LABORATORY INSTRUMENTS

Their Design and Application

by

A. ELLIOTT, Ph.D., D.Sc.

Courtaulds Ltd.

and

J. HOME DICKSON, M.Sc.

Royal Naval Scientific Service

SECOND EDITION
REVISED

1960

CHEMICAL PUBLISHING CO., INC.

212 Fifth Avenue   New York, N.Y.

1960

CHEMICAL PUBLISHING CO., INC.
NEW YORK   N.Y.

PREFACE TO THE SECOND EDITION

THE demand for a second edition has given us the opportunity to revise the book very completely, correct some doubtful points, bring the matter up to date and add much new material.

The chapter on properties of materials has been expanded to include a fuller account of plastic materials, in which field there have been important developments. The same chapter also introduces the subject of corrosion-resisting metals, and a complete new chapter has been added on the subject of corrosion in laboratory instruments. Personal experience has shown how troublesome corrosive agents may be in some laboratories, and it is hoped that this chapter will be of value to many.

Some new figures have been prepared to amplify the section on cross-spring pivots, which are finding new applications as they become better known, and additional figures have been added to illustrate the subject of errors in instruments.

The appendix on optical crystals has been enlarged into a chapter with the latest possible information on the refractive index of materials useful in infra-red spectrometry. A complete new section on radiation has necessitated another new chapter which includes the section on photometry. Some new matter has been added on colour vision, to the diagrams of photographic lenses, and in the chapter on photography. Photographic resolution has been treated much more fully.

Some new information on glass protection against radiation hazards which arrived too late for incorporation in Chapter 12 has been added as Appendix IV.

As in the first edition, we have confined ourselves almost wholly to mechanical and optical matters, since any adequate treatment of electronic instruments would have made the scope of the book much too wide.

The revisions and additions have been prompted by the many helpful criticisms and suggestions of friends and colleagues to whom we are very grateful. Research units and establishments in many parts of the world and many firms have also suggested improvements which we have endeavoured to include and have provided us with much interesting new matter. We hope that this new edition will prove to be a considerable improvement on the first edition.

A. ELLIOTT
J. HOME DICKSON

PREFACE TO THE FIRST EDITION

THE present-day trend towards specialisation is making it more difficult for students in Universities and Technical Colleges to obtain the wider general training which is so necessary for successful research work.

In any research organisation the worker is often called on to design and construct his own instruments or to guide others in their construction, and he finds his training inadequate to cover the many ramifications involved in this aspect of the work.

It is especially to provide some guide to these ancillary processes and components that this book has been written. The chief aim has been to present the principles on which good design is based, and many examples of the application of the principles have been given. No attempt has been made to cover the entire field of instrument design, but the authors have endeavoured throughout to show the interrelation of good design, material, and method of construction, so that the best results may be obtained with moderate or limited means.

The first few chapters deal with the properties of various materials and their treatment and use in the construction of instruments. A number of workshop processes are described and the accuracy attainable in the various processes is discussed. There is a chapter on the preparation of drawings for workshop use and their reproduction. Succeeding chapters are devoted to methods of construction to suit special requirements and in particular the kinematic design of instruments is treated at some length. Chapters on vibration insulation, sensitivity and methods of measurement follow.

Since optical instruments of many kinds and photography play such a large part in modern research work the remainder of the book is concerned with such instruments and methods. Chapters on glass and on the uses and working of glass are followed by a description of a number of optical instruments and devices. There are many tables and diagrams illustrating the uses of lenses, mirrors and prisms and there is much information which is not generally included in books on optics or in the normal college courses. Finally there is a chapter on the applications of photography and several appendices containing miscellaneous information.

vii

In compiling such a book, based as it is on the accumulated experience of the authors, during many years of research work, there must necessarily occur many items of information collected from a number of sources. Copious references and acknowledgements have been made throughout the book and there has been added a collected list of acknowledgements but the authors must repeat here that they are indebted to many others whose names may not occur in these lists and we take this opportunity of thanking all those whose help, through the years, has made this book possible.

A. ELLIOTT
J. HOME DICKSON

ACKNOWLEDGEMENTS

Acknowledgements are due to the following firms, publishers and authors for permission to reproduce figures, tables and extracts :—

Messrs. Longmans, Green & Co., Ltd. and Mr. W. Steeds, from *Engineering Materials, Machine Tools and Processes*, Table 2.1.

Messrs. Johnson, Matthey & Co., Ltd., from *Beryllium Copper*, Figs. 3.1, 3.2, 3.3, and Table 3.5.

Messrs. Macmillan & Co., Ltd. and Mr. F. H. Rolt, from *Gauges and Fine Measurements*, Figs. 6.4, 6.17 and 7.7. We are indebted to Mr. Rolt, both personally and through his book, for much information.

Messrs. Mercer, Ltd., for Fig. 7.4.

Dr. J. A. Haringx and the Editor of *Philips' Technical Review* for Figs. 9.5 to 9.14.

The Dow Corning Corporation, Midland, Michigan, U.S.A., for Fig. 10.3.

Messrs. Imperial Chemical Industries, Ltd., and the *British Catalogue of Plastics* for Table 3.4.

Messrs. Aero Research, Ltd., for Table 4.1.

The Copper Development Association, The British Cast Iron Research Association, Messrs. Firth-Vickers Stainless Steels, Ltd., The British Iron and Steel Research Association and Messrs. High Duty Alloys, Ltd., for information used in Table 3.2.

Messrs. Firth-Vickers Stainless Steels, Ltd., Messrs Imperial Chemical Industries, Ltd., and Messrs. Murex Ltd., for Table 3.3.

The British Standards Institution for Table 4.2. and Figs. 5.1, 5.13 and 5.15.

The Director of the National Physical Laboratory for Figs. 6.15 and 6.16.

The Watts Division of Messrs. Hilger and Watts, Ltd., for much information on liquid levels.

Dr. W. H. J. Vernon for Fig. 19.1.

Dr. U. R. Evans and Mrs. V. E. Rance for help in connection with the chapter on Corrosion.

Mr. H. L. Bennister for Table 19.1.

The Controller of H.M. Stationery Office for Table 19.2.

Mr. H. J. Davies for information on the accuracy of machining operations.

Sir Isaac Pitman & Sons, Ltd., and Prof. L. C. Martin, from *Technical Optics*, Vol. I, for Figs. 12.5, 12.6, 12.12, 12.13, 16.5, 16.6, and from *Introduction to Applied Optics*, Vol. II, by the same author, Fig. 15.17 (g).

ACKNOWLEDGEMENTS

Sir Isaac Pitman & Sons, Ltd., and Messrs. K. J. Habell and A. Cox, from *Engineering Optics* for Figs. 15.8, 16.13–16.17.

Blackie & Sons, Ltd. and Prof. L. C. Martin and Mr. B. K. Johnson from *Practical Microscopy* for Fig. 15.12.

Hutchinson & Co., Ltd., from *Scientific Instruments*, Vols. I and II (edited by H. J. Cooper) for Figs. 15.1, 15.2, 15.11, 15.13.

Clarendon Press, Oxford, and Mr. E. J. Bowen, from *Chemical Aspects of Light* for Tables 18.5, 18.6.

Hilger & Watts, Ltd., and the late Mr. F. Twyman, from *Prism and Lens Making* for Figs. 14.3, 14.4, and 14.6 to 14.10.

McGraw Hill Publishing Co., Ltd., from *Handbook of Photography* (edited by K. Henney and K. Dudley) for Figs. 18.2, 18.3, 18.10 to 18.13, 18.15, 18.17, 18.18.

McGraw Hill Publishing Co., Ltd., and Messrs. A. C. Hardy and F. H. Perrin, from *Principles of Optics* for Fig. 15.4 and Table 15.3.

Hutchinson & Co., Ltd., from *Glass* (edited by J. Home Dickson) for Tables 12.1 and 12.2.

Hilger & Watts, Ltd., for Figs. 7.6, 17.18, 17.19 and for information on liquid levels.

Chance-Pilkington, Ltd., Bausch & Lomb, Ltd., Parra-Mantois and Schott & Gen. for data and information on Glass.

Kodak, Ltd., for numerous figures and extracts from the *Kodak Data Book*, for a number of original photographs and for much information.

J. H. Dallmeyer, Ltd., Ross, Ltd., Taylor, Taylor & Hobson, Ltd., Wray, Ltd., for information regarding their lenses.

R. & J. Beck, Ltd., for the loan of blocks, Fig. 15.17(f).

The Institute of Physics and Mr. E. W. Taylor for the table and diagrams of eye-pieces published in the *Journal of Scientific Instruments* (Table 15.4).

The Royal Photographic Society for figures and diagrams and for the loan of blocks from *The Photographic Journal*.

The Optical Society of America for numerous extracts, figures and tables from *The Journal of the Optical Society of America*.

Longmans, Green & Co., Ltd., for permission to publish data from *Physical and Chemical Constants*, Kaye & Laby.

The Harshaw Chemical Co. for permission to publish data on optical crystals and for much information.

Barr & Stroud, Ltd., for Figs. 12.7, 12.8, 13.4, 13.6.

Clarendon Press, Oxford, and Messrs. Smith, Jones and Chasmar from *Detection and Measurement of Infra Red Radiations* for Table 17.4 and Fig. 17.4.

Mr. J. W. Herkes for assistance in preparing a number of the figures.

Our indebtedness to *The Journal of the Physical Society, Monthly Notices of the Royal Astronomical Society, Journal of the British Astronomical Association, Journal of Scientific Instruments, Journal of the Optical Society of America,*

ACKNOWLEDGEMENTS

Photographic Journal, Nature, etc. and to many books, periodicals and published and unpublished matter cannot be adequately acknowledged. Where specific articles or papers have been consulted or used references have been given in the text and at the ends of the chapters, but it is feared that in many cases we have failed through over familiarity with the subjects, to make proper acknowledgement and we ask for the indulgence of authors, publishers and others for any omissions of this kind which will be rectified in any subsequent edition. We must also add our sincere thanks to Mr. G. Parr, Mr. E. W. Hamilton and Mr. P. C. Found of Messrs. Chapman & Hall, Ltd., for their help with the figures, constant care with a difficult production and for their kindness and courtesy while the book was proceeding through the press.

A.E.
J.H.D.

CONTENTS

xiii

CONTENTS

Appendix

Chapter 1

GENERAL CONSIDERATIONS

RECENT years have seen a great extension in the use of physical methods in widely differing fields. In all branches of industry, in medical and biological research and in the defence services such methods are used, while many who received their first training as chemists find themselves using the tools of the physicist during the greater part of their working time. The various needs of such workers are partly met by the output of the scientific instrument firms, but new fields of research demand new methods, and much routine test equipment is so specialised that it must be designed for a particular purpose. Some instrument manufacturers undertake the design and construction of special apparatus and in certain classes of work this is undoubtedly the best solution. It is, however, not always satisfactory, unless there is very close co-operation. In every research establishment, a considerable amount of equipment is made by the workshop, usually to the design or instructions of the research worker. It is chiefly to meet the needs of such cases that this book has been written, though it is hoped that it may be of use to the professional instrument designer as well. Apparatus for teaching purposes in universities and technical colleges is often of poor design, and not always suited to its purpose. In this field, too, the appreciation of the principles of good design are important.

Good design will take into account the imperfections of current workshop practice and the limitations imposed by the properties of the materials available. For this reason, we have put these two subjects first and have tried to present a picture of what can be expected of a good workshop, and how design can keep the inevitable errors of performance within acceptable limits. The design of many commercial instruments is capable of considerable improvement in this respect, though the work of the best firms is above reproach. The subject owes much to the early work of Kelvin, Clerk Maxwell and Darwin, but has been greatly extended and ably expounded by the late Professor A. F. C. Pollard, who died while the first edition of this book was being written.

Since the eye is the organ chiefly used in accurate perception, the majority of instruments are made for visual observations. Accordingly, we have considered the properties and manufacture of optical components as well as the properties of the eye. In many instruments the optical parts may play only a subsidiary rôle (often to provide an enlarged image for observation) but are nevertheless very important.

World War II brought home to many academic scientists the importance of the human observer and his relation to the instruments he used. The services rightly insisted that an uncomfortable observer was an inefficient observer, and much attention was paid to comfort. Faulty observation in the laboratory is not deadly as, for instance, in the cockpit of a night fighter plane, but it should be avoided if possible, and instruments should not cause strain or fatigue. It is, however, difficult to reach this ideal at the first attempt, and usually re-design is needed to achieve the best results.

When the principles of sound design are understood, a good deal of work can be done on paper with the assurance that the instrument will function properly when made. Many instances arise, however, when it is impossible to visualise the arrangement and forecast how it will work. This is often the case when a mechanism depends on the action of springs, for instance. In such cases it often saves time if a rough model of such a part is made. Sometimes a " space model " of a part is useful. This is a model, usually made in wood, having the external dimensions of the actual instrument which it represents, but not capable of working. It is useful when the part has to be fitted in some larger assembly.

Optical arrangements are often set up in rough form, using simple components such as spectacle lenses, before the mechanical parts are designed. It is often found, contrary to expectation, that the mechanical parts of an optical instrument are the most difficult to design and make satisfactorily.

Opinions differ as to the extent to which apparatus constructed in the laboratory should be of a makeshift character when it is only to be used for a short time. If the apparatus is made with the least possible expenditure of work, it is true that workshop time may be saved, but a great deal of time may be wasted later by the experimenter who has to try to make defective apparatus work. It usually pays to have research apparatus soundly constructed, and this is true of the smaller parts of research equipment such as mountings, stands, adjustable holders, etc., as well as of the larger instruments. At the same time, it will be realised that nothing is gained by a super-fine finish, and the condition of much of the material surfaces used in research apparatus is of no importance whatever. This is hardly the case with apparatus used in teaching, for it seems that in many cases students produce better work if they feel that they are using good instruments. Elementary students are only able to judge the performance of an instrument to a limited extent, and appearances count for something. For this reason, some attention may be given to finish as well as to function in apparatus for teaching. It is, however, useful to have apparatus in which the difference can be seen between those parts which require accuracy in manufacture and those which do not, provided that the difference is made clear.

CHAPTER 2

THE ACCURACY ATTAINABLE IN MACHINING OPERATIONS

In order that full advantage may be taken of modern machine tool developments, some account of various manufacturing processes, and of the accuracy of the work done in them, will be given in this chapter. Even though the workshop in which the construction of an instrument is carried out may not be provided with all the equipment described, it is frequently possible to send out a portion of the work to a general engineering shop, for a particular type of machining, provided that the design is suitable. Many processes which are of use in mass production are not described, because they involve considerable expense in the preparation of the special tools, etc., and are uneconomical for small-scale production. Such operations as die-casting and pressing come in this category.

The designer must pay particular attention to the way in which work is held or clamped in the various types of machines. Considerable difficulty may arise in machining operations if suitable provision for holding has not been made. Sometimes it may be necessary to provide, in a casting, pieces which serve no other purpose than to assist in holding the work ; these pieces are cut off after finishing. Naturally, it is much easier to provide for such pieces before the work is cast than afterwards. Attention must also be given to the need for sufficient rigidity in the work to enable it to be machined properly, quite apart from the rigidity required in the finished instrument. It is, for example, difficult or impossible to mill a flat surface on the outside of a thin-walled, hollow box. The accuracy of the work produced is often governed by the rigidity of the work, but the standard of rigidity required for best performance varies with the machining process employed, e.g., a surface grinder will produce satisfactory results with less rigid work than would be required for milling.

In the following account, an attempt has been made to state the accuracy with which work may be produced by various operations. Naturally, this depends to a great extent upon the combination of machine and operator. The accuracy claimed should certainly be reached with skilled use of modern machines ; in most cases the limits stated are demanded in high-class production work and no great difficulty should arise in working to them in individual jobs, should this be necessary.

Nominal size, tolerance, limits, allowance

These terms are in common use in engineering practice. The " nominal size " is self-explanatory. The use of the word " tolerance " indicates that it is recognised that no work is perfectly accurate, and " tolerance " is defined by the British Standards Institute as " a difference of dimensions prescribed in order to tolerate unavoidable imperfections of workmanship." H. J. Davies[1] amplifies this with the remark that the word unavoidable is to be read as " unavoidable, consistently with reasonable cost of production for the kind of work referred to," and this should always be kept in mind. " Limits " are the dimensions between which must lie the dimension of the work ; the difference between a limit and the nominal size is equal to the tolerance. The term " allowance " is quite different in meaning from tolerance. It is used to indicate the difference between the dimensions of two components which must fit. The fit may be an " easy running fit," " sliding push fit," " driving fit," etc., and the allowance depends on the class of fit.

Much of the utility of the " limit gauge system " whereby work is simply kept within the limits given, and no attempt is made to reproduce exactly the given nominal size, is connected with the interchangeability of components in mass production, and consideration of the system is outside the scope of this book. It will frequently, however, be necessary to have certain parts of an instrument made to a given tolerance. Reference may be made to Chapter 5 for methods for indicating tolerances on a drawing.

Lathe turning is by far the commonest machining operation and warrants consideration at some length. A diagram of a lathe is given in Fig. 2.1. The work is made to rotate by means of its connection to the lathe spindle, and metal is removed by a chisel-like tool held securely in a tool post. There are two methods of holding the work. It may be held rigidly in a chuck or other device which is fixed to the spindle, in which case the figure cut by the tool will be a solid of revolution coaxial with the lathe spindle, or it may be held between centres, as in Fig. 2.2. Centring holes are made in the work to take the lathe centres in the latter case, and the work is driven round by a

" dog " attached thereto, as shown. It must be noted that when turning between centres a solid of revolution is generated whose axis coincides with a line joining the points of the two centres, unless the centre in the lathe spindle (which is called a " live " centre because it rotates) is not true, in which case the axis will be on a line joining the back (" dead ") centre and the centre of rotation of the circle described by the point of the " live " centre. The axis of the spindle is intended to be parallel to the bed of the lathe, along which the saddle carrying the tool post and tool is moved by a screw

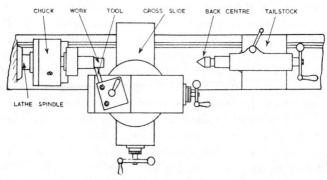

CHUCK   WORK   TOOL   CROSS SLIDE   BACK CENTRE   TAILSTOCK

LATHE SPINDLE

Fig. 2.1.—Chief parts of instrument maker's lathe. The drive for the spindle at the left hand side is not shown. Work is held in a 3–jaw chuck.

connected to the spindle by gears. In order that the depth of cut made by the tool may be varied, a cross slide is carried on the saddle, so that the tool may be moved in a direction at right angles to the bed. Motion of the tool along the cross slide enables the work to be " faced," the surface produced being a plane at right angles to the axis of the spindle. Conical surfaces may be cut by setting the cross slide at an angle different from 90° to the lathe spindle.

When the work is held in a chuck, it may, if long, be supported at its free end by the back centre, fitting freely in a hole made in the work for the purpose. If the work is short, or sufficiently rigid, the back centre will not be used. In this case, it is possible to turn cylindrical surfaces, all concentric with the lathe spindle, and the accuracy of the surfaces, apart from some important factors considered below, will depend on the accuracy with which the spindle is aligned with the bed, and on the straightness of the bed. So far as the first factor is concerned, the spindle should not be out of alignment by more than

6

0·0005 in. in a distance of 1 ft.[1] The departure from straightness of the bed in a lathe having any pretensions to accuracy should be very small.

If the back centre is used to support the work there will be a conflict between the stiffness of the work and of the machine unless the point of the back centre is in the line of the spindle axis. Since, however, the tailstock which carries the back centre can be set over, that is moved parallel to itself in a horizontal plane at right angles to the bed, this condition can be satisfied by the operator. No new errors need be introduced by using the back centre. It should be noted that a slight error of alignment of spindle and bed in a vertical

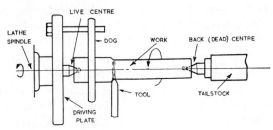

Fig. 2.2.—Work supported between centres, driven by dog.

plane, or a small error in the height of the back centre above the bed, produces a negligible error in the work owing to the fact that the turning tool is applied to a point on the work at the same height above the bed as the centres.

When turning between centres, a method which should always be employed for long work if possible, conical surfaces, with the cylinder as a special case, are produced by setting over the back centre by an appropriate amount. This is completely within the control of the operator, and want of alignment of spindle and bed is of no consequence.

It frequently happens that work must be removed from a lathe before turning is completed. This may be for some fitting operation, or it may be necessary to reverse the work in order to turn that portion which was held in the chuck or in the dog. In such a case, the automatic self-centring chuck cannot always be relied on to hold the work true after replacement, especially if the work has been reversed and the diameters of the two ends are different. If a lathe provided with collet chucks is used, the work may be taken out and replaced true, but as the collets fit within the hollow lathe spindle, only small diameter work can be held in them. One great advantage of turning between centres is that work may be reversed and replaced accurately, provided that the live centre runs true. This can always be arranged for by truing it *in situ*. As an example of the need for considering the machining operations when designing components, consider the piece of work shown in Fig. 4.2 and suppose that the internal and external cylindrical surfaces must be coaxial. The work cannot be held between centres, and if held in a chuck it would be difficult to ensure that the surfaces were coaxial after reversal of the work. The operation could be performed accurately if the internal surface were first bored, then a cylindrical rod were turned between centres to fit tightly in the hole in the work. The bar would be replaced between the lathe centres and the external surfaces could then be turned up. A good deal of labour could have been saved if the work had been cast with a prolongation for the purpose of holding the work. All the cylindrical surfaces could then have been turned up without removing the work from the chuck. The extra piece of metal would be removed by a " parting off " tool.

There remain to be considered several other sources of error in lathe work. It is inevitable that the spindle should have some play in its bearings, hence the position of the spindle axis is indefinite to this extent. Next the material of the machine not being perfectly rigid, some yielding must occur during cutting. Unless the lathe is very badly designed, the yielding should not be appreciable when taking fine finishing cuts with a sharp tool. More important is the yielding of the work. This may, in extreme cases, make it impossible to produce the required shape. The magnitude of the error produced in a given piece of work depends very much on the cutting tool used, and hence is to some extent conditioned by the skill of the operator. Mention of the cutting tool brings us to the last major source of error, which arises from a peculiarity of the cutting operation. During the removal of metal by a lathe tool, a small quantity of the metal sometimes adheres to the edge of the tool, producing what is known as a " built-up edge." The effect is virtually to increase the size of the tool slightly, making the cut deeper. When taking fine cuts for finishing, the built-up edge may be formed and destroyed alternately, producing irregularity in the dimensions of the work. The effect is most marked with tools made of high speed steel, less so for carbon steel, and for tools with a cutting edge of tungsten carbide or diamond, it is negligible. Tungsten carbide and diamond tools are harder and can be brought to a much keener edge than steel, with the consequence that lighter cuts may be taken. This at the same time allows work to be made to finer limits and reduces errors due to elasticity of the work. It appears that the introduction of these new cutting materials has increased the accuracy of turning so much that it now compares in accuracy with grinding. The turned surface so produced is smoother than a ground surface. Diamond and tungsten carbide tools are very suitable for turning soft materials such as brass and gunmetal, as well as hard materials.

Limits of accuracy to be expected in turning

It should be possible, using carefully sharpened tools of carbon or high speed steel, to keep within a tolerance of $\pm$ 0·0003 in. by turning work held in a chuck for short work, or by turning between centres for long work, provided that the work is sufficiently rigid. By using a file and emery cloth for finishing, the work being rotated in the lathe at high speed, the tolerance can be kept within $\pm$ 0·0002 in. and a good deal can be done by careful filing to rectify turning errors due to elasticity of the work. Much, however, depends on the operator's skill in filing, and the process is more akin to hand finishing than to machining. To some extent it shares with hand finishing the characteristic that any degree of accuracy can be produced by the exercise of sufficient skill and patience by the operator.

With tools of tungsten carbide or diamond, and a very good lathe, work can be turned to limits differing by 0·0002 in., i.e., a tolerance of $\pm$ 0·0001 in. This is actually the tolerance adopted by one firm for the bore of internal combustion engine cylinders, finished by tungsten carbide tools, but it is not easily attained. Production work of this high precision is done on specially built, rigid machines with a very slow rate of advance of the tool. For many purposes, of course, such accuracy is not required.

Plain milling

The essential features of a plain miller are shown in Fig. 2.3. The work is held on the table, either in a vice or by clamps and the table is moved by power in a horizontal direction (longitudinal power feed), perpendicular to the spindle on which the cutter is mounted. The shape of the cutter varies according to the surface which it is required to produce. Cutters for flat surfaces (including a facing cutter) and for vee surfaces are shown in the same figure. In order to deal with surfaces wider than the cutter, a hand operated cross motion is provided, which moves the table parallel to the spindle. In addition to the horizontal power feed, a vertical power feed is provided on some machines. This enables flat surfaces at right angles to be cut, first a horizontal surface being cut by the horizontal feed, then a vertical surface is cut using the vertical feed.

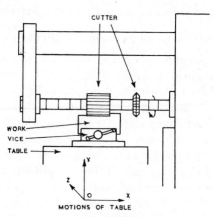

FIG. 2.3.—Chief parts of plain miller, showing flat face being milled on work. Motion is in direction OZ for this operation.

Milling is an operation in which large amounts of metal may be removed, using heavy cuts. It is also an operation which results in very heavy stresses being set up both in the work and in the machine, much greater than for example in turning. This is due in the first place to the fact that a wide surface, very commonly 2 or 3 in. or more in width, is cut at once by the milling cutter, whereas in a lathe the cut is much narrower, perhaps less than 0·1 in. Another reason for the greater stresses in milling lies in the fact that the cutter edges are frequently much less keen than the edge of a turning tool, and greater force is needed to ensure penetration of the work by the tool. Milling cutters are very expensive, consequently they are not ground more frequently than is necessary. It will be realised that the work must be capable of being rigidly supported to mill it accurately. Lack of rigidity of the work results in surfaces which deviate more or less from the surface it is intended to produce. The type of surface obtained is also often unsatisfactory, as " chatter " may be set up and a rippled surface produced by vibration when the work is not rigid enough.

Besides the plain miller referred to above, there is the universal miller in which, in addition to the movements found in the plain miller, the table and longitudinal power feed can be rotated about a vertical axis, and the work can be mounted between centres on the table and rotated by power. These movements are used to mill spirals, worm gears, etc. Consideration of the universal miller is outside the scope of this book.

Milling does not rank as one of the most accurate of machining operations, and unless special precautions are taken, it cannot be relied upon to produce work with a smaller tolerance than some thousandths of an inch ; the accuracy depends very much on the condition of the cutter. It is, however, a very useful method, and the accuracy of shape (as distinct from accuracy of size) is high.

Surface grinding

The surface grinder (Fig. 2.4) is much used in high-class production work, and is being used to an increasing extent in the construction of accurate instruments. In essentials it resembles a plain miller with a high speed grinding wheel in place of a steel cutter. The longitudinal power feed moves the table backwards and forwards automatically at a rather rapid rate, and the cross feed automatically advances the table at right angles to the longitudinal feed by a small fraction of an inch during each oscillation. The grinding wheel, which is narrow (about $\frac{1}{2}$ in. wide in a small machine), passes over each part of the work in turn, producing a surface which is a good approximation to a plane. In small machines the work cannot be moved by power in the vertical direction, hence rectangular surfaces can only be produced by re-setting the work.

The wheel is made from grains of abrasive material, suitably cemented together. The abrasive material is crystalline, and the edges of the crystals act as numerous small cutters, removing material from the work. These edges become blunted with use, but the bonding material breaks down, and new grains are exposed. If the bond is suitable for the work, the abrasive grains never become too dull to cut, but break away before this condition is reached. A consequence of this is that, since the cutting tools are always sharp, very light cuts can be taken and the stresses set up are correspondingly small.

Cuts made with a small grinder are commonly not much more than about 0·001 in. deep, and the depth can be regulated to 0·0001 in. The process, which is usually employed as a finishing process, is very much more accurate than milling, and demands less rigidity in the work.

Grinding may be applied to hardened steel, as well as to mild steel and cast iron. It is not impossible to grind softer materials such as brass and gunmetal, but a different type of wheel is required from that used for iron and steel. Generally it will be found that requests to grind soft metals meet with no favour from the machinist.

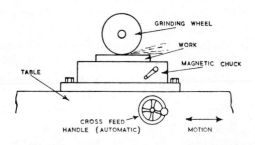

FIG. 2.4.—Essentials of a surface grinder.

Since grinding is commonly applied only to iron and steel, the work is frequently held on a magnetic chuck. This accessory is very useful for many classes of work, and doubtless adds to the accuracy with which parallel surfaces can be produced. The magnetic chuck is usually used to hold thin sheets or strips which are to be ground on the flat surface. If, however, the face which is applied to the chuck is not quite flat, it will be pulled flat by the magnetic force, hence the upper surface will be ground parallel to the lower, But on releasing the work, elasticity will cause the lower surface to regain its former figure, or something like it, and the work will no longer have flat surfaces. The extent to which a moderately stiff, slightly curved piece of iron or steel will be straightened out by a magnetic chuck is surprising. For example, a strip of mild steel of 1 in. by $\frac{1}{8}$ in. section, 3 in. long, was bent into an arc such that the straight line joining the ends of the strip was 0·01 in. distant from the surface at the middle point. On laying the strip on the magnetic chuck, concave side down, and applying the magnetic flux, the centre of the strip was pulled down through a distance of 0·006 in. Evidently such a strip could not be ground to surfaces which would be flat after removal from the magnetic chuck. In such a case the work would be fixed to a more rigid piece of metal which could then be mounted on the chuck. After one flat surface had been ground on the work, no further difficulty would arise in using the magnetic chuck.

Surface grinding can be used to produce small parts (say up to 2 in. long) with surfaces flat and dimensions accurate to about ± 0·0001 in., under good conditions.

A very accurate form of surface grinding is possible without a surface grinder of the type shown in Fig. 2.4 ; it is known as " spot grinding " and has been used by the National Physical Laboratory to produce accurate squares, etc. The work is held by hand on a surface plate over which it is moved, and the upper surface is removed by a grinding wheel suitably placed. The work is moved about until the wheel ceases to grind, and the ground surface is then parallel to the surface plate. Evidently parallel ground surfaces can be made by two spot grinding operations. The method, which does not require expensive equipment, should be useful when very high accuracy is required on small parts.

Centre grinding

The most accurate cylindrical grinding is done with the work supported between two dead centres. The work is driven round by means of the headstock spindle, but as the connection between the two is not rigid, any play which the spindle has in its bearings is not communicated to the work, and true surfaces of revolution are produced by the grinding wheel. What was said about the action of abrasive wheels in the last section applies naturally to cylindrical and taper grinding. Surfaces with a high degree of smoothness can be produced by the use of fine grained wheels, but in general the ground surface is not so smooth as that produced by turning with diamond or tungsten carbide tools. The accuracy of figure produced by grinding is high, and tolerances within 0·0001 in. are possible, but the depth of surface irregularities becomes important for such fine work. Lapping is more satisfactory for tolerances as small as this.

Lapping

Lapping is used as a finishing process both for producing a smooth finish and for producing accurate dimensions. To lap a surface, a piece of soft metal (called a lap and usually made of lead, gunmetal, copper or sometimes cast iron or mild steel) is prepared which will as far as possible fit the surface to be lapped. The surfaces of lap and work are moved over each other with a little fine abrasive between them, the motion being such that as far as possible all parts of the two surfaces come in contact with each other. Lapping can be successfully applied to plane, spherical and cylindrical surfaces. For other figures it is not so satisfactory. The accuracy obtainable by hand lapping appears to be limited only by the skill and patience of the operator. As an example of the accuracy of hand lapping applied to plane surfaces, the slip gauges introduced by Johansson and now made by several firms have flat, parallel faces, accurate to size within 2 millionths of an inch in the smaller sizes. Lapping of this kind is naturally highly specialised and generally only employed on gauges or flat reference surfaces.

Cylindrical lapping, in which the work is rotated in a lathe and the lap held by hand, is a fairly common finishing operation applied to ground work. Lapping machines for plane, cylindrical and spherical surfaces are employed in engineering, but the only products of these machines which are likely to be used in small scale instrument work are standard articles, such as steel rollers, taper pins, etc.

Lapping is essentially the same process as the grinding of optical parts (Chapter 14), applied to metal instead of to glass. It has the same characteristic that a very crude machine can be used to produce the most accurate work.

Spinning

Spinning differs from the other operations considered in this chapter in that metal is not cut away to obtain the required shape, but is worked into shape by a process not unlike that used by a cook shaping pie-crust. Spinning is used for making hollow, thin-walled objects whose surfaces are solids of revolution, such as metal beakers, hemispherical bowls, etc. It is most easily applied to soft metals such as aluminium. The work is done on a lathe, and requires in addition to the lathe only a few simple tools and appliances. No hesitation need be felt in introducing the process into a workshop so equipped.

The shape to be formed is first turned in the lathe in hard wood, the wood being gripped in some form of chuck. A circular disc of metal of the required thickness is held between the wood and a special spinner's centre which fits in the lathe tailstock in place of the ordinary pointed centre. The centre of the disc is adjusted to the axis of the lathe and clamped to the wood by means of the spinner's centre, then as the work revolves in the lathe it is gradually pressed to the shape of the wood by means of a smooth blunt tool resembling a burnisher. Friction between the wood and work is sufficient to rotate the latter. Spinning is particularly useful when very light objects are required, such as dust caps for lenses, etc. Details of the process may be found in references 2 and 3.

Location of holes with respect to other holes and to edges and surfaces

By the use of a steel rule and scriber, work can be marked out with an error which should not exceed about 0·01 in. and the positions of the centres of holes defined by intersecting lines to the same order of accuracy. With care in drilling, little accuracy should be lost, unless the hole is a deep one, in which case the drill, not being rigid, may not run true.

If higher accuracy is required, greater accuracy in marking out (with an error which in favourable circumstances need not be more than a few ten thousandths of an inch) may be obtained by setting the scribing point, held in a suitable fixture, with the help of a micrometer or gauge blocks. The flat surface is supported on a surface plate, which is a rigid plate, usually of cast iron, whose upper surface has been rendered plane by careful machining or scraping, and the scribing point set at the required distance from the flat base of its support. A small centre-punch mark is made where the hole is to be made, using a special fixture for holding the punch. The work is now put in a lathe chuck provided with independent jaws, and adjusted until the centre punch mark is on the axis of rotation of the spindle, and clamped. A small hole is now drilled, using a drill held in a chuck fitting the taper hole in the tailstock. This drilled hole will probably be eccentric ; it is corrected by boring with a stiff turning tool or boring bar held in the tool post, and a hole in the desired position produced in this way. The method allows of an error as small as a few ten thousandths of an inch. This and other somewhat more accurate methods have been developed in connection with the making of jigs and fine tools ; they require considerable skill and are by no means rapid. From the above brief account some idea of the difficulties encountered in locating holes accurately may be formed. Further details may be found in ref. 1. The limit of accuracy in position of holes is about 0·0001 in. when extreme care is taken. Optical methods for locating holes are described in ref. 5.

TABLE 2.1—*Accuracy of Holes*[4]

Operation	Error in Size	Error in Roundness	Straightness
	Inches	Inches	Inches/foot
Drilling	0·005	0·005	0·008
Reaming	0·001	0·0005	0·004
Grinding	0·0002	0·0002	0·0002

REFERENCES

[1] DAVIES, H. J., *Precision Methods in the Workshop* (London, Arnold, 1946).
[2] REAGAN, J. E., and SMITH, E. E., *Metal Spinning* (New York, Bruce Publishing Co.).
[3] MACHINERY'S Yellow Back Series, *Metal Spinning* (London, Machinery Publishing Co. Ltd.).
[4] STEEDS, W., *Engineering Materials, Machine Tools and Processes.* (London, Longmans, 1954).
[5] HABELL AND COX, *Engineering Optics* (London, Pitman, 1953).

General References

SMITH, R. H., *A Textbook of Advanced Machine Work* (Boston, U.S.A., Industrial Education Book Co., 1930).
CHAPMAN, W. A. J., *Workshop Technology*, Parts 1 and 2 (London, Arnold, 1951—1955).

CHAPTER 3

PROPERTIES OF MATERIALS USED FOR GENERAL CONSTRUCTION OF INSTRUMENTS

IT is essential that the designer of an instrument should have some knowledge of the properties of materials which are available for their construction ; a brief account of the properties of some of the more useful materials is therefore given below.

Wood

Formerly wood was employed in instrument making to a much greater extent than at present. It may be said that where a high degree of accuracy and stability are required, wood is quite unsuitable, as its dimensions are subject to change with temperature and humidity. None the less, there are many cases where, owing to the ease with which it can be worked, wood may be employed. Not every instrument, even of those used in accurate measurements, requires high constancy of dimensions ; in electrical measurements, for instance, limits to accuracy are often set by other circumstances. Wood may frequently be employed for stands and instrument cases.

The decrease in dimensions which occurs as wood becomes dry takes place chiefly across, rather than along the grain, and occurs to a less extent in the parts of the wood near the centre of the tree than in those near the outside. In consequence of this, there is a pronounced tendency for boards to contract more on one side than on the other, and to become warped. The extent to which warping occurs depends to a considerable extent on the treatment of the wood before sawing into boards, and is more pronounced in some species of wood than in others. When it is required to overcome this tendency, the wood is " clamped " by a strip of the same wood joined to each end, with the grain running perpendicular to the grain of the main piece. Drawing boards are always treated in this way, and the same method is employed in camera construction.

In spite of the disadvantages associated with wood on account of shrinkage, etc., no alternative material has yet been found to replace it in certain kinds of work. Its elastic properties are unique ; no other material combines in the same way the ability to absorb mechanical shock, to bend and to recover its shape, being at the same time easily worked with hand tools. Into what other materials suitable for constructional purposes, for instance, can nails be driven, or drawing pins, etc., inserted ?

The following list contains only a few kinds of wood, but for instrument work it will not usually be necessary to go outside it.

Pine :—Oregon pine, red pine and Siberian pine are all very suitable for stands, being straight grained, easily worked and containing few knots. Yellow pine is one of the best woods for pattern making, but is expensive and not very readily obtainable. Its value for pattern making lies in the fact that it is less liable to warp than most woods when placed in wet moulding sand. For laboratory use it is rather too soft.

Mahogany :—Very many varieties of mahogany are in use. Spanish mahogany is probably the best from the instrument maker's point of view, but is extremely dear and difficult to obtain. It is, compared with other woods, very stable as regards dimensions, and takes glue well, also its compactness renders it suitable for working to fairly close limits. Plate holders for cameras and spectrographs are frequently made of this mahogany.

There are many inferior varieties of mahogany on the market ; one of these, known as gaboon mahogany, is frequently met. It is pink in colour, and rather soft. It is much used in the form of plywood (see later).

Steel screws and nails should not be used in mahogany, as excessive corrosion of the metal occurs, and this in turn destroys the surrounding wood.

Teak is an excellent material, being straight grained, strong, hard and very durable even when exposed to the weather. It is, when properly seasoned, little liable to warp or shrink and stands extremes of temperature well. For this reason it is always recommended for apparatus to be used in tropical climates. The best variety, tectona grandis, comes from Burma. There are inferior varieties on the market. Teak is rather expensive, but if wood is to be employed at all in instrument construction, teak may be expected to give the most satisfactory results. Steel screws, etc., should not be used in teak (see preceding paragraph).

Afrormosia is one of several African hardwoods which have to some extent replaced teak in recent years. It is a hard, stable wood which is fairly easily worked ; it is however liable to become discoloured when used for draining boards, and is somewhat liable to split when nailed.

Iroko is also a tropical African wood and has many of the virtues of teak. Its stability is comparable to that of teak, but specimens with irregular grain should not be used if stability is important.

Boxwood is very hard and one of the closest grained of woods, yellow in colour and, if of the best quality, not very liable to shrink or warp. It is employed for carpenters' rules and the less accurate variety of scales used in laboratories. Some varieties of boxwood are not very good as regards warping ; many of the boxwood metre rules in elementary teaching laboratories will be found on inspection to be far from straight. Occasionally it is useful for formers on which small coils are to be wound, as it is more free from magnetic materials than metals usually are.

Plywood was formerly made chiefly of birch, but many other woods are now made up into plywood. The number of plies used varies from three upwards, depending on the thickness. Layers are built up with the grain running perpendicular to the grain of the adjacent layers, and the tendency of wood to split easily along the grain is by these means counteracted. Shrinkage, which in wood takes place chiefly across the grain, is also reduced. Birch plywood is the hardest of the common plywoods, but differential shrinkage in the plies often gives rise to rather bad warping, unless the plywood is half an inch or more thick. Plywood made from Oregon and other pines is now fairly common, and is as a rule much flatter than birch. For many purposes, gaboon mahogany, which is also fairly free from warping, may be recommended. It is very useful for pattern-making, particularly where it is required to keep the casting thin.

During the recent war there was a great increase in the use of plywood for aircraft and other constructional purposes. The need for weather resistance led to the use of waterproof cements, and synthetic resins were much used for this purpose. Plywood impregnated throughout with synthetic resin has also been made. Such materials are much more stable than the older plywoods.

Metals

It will be realised that only a very brief account of the more important metals and alloys can usefully be given here. As a rule, only small quantities of material are purchased for the kind of instrument construction considered in this book, consequently except by special arrangement with manufacturers, the best must be done with what the market affords. Many steels, for example, can be produced for special purposes, but if such materials are required it is advisable to consult one of the larger steel manufacturing firms, some of whom are sufficiently interested in scientific work to go to the trouble of supplying small quantities of special materials for research purposes.

Mechanical properties of metals such as the maximum stress and yield point, which are of great importance to the engineer, are in most instances of much less importance to the instrument maker, for it is usually possible, in instrument design, to allow such generous proportions that the question of breakage under normal conditions never arises. Usually rigidity rather than high breakage loads is demanded of scientific apparatus.

The nomenclature used in connection with metals and alloys is often very confused : not only are different names given to the same alloy, but the same name is sometimes given to alloys of different composition. The composition is of more importance than the name, but is not always easily ascertained when purchasing stock in small quantities.

The most generally useful metals for ordinary instrument construction are given below, with brief notes on their properties.

Wrought iron :— This is iron of high purity, containing less than 0·25% of carbon, and small amounts of other impurities such as sulphur and phosphorus. It is, by comparison with steel, soft but tough, and tends to bend rather than break. It is not sufficiently fluid even at high temperatures to be cast, and is used chiefly for hot forged and welded work, such as is done by blacksmiths. On account of the method of production, and the presence of some impurity, wrought iron has a fibrous structure and is weaker in a direction across the fibres than along them. It is used much less now than formerly, having been largely replaced by mild steel, which is cheaper.

Mild steel contains from 0·25% to 0·5% of carbon, with small amounts of sulphur and phosphorus. Vast quantities are used in engineering construction, shipbuilding, etc., and it is obtainable as sheet, rod, tube, channel, girder, etc. Mild steel can be worked cold or hot ; it can be forged and welded. Much of the mild steel on the market is hot rolled, and is covered with a dark blue oxide, which to some extent protects it from rusting. It can also be obtained in the form of " bright drawn " rod and bar. The hot rolled material is supplied roughly to the nominal size, but is not very accurate, though good enough for many purposes. The bright drawn material is very good as regards shape and dimensions, though its surface is in a state of considerable strain as a result of having been drawn through dies. If part of the surface is removed, some deformation may occur owing to the release of strain.

Mild steel, when heated to redness and quenched in water, hardens very slightly. It may, however, be surface hardened (see later : case hardening). Its mechanical properties are good, and it is easily machined. As it is supplied rolled or drawn, it has a close compact structure and is not porous. It is consequently very suitable for high vacuum apparatus, provided that precautions are taken against rusting.

Case Hardening

When only the outer surface is required to be hard, mild steel or wrought iron may be used for construction of the object which can then be case-hardened. This may be carried out by heating the work to a red heat, coating the surface with potassium ferrocyanide, and quenching in cold water. This process gives a thin skin (about 0·01 in. deep) of hard steel over the core of wrought iron or mild steel, which remains soft and ductile. If a deeper covering is required, the work may be put in a box packed with animal charcoal and heated to redness for a number of hours, or even days. The carbon penetrates to a depth depending on the time of treatment. In place of potassium ferrocyanide, or animal charcoal, case-hardening powders may be obtained which are claimed to be much more rapid and safer in use. For example, Messrs. Alfred Herbert Ltd. supply a case hardening powder which it is claimed will give a carbon penetration of 1/16 in. in about two hours.

Hard or carbon steel contains from 0·5% to 1·5% of carbon, with very small traces of impurity if of good quality. There is not a sharp distinction between mild and hard steel ; the properties vary according to the carbon content, though many other factors affect the quality (impurities, heat treatment in manufacture, method of pouring in casting, etc.). Hard steel can be made by various processes, but practically all the hard steel now made is cast in ingots, which are then worked into the required form. In consequence of this it is usually rolled into the shape in which it appears on the market.

Hard steel possesses the invaluable property that it can readily be converted from a glass hard substance to one which is soft enough to be machined (with a tool of the same material in a suitably hard condition) and vice versa. Cooling slowly from a temperature of 740° C. produces the " soft " or annealed form ; quenching in water or oil from the same temperature makes the steel glass hard. By raising the temperature of the hardened steel, varying degrees of softness, with an accompanying decrease in brittleness, are obtained. This operation is called " tempering."

TABLE 3.1—*Tempering of Carbon Steel*

Colour	Temperature (° C.)	Uses
Dark blue	316	Hand saws
Blue	293	Smith's tools
Bright blue	288	Springs
Purple	277	Wood turning tools
Brown-purple	266	Axes, wood-working tools
Brown	254	Scissors, punches
Golden yellow	243	Penknives, hammers
Straw	230	Razor blades
Pale yellow	221	Small lathe turning tools

Grades of Carbon Steel

1·5% carbon. This steel is used for razors and surgical instruments, as it can be given a very keen edge. It is practically impossible to forge it.

1·375% carbon. This is more easily worked than 1·5% carbon steel, and can be welded with difficulty.

1·25% carbon. Used for lathe tools, drills, milling cutters, etc.

1·125% carbon. Can be given a good edge, and is more easily worked than the steel of higher carbon content. It is used for wood-working tools, taps, dies, etc.

1% carbon. Used for edged tools such as cold chisels which receive severe usage.

0·825% carbon. Tough, but does not harden well. Used for cold setts and tools which receive heavy blows.

0·75% carbon. Very tough. Used for hammers, dies for pressings, etc.

Whilst the above grades are all made and used in industry, it may be well to point out that a single medium grade, suitably heat treated, will cover very many different purposes. The steel known as " silver steel " is a high quality carbon steel, of great purity ; the term "silver" steel is a misnomer, as it contains no silver, and is not an alloy steel in the usual sense of the word. By hardening and re-heating to temperatures varying from 200° C. to 300° C., material suitable for a variety of objects, from lathe tools to springs, is obtained.

Silver steel stock bar in 13 in., 37 in. and 78 in. lengths is available to $\pm$ 0·00025 diameter in all diameters from $1\frac{1}{4}$ in. to 0·013 in. This material can be purchased in very small quantities, if required, from any metal merchant.

Stabilisation

Carbon steel which has been hardened will change in dimensions by measurable amounts for months or even years if it is not treated suitably to relieve the strains introduced by the hardening process. This makes " stabilisation " imperative if the steel is to retain its size and shape accurately. The process recommended by the National Physical Laboratory is a 5 hr. treatment at 150° C., followed by slow cooling. More information on the subject is contained in ref. 14, which contains much that is useful to both the designer and the constructor of accurate mechanism.

Alloy steels

An enormous number of steels alloyed with other metals is made, but in addition to the stainless steels only one, which has become fairly standard and is known as " high speed " steel, will be mentioned. A typical composition is carbon 0·65%, silicon 0·20%, manganese 0·20%, sulphur and phosphorus not more than 0·04%, tungsten 14%, chromium 4%, the remainder being iron. Vanadium and cobalt are also found in some high speed steels.

When this steel is heated to about 1150° C. and quenched in oil or water, or in a blast of cold air, it becomes very hard and in this condition is used as a cutting material for steel and other metals. Unlike plain carbon steel, which begins to lose its hardness when heated above 200° C., high speed steel retains its hardness up to about 535° C., i.e., a dull red heat. In consequence of this, machine tools using high speed steel cutting edges can be run at speeds which cause the tool to become red hot. It is a useful material for glass-cutting knives, as it can be used for cutting hot glass.

High speed steel has now to a great extent replaced carbon steel for lathe tools, drills, milling cutters, hacksaw blades etc. because tools made of this material retain their cutting edges much better under all conditions.

Cast iron

Along with mild steel, this is the most useful ferrous material for general construction. It has widely varying composition, according to the raw material employed and subsequent treatment. The carbon content is high, from about 1·5% to 5%, and a good deal of impurity is present of which silicon is usually the most plentiful. Three varieties are distinguished, namely grey, white and mottled cast iron—the last being a mixture of grey and white.

Grey cast iron is largely used for castings ; the grey colour is due to free carbon in the form of graphite present in the metal. It is soft, rather brittle, and has a low tensile strength. but is cheap and machines well and is used for many purposes where rigidity, but not great strength, is required.

Iron castings are not so tough and strong as good brass and gunmetal castings. The quality of iron castings varies considerably from one foundry to another : some foundries specialising in small castings turn out very good, smooth and sound work.

Cast iron cannot be forged or welded by a smith as it crumbles to pieces under the hammer at red heat. It is, however, possible to mend a broken cast-iron article by pouring molten cast iron around the fracture : the process is known as " burning on." Arc and flame welding are also possible.

White cast iron contains carbon combined with iron, with little or no free carbon, and the silica content is lower than in grey cast iron. It is much harder than grey iron. White cast iron is used in the manufacture of malleable castings. The objects, having been cast in white iron containing 1–2% carbon, are packed in boxes with some material which will prevent the castings sagging at high temperature, and maintained at a temperature in the neighbourhood of 800° C. for a number of hours. The carbon is precipitated out in the form of a powder, with well separated particles, within a matrix of iron with a low carbon content. The resulting iron is very much stronger, tougher and more ductile than grey cast iron, and is at the same time easily machined. Malleable castings are also produced by heating white cast iron embedded in an oxidising agent such as hematite or oxide of manganese for a period of from three days to a fortnight, which to a large extent removes the carbon.

Nodular or spherulitic graphite cast iron[1] is a grey cast iron which has some of the properties of malleable castings in the " as cast " form, that is without any lengthy heat treatment. The carbon in nodular cast iron is in the form of graphite, but instead of it being in flakes which produce a weak and brittle material (as in grey cast iron) it is in a rounded form which does not interrupt the continuity of the metallic matrix. The nodular form can be given to cast irons of fairly widely differing compositions. The process, which is a fairly recent development, consists in adding certain materials (cerium or magnesium) to the molten iron just before casting. Nodular cast irons have, in general, higher tensile strengths (25–40 tons/sq. in.) and greater shock-resistance than grey cast irons, and are to some extent ductile. By suitable heat treatment, greater ductility may be obtained. The solidification shrinkage of nodular cast iron is greater than that of ordinary cast iron.

Internal damping

In many structures it is important that any vibrations set up within the structure should disappear quickly, and internal frictional damping is an important agency in achieving this. Cast irons have, in general, high internal damping and this is one reason why they are so much used for instrument and machine tool construction. The damping may be measured by observing the torsional vibrations set up in a machined specimen when it is released after having been stressed in torsion to a suitable amount. According to ref. 1, the cast irons commonly used in engineering lose from 8 to 15 per cent of their vibrational energy per cycle when given an initial stress of 2 tons per sq. in., whereas for steels the figure is in the neighbourhood of 1 per cent. For nodular cast irons an intermediate figure is found.

Stainless Steel and Iron

The outline of the properties of stainless steel and iron which follows is not intended to be a complete guide to the working of these materials, but rather to indicate what can be expected from them with different kinds of treatment. A detailed account of stainless steel and iron may be found in ref. 2 from which source most of the information below has been taken.

Stainless steel and iron contain chromium, and owe their corrosion resisting properties to a film of chromium oxide. The classification is to some extent arbitrary, since a considerable range of composition and properties is covered by the quite large number of types available. Stainless steels may conveniently be subdivided as follows.

(1) Hardenable stainless steels, which contain carbon and which can be hardened, softened and tempered by heat treatment in much the same way as plain carbon steel (though with a different temperature schedule). This group contains the original Brearly cutlery steel containing 0·3 per cent carbon and 12 to 14 per cent chromium. Later developments have shown that resistance to a greater range of chemicals is obtained by increasing the chromium content up to 20 per cent, while it has been found advantageous for some purposes to reduce the carbon content and to add about 2 per cent of nickel.

(2) Stainless irons with a low carbon content containing about 16 per cent chromium. These materials are not hardenable to any great extent by heat treatment. They are ductile and may be used in cold-working processes. Like the steels of group (1), they are magnetic.

(3) Non-hardenable, austenitic stainless steels, containing usually 16 to 20 per cent chromium and about 6 to 8 per cent nickel, in addition to small amounts of other elements which improve the corrosion resistance in certain circumstances (see below). These steels are non-magnetic and show superior corrosion resistance compared with classes (1) and (2).

Material of groups (1) and (3) is now available in the form of rod, sheet, wire, etc., and should find application in instrument construction where resistance to atmospheric or chemical corrosion, along with high mechanical strength is required.

Stainless cutlery steel

Cutlery steel manufactured in England is practically standard with a composition of 12 to 14 per cent chromium and 0·3 per cent carbon, the remainder being iron. It may be softened by tempering, in which case it is heated to a temperature in the range 580–750° C. and then cooled (the rate of cooling is of no importance) or by annealing, when it is heated to 850–880° C. and cooled slowly. Hardening is effected by heating to about 950° C. and cooling in air, water or oil. This operation, which is necessary if the best mechanical and corrosion resisting properties are to be obtained, should be followed by tempering. If reheated to a temperature of from 200–400° C., increased toughness is obtained without any material decrease in hardness.

Cutlery steel in the soft condition can be machined, and machining difficulties are about the same as experienced with plain carbon steel of the same tensile strength. It is sufficiently magnetic to be held on a magnetic chuck for grinding. Forging of cutlery steel can be carried out, but is difficult, both in respect of the great mechanical work necessary and also of the attention which must be paid to temperature control. Welding may be carried out with the oxy-acetylene or atomic hydrogen flame, or electrically, and welds may be made to mild steel, but the process demands care and knowledge of the material on the part of the operator.

The physical properties of a stainless cutlery steel are given in Table 3.2, and the resistance to various corrosive agents is shown in Table 3.3.

Austenitic steels

These steels contain, or should contain, their carbon in the form of " austenite," which is a solid solution of carbon in iron. The austenitic form is obtained by heating to a temperature within the range 1000–1200° C. (depending on the composition) and quenching. Slow cooling from 1000° C., or re-heating of the austenitic steel to a temperature between 500 and 900° C. causes the precipitation of particles of metallic carbide from solution, and this is fatal to corrosion resistance. Stainless steels in this condition are subject to a dangerous form of corrosion in the presence of chemical reagents which may penetrate the metal without noticeably affecting the external surface. Because of the change in composition resulting from heating in the range 500–900° C. welding of the older types of austenitic steel must be followed by heat treatment of the whole article to obtain the austenitic form, for the fringes of the weld are bound to include regions which have been heated to temperatures within the dangerous range. If the weld is not subjected to corrosive action, heat treatment is not, however, necessary. The need for heat treatment after welding has been eliminated by adding small amounts of certain metals to the steel, which have the effect of delaying the precipitation of metallic carbide sufficiently to allow a weld to be formed without destruction of the austenitic structure. The austenitic steels can be welded to other steels.

As mentioned above, steels of group (3) cannot be hardened by heat treatment, but they harden readily on being worked (work-hardening) and this may cause difficulty in machining unless attention is paid to the effect. Sharp cutting tools must be used, and they must be made to cut, and to continue cutting as soon as they are in contact with the metal. Stiff cutting tools and short drills should be used so that the necessary pressure can be applied. It is difficult to drill small diameter holes ; holes of 1/32 in. or less diameter, if of any depth, are practically impossible in these austenitic steels.

In the soft condition, austenitic stainless steels are practically non-magnetic ; they become slightly magnetic when work-hardened, but cannot be held on a magnetic chuck. Stainless steel is used to a considerable extent in the form of castings.

The physical properties of a typical austenitic steel are given in Table 3.2, and the corrosion resistance of the same steel to various agents is shown in Table 3.3.

Iron–Nickel alloys–" Invar "

The work of Guillaume disclosed that the addition of nickel to iron produces an alloy of low thermal expansion ; moreover, by using different proportions of the constituents, alloys covering a range of expansibility can be had. These alloys have other good properties ; they have good corrosion resistance, high tensile strength and can be cold or hot worked, and welded. Machining is somewhat difficult on account of toughness and ductility.

The best-known alloy of this class is " Invar " (36% nickel), with the low coefficient of expansion of $1 \cdot 5 \times 10^{-6}$ per ° C. between 0° C. and 100° C. The minimum value is at about 32° C., and the coefficient becomes somewhat higher at low temperatures ; at high temperature the coefficient becomes quite large (approximating to 18×10^{-6} per ° C. at 700° C.). For temperatures above normal, other alloys are available with lower expansion coefficients. A 42% nickel alloy has low expansion between normal temperature and 300° C. (about $5 \cdot 4 \times 10^{-6}$ per ° C.).

" Invar " is subject to small dimensional changes after manufacture, and is not considered suitable for standards of length of the highest accuracy, though it can be improved by suitable heat treatment. It is much used for the low expansion component in bimetallic strip for temperature indication and control, for surveying tapes, etc., and in general for any application requiring constancy of length under varying temperature conditions.

Alloys of controlled expansion properties are also of great use in glass-to-metal seals. These may be, for example, a 42% nickel alloy covered with a borated copper layer (Dumet) which is suitable for sealing into soft soda glass. For hard glasses, alloys of cobalt, iron and nickel have been developed. (Fernico, Kovar, etc.)

Guillaume also discovered that a certain nickel-iron alloy had a modulus of elasticity which was independent of temperature around normal temperatures. This particular alloy was, however, so sensitive to change of composition that manufacture was practically impossible. The addition of other elements reduces this sensitivity and such an alloy (Elinvar) is much used for hair springs in precision watches, etc. The range of elasticity is rather low, which makes it unsuitable for many kinds of measuring instruments.

References 15 and 16 may be consulted for further information concerning iron-nickel and related alloys.

Copper Alloys

A selection of the most useful copper alloys for general construction of instruments has been made from the very large number of materials in which copper is the chief constituent, and others are included in the section on materials for springs (see p. 49). Other alloys, particularly high tensile and high corrosion resisting alloys will be found described in refs. 3, 4, 5 and 13. We are particularly indebted to the Copper Development Association for information on the subject.

Cartridge brass

Cartridge brass contains 70 per cent copper and 30 per cent zinc. It is the most ductile of brasses, and is used for cold drawing, spinning and pressing. The material work-hardens, and has to be frequently annealed by heating to about 600° C. if successive drawing operations are to be carried out. The finished objects should be heated to about 250° C. for 30 min. to remove internal strains. If this is not done, ammonia fumes, if present in the atmosphere, may cause " season cracking."

Muntz metal

Muntz metal, containing 60 per cent copper and 40 per cent zinc, belongs to the less ductile group of brasses. It may be used for castings, or for hot forging, rolling, etc., but is not ductile enough for cold working. It may be had in the form of hot rolled sheet, hot rolled rod or extruded sections. Muntz metal may also be used as a brazing alloy for steels.

Turning brass

Turning brass is 60 : 40 brass to which has been added 0·5 per cent to 3·5 per cent of lead to improve the machining qualities. The lead has little effect on the tensile strength, but lowers the ductility. It is much used for turning in automatic machines, and may be used for castings. The properties of this alloy are given in Table 3.2.

TABLE 3.2—*Properties of*

Particulars	Grey Cast Iron	Mild Steel	Stainless [1] Cutlery Steel	Stainless [2] Steel	Admiralty Gunmetal
Condition	As cast	Wrought	Oil quenched at 950° C. Tempered at 400–500° C.	Quick cooled 1050° C.	Sand cast
Composition, per cent			Chromium 13 Carbon 0·3 Silicon 0·4 Manganese 0·3	Carbon 0·07 Silicon 0·30 Manganese 0·80 Chromium 17·75 Nickel 9·5 Molybdenum 2·60	Copper 88 Tin 10 Zinc 2
Hardness*	130–230 (B)		450 (B)	180 (B)	
Tensile Strength, tons/sq. in.	9–28	24–40	95	40	19
Modulus of Elasticity in Tension, lb/sq. in.	13·5–19 × 10⁶	30		29 × 10⁶	15 × 10⁶
Modulus of Elasticity in Torsion, lb./sq. in.	5–8 × 10⁶	11–12 × 10⁶			Approx. 5 × 10⁶
Electrical Resistivity, microhm—cm.	75–100		50–55 at 20° C.	73 at 20° C.	15
Thermal Conductivity, cal/sec/cm²/°C./cm.	0·1–0·135		0·05	0·039 at 20° C.	0·14
Coefficient of Thermal Expansion per °C.	11·1 × 10⁻⁶ (0°–100° C.)		11 × 10⁻⁶ (20°–200° C.)	16 × 10⁻⁶ (20°–100° C.)	18 × 10⁻⁶
Specific Heat, cal./gm./°C.	0·125			0·12	0·09
Density, gm./c.c.	6·8–7·2	7·8	7·74	7·96	8·8
Melting Range : Solidus °C. Liquidus °C.					840 1015

[1] Firth-Vickers Type F.H.; B.S. En. 56D; American I.S.I. Type No. 420.
[2] Firth-Vickers Type F.M.B.; B.S. En. 581; American I.S.I. Type No. 316.

* B = Brinell hardness number. V = Vickers hardness number.

Note to Table (3.2) :—The data are taken chiefly from the references at the end of Chapter III. I

Clock brass

Clock brass in the form of hard sheet is particularly useful for instrument work. It is made by adding about 1 per cent of lead to an alloy of 65 per cent copper with 35 per cent zinc. This material machines cleanly and drills without burrs. It is suitable for engraving.

Admiralty gunmetal

For instrument castings which have to be machined, and in which corrosion resistance and good mechanical properties are important,

Metals for Construction

Turning Brass	Phosphor Bronze	Beryllium Copper	Hiduminium "Du."	Hiduminium "Y."	Hiduminium R.R. 50	Hiduminium 20 (D.T.D. 424)
Extruded	Wrought	Heat treated	Heat treated and aged	Cast, heat treated and aged	Cast, heat treated 8–16 hrs. at 155–170° C.	Cast
			Copper 3·5–4·8 ; Magnesium 0·4–0·9 Silicon 0·7 max. ; Iron 0·7 max. Manganese 0·4 –0·7 ; Titanium 0·3 max Aluminium Remainder	Copper 3·5–4·5 ; Magnesium 1·2–1·7 Silicon 0·6 max. ; Iron 0·6 max. Silicon and Iron 1·0 max. Nickel 1·8–2·3 Lead 0·05 max Tin and Zinc 0·10 max. Titanium 0·2 max. Aluminium— Remainder	Copper 0·8–2·0 Magnesium 0·5–0·2 ; silicon 1·5–2·8 Iron 0·8–1·4 Nickel 0·8–1·75 ; Titanium 0·05–0·25 Aluminium —Remainder	Copper 2·0–4·0 Magnesium 0·15 max. ; Silicon 3·0–6·0 Iron 0·8 max. Manganese 0·3–0·7 ; Nickel 0·35 max. Zinc 0·5 max. Aluminium —Remainder
Copper 57 Zinc 40 Lead 3	Copper 95 Tin 5 Phosphorus0·1					
27	220 (B) 21–48	350–420 (V) 75–100	110–130 (B) 25–27	100–125 (B) 14	65–80 (B) 10	55–75 (B) 9·0
15 × 10⁶	16 × 10⁶	18–19 × 10⁶	10–10·5 × 10⁶	10–10·5 × 10⁶	10·0–10·5 × 10⁶	10–10·5 × 10⁶
Approx. 5 × 10⁶	Approx. 6 × 10⁶	6·5–7·0 × 10⁶				
7·2	9·6	6·8–7·4	5·3		4·25	
0·29	0·19	0·23–0·28	0·35		0·415	
20 × 10⁻⁶	17 × 10⁻⁶	17 × 10⁻⁶ (0°–100°C.)	23·7 × 10⁻⁶ (20°–100° C.)	22·5 × 10⁻⁶ (20°–100° C.)	22·0 × 10⁻ᶜ (20°–100° C.)	
0·09	0·09	0·10	0·21–0·22	0·21–0·22	0·21–0·22	0·21–0·22
8·5	8·9	8·24	2·79 510–640 approx.	2·79 510–640 approx.	2·75 510–640 approx.	2·75 510–640 approx
875 890	940 1050					

many cases they can be regarded only as typical, and variations in individual cases are to be expected.

gunmetal is one of the best materials. Admiralty gunmetal contains 88 per cent copper, 10 per cent tin and 2 per cent zinc. Corrosion resistance to sea water is good, hence it is employed for sea-fittings.

Porous bronze

It is possible to make a porous bronze by sintering together a mixture of copper and tin powder. Such a material is capable of retaining oil, and hence is very suitable as a bearing material. Porous bronze containing graphite can also be made, and this may be used for bearings in situations where oil lubrication is difficult or undesirable.

Aluminium and Aluminium Alloys

Aluminium has only become a commercial product within recent times, and it may be expected that the future will see not only greater applications of aluminium and aluminium alloys at present known but also the development of new alloys. Besides its low specific gravity (2·67) which makes it exceedingly useful where lightness is required, aluminium is valuable for its high electrical and thermal conductivities.

" Pure aluminium," by which is meant aluminium as pure as the ore used and method of manufacture allow, contains usually between 98 and 99 per cent of aluminium. It is used in the form of sheets, tube, rod and wire. The high degree of flatness and polish of commercial aluminium sheet is noteworthy. Aluminium can be forged and otherwise hot worked at temperatures between 400 and 450° C. ; it can also be cold worked. Cold working increases the tensile strength considerably. The metal does not machine easily, as it tears and sticks to the tool, but the use of turpentine as a lubricant in cutting improves it considerably in this respect. It is not employed for castings except when alloyed with other metals. One of the disadvantages of aluminium is that, although it can be soldered with a suitable solder, the joint usually becomes unsound after exposure to steam, hot water or even to a moist atmosphere. Soldering of aluminium without the use of flux may now be done by means of ultrasonic soldering irons which remove the aluminium oxide scale under a layer of molten solder, so allowing the aluminium to become tinned. Convenient equipment for this process has been developed by Mullard Ltd. The joints require a waterproof coating to protect them from corrosion. Aluminium can be welded by the usual methods if a suitable flux is used for dissolving the oxide.

A recent important contribution to the problem of soldering aluminium and its alloys has been made by the Sheffield Smelting Company with " Thesscal A " hard solder and flux. These materials allow strong joints to be made between aluminium and most metals at operating temperatures between 450° and 500° C. Moreover, joints between aluminium and duralumin are corrosion-resistant to salt spray and standard accelerated corrosion tests.

Aluminium alloys

From the very large number of aluminium alloys now available, a few have been selected as of special interest. These are described briefly below; their composition and properties are given in Table 3.2. Many more alloys will be found described in ref. 3.

Duralumin is not a casting alloy, but may be cold worked, or hot worked at about 400° C. Cold working hardens the alloy. The effect of heat treatment is important. The work-hardened alloy can be softened by heating to between 325° C. and 350° C., and it remains soft after cooling (whether this be rapid or slow). If, however, the alloy is taken up to 460°–480° C. and quenched, it is soft for a short period (less than an hour, with some compositions) and then begins to harden, increasing greatly in tensile strength at the same time. This process is complete after about ten days at normal temperature, or a shorter period at higher temperature. Heating to 350° C. completely removes the effect of this " age hardening " and the alloy becomes soft again. The temperatures for heat treatment naturally vary somewhat with the actual composition.

Duralumin is available in the form of sheet, bar, rod and tube, as well as in channel and special sections. It is not a satisfactory metal for welding.

Y-alloy, which was developed at the National Physical Laboratory, is very suitable for castings. It responds to heat treatment in the same way as duralumin, but the temperature to which it must be heated before quenching is higher, between 500° and 520° C. The alloy machines well, and retains its high strength at elevated temperatures, hence it has been much used for pistons in internal combustion engines.

Hiduminium R.R. 50. This alloy, one of a series developed by Rolls Royce Ltd. and manufactured by High Duty Alloys Ltd., is a general purpose casting alloy of good ductility and mechanical strength. Casting is followed by heat treatment for 8–16 hrs. at 155–170° C., after which the alloy may be quenched in hot water or cooled in air. This moderate treatment (unlike the heat treatment required in some light alloys) does not produce internal strain. The alloy is therefore suitable for use in castings where large variations in cross-section occur.

D.T.D. 424

Very many castings are made in this general purpose alloy, which is of moderate strength and has fairly good corrosion resistance. It is made to the Ministry of Supply Aircraft Specification and is generally used as cast, but the tensile strength may be improved by heat treatment.

General remarks on the use of light alloys

Light alloys have many applications in instrument work, but should be used with caution when high dimensional stability is required. Their reputation in this respect is not good, but some alloys are much better than others. An alloy free from severe internal strain would naturally be the best choice.

Aluminium and its alloys are not very subject to corrosion in a fairly dry atmosphere, but moisture, alkalies and salt water cause serious corrosion. The corrosion may be more serious than inspection suggests, as in some cases it penetrates the inter-crystalline boundaries and extends into the interior of the metal, reducing its strength. Aluminium alloys should be protected if they are exposed to moist conditions ; the usual and generally most satisfactory method is by anodic oxidation. In this process, the alloy is made the anode in a bath of dilute chromic acid, a carbon or stainless steel rod being used as cathode. With a suitable current density, a hard, adherent film of aluminium oxide is formed. This material is chemically identical with sapphire, one of the hardest of gems, and is a very efficient protecting agent. It may be coloured by means of dyes if desired.

Because of the possibility of electrolytic action between aluminium and brass, it is necessary to take certain precautions when these metals are used together (see Chapter 19 where corrosion in metals is considered in more detail).

It may be useful to explain here that the same stiffness may be obtained for a smaller weight by using a light material in place of a heavy one. Consider the bending of a rod of circular cross section. The bending with a given load and a given length of rod is inversely proportional to the fourth power of the radius of cross section (γ), and inversely proportional to Young's modulus of elasticity for the material (E). For two rods of different material to be equally stiff,

$$E_1 \gamma_1^4 = E_2 \gamma_2^4 \text{ or } \left\{\frac{\gamma_1}{\gamma_2}\right\}^4 = \frac{E_2}{E_1}$$

If the masses per unit length and densities of the rods are M_1, M_2 and ρ_1, ρ_2 respectively,

$$\frac{M_1}{M_2} = \frac{\pi \gamma_1^2 \rho_1}{\pi \gamma_2^2 \rho_2}$$

$$\text{Hence } \frac{M_1}{M_2} = \sqrt{\frac{E_2}{E_1}} \cdot \frac{\rho_1}{\rho_2}$$

Comparing the mass per unit length of solid rod required to produce the same stiffness, for steel and duralumin (for example), we have

$$E \text{ steel} = 30 \times 10^6 \text{ lb. per sq. in.}$$
$$E \text{ duralumin} = 10 \times 10^6 \text{ lb. per sq. in.}$$
$$\rho \text{ steel} = 7\cdot8 \text{ gm. per cc.,}$$
$$\rho \text{ duralumin} = 2\cdot79 \text{ gm. per cc.,}$$

whence by substitution in the formula above it is seen that the steel will be $1\cdot62$ times as heavy as the duralumin rod.

Corrosion-resistant metals (non-ferrous)

Mainly because of their resistance to corrosion, the metals titanium, tantalum and zirconium are of considerable use in chemical engineering, and titanium with its low density ($4\cdot51$ gm/cc.) is a structural material of importance in the aircraft industry and elsewhere where a high ratio of strength to weight is required. Applications to the construction of laboratory instruments are not at present sufficient to warrant a detailed discussion of their properties here, but reference to the commercial publications listed at the end of this chapter may be made for information on properties, methods of working and availability. It has, however, been thought desirable to list their properties as corrosion resistant materials (Table 3.3), so that they may be compared in this respect with two typical stainless steels. The information in this table is taken from references 21–23.

TABLE 3.3—*Corrosion Resistanc*

No.	Reagent	Stainless cutlery steel [1]			Stainless Austenitic steel [2]		
		Concn. % by wt.	Temp. ° C.	Behaviour	Concn. % by wt.	Temp. ° C.	Behaviour
1	Acetic acid	100	20	Unaffected	100	20	Unaffected
	Acetic acid	5, 15, 33	20	Attacked	5, 15, 33	20	Unaffected
	Acetic acid	Up to 100	b.p.	Attacked	Up to 100	b.p.	Slightly attacked
2	Ammonium hydroxide	Up to 100	All	Unaffected	Up to 100	All	Unaffected
3	Aqua regia						
4	Chlorine gas (moist)		20	Attacked		20	Attacked
5	Chlorine gas (dry)						
6	Chromic acid						
7	Ferric chloride	5, 10, 50	20	Attacked			
8	Hydrochloric acid	0·25–conc.	20–b.p.	Attacked	v. dil.		Only resistant in very dilute solution
	Hydrochloric acid						
	Hydrochloric acid						
9	Nitric acid	72	20	Unaffected	72	20	Unaffected
	Nitric acid	33	20	Unaffected	33	20	Unaffected
	Nitric acid	1, 5, 10	20	Attacked	1, 5, 10	20	Unaffected
	Nitric acid	33	b.p.	Attacked	33	b.p.	Practically unaffected
10	Oxalic acid	5	20	Attacked	5	20	Unaffected
	Oxalic acid	5–20	60	Attacked	5–20	60	Resistant except in higher concentrations
11	Phosphoric acid	0·25–conc.	20–80	Attacked	0·25–conc.	20–80	Unaffected
	Phosphoric acid	0·25–conc.	b.p.	Attacked	0·25–conc.	b.p.	Resistant except in higher concentrations
12	Potassium hydroxide			Resistant except to hot, strong solutions			Resistant except to hot, strong solutions
13	Sodium hydroxide	33, 66	20	Attacked			Resistant except to hot, strong solutions
	Sodium hydroxide						
14	Sulphuric acid	0·25–conc.	20–b.p.	Attacked	Satisfactory in some cases up to 10% at 20° C		
	Sulphuric acid						
	Sulphuric acid						
	Sulphuric acid						

[1] Firth-Vickers Type F.H., Brit. Stand. Spec. En. 56 D; American I.S.I. Type No. 420.
[2] Firth-Vickers Type F.M.B., Brit. Stand. Spec. En. 581; American I.S.I. Type No. 316.
* A—rate of penetration less than 0·005″ per year.
B—rate of penetration 0·005–0·010″ per year.
C—rate of penetration more than 0·010″ per year.

Plastic Materials

In recent years a remarkable number of organic materials, many of them synthetic, have appeared on the market under the collective name of " plastics." For a comprehensive treatment of these materials one of the references at the end of this chapter may be consulted. A few, however, are of sufficient interest to the instrument designer to be described here. Many of the materials are chiefly valuable because, being suitable for moulding, they enable large numbers of articles to be produced cheaply. This aspect of plastics will not be our chief concern, and the selection will be mainly based on specially valuable physical properties which some of these materials possess. A table of properties is given below. The information is taken chiefly from ref. 6 and from manufacturer's data sheets.

Some Metals

No.	Tantalum Concn. % by wt.	Temp. °C.	Rating*	Titanium Concn. % by wt.	Temp. °C.	Rating*	Zirconium Concn. % by wt.	Temp. °C.	Rating*
1	0–100	20–392	A				5–99·5	60, 100	A
2				28	20–100	A	28	20–100	A
3		19–60	A		19–60	A		19–60	C
4		20	A		20, 75	A		20	C
5		20	A		30	C			
6	Conc.	100	A	10	b.p.	A	10, 20, 30	20, 50, 100	A
7	5–30	19–b.p.	A	1–20	19–100	A	2·5–30	19–100	C
8	19	19–100	A	3·5	20	A	5	20–100	A
				3·5	70	B			
				3·5	b.p.	C			
9	10–conc.	19–100	A	5–conc.	35–100	A	10–conc.	19–100	A
10	Sat.	20–96	A	1–25	35–100	C	1–25	100	A
11	85	145–210	A	5–30	35	A	10–85	20–100	A–B
				35–85	35	B			
12	5	110	A	10	b.p.	A	10–40	20–100	A
13	5	100–110	A	10	b.p.	A	10–50	20–100	A
14	40	100–110	C	Fused		C	Fused		A
	20	19–300	A	5	35	A	10	20–100	A
				10	35	B			
				30–50	35	C			
				60–70	35	B			

Plastics are compounds which are polymers, that is to say the molecules of which they are composed have been made by the linking up of a large number of similar units, often of quite simple structure. They are divided into two not sharply defined types. The thermo-plastic type become soft when the temperature is raised ; they may or may not melt when the temperature is still further raised, and then harden again on cooling. The other type, known as thermo-setting, are polymerised by the action of heat (usually in the presence of a catalyst to hasten the process) and do not again become soft once the polymerisation has occurred. Such plastics do not melt, but remain hard until raised to a temperature at which decomposition occurs. They may be shaped by filling a mould with the unpolymerised powder, and applying pressure at an elevated temperature. The thermoplastic type may be moulded by forcing the heat-softened, polymerised material under pressure into a steel mould (injection moulding). In addition, sheets of the polymerised material may be softened by heating and bent into shape. After cooling, the material hardens and then retains its shape at normal temperature. Both types can of course be fabricated by cutting to shape from the polymerised sheet.

Phenol formaldehyde resin is the material in the proprietary product " Bakelite," but is manufactured by a number of firms under various names. It is thermo-setting. The pure polymer is relatively little used, and most of the material contains one or other filler such as paper, fabric, wood flour, mica, etc. Quantities are used for moulded articles.

Phenol formaldehyde has been particularly successful for bonding together paper or woven fabric laminations to make a strong, tough material which can be obtained in the form of rod, tube or sheet. It can be easily machined, sawn, filed, etc., with metal-working tools, though it dulls the cutting edge of the tool rather rapidly. The resistance to organic solvents is extremely high, and the material is practically unaffected by weak acids or weak alkalies. The electrical resistance is high, making it suitable as an insulator for many purposes ; the degree of insulation depends to a considerable extent on the filler used.

It will be realised that the laminated sheet has properties which make it very useful in electrical and other instrument construction. The dimensional stability is fairly good, though far inferior to that of metals. One or two particular applications may be mentioned. The fabric filled sheet is much used for gear wheels, since it is found to give long life and silent running, and may be lubricated with either oil or water. For the same reasons, the material is used for bearings, even in heavy machinery such as rolling mills. Where gears or bearings have to run immersed in water, laminated phenol formaldehyde may be employed.

The laminated or filled phenol formaldehyde is always dark in colour, usually brown to black. When sufficient precautions are taken to obtain the polymer in a pure state, however, it is transparent and practically colourless. In this condition it may be dyed to produce any colour. The pure resin is available in the sheet form. The syrup from which the polymer is made may be cast in lead moulds, which are cheap to make, polymerisation taking place in the mould. Polymerisation may take some weeks at a temperature of 80° C. The material so obtained is to some extent thermo-plastic, and sheet may be bent after softening at a temperature of about 82° C. for a short time. It retains the bent shape after cooling.

Cast phenol formaldehyde resin is made with a graphite filling for light duty bearings.

Polymethyl methacrylate is in many ways one of the most outstanding contributions which the plastics chemist has made. It is completely colourless and very transparent, has excellent machining properties and high dimensional stability. Although not so tough as laminated phenol formaldehyde resin, it is very strong, and does not splinter or fracture, as glass does. It is very durable and weather resistant, and completely waterproof.

Polymethyl methacrylate is manufactured in the United Kingdom by I.C.I. under the names " Perspex," " Transpex I," " Diakon," " Kallodent," " Kallodentine " and " Kallodoc." It is available in sheets up to 1 in. thick either plasticised or unplasticised, and in block form 1 in. to 2 in. thick in the unplasticised form only. Rod is available in the unplasticised form. The following notes refer to " Perspex " and are based on the more complete information contained in ref. 17.

Polymethyl methacrylate consists of long-chain molecules which are not chemically linked with neighbouring chains, and belongs to the thermo-plastic group of polymers. It softens on heating, and may then be easily bent, and becomes rigid on cooling, retaining the form it received when soft. If, however, it is again heated to the softening point without constraint, it will assume the form in which it was originally cast. The plasticised form deforms under load at a temperature of 75–80° C.; for the unplasticised form this temperature is about 5° C. higher. To soften the material for hot-working, the temperature should be raised to 130–140° C. in a thermostatted oven or an oil bath. Rapid decomposition may take place above 155° C. The hot polymer may easily be bent or moulded with the aid of wooden press tools, or stretched over formers. It may be blown either free or into moulds. If wood tools are used, it is recommended that they should be covered with cloth having a short pile, such as glove fabric, to avoid damage to the polymer surface.

The mechanical stability of polymethyl methacrylate is good, but there is an initial change in dimensions when a sheet is heated for the first time, a shrinkage of 1·2–1·8 per cent occurring when the temperature is kept for an hour at 105° C. For a temperature of 140° C., the corresponding figure is 2 per cent. No further shrinkage takes place on reheating, however. The effect of water on dimensions is quite small, an increase of 0·04–0·10 per cent being observed when a specimen is immersed for a week in water at 20° C. These figures for dimensional change are the same for plasticised and for unplasticised "Perspex."

Polymethyl methacrylate may be sawn, drilled, turned, milled etc. with metal-working tools without any special precautions save the need to avoid overheating, especially when drilling. This is necessary because the low thermal conductivity greatly retards the rate of removal of heat. A better surface finish is obtained by the use of a lubricant such as soluble oil, water or a standard cooling oil. Swarf should not be allowed to remain on the surface of the material, since this may lead to crazing.

Polymethyl methacrylate is readily soluble in a number of organic liquids and in consequence may easily be cemented. For joints up to $\frac{1}{2}$ in. width, one of the edges to be cemented may be dipped in, for instance, chloroform for about a minute and then after shaking off the excess solvent it is applied to the other surface and pressed down firmly. When this technique is used, the gap before cementing should not exceed about 0·001 in. Such joints are very strong and quite invisible after the surface has been cleaned up. It is advisable to keep the concentration of solvent low in the neighbourhood of the joint to minimise the possibility of solvent crazing. This is assisted by working in a well-ventilated fume cupboard, which is necessary in routine work for the protection of the operator. Proprietary cements with varying degrees of gap-filling properties are available.

The electrical properties are good, and polymethyl methacrylate has extremely high surface resistivity, even under moist conditions. For this reason it is very suitable for the insulated parts of electrostatic apparatus. It is difficult to make an accurate comparison with other first-class insulators, but it appears to be comparable with fused silica in the matter of surface resistivity.

Contrary to statements which have sometimes been made, polymethyl methacrylate cannot be moulded directly from powder or syrup to form high quality optical components, since the refractive index of such moulded components is not uniform throughout.

The unplasticised material can, however, be worked by normal optical grinding and polishing methods into lenses, prisms, etc. As the density is only 1·18–1·20 gm. per cc. such components are much lighter than similar glass ones. There are methods whereby blanks of optical parts, machined to fairly close limits, can be optically surfaced without the use of abrasives, but the techniques are really only suitable for quantity production, as they require expensive tools. It is, however, an important advantage of these methods that the tool can be given an aspheric surface, which is later imparted to the work. The cost of making components from an aspheric tool is no more than that of using a spherical tool, and if the demand is sufficiently high, aspheric lenses (which when properly designed may have considerable advantages over spherical lenses) can be produced at moderate cost. The softness of perspex, as compared with glass, is a great disadvantage of the material and unless great care is taken, the life of perspex optical parts is much less than that of glass ones.

The chief uses of polymethyl methacrylate for optical work appear to be :—

(a) Where lightness and freedom from risk of fracture are of paramount importance, as in ophthalmic work.

(b) In making very large optical components where definition standards are less exacting than in, say, photographic lenses. The advantage of perspex for large lenses, apart from lightness, lies in the greater ease in making large homogeneous blocks, as compared with optical glass.

(c) When the use of aspheric surfaces confers a great advantage and the number of components required justifies the cost of making the tools. Hand magnifiers giving a flat field may be mentioned as an example.

Polystyrene, like polymethyl methacrylate, is a clear, transparent plastic. It is almost colourless, though in thick pieces a slight yellow colour can usually be detected. It is thermoplastic, and is much used for injection moulding of small articles. Being itself colourless, the use of dyes or pigments enables a material of any colour to be produced.

Optically, polystyrene resembles flint glass, having a refractive index 1·59 and high dispersion (see p. 201). Like polymethyl methacrylate, it is made under controlled conditions to give a homogeneous material for optical manufacture. This material is known as " Transpex II," and is made by Imperial Chemical Industries. It may be used in conjunction with Transpex I to produce an achromatic combination of lenses.

Polystyrene is fairly hard and glass-like, and is more easily fractured than perspex. It is, however, quite easily machined. It is rather prone to show stress cracks when moulded, and a sheet which is exposed to the action of solvent vapour (for example, benzene or carbon tetrachloride) will often develop a large number of small surface cracks. It is a valuable material where resistance to acids or alkalies is required, and is not attacked by hydrofluoric acid. Water resistance is very good, but it is not completely non-absorbent of water (see Table 3.4).

It is in electrical work that polystyrene is outstanding. Its resistivity is very high, and the power loss when it is used as a dielectric at high frequencies is low. For this reason it is made into foil to be used as the dielectric in condensers ; moulded or machined components are used for many insulating parts in high frequency systems. Like " Perspex," it may be formed from sheet, and components can be cemented together very readily.

Polyethylene

Essentially, polyethylene consists of long hydrocarbon chains $-CH_2-CH_2-CH_2-$. However, this simple molecular structure is occasionally interrupted at places where the chain branches to form two chains and these places occur quite at random. The extent to which chain branching occurs has an important influence on the physical properties of the polymer. Complete absence of branching gives a material which is neither tough nor flexible. With a many-branched polyethylene, a flexible material is obtained, but the melting point may be undesirably low, and for most purposes a moderate degree of branching will produce the most satisfactory compromise. The original high-pressure method of polymerisation developed by Imperial Chemical Industries tends to give a more highly branched material than the more recent low-pressure process of Ziegler (operated in the United Kingdom by one of the Shell Group of companies). The density depends to some extent on the degree of chain branching, and the low-pressure type of polyethylene is sometimes referred to as " high-density " polyethylene. The following remarks (except where otherwise indicated) apply to both types.

Polyethylene is a rather soft, waxy, usually translucent polymer with considerable flexibility but without rubber-like properties at room temperature. Its physical properties (particularly some mechanical properties) depend on molecular weight, and a range of

TABLE 3.4—*Properties of Some Plastics*

	Phenol Formaldehyde Resin			Cast—no filler	Polymethyl methacrylate, unplasticised	Polystyrene	Polyethylene	Polytetrafluor-ethylene	Polyvinyl chloride
	Cellulose paper base	Cotton fabric base	Glass fabric base						
Specific gravity	1·30–1·36	1·30–1·36	1·4–1·8	1·26–1·335	1·19	1·05	0·918–0·921	2·1–2·3	1·44
Refractive index n_D				1·58–1·66	1·490	1·59	1·51		ca. 1·52
Tensile strength, lb. per sq. in.	7000–25000	8000–12000	11500–40000	2000–9000	8000–10000	7000	1560–2500	1500–2500	7000–8000
Modulus of elasticity in tension, lb. per sq. in.	$4–30 \times 10^5$	$3·5–15 \times 10^5$	$10–20 \times 10^5$	4×10^5	$3·9–4·4 \times 10^5$	$5·2 \times 10^5$	$0·25 \times 10^5$	$0·58 \times 10^5$	$4·4–5·0 \times 10^5$
Impact strength (Izod)					0·25–0·35	0·3	>3·0	4·0	4·0
Linear expansion, per° C.	$17–25 \times 10^{-6}$	$17–30 \times 10^{-6}$	$17–25 \times 10^{-6}$	$50–150 \times 10^{-6}$	90×10^{-6}	$60–80 \times 10^{-6}$	280×10^{-6}	$80–150 \times 10^{-6}$	80×10^{-6}
Specific heat, cal./°C./gm.	0·3–0·4	0·3–0·4	0·3–0·4	0·3–0·4	0·35	0·32	0·55		0·24
Thermal conductivity, cal./sec./cm.³/°C./cm.	$5–8 \times 10^{-4}$	$5–8 \times 10^{-4}$	$5–8 \times 10^{-4}$	$3–5 \times 10^{-4}$	$3·5 \times 10^{-4}$	$2·5–3·3 \times 10^{-4}$	$8·1 \times 10^{-4}$	$5·9 \times 10^{-4}$	$4·0 \times 10^{-4}$
Heat resistance, °C.	100–121	100–121	250	<80	80–85	95	95	250–300	60
Vicat softening point, °C.					100–112		83–98		83–87
Volume resistivity, ohm-cm.	$10^{10}–10^{13}$	$10^{10}–10^{13}$			$>10^{15}$	ca. 10^{19}	ca. 10^{19}	$>10^{19}$	10^{15}
Dielectric strength, volts per 0·001 in., $\frac{1}{16}$ in. sheet	250–600	150–400			390	1000	1000	500	350
Dielectric constant	3·6–5·5	4·5–7	3·7–5·0		3·0–3·6	2·5	2·3	2·0	3·0–3·2
Water absorption, $\frac{1}{8}$ in. sheet, per cent	0·3–9·0 (24 hrs.)	0·3–2·3 (24 hrs.)	0·3–2·3 (24 hrs.)		0·3–0·7 (7 days)	0·04–0·06 (24 hrs.)	0·15 (1 year, 1 mm. thick)	Nil	0·02 (24 hrs.)
Effect of sunlight	Lowers surface resistivity				Very slight	Yellows slightly	Crazing	None	Weathers well
Resistance to acids	Decomposed by oxidising acids				Affected by oxidising acids	Some attack	Very good	Complete	Very good
Resistance to alkalies	Decomposed by strong alkalies				Very good	Very good	Very good	Complete	Very good
Resistance to organic solvents	Good	Good	Good	Good	Attacked by many	Attacked by many	Resistant to most solvents	Complete	Swollen by aromatic and chlorinated hydrocarbons
Clarity	Opaque	Opaque	Opaque	Transparent when pure	Very transparent	Transparent	Translucent to opaque	Translucent to opaque	Transparent to opaque

polyethylenes of various molecular weights is available. The flexibility at low temperatures which is a useful property of polyethylene is greater the higher the molecular weight. The brittle point of the highest molecular weight polyethylene made by Imperial Chemical Industries is about −100° C.

Polyethylene has two outstanding properties, namely its excellence as an electrical insulator (even in humid conditions) and its chemical inertness. It is cheap and is used in large quantities for insulation, and for laboratory, household and photographic purposes for containers of acid, alkali and other liquids. There are no solvents for polyethylene at room temperatures, but at higher temperatures it is dissolved by hydrocarbons and by chlorinated hydrocarbons. It is resistant to most inorganic liquids, but is to some extent oxidised by strong nitric acid. Polar organic liquids such as alcohols, organic acids, esters, amines, phenols and nitro-compounds produce cracking of the surface if the polyethylene in contact with these liquids (or their vapours) is stressed. Unstressed polyethylene is not affected in this way.

A disadvantage of polyethylene is the degradation produced by exposure to ultra-violet radiation (e.g. to strong sunlight) which causes crazing of the surface and embrittlement. The only known way of avoiding this is to incorporate about 2 per cent of a suitable black pigment in the polymer. Suitably blackened polyethylene may be used for outdoor purposes, and has been shown to be little affected by several years of outdoor exposure in the tropics.

Polyethylene is thermo-plastic. The yield point is at about 90°C., and the material has a sharp melting point at 111° C. It is used for injection moulding and may be extruded. Castings of polyethylene are readily made, since the melted material flows easily. It is also possible to make articles, when of suitable shape, by dipping a former into molten polyethylene. After removal and cooling, the polyethylene is separated from the former. In all these methods of fabrication, allowance has to be made for the large volume shrinkage (16 per cent) which occurs in cooling from the melting point to room temperature. For casting, a material of suitable molecular weight should be specified.

The rather low melting point allows polyethylene components to be welded readily, using a gas torch with a stream of nitrogen blowing on the joint. As there are no cold solvents for polyethylene, cementing is not a satisfactory method of joining.

In addition to being inert, polyethylene has very little tendency to stick to other materials (except when electrostatically charged) and may therefore be used for coating rollers, etc., used in the manufacture of films of other materials.

Polyethylene is one of the best of electrical insulators. The specific resistance is extremely high, and it is practically unaffected by moist conditions. The power loss when used as a dielectric at high frequencies is very low. For these reasons, polyethylene is now extensively used as the insulator in cables, particularly in concentric cables for high frequency work. It is not necessary to sheath these cables in lead to protect them against the action of water.

The use of polyethylene coatings for protection against corrosion is dealt with on p. 489.

Polytetrafluorethylene (P.T.F.E.)

Polytetrafluorethylene was first developed commercially in the United States, where it is manufactured by du Pont de Nemours under the name " Teflon." It is also made in Great Britain by Imperial Chemical Industries, Ltd., whose product is known as " Fluon." Polytetrafluorethylene consists of long chains of carbon atoms to each of which are attached two atoms of fluorine —CF_2. CF_2. CF_2. CF_2—. The polymer is analogous to polyethylene, with the hydrogen atoms replaced by fluorine. Information in the following account is taken from ref. 18 and refers to " Fluon."

The polymer, as made, consists of a granular white solid whose bulk density is about 0·5 grams per cc. By moulding under pressure, followed by sintering at a temperature above 327° C., or by extrusion at about 400° C., a compact, waxy material of density 2·1–2·3 grams per cc. is obtained, whose colour varies from white to blue-grey. It has a transition point at 20° C., when (with increasing temperature) an increase in volume of 1 per cent occurs, and a second transition point at 327° C. at which the volume increases by 25 per cent and the polymer becomes amorphous, translucent and similar in its physical properties to a hard rubber. Decomposition occurs slowly above 400° C. The serviceable temperature range, −100 to 250° C. is remarkable, and exceeds that of any other plastic. It is flexible in thin sheets, even at −75° C. For some purposes, it may be used up to 300° C., and it is not inflammable.

Another outstanding characteristic of polytetrafluorethylene is its chemical resistance. No solvents or swelling agents are known, and the only chemicals known to attack it (within the working temperature range) are fluorine and molten alkali metals. In this respect it is more inert than gold or platinum. The surface is not wet by water, nor is there any measurable water uptake. The surface is inert, and there are no adhesives, though polytetrafluorethylene can be welded to itself by a suitable technique. The non-sticking properties make it of great use in the processing of sticky materials. Another surface property of interest is the very low coefficient of friction, which is about the same as that of wet ice on wet ice.

Polytetrafluorethylene is an excellent electrical insulator, with properties similar to that of polyethylene. An important property is that no conducting path is formed if arcing occurs across the surface. The polymer may be moulded over metal rods, and if metal inserts are forced into holes of suitable dimensions in the polymer, they remain tight because of the elastic memory of polytetrafluorethylene.

Naturally with a material which can neither be cast from the melt nor from solution, and for which no satisfactory adhesives exist, there are some limitations on methods of fabrication. The material machines easily with sharp tools, however. Machining is best carried out with high speeds and deep cuts. For hand operations, wood-working tools are suitable. Thin films are made by the technique used for cutting veneers, and long lengths of film (0·001 in. and upwards in thickness) are made by " peeling " from the periphery of a circular disc on a lathe. To obtain non-porous films, the parent block or disc must have been sintered under pressure.

The normal method of fabrication from the powder is cold-moulding, followed by sintering for about ninety minutes at 360° C. The process is suitable for simple shapes in which the minimum dimension lies between 0·050 in. and 1 in., and may be carried out in mild steel moulds. The weight of powder, calculated from the density, is spread evenly in the mould, and subjected to a pressure of between 2,000 and 3,000 lb. per sq. in. This operation is done slowly, to allow air to escape from the powder (about fifteen seconds is a suitable time) and the formed polymer is removed after a few seconds, and baked at 360° C. till it becomes translucent. Air circulation and thorough extraction of fumes are necessary, since these may be toxic. Dust from polytetrafluorethylene should not be inhaled, and such dust should not be allowed to come in contact with burning materials (e.g. tobacco), since at high temperatures toxic products may be formed.

Polytetrafluorethylene is obtainable as rod, sheet, rings, tape, cord etc. and is made into gaskets, O, U, and V rings, flexible bellows, as well as terminal blocks, valve sockets, screws, bolts etc. It is usefully employed as a bearing material to reduce friction. A metal-polymer sliding contact will work dry, but the application of oil reduces friction further. Such combinations have been used in rotary bearings and also in kinematic slides.

Some quantitative data are given in Table 3.4.

Polyvinyl chloride

Plasticised polyvinyl chloride has been known for a number of years as film, sheet and tube for purposes which require a flexible and sometimes a rubber-like material which is impervious to many liquids. It is much used as an insulating cover for electric wire and cable. Being unaffected by aliphatic hydrocarbons and oils, it has many applications in the form of pipe. More recently, improvements in manufacture have led to a considerable use of the unplasticised, rigid polymer in the form of sheet for a variety of constructional purposes. It is manufactured by a number of companies; the information given below refers to the product of Imperial Chemical Industries, Ltd.

In addition to its resistance to many solvents, polyvinyl chloride possesses high impact strength and rigidity even in thin sheets, which makes it suitable, for instance, for protective helmets. It is transparent and colourless, but is available in coloured form; the natural material is not, however, so transparent as polymethyl methacrylate. It has very good dimensional stability; the increase in length produced by immersion in water at 20° C. for one month is only 0·05 per cent. Heating to 120° C. may cause a shrinking of up to 2 per cent however. Polyvinyl chloride is thermo-plastic, and may be shaped, like polymethyl methacrylate, by moulding, pressing etc. while hot, the temperature for these operations being 120° C. It is not suitable for situations where the temperature will rise to 60° C. or more. Machining is easily carried out with metal-cutting tools, but soluble oil or a light mineral oil should be used as lubricant.

The majority of simple solvents do not dissolve polyvinyl chloride at room temperature, and hence solvent cementing cannot be carried out, but suitable proprietary cements are available. It is resistant to strong acids and strong alkalies, to aqueous solutions of most inorganic salts and to many organic liquids but is swollen by aromatic and by chlorinated hydrocarbons.

Welding may be done by means of a hot-air torch and filler rod of polyvinyl chloride, the parts to be welded being preferably bevelled and clamped with a small separation ($\frac{1}{32}$ in.) between them, so that a space is made into which the softened polymer of the filler rod may be pressed. This pressure is applied by hand. The aim should be to produce a weld of the same length as the original length of the rod used for the weld, which will ensure that a strain-free joint is made.

Some of the physical properties of polyvinyl chloride are given in Table 3.4.

Silicone elastomer

The development of polymers based on the silicon-oxygen chain

$$-\overset{|}{\underset{|}{Si}}-O-\overset{|}{\underset{|}{Si}}-O-$$ by the Dow Corning Corporation of America has

produced the many materials with unusual properties known as " silicones." Among these are certain rubber-like materials which are of use where flexibility is required, for example as gaskets, tubing, pressure couplings etc. The following brief account of the properties of these silicone elastomers is taken from ref. 20, in which a more detailed description will be found.

The properties which make silicone elastomers useful are chiefly their chemical inertness and the wide range of temperatures over which they may be used. They contain no plasticiser or solvent, and grades are available which do not stiffen appreciably until temperatures between $-80°$ and $-90°$ C. are reached (natural rubber is stiff and brittle at $-55°$ C.). Long exposure at $150-180°$ C. is practically without effect, and exposure for short times at $250-300°$ C. is without serious effect. The decomposition temperature is about $400°$ C.

The mechanical strength and elongation at break are lower for silicone elastomers than for natural rubbers, but are maintained at the temperature extremes mentioned above, under conditions when natural rubbers quickly deteriorate. Elongations up to 500 per cent are possible, with tensile strengths up to about 1,000 lb./sq. in.

Silicon elastomers are suitable for electrical insulation, and as with mechanical properties, the electrical properties are largely constant over a wide temperature range. The water-repellent characteristic of the silicones is a useful property, and ensures that the surface resistance remains high in humid conditions.

Silicone elastomers are inert chemically, but are swelled by the lower hydrocarbons, strong acids and alkalies, chlorinated solvents and reducing agents. Gases diffuse much faster through silicone elastomers than through other rubbers. They may be used as gaskets in vacuum work down to pressures of about 10^{-5} mm. of mercury, the limit naturally depending on the rate of pumping and other conditions.

Materials for Springs

The physical properties of materials for springs play a very important part in the functioning of measuring instruments. Suitable properties are found in few materials, and steel, phosphor bronze, beryllium copper, silicon bronze and fused silica are almost the only materials used. Elinvar, referred to above under the heading " Iron-nickel alloys," is used where constant elasticity under varying temperature conditions is essential.

Elastic properties

The more important elastic properties are shown in Table 3.2 and in Figs. 3.2 and 3.3. The endurance limit is obtained by reversing the stress a sufficient number of times until fracture occurs. A plot of the reversed stress against the logarithm of the number of reversals to cause fracture is made (see Fig. 3.1), which gives this curve for

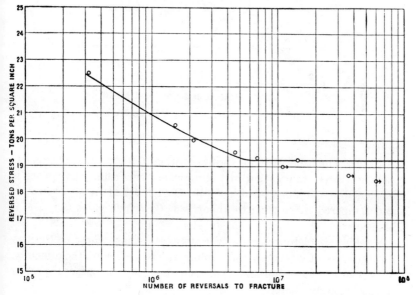

FIG. 3.1.—Typical endurance limit curves for Mallory 73 Beryllium Copper in reversed bending. Arrow heads indicate unbroken test pieces.

(*Mallory Metallurgical Products Ltd.*)

beryllium copper, from which may be read off the reversed stress at which the curve becomes horizontal. Below this stress value the number of reversals for fracture becomes extremely high, and this is taken as the endurance limit.

In the following section a few particulars are given concerning the composition, properties and use of spring materials.

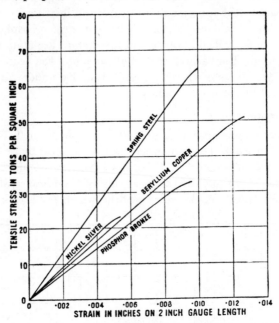

Fig. 3.2.—Tensile stress-strain curves for spring materials in strip form.
(*Mallory Metallurgical Products Ltd.*)

Steel. The usual steel for springs contains 0·9 per cent–1·0 per cent carbon. After fabrication in the annealed condition, the spring is hardened by heating to about 740° C., quenched in oil or water, and tempered by heating to about 288° C., which gives the steel a blue colour.

Steel is satisfactory for most springs except those whose deflections form the basis for accurate measurements. In such cases the difficulty of preventing corrosion and to some extent its magnetic properties render steel unsuitable.

Phosphor bronze is an alloy of copper with tin and a small amount (0·1–0·5 per cent) of phosphorus. It has been widely used for electrical instruments, where the spring usually also carries the current to the moving coil. Until the advent of beryllium copper, no other material was satisfactory for this purpose, which demands a high electrical conductivity and absence of magnetic effects in addition to good elastic properties.

Phosphor bronze can be annealed by heating, but hardening is

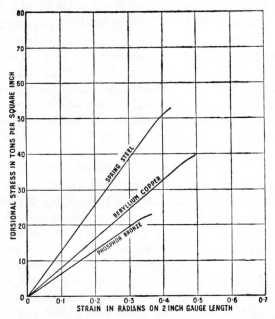

FIG. 3.3.—Torsional stress-strain curves for spring materials in the form of 0·10 in. diameter wire. (*Mallory Metallurgical Products Ltd.*)

only accomplished by cold working. This is a disadvantage, since the formed spring cannot be silver soldered without softening occurring. An even more serious drawback in precision instruments is the presence of internal stresses in a cold-worked material which are responsible for lack of stability, and for a rapid change in properties at elevated temperatures. Suitable heat treatment may relieve some of the stress, but there is risk of softening. The corrosion resistance of phosphor bronze is good.

Beryllium copper is of much more recent introduction than the other spring materials, but because of its excellent properties it is already widely used. An improved alloy containing cobalt in addition to beryllium and copper is produced by Mallory Metallurgical Products Ltd. under the name " Mallory 73 "; the following brief account refers to this material, and is taken from a more comprehensive booklet (ref. 8). A material of similar properties (also containing cobalt) is made by the Telegraph Construction and Maintenance Company Ltd.

The chief physical properties are given in Table 3.2, and stress-strain curves are shown in Figs. 3.2 and 3.3. It will be seen that the limit of proportionality extends to higher strain values (both for tension and torsion) for beryllium copper than for steel. For springs in instruments this figure is usually more important than the limit of proportionality for stress. The endurance value for reversed bending is high, which renders the material suitable for springs which have to survive a large number of reversals ; see Fig. 3.1. For electrical instruments, the material is quite outstanding on account of the good electrical conductivity.

Probably the most important feature of beryllium copper is that it is a precipitation hardening alloy. The hardening is brought about by heating for a controlled time at a temperature between 300° C. and 320° C. (see Table 3.5). Hardening may be applied to the annealed or to the cold-worked material. By the heat treatment, the strains set up in cold working (which includes the rolling of sheet, etc., as well as the bending to form a spring) are removed. This results in high stability of the hardened spring, and hence good zero-keeping properties when beryllium copper is used for the control spring in measuring instruments. The superiority of the alloy over other materials is especially marked in components which undergo great deformation in manufacture, e.g., flexible metal bellows and corrugated diaphragms. Besides stability, a high degree of reproducibility can be obtained when springs are made from the annealed or lightly worked material.

TABLE 3.5—*Heat Treatment of Mallory 73 Beryllium Copper*

Temper	Heat Treatment
Annealed	2 hrs. at 310–320° C.
Quarter-hard ⎫	
Half-Hard ⎬	1 hr. at 300–310° C.
Hard ⎭	

Beryllium copper may be silver soldered before hardening, or soft soldered after hardening, without any effect on the final properties. It is available either annealed or with various degrees of cold working, and may be had in a variety of forms suitable for instrument work, including wire and precision rolled fine strip down to 0·010 in. by 0·0005 in. Tube (including Bourdon tube) is also available. Beryllium copper possesses good resistance to corrosion.

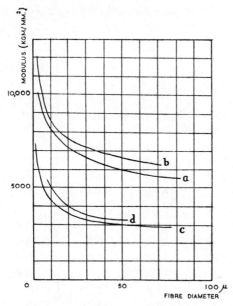

Fig. 3.4.—Elastic properties of fused silica fibres (Reinkober).
(*a*) Modulus of elasticity (old fibres).
(*b*) Modulus of elasticity (etched fibres).
(*c*) Modulus of torsion (old fibres).
(*d*) Modulus of torsion (etched fibres).

Fused silica is unique in many of its properties. It is one of the best electrical insulators, has the smallest known coefficient of thermal expansion, and is the most dimensionally stable material known. For an account of the methods of working and the use of fused silica, refs. 7, 9, 10 and 11 may be consulted.

The elastic properties are extremely good, and proportionality between stress and strain holds up to the breaking point. Internal friction is very low, and a weighted rod of fused silica set vibrating or oscillating in vacuo will remain in motion for a considerable time.

The elastic moduli of fused silica fibres, as well as the breaking strength, are highest for the finest fibres. Fig. 3.4 shows values of Young's modulus and of the rigidity modulus for a range of fibre diameters, and shows the difference between the properties of old fibres and those whose surfaces have been cleaned by etching. Table 3.6 gives the breaking strength and breaking stress for old and new fibres.

TABLE 3.6—*Strength of Silica Fibres*

Old Fibres			New Fibres		
Diameter	Breaking strength	Breaking stress	Diameter	Breaking strength	Breaking stress
microns	gm.	kgm./mm.^{2}	microns	gm.	kgm/mm.^{2}
2·25	2·18	555·2	1·5	1·42	915
8·4	9·36	168·4	1·7	1·97	889
13·7	20·50	138·2	2·2	2·82	770
18·7	27·71	99·5	3·7	6·12	565
20·4	33·24	101·6	5·0	9·30	471
25·9	40·80	75·4	5·6	12·85	528
33·4	55·98	63·9	7·4	16·60	383
46·4	83·00	49·0	7·9	18·63	371
51·8	93·85	44·5	8·8	19·3	315
65·3	136·6	40·8	11·1	26·6	273
75·7	174·5	38·8	12·2	31·4	266
93·0	219·5	32·3	14·7	39·1	230
			15·0	43·2	245
			16·3	49·7	237
			16·7	45·5	207
			20·7	62·4	184
			22·4	64·0	161
			24·5	82·1	171
			25·1	97·6	166
			31·4	111·8	146

(Data from O. Reinkober, ref. 12.)

The use of quartz fibres in electrometers, galvanometers and torsion balances is well known. Such fibres are made conducting, when necessary, by sputtering or evaporating a film of gold on the fibre.

Fused silica is also ideal for spiral springs for precision weighing. The material can be used over a wide range of temperature (though with a correction for change of elastic properties); it is chemically inactive at room temperature except to hydrofluoric acid, and (to some extent) alkalies. The temperature coefficient of each of the elastic moduli is $1 \cdot 3 \times 10^{-4}$ per °C., according to Boys.

REFERENCES

[1] DRISCOLL, W. J. (British Cast Iron Research Association), "Cast Iron" in Kempe's Engineers Year Book, 1952, Vol. 2.

[2] MONYPENNY, J. H. G., Stainless Iron and Steel (London, Chapman and Hall, 3rd edition, 1951).

[3] JUDGE, A. W., Engineering Materials, Vols. 1–3 (London, Pitman, 1943–7).

[4] AITCHISON, L., and BARCLAY, R. W., Engineering Non-Ferrous Metals and Alloys (London, Hodder and Stoughton, 1923).

[5] STOUGHTON, B., and BUTTS, A., Engineering Metallurgy (New York, McGraw-Hill, 1938).

[6] British Catalogue of Plastics (London, National Trade Press Ltd., 1947).

[7] STRONG, J., Modern Physical Laboratory Practice (London, Blackie, 1940).

[8] Beryllium Copper (London, Mallory Metallurgical Products Ltd.).

[9] KIRK, P. L., and CRAIG, R., Rev. Sci. Inst. 19 (1948), 777.

[10] KIRK, P. L., and SCHAFFER, F. L., ibid. 19 (1948), 785.

[11] SHEFT, I., and FRIED, S., ibid. 19 (1948), 723.

[12] REINKOBER, O., Phys. Zeits., 38 (1937), 112.

[13] Copper and its Alloys in Engineering and Technology (Copper Development Association, 1948).

[14] Notes on Gauge Making and Measurement, National Physical Laboratory (London, H.M. Stationery Office, 2nd Ed., 1946).

[15] Iron-nickel and Related Alloys of the Invar and Elinvar Types (30% to 60% Nickel) (New York, The International Nickel Company, 1949).

[16] BUCKNALL, E. H., J. Birmingham Metallurgical Society, 29 (1949), 55.

[17] Perspex Acrylic Materials (Imperial Chemical Industries Ltd.).

[18] "Fluon" Polytetrafluoroethylene (Imperial Chemical Industries, Welwyn Garden City, Herts).

[19] "Darvic" P.V.C. Sheet (Imperial Chemical Industries Ltd., Welwyn Garden City, Herts, 1954).

[20] BAKER, C. J., "Silicone Elastomers", Research 6 (1953), 458.

[21] The Corrosion-resisting properties of Firth-Vickers Steels (Firth-Vickers Stainless Steels Ltd., Sheffield, 1955).

[22] Wrought Titanium (Imperial Chemical Industries Ltd., Birmingham, 1955).

[23] Tantalum and Zirconium (Murex Ltd., Rainham, Essex).

CHAPTER 4

CASTING AND JOINTING OF METALS

Casting

WHEN an object is to be produced as a casting, a pattern, usually
in wood, of the same shape but slightly larger than the object is first
made. This is sent to the foundry, when a mould is prepared from the
pattern. The procedure adopted in making the mould varies with the
shape of the pattern, but the method adopted for patterns of a
simple form is shown in Fig. 4.1. The lower half of a moulding box or

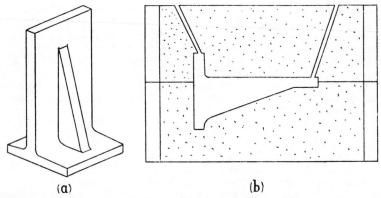

(a)   (b)

FIG. 4.1.—(a) Pattern from which a casting is to be made, and
(b) Moulding box filled with sand, showing mould formed by removal
of pattern.

" flask " is filled with moulding sand and smoothed off. The pattern
is then pushed down into the sand to a point which will readily permit
withdrawal of the pattern. The sand is again smoothed off round the
pattern and a thin layer of dry sand is applied to the moulding sand
to make it come away easily from the sand in the upper part of the
box, which is now put on. It is accurately located with respect to the
lower half by dowels or other means. The upper half is now packed
with sand and rammed down, after which it is removed and the
pattern taken out, leaving the desired hollow form in the sand in the
upper and lower parts. These are again put together and molten metal

is poured in through a hole made for the purpose. Sometimes the "parting" or dry sand layer is taken above or below the plane where the two parts of the moulding box meet ; this enables moulds to be made from patterns which would not withdraw if moulded in the way described above. After solidification and cooling, the resulting casting is removed. It will, owing to thermal contraction, be smaller than the pattern, however, and this is the reason for making the pattern slightly oversize. It is not necessary to allow for this in making a drawing for the pattern, as the pattern-maker will make the pattern using a "contraction rule," on which the divisions marked "inches" are really slightly larger than a true inch, to allow for contraction. Contraction rules for the commoner cast metals can be purchased.

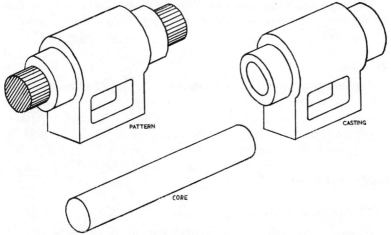

PATTERN

CASTING

CORE

FIG. 4.2.—Pattern and core required to make a casting with a hole right through.

It will be evident that only patterns can be used which are so shaped that they may be withdrawn from the moulding sand without destroying its form. Patterns are usually made slightly tapered so that they withdraw more readily (see for example Fig. 4.1) and re-entrant angles are rounded off. If the casting must be produced with a hole in it, and the hole is a deep one, or in such a position that the pattern could not be withdrawn from the mould without tearing away the sand in the hole, a "core" of baked moulding material must be made by the moulder and placed in the correct position within the mould. Fig. 4.2 shows the pattern and core required to produce the casting. Usually the pattern-maker must provide a core-box, which is a wooden mould for making the core. In the case of cylindrical cores of sizes such as 1 in., 2 in., etc., the foundry will usually have core-boxes of the right diameter, and can make a core and cut it off to the right length. The provision of projections on the pattern is necessary in order that the core can be supported in the mould. It is for the pattern-maker to provide such projections as may be necessary as well as to make the core-box, but the designer must realise that if he designs castings requiring cores, the expense of the work will be increased thereby. The projections referred to above are known as " core prints " and are painted black to distinguish them from the other parts of the pattern. The advantages to be gained from the use of castings are considered at the end of this chapter.

The inspection of light alloy castings by X-rays is now common. The lowest voltage X-rays capable of penetrating the specimen so as to obtain a radiograph in an economical time are employed[7,8].

Jointing

The surfaces of metals may be joined by means of an intermediate metal (usually an alloy) which by the application of heat is made to flow and adhere to the metals, as in soldering (hard or soft) and brazing. If the two surfaces to be joined are of the same metal, in certain cases they may be made to fuse together at a suitable temperature (welding). Finally, the surfaces may be held together by mechanical forces produced by screws, rivets, etc.

Soldering and brazing

Where no great mechanical strength is required, or where strength is provided by other means, and it is only required to make a joint tight, soft solder (tin 2 parts, lead 1 part) may be used. It is very suitable for electrical connections. Cored solders, which contain a core of flux in a thin rod of solder, are very convenient. For vacuum tight joints, some trouble may arise due to slight porosity of the solder.

Hard solders, which commonly contain silver, are now available with a range of melting points in the region of 600–900° C. These materials should be used with the special fluxes sold with them. They are in general very easy and economical in use, and the tensile strength is in the neighbourhood of 20 tons per sq. in. Most constructional metals except the light alloys can be silver soldered.

Silver solders are also available with melting ranges (solidus) in the neighbourhood of 220–275° C. Although not so strong as the so-called hard solders, they are much stronger than the lead-tin solders, and are in general more resistant to corrosion. The fluxes commonly used for lead-tin solders are suitable[1].

Aluminium and the light alloys have long been known as difficult to solder, but the position has improved considerably in recent years (see p. 32).

Brazing resembles soldering, but spelter (copper-zinc alloy) is used as the jointing material. Brazed joints are strong mechanically, but some difficulty may be experienced in getting the spelter to flow properly. It is difficult to braze brass, as the margin of temperature between the melting point of brasses (890–950° C.) and that of spelters (which are really brasses of high zinc content) (850–950° C.) is very narrow. Cast iron cannot easily be brazed.

Useful information on soldering will be found in ref. 2 and the properties of tin solders are described in ref. 3.

Welding

To produce a welded joint, the surfaces to be joined are heated locally until a temperature is reached at which they will fuse together, or molten metal of a character similar to those which are to be united is run into the joint. In the oldest form of welding (smithy welding) the metals are heated in a forge and united by the skilled use of a hammer. This method is of limited application in instrument work. It is possible to join aluminium sheet by pressure alone if the surfaces are cleaned with a rotary wire brush to remove all traces of oxide. The two surfaces can then be hammered or pressed together to form a joint which is virtually a molecular bond. The method is really more of theoretical than practical value, however.

Electric welding. Two systems will be briefly described. In arc welding an arc is struck between the work and an electrode, which may be of carbon or of metal similar in composition to the work. Intense heat is produced at the parts of the work to be joined, and these are fused together; gaps may be filled up with metal from the electrode, or scraps of metal are melted on if a carbon electrode is used. It is usual to prepare the surfaces of a butt joint so that an open vee is left which can be filled up with molten metal.

In resistance welding, a heavy current is passed through the work, which heats up at the joint to be made, where the electrical resistance is high. Though various forms of resistance welding are in use, we may mention as the method most useful in laboratory practice, the process known as spot welding. This is particularly useful for joining articles made of sheet metal, in place of riveting, or for joining wire to wire or wire to sheet as in the construction of valve electrodes, etc. In spot welding, the articles to be welded are held between two copper electrodes of small area (approaching " point contacts "), between which a heavy current is passed for a short time. With clean copper electrodes, most of the heat generated is produced at the surfaces of the two parts of the work which have to be joined, and at this point fusion occurs. A number of such spot welds may be made to weld a long seam. The current is taken from a low voltage transformer with high current output. Spot welding apparatus often forms part of the equipment of a laboratory workshop.

Flame welding. For welding purposes, an oxy-hydrogen or oxy-acetylene flame is commonly employed to heat the work at the joint to the fusion point, and the joint is filled with metal melted from a strip or rod of similar composition. As in electric welding, the surfaces of joints are usually finished to give a vee which can be filled up with molten metal.

Flame cutting. Though not a welding process, flame cutting may conveniently be mentioned here. This is accomplished on iron and steel by heating the metal locally and applying a jet of oxygen, which burns it and also blows away the molten oxide of iron, so that the metal is cut through. Steel plate up to nearly 2 ft. in thickness can be cut in this way. A refinement of flame cutting consists in controlling the movement of the blowpipe flame by means of a pantograph, so that a pointer is made to follow a drawing, and the flame traces out the same shape on the metal. This method is used to a considerable extent in producing complicated shapes from sheet steel. It produces a remarkably good finish on the cut surface. In cases where iron castings are unsuitable, e.g., in high vacuum work, or for heavy electromagnet cores, flame cutting may solve a difficult problem.

General observations on welding

Welding is most commonly employed for joining wrought iron and mild steel, but with suitable technique it may be employed on cast iron, alloy steels (including stainless steels ; see, however, p. 27), copper alloys (gun metal, brass, etc.), aluminium, etc. Some of these metals are difficult to weld, and steel containing more than 1·25 per cent carbon is considered unweldable by some.

If work is sent out to be welded, it will probably be advisable to let the welding firm shape the surfaces of the joint according to their requirements. Sound welded joints are quite satisfactory for high vacuum and high pressure work, but as the soundness of a weld cannot be ascertained by inspection, a test should be applied. For high pressure apparatus, an hydraulic test is desirable. Vacuum apparatus may be tested by filling with air under pressure from a hand pump and immersing in water, when the presence of air bubbles from the joint will speedily reveal a leak. Radiographic inspection of welded structures is now common, and for many applications such as pressure vessels, gas holders etc. it is mandatory. Initially X-rays were used but now gamma rays are extensively used and a range of sources is available. The radio-active source must be chosen according to the thickness and kind of metal to be examined. Information on sources, method of use, safety precautions etc. may be found in Kodak Data Sheet IN-16 (ref. 5), and other references to radiographic testing are given at the end of this chapter. The best results in welding are obtained when the parts to be joined are of equal thickness.

Resin-Bonded Construction

The development of epoxy resins for use as cements by Ciba Ltd. of Basle has been an outstanding contribution to technology, which has had great effects on methods of construction and assembly in many fields. The Ciba epoxy resins (made in the United Kingdom by Aero Research Ltd., Cambridge, and in the U.S.A. by Ciba Ltd.) are known as " Araldite " resins and now cover materials with a range of properties. The same basic materials find application for paints and varnishes (Chapter 19). They are, generally, thermal-setting resins of great strength and chemical stability, and their adhesion to most materials is remarkably good. They need not (except for convenience in some applications) contain any solvent, and hence the setting process is accompanied by little change in volume. They are easy to apply, either on a small or a large scale. Besides being used as adhesives, suitable modifications of epoxy resins are finding many applications as casting resins. For instance, press tools and tools for moulding plastics can be made cheaply from epoxy casting resins, which are strong enough to give satisfactory performance in many cases. They are also used as " potting " resins to surround electrical components (e.g. transformers) with a solid, water- and oil-proof protecting sheath.

It is not practicable to describe here the many kinds of Araldite resins and hardeners which are now available, and the makers' literature should be consulted for information on the full range. The following notes refer to two types which we have found useful in the construction of laboratory instruments, and which are particularly convenient for small-scale, occasional use. For large-scale applications Araldite resins are available in other forms which may in some circumstances be more suitable.

The epoxy resins are particularly useful because they bond very strongly to light alloys, which present difficulties when joined by solders (see, however, p. 32). In addition, since they can be set at temperatures well below the melting point of soft solder, the assembly of complex structures of other metals is facilitated by the use, if necessary, of brazing, soft soldering and epoxy resin to add further components without disturbing the previous assembly. Multiple assembly can be carried out with epoxy resins alone, however, for the bond formed by heat treatment is not affected by up to at least three subsequent treatments. In using adhesives it is important that no air bubbles should remain in the joint as the loss of strength is catastrophic, a "start" allows local stresses to rise to enormous values greatly exceeding the parting stress of the normal material. Both surfaces to be joined should be coated thinly with the cement, and the parts so applied to each other as to exclude possible air pockets.

Araldite Type I

This is the name now given to the original Araldite resin, which is available in the form of sticks (like sealing-wax) which soften at temperatures below 100° C. and flow freely at 100–120° C. Metal surfaces should be shot blasted, sanded or chemically cleaned, and light alloys will form a stronger bond with the resin if they are anodised or pickled in a mixture of chromic and sulphuric acids (D.T.D. specification 915A). After cleaning, the metal surfaces should be heated to 100-120° C. and a coating of resin applied to the joint either by rubbing the Araldite rod on the metal or by dusting with powder. Usually some form of light clamp is needed to prevent movement of the parts after assembly, but there is no need for much pressure. The parts should be stoved according to a schedule from Table 4.1, when polymerisation will occur and a strong joint will be formed.

Maximum bond strength is obtained with temperatures of 180–190° C.; the times in Table 4.1 are minimum values, and for joints which have to stand severe conditions of exposure it is recommended that they be increased by 50 per cent. At about 180° C., the stoving times may be increased fourfold without harmful effects. The strength of the cured joint varies but little with temperature up to 100° C., but further increase in temperature rapidly reduces it, and at 120° C. the strength is less than one-third of the value at 20° C.

Araldite Type I is available in a " silver " grade to produce a metallic appearance. In our experience, this material resists penetration by some organic solvents better than the " natural " grade. Anodised light alloy strips 1 in. wide, with an overlap at the joint of 0·5 in. have a shear strength of about 2,200 lb. per sq. in.; with chrome-pickled specimens the strength is about 3,200 lb. per sq. in.

Metals may be bonded to glass with Araldite, but differential expansion causes strain to be set up, and fracture of the glass may occur with large pieces. Iron or steel and glass may be bonded without subsequent breakage if the shape and size do not produce too great a local concentration of strain. These strains may be avoided by using a resin which sets at or slightly above room temperatures.

TABLE 4.1

Temp. °C.	240	220	200	190	180	170	160	150	140
Curing time	10 min.	20 min.	40 min.	50 min.	1 hr.	2 hr.	3 hr.	5 hr.	7 hr.

Cold-setting Araldite

Several types of epoxy resins are available in the form of viscous liquids which when mixed with a suitable liquid hardener will set to the solid form in some hours at room temperature. This form of Araldite possesses some obvious advantages over those which require stoving at a high temperature. At the present time, however, neither the mechanical strength nor the resistance to chemicals is as good as with Type I. A considerable improvement in these properties is obtained by heating to, say, 80° C. for about an hour. A particularly convenient form of resin for small-scale application is available; resin and hardener are each supplied in a separate collapsible tube and only require to be mixed in equal proportions to make a cold-setting adhesive.

Araldite resins possess very good electrical insulating properties, and find many applications in electrical industry. They are used for bonding porcelain and other insulators to metal, as insulating coatings for wire, and for embedding components in a solid resin matrix to give protection against humidity etc. Some of the applications of epoxy casting resins are described in ref. 4.

TABLE 4.2—*Dimensions of Small Rivets* (See Fig. 4.3)

(Data from British Specification 641, 1935)

Snap (round) head	Pan head	Mushroom head
Ferrous and non-ferrous A = 1·75D B = 0·75D RR = 0·885D	Ferrous and non-ferrous A = 1·6D B = 0·7D	Ferrous and non-ferrous A = 2·25D B = 0·5D R = 1·516D

Flat head	Countersunk head (60°)	Countersunk head 90°
Ferrous and non-ferrous A = 2D B = 0·25D	Non-ferrous A = 1·75D B = 0·65D C = 0·4D E = 0·79D	Ferrous and non-ferrous A = 2D B = 0·5D

Countersunk head (120°)	Countersunk head (140°)
Ferrous A = 2D B = 0·29D	Non-ferrous A = 2·75D C = 0·4D E = 0·79D

Jointing by mechanical means

Rivets. Various types of rivets are shown in Fig. 4.3. When it is not necessary to take the structure apart after assembly, a riveted joint may be used. Rivets are made in a variety of metals, varying in hardness. The pressure between the surfaces of a joint is readily controlled during the riveting process, and when steel rivets are used the pressure remains fairly constant in spite of mechanical stresses to which the joint may be subjected during use. For this reason, single rivets are employed in the joints of scissors, pliers, etc.

The hollow rivet, particularly if made in a suitable light alloy, may be very quickly secured by the aid of a punch and hammer. It is frequently used in light constructions.

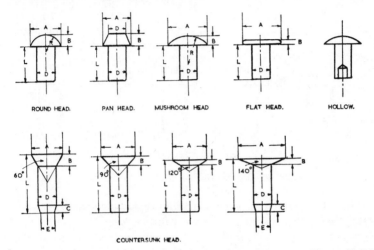

ROUND HEAD.   PAN HEAD.   MUSHROOM HEAD   FLAT HEAD.   HOLLOW.

COUNTERSUNK HEAD.

FIG. 4.3.—Various rivets. The relative dimensions of rivets according to B.S.S. 641, 1935, are given in Table 4.2.

Duralumin rivets have a valuable feature, for they may be softened by heating to 460–480° C. (as mentioned earlier), which makes riveting easy. They will harden without further treatment in a few hours, increasing greatly in tensile strength. The softened rivets may be kept in that condition if held at the temperature of solid carbon dioxide (Drikold, Cardice, etc.).

Screws are the usual fastenings employed in instruments, where it is frequently necessary to take the assembly apart. A variety of screw heads is shown in Fig. 4.4. Countersunk headed screws are usually employed when no projecting head can be allowed. They call for accurate workmanship, however, as the conical head is pulled into the countersunk hole, and it is not satisfactory to drill the clearance hole extra large to allow for lack of accurate location. An alternative is to employ a cheese-headed screw in a counter-bored (flat bottomed) hole. This allows slight adjustment of the parts before the final tightening of the screw. The cheese-headed screw is on the whole the most useful.

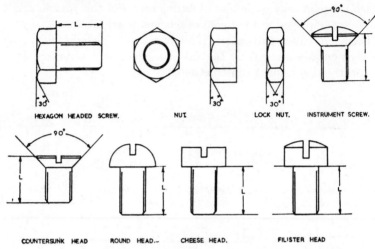

HEXAGON HEADED SCREW.   NUT   LOCK NUT.   INSTRUMENT SCREW.

COUNTERSUNK HEAD   ROUND HEAD.   CHEESE HEAD.   FILISTER HEAD

FIG. 4.4.—Types of screw heads and plain nuts.

When it is required to take apart and replace the parts very accurately, the screws should not be used for location, only for clamping the parts together, and the clearance hole under the screw head should be of ample size. Accurate location is obtained by taper pins fitting in holes. The holes should be drilled through both parts when these are clamped in correct location, and a taper reamer (to suit the pin) run through the holes (see Fig. 4.5). The pins will thereafter enable the

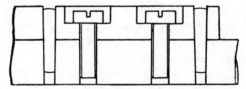

FIG. 4.5.—Use of taper pins to secure accurate location of a removable part. The counterbored holes are used when screw heads must not project.

parts to be accurately replaced. Parallel instead of taper pins (known as dowels) are often used for the same purpose. Countersunk head screws are not suitable in these cases.

A special type of screw which is being increasingly used is the socketed cap (" Allen ") screw (Fig. 4.6) which is pierced by a hexagon in the head. A hexagonal key is used for turning. The following advantages of this " Allen " screw may be noted.

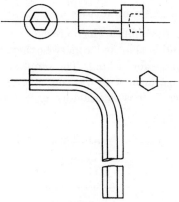

(*a*) Pressure is more under control using a key than a screwdriver in a slotted head.

(*b*) The screw is not readily injured by frequent use of the key. A screwdriver slot, on the other hand, is quickly spoiled. This is especially the case with small screws, and with grub screws, which have no head.

FIG. 4.6.—Hexagon socketed cap screw and wrench.

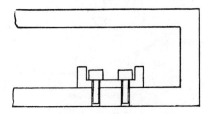

(*c*) The socketed screw can be turned in situations where there is no room for either a screwdriver or a spanner. Fig. 4.7 gives an example, and suggests that this type of screw may often solve the difficult problem of accessibility in instruments.

FIG. 4.7.—Showing the use of socketed cap screws in a situation inaccessible to a screwdriver or spanner.

Articles made in soft metals, wood or plastic materials which have to be frequently taken apart may usefully be provided with insert bushes. In the form made by Guest, Keen and Nettlefolds Ltd. these are of cadmium-plated steel, threaded externally with a very coarse, hardened thread, and internally with standard B.A. threads. They may be pressed or hammered into holes of the correct size, cutting their own threads as they enter, and may equally well be driven into " blind " or " through " holes.

Finally may be mentioned the self-tapping screw, which is to a certain extent self-locking. This resembles a wood screw, but is driven (by turning) into an untapped hole in soft metal or plastic material such as phenol formaldehyde resin. It is used a good deal on mass produced articles, but is not suitable in accurate work.

Locking of screws and nuts

Assemblies which are subject to vibration should have their screws and nuts locked, otherwise they will shake loose. Various methods are in use for locking. The simplest is to paint over the screw or nut with a varnish. This was common on service instruments during the recent war. It is satisfactory except where the parts have to be removed

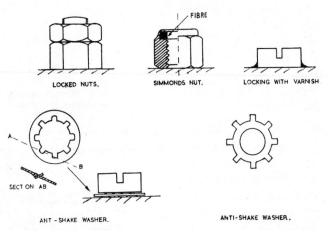

FIG. 4.8.—Methods of locking screws and nuts. The Simmonds nut is self-locking.

occasionally. In such cases, anti-shake washers are often used (Fig. 4.8). These washers have sharp projections which bite into the surfaces in contact with them, when the screw is tightened, so preventing movement. Locking washers of many types are available.

Where a more positive method is required, the screw head may be drilled radially to take a wire which is secured at both ends to adjacent parts of the instrument.

Nuts may be locked by means of the above devices, or two nuts may be used to lock one another, as in Fig. 4.8. For this purpose, the nuts are usually thinner than standard nuts, and are chamfered on both sides, as shown in Fig. 4.4.

A useful nut which needs no separate locking device—the Simmonds nut—is also shown in the same figure, This nut has a fibre collar through which the screw is forced. The friction between fibre and screw prevents the nut shaking loose. All-steel nuts made from one piece, without auxiliary fastening devices, but in which there is a considerable frictional force between nut and screw are also available.

Relative advantages of cast and built-up work

Unless one is accustomed to have castings made for workshop purposes, it may seem a wasteful process to have a pattern made for an instrument of which only one may be required, and that perhaps for a limited amount of work. It is probably true to say that the advantages of castings are not appreciated by many who are engaged in scientific work, and who from time to time require special apparatus to be constructed.

The use of castings enables the designer to consider the production of much more complicated forms than would be projected if the work were to be built up, for the construction of the pattern in wood is relatively easy. Not that complicated forms are in themselves desirable, but sometimes the distribution of metal in such a way as to obtain the greatest rigidity for a given weight demands a complicated form.

Great rigidity is easily obtained in a casting by adding flanges or other stiffening pieces, much more readily than in built-up work, and the importance of rigidity is sometimes overlooked. Usually castings will be either in iron, brass, gunmetal, or light alloy, all of which machine well. In this respect cast iron is superior to mild steel. If light components are required, one of the aluminium alloys such as Y-metal or other casting alloys may be employed.

It will be found that much time may be saved in the machining operations by using suitably designed castings. Machining is usually applied to surfaces which have either to slide smoothly over one another, or have to be clamped together. In the latter case machining is used to produce surfaces which will clamp without distortion. Frequently these machined surfaces need be only a small fraction of the whole surface ; indeed, it is often advantageous to reduce the areas of surfaces in contact, as in that way more definite location of the surfaces is obtained and the arrangement may be made to approach a kinematic one.

By raising the surface of the parts which are to be machined above the surface of the remainder of the work, it becomes possible to finish these raised portions without touching the remainder. Between $\frac{1}{8}$ in. and $\frac{1}{4}$ in. should be left on these surfaces for machining, as the outer skin of a casting should be removed in the cleaning up process.

A further point which is sometimes of great importance lies in the great difference in elastic properties of, say, cast iron and mild steel. The internal damping of vibrations in cast iron is far greater than in mild steel, hence if it is important not to transmit vibrations from one part of a structure to another, cast iron may be chosen in preference to steel.

Naturally there are many cases where it is of advantage to employ a built-up structure. Iron castings are brittle, and sometimes it is advantageous to employ mild steel structures. For vacuum work, also, cast metal is unsuitable, as it is to some extent porous, and in such work it is usual to employ rolled or drawn metal to ensure freedom from leaks. It is possible to have steel plate cut accurately to a given shape by the oxy-acetylene process, which may save a great deal of sawing and machining.

REFERENCES

[1] *Thesso Silver Solders, Brazing Alloys and Fluxes* (The Sheffield Smelting Company, Ltd.).

[2] NEWMAN, A. S., and CLAY, R. S., *J. Sci. Inst.* **10** (1933), 333.

[3] NIGHTINGALE, S. J., *Tin Solders* (London, British Non-Ferrous Metals Research Association, 1942).

[4] *"Araldite" Resins in the Electrical Industry* (Aero Research Ltd., Duxford, Cambridge).

[5] *Weld Radiography*, Kodak Data Sheet IN-15 (Kodak Ltd., London).

[6] *Gamma Radiography*, Kodak Data Sheet IN-16 (Kodak Ltd., London).

[7] CROWTHER, J. A., *Handbook of Industrial Radiology* (London, Arnold, 1949).

[8] ST. JOHN, A., and ISINBERGER, A. R., *Industrial Radiology* (Wiley, 1942).

Chapter 5

PREPARATION OF DRAWINGS

THE instructions given to instrument shops vary from the roughest freehand sketches to fully detailed drawings. When it cannot be foreseen how one part of an instrument fits another, scale drawings should be made. High accuracy is not expected in a drawing, however, as the work will be constructed according to the dimensions written on the drawing, not by " scaling " the drawing. One reason for this is that paper on which drawings are made is subject to dimension changes, chiefly on account of changes in moisture content.

When much work has been spent on a drawing, it is advisable to retain the original and supply the workshop with a copy, since drawings soon become soiled and illegible in a workshop. As will be seen from later paragraphs, little extra work is needed to produce a copy.

The recommendations in this chapter are in line with those in British Standard Specification 308 : 1943 on Engineering Drawing Office Practice.

Materials for drawing

In a large drawing office serving a production workshop, drawings are made in pencil on either drawing paper (which is tough and opaque) or on detail paper (a thinner, more translucent paper of fine texture). Then they go to the tracer who makes a tracing in Indian ink on tracing cloth or paper. Prints are made from the tracings (see below) and these prints, not the original drawings or tracings, are given to the workshop. This method produces the clearest results, and ensures that originals are not spoilt by use. It is, however, uneconomical when scientific or technical staff have to produce their own drawings and have not a staff of tracers.

For very many of the requirements covered by this book, the best procedure (when pencil sketches are not sufficient) is to make the drawing on a good quality tracing paper, in pencil. Prints may be made direct from such drawings. If necessary, dimension figures and arrows may be added in ink. To facilitate drawing it is useful to pin the tracing paper over squared graph paper, thus saving time as there is no need to measure with a scale. Pads with squared undersheets are readily available.

Paper is available in rolls 30 in. and 40 in. wide, and also in pads of various sizes ; the latter are very convenient. Good paper should stand the use of an eraser without showing the erased mark on a print, but not all grades are equally good in this respect. If it is intended to print direct from tracing paper, it is advisable to make a trial by printing from an erased drawing, as it is difficult to judge by eye what will show in a print, For pencil drawings, the paper should be unglazed. A 2H pencil is, on the whole, most suitable.

If ink tracings are required, tracing paper is quite satisfactory. Where extra permanence is required, glazed tracing cloth may be used. The unglazed side of the cloth is dusted with french chalk, which is then wiped off with a cloth. This treatment causes the ink to take more readily.

Assembly and detail drawing

A complete set of drawings consists of a numbered drawing of every part (or " detail ") to be made by the workshop, together with an assembly drawing showing how all the details fit together. The assembly drawing should show the number of each detail and indicate, by means of arrows, where the details are placed. In addition, any standard parts (such as screws, nuts or other purchased components) are shown on the assembly drawing. A list of parts required is appended, giving the name and number of each part, and showing whether it is a standard or a specially made part. It may also be necessary, in a complicated assembly, to show separately some of the components put together in a " sub-assembly."

To what extent the orthodox procedure outlined above is followed will depend on circumstances. If several instrument makers are employed together on one job, it is very desirable.

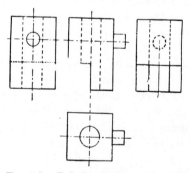

FIG. 5.1.—Relative positions of various views of an object using British standard projection. (B.S. 308 : 1943.)

Method of projection

The British standard method of placing the various views of an object (known as " first angle projection ") is shown in Fig. 5.1. In America, a different convention is used, which is shown in Fig. 5.2. This is known as third angle projection and is becoming more common in Great Britain.

No more views should be given than are necessary for complete information.

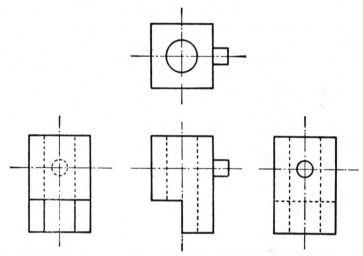

FIG. 5.2.—Relative positions of views in American projection. (B.S. 308 : 1943.)

Types of line. Two thicknesses of line, along with the use of interruptions, are used with the special significance shown in Fig. 5.3. The thick lines should be from two to three times as broad as the thin lines.

Scale. The scale of the drawing must be clearly stated. Full scale should be used unless there is a good reason for a different choice.

Sections. The proper use of sections is essential to clarity. In drawing a section, all the edges which would be produced by a cut through the section plane are shown, and the sectioned material is indicated by hatching. All lines which can be seen *below* the section plane are shown in full line ; those *above* the section plane are not drawn. Examples of sections are shown in Figs. 5.4 to 5.8. It is not usual to show standard parts in section, the exterior view being given instead.

Screw threads. The usual method for indicating screw threads is shown in Figs. 5.9 to 5.12. This method saves the time-consuming work of drawing the actual thread. If necessary, a more realistic method may be used as shown in Fig. 5.13. When left-handed screws occur, this must be stated, and in all cases the necessary information on number of threads per inch (T.P.I.), diameter and thread form (e.g. Whitworth, B.A., etc.) should be given on the drawing.

TYPES OF LINES

For general engineering drawings the types of lines shown in Fig. 2 should be used.

a. ————————————————————————
Continuous (thick)

Use for : Visible outlines ; border lines of sheets.

b. ————————————————————————
Continuous (thin)

Use for : Dimension lines : projection or extension lines for dimensions ; hatching or sectioning ; pointer lines for notes and for adjacent parts.

c. — — — — — — — — — — — — — — —
Short dashes (thin)

Use for : Hidden details ; existing installations or portions to be removed.

d. ——————— — ————— — ————— — ——————— — ———————
Long chain (thin)

Use for : Centre lines ; path lines (indicating movement) ; cutting planes or section lines (i.e., traces of cutting planes).

e. — · — · — · — · — · — · — · — · — · — · — ·
Short chain (thin)

Use for : Developed or false views ; adjacent parts.

f. ∿∿∿∿∿∿∿∿∿∿
Continuous wavy (thick)

Use for : Irregular boundary lines ; short break lines.

g. ————/\/\/————/\/\————/\/\————
Ruled line and short zig zags

Use for : Long break lines.

FIG. 5.3.—Types of line. (B.S. 308 : 1943.)

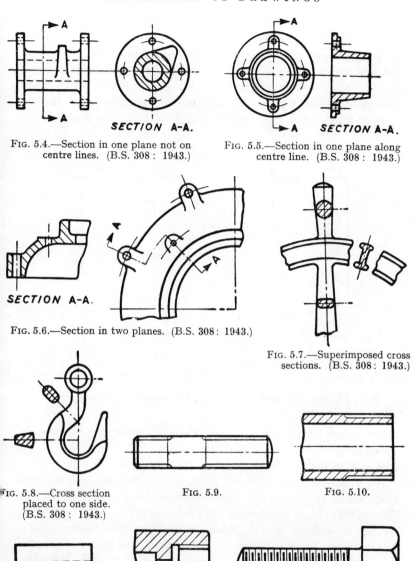

FIG. 5.4.—Section in one plane not on centre lines. (B.S. 308 : 1943.)

FIG. 5.5.—Section in one plane along centre line. (B.S. 308 : 1943.)

SECTION A-A.

FIG. 5.6.—Section in two planes. (B.S. 308 : 1943.)

FIG. 5.7.—Superimposed cross sections. (B.S. 308 : 1943.)

FIG. 5.8.—Cross section placed to one side. (B.S. 308 : 1943.)

FIG. 5.9.

FIG. 5.10.

FIG. 5.11.

FIG. 5.12.

FIG. 5.13.

FIG. 5.9–5.13.—Conventional representation of screw threads. (B.S. 308 : 1943.)

75

Dimensions and tolerances

Dimensions must be clearly indicated. Unless there is a good reason for doing otherwise, dimensions are better kept in inches (rather than feet and inches) up to at least 2 ft. Similarly, metric measurements should be kept in millimetres for dimensions below 1 m. Each dimension should be given only once on a drawing, to reduce the risk of error when dimensions are altered. If a dimension is not shown

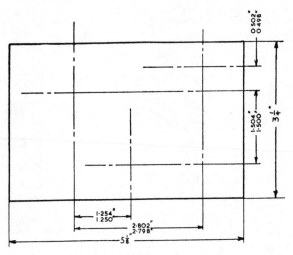

Fig. 5.14.—Method of indicating dimensions and tolerances.

of the correct length on a drawing, the figures indicating it should be underlined, or followed by the letters " N.T.S." (" not to scale "). This will be the case when breaks are used (see Fig. 5.15).

The dimensions which do not require to be very accurately reproduced are usually given as vulgar fractions. In some workshops it is the rule that vulgar fractions imply a tolerance of $\pm$ 1/64 in. This is a very convenient convention. When the work has to be more accurate, decimal fractions must be given. Here again, some workshops produce dimensions (when given in decimals) to a standard tolerance (for example, $\pm$ 0·005 in.). When the dimensions must be kept within a given tolerance, the two extreme permissible dimensions may be stated, as shown in Fig. 5.14.

To avoid adding up tolerances on individual dimensions, it may be necessary to state a number of dimensions from a common datum line. Such a line may be a machined face, or the centre of a hole. An example of the second case is shown in Fig. 5.14.

Additional instructions.—Other information required by the workshop will be as regards material, machining operations and finish. There are standard abbreviations for material and machining in B.S. 308: 1943. A more recent specification (B.S. 308: 1953) deals, in addition, with geometrical tolerances for straightness, flatness, parallelism, squareness, angularity, symmetry, concentricity, roundness and position, and replaces B.S. 308: 1943.

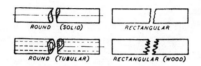

ROUND (SOLID)   RECTANGULAR

ROUND (TUBULAR)   RECTANGULAR (WOOD)

FIG. 5.15.—Conventional " breaks." (B.S. 308 : 1943.)

Reproduction of drawings

Tracings may be copied photographically by contact printing on (among various materials) ferro-prussiate paper or dye-line paper. The first method gives the familiar blueprint, with white lines on a blue ground. The second method gives black or at least dark lines on a light ground. Ferro-prussiate paper requires only washing in plain water, and dye line requires either a semi-dry development, or treatment with ammonia fumes. Dye line prints are more quickly processed than blue prints, since the latter have to be dried.

For occasional use, ferro-prussiate paper is perhaps more convenient, since it can be printed in daylight, the printed image being visible before washing. Dye line prints require a timed exposure, as the print is invisible before development. The variation in daylight intensity makes timed exposures difficult.

For small prints (say up to 15 × 20 in.) printing can be done with a 400 watt mercury discharge lamp arranged co-axially inside a glass cylinder of about 10 in. diameter. The tracing and paper are stretched round the outside of the cylinder. Since the exposure is of the order of 30 secs., the paper can be held by hand. Larger prints require a more elaborate arrangement to ensure good contact between tracing and print, and to get uniform exposure.

Opaque drawings may be copied by the reflex process, using a special grade of bromide paper. The bromide paper is laid with the emulsion side in contact with the front face of the drawing and covered with a sheet of plate glass, pressed firmly into contact. Exposure is made through the *back* of the bromide paper. After the usual processing, a reversed negative is obtained. A second printing operation reverses this and gives a positive. There is some risk that faint lines will be lost unless great care is taken to get the exposures correct. With small sheets of paper, the necessary close contact can be obtained by pressure applied mechanically. With larger sizes, however, this may be difficult and apparatus is available in which a vacuum pump is used to produce suction in order to keep paper and original in contact.

Reflex paper keeps well, but ferro-prussiate and dye line paper deteriorate after some months. Storage in a refrigerator is an advantage, particularly if the paper is put in an air-tight metal container with a desiccant such as silica gel.

REFERENCE

Engineering Drawing Office Practice, British Standard Specification, 308 (1953).

CHAPTER 6

CONSTRAINED MOTION AND CONSTRAINTS

SCIENTIFIC apparatus and measuring instruments almost always contain moving parts whose motion is restricted or constrained in some way. By far the commonest restriction is that of rotation about a fixed axis, or of translation in a straight line. Consideration of the necessary and sufficient conditions which are needed to achieve this appears to have been first made by Clerk Maxwell. The principles of kinematic or geometric design lead to the definite and accurate location of the various parts of an instrument, and found frequent and highly successful application in the work of Sir Horace Darwin at the Cambridge Scientific Instrument Company. An interesting historical account with an extensive bibliography may be found in Pollard's article[7] and more recently various authors have discussed the subject[14]. A number of uses of kinematic design in modern instruments may be found in these references.

Kinematic or Geometric Design

Degrees of freedom

The number of degrees of freedom possessed by a body is equal to the number of independent co-ordinates required to specify its position with respect to a chosen frame of reference. A point free to move in space has three degrees of freedom, a solid body under the same conditions has six degrees of freedom. The independent co-ordinates may be chosen in a variety of ways, but the number required remains the same. For our purpose, it is convenient to think of a free body as capable of rotation about each of three axes, and at the same time capable of motion of translation (i.e., without rotation) along each of three different directions. In this system, three linear and three angle co-ordinates specify the position of the body. Degrees of freedom may be removed from a body by constraining it in such a way that the magnitude of some co-ordinates remains fixed. For example, if a point particle be constrained to remain on a plane, it loses one degree of freedom. Two of the three co-ordinates required to specify its position may be taken on the plane, and can be varied ; the other co-ordinate, owing to the restriction that the point remains

79

on the plane, is fixed. Hence a point constrained to move on a plane has two degrees of freedom. Similarly we see that a point constrained to remain on a straight line has only one degree of freedom. The line may be defined by the intersection of two planes, hence simultaneous contact between the point and any two planes will remove two degrees of freedom. Contact between the point and three planes removes all three degrees of freedom. It is readily seen that the point has one degree of freedom for very small displacements if it is in contact with any two surfaces, whether plane or not, but one degree of freedom for displacements of finite magnitude requires that both the surfaces be plane. Simultaneous contact with any three surfaces leaves the point with no degrees of freedom.

The case of a rigid body may be approached by considering such a body supported by three points resting on a plane. The body will then have two freedoms of translation and one freedom of rotation (about an axis perpendicular to the plane). A fourth degree of freedom may be removed by causing a point on the body to remain in contact with any plane surface not parallel to the first plane ; the body is then capable of translational motion in a line parallel to the intersection of the two planes or of rotation about a vertical axis through the point of contact of the body with the second plane. A fifth degree of freedom is removed if a point on the body is made to remain in contact with a third plane, not parallel to either of the other planes ; this leaves only freedom of rotation about an axis perpendicular to the first plane, but the axis is not fixed. All six degrees of freedom are removed by contact between a sixth point on the body and a fourth plane, not parallel to any of the first three. Evidently, in this case, since no motion of the body relative to the constraining surface can take place, it is immaterial whether these surfaces be plane or not.

In general, each successive point contact between the body and external (supposed fixed) surfaces removes one degree of freedom, but on the form of these surfaces depends the type of freedom remaining (i.e., whether of translation, or of rotation about a fixed or a moving axis). For example, contact between three points on the body and a plane surface leaves two freedoms of translation and one of rotation, whereas if a spherical instead of a plane surface were employed three degrees of freedom of rotation about fixed axes would remain.

The most important practical cases of constrained motion are those where the body has one degree of freedom for motion of translation, or one degree of freedom for rotation (about a fixed axis), and the case of no degrees of freedom. In all these cases, it is desirable that Maxwell's condition shall be fulfilled, namely that when one of the constraining surfaces is moved parallel to itself, the corresponding point should move in a direction normal to the surface.

For a body to be capable only of motion in a straight line, five point contacts with the constraining surfaces are necessary. The surfaces must be those of a prismatic body, or bodies (in the case of more than one body, their axes must be parallel). Certain cases, which may be thought of as limiting cases, are excluded, e.g., if four points are on concentric cylindrical surfaces, the fifth point must not be on such a surface concentric with the others. Also not more than three points must rest on a given plane surface. The necessary conditions can be met in an infinite number of ways, but when the practical problem of constructing the necessary surfaces on material bodies is considered, it is seen that only flat, cylindrical and spherical surfaces, which are easily produced, are of importance. Point contacts are obtained (to the extent to which the surfaces may be considered perfect and unyielding) between sphere and plane, sphere and cylinder, and cylinder and cylinder (in the last case with their axes not parallel).

If the motion of a body is to be restricted to rotation about a fixed axis, then five points must remain in contact with a surface of revolution, or concentric surfaces of revolution. Limiting restrictions are that not more than three points must make contact with a spherical surface, or with two concentric spherical surfaces, whereas not more than four points may make contact with a given cylindrical surface, or with two coaxial cylindrical surfaces.

In the foregoing discussion, it has been assumed that the chosen points on the body remained in contact with the (fixed) constraining surfaces, but this is in general true only if some force is applied to the body to produce a reaction at each of the contacting surfaces; the applied force must obviously be great enough to overcome

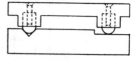

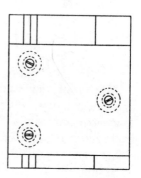

Fig. 6.1.—Kinematic slide allowing movement of a carriage in a straight line.

any forces tending to separate the surfaces which arise during the use of the instrument of which the body forms part. If Maxwell's condition (above) is fulfilled, then a force applied to the constrained body by one of the points of contact on the constraining surfaces cannot, in the absence of friction, produce reactions at any of the other points of contact. Hence the force required to maintain contact must be applied elsewhere than at the points of contact. In many cases (e.g., Figs. 6.1 and 6.2.) the weight of the constrained body provides the necessary force. In other cases, particularly in an instrument which is of a portable nature, other means, usually some form of spring, must be employed (see for example Fig. 6.5).

We now consider some of the more useful ways of realising these types of constrained motion, and of complete absence of motion, by applying the foregoing principles. The arrangements are usually spoken of as geometric or kinematic.

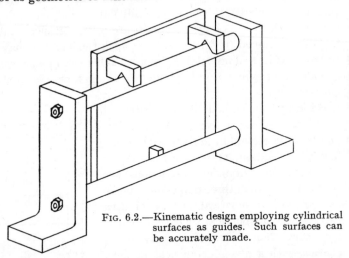

FIG. 6.2.—Kinematic design employing cylindrical surfaces as guides. Such surfaces can be accurately made.

Motion of translation. Figs. 6.1 and 6.2 show ways in which rectilinear motion of a carriage relative to a frame may be obtained by geometric constraints. The cylindrical surface being the easiest to generate accurately, preference would be given to the arrangement in Fig. 6.2, which is excellent where the distance to be traversed is not great ; it is, however, not very suitable for such a purpose as an optical bench unless the rods are of ample diameter and are themselves mounted on a length of girder or channel. In such a case it would be preferable to employ a hollow cylinder of large diameter to carry the slide on which the two vee surfaces slide. Rotation of the slide would be prevented by an arm on the slide making contact with a cylindrical rod parallel to the first cylinder. If it were arranged that most of the weight of the slide were taken by the hollow cylinder, the rod could be made fairly light. To fulfil the requirements of geometric design, the vee surfaces on the carriage should be rounded to make a point contact on the cylindrical surface.

If vee shaped constraining surfaces are employed, as in Fig. 6.1, difficulty may be found in machining them accurately. If milled, their surfaces will generally be more or less uneven. To some extent this may be remedied by lapping the vee with a cylindrical rod of the same diameter as the spheres which are to slide in them. An advantage of the vee shaped constraining surface is that it can be machined out of the bed of the instrument, which enables rigidity to be obtained.

A simple form of slide, which is very easily constructed, is shown in Fig. 6.3. For the guiding surfaces, mild steel bar purchased ready ground may be used ; this

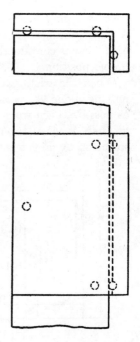

Fig. 6.3.—Kinematic slide. The spheres are fixed to the carriage.

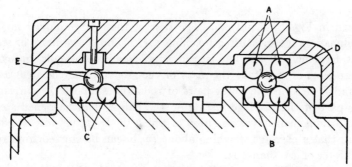

Fig. 6.4.—Carriage of Wickman gauge, giving very free motion by the use of rolling spheres D and E.

ensures a high degree of approximation to straight line motion. A disadvantage of the arrangement is that, unless the width of the bar is considerable, the slide is rather easily tilted from its proper position.

When the frictional forces to which a member is subject when moving along its constraining surfaces are to be kept as small as possible, even when the thrust between the slide and the ways is great, it is usual to employ rolling spheres in place of the sliding surfaces. Arrangements in which rolling spheres are employed are

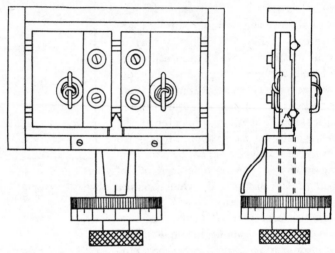

FIG. 6.5.—Symmetrically opening slit for optical instruments. Rolling motion of spheres is employed. The figure is drawn in American projection ; the side view shows the end plates removed.

shown in Figs. 6.4 and 6.5. The first of these is employed in the Wickman gauge measuring machine. *A, B* and *C* are pairs of steel rods, hardened, ground and lapped, supported in rectangular grooves. These pairs of rods take the place of vee-grooves, and the steel balls *D* and *E* rest on the lower pairs of rods and support the carriage. The part of the carriage resting on the ball *E* is of hardened steel. This arrangement gives a motion in which the frictional forces are so small that a carriage weighing about 75 lb. can be started from rest by a force of less than 2 oz.

Another application of rolling spheres is seen in the symmetrically opening slit shown in Fig. 6.5. Attention may be drawn to the use of a strong spiral spring to keep the various surfaces in contact; a small component of the tension of the spring is used to move the two slit jaws towards each other.

When an arrangement of rolling spheres is employed, the extent of the travel is limited to somewhat less than the length of the sliding part, assuming that the bed is longer than this. The accuracy of the motion depends on the accuracy of the spheres, whereas this is not the case when sliding friction is used, with spheres fixed to the moving member. Although commercial steel balls are accurate in size and

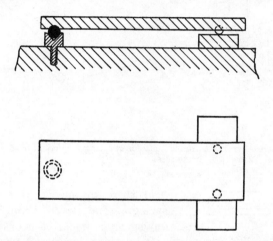

FIG. 6.6.—Simple kinematic arrangement giving rotation about a vertical axis.

shape to within 0·0001 in. it must be remembered that this figure represents about five wave-lengths of light in the middle of the visible spectral region, and departure from sphericity of this amount would be significant in some cases.

Arrangements for securing rotation about a vertical axis are shown in Figs. 6.6. and 6.7. In Fig. 6.6, free rotation is obtained by the movement of a ball in a vertical rod, whose end is bored with a conical hole. To be strictly kinematic, the hole should have the form of a three-sided pyramid. Since, however, very accurate conical holes can be turned in a lathe, the departure from kinematic conditions can usually be tolerated. Movement is further restricted by the contact of two steel balls on a flat, horizontal plate. For many purposes very satisfactory results may be obtained by using plate glass for the horizontal surface, and a simple and cheap construction is possible.

Fig. 6.7 shows the micrometer mechanism for rotating a plane mirror in an infra-red spectrometer and illustrates some points in connection with instrument design. As in Fig. 6.6, a conical hole in the end of the rotating shaft is supported by a steel ball. The additional constraints are furnished by a vee support in which the shaft rests,

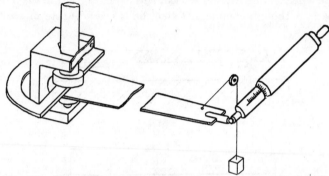

Fig. 6.7.—Micrometer movement for rotating a vertical shaft, using kinematic principles.

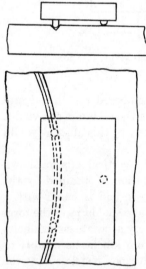

Fig. 6.8.—Arrangement for rotating a carriage round an arc of large radius.

held there by means of a stiff leaf spring. The lever through which movement is imparted is of duralumin 1/16 in. thick, but broad to give stiffness in the required direction. A steel ball at the end of the lever is held in contact with a micrometer head by a weight on a cord passing over a pulley, which ensures a constant thrust. The end of a commercial micrometer head is flat and perpendicular to the screw axis to a high degree, hence it is not essential that the ball should always touch the micrometer end at the same point. A counterpoise weight is added to ensure a vertical thrust on the steel pivot ball.

The relation between micrometer movement and mirror rotation is only linear in approximation for small rotations. A correction for this could be calculated, but as a spectrometer requires calibration, the matter is of no consequence.

To produce rotation about a point, it is of course not necessary that one of the points of support should coincide with the rotation centre. The use of a circular vee groove and a flat surface as shown in Fig. 6.8 enables rotation to be obtained about a distant axis. If the radius of the circular vee is small enough to allow the groove to be cut in the lathe, a good surface can be obtained on the sides of the vee. This may be contrasted with the difficulty in making a good straight vee, referred to earlier.

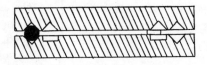

Rolling instead of sliding contacts may be used in circular grooves (Fig. 6.9), but there are objections. Since a ball rolling in such a groove is in contact with two surfaces of different curvature, slipping and hence sliding friction must occur to some extent. More serious, however, is the fact that if the upper and lower grooves have different radii of curvature, the centre of rotation is indeterminate. Evidently, if the two balls were fixed to, say, the lower groove, rotation of the

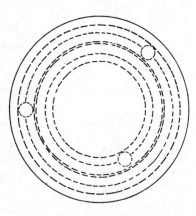

FIG. 6.9.—Rotatory motion using rolling spheres.

upper member would take place about its own centre. Conversely, if the balls were fixed to the upper member, the centre of rotation would coincide with the centre of the lower member. Since the balls could only fit in the grooves when a certain amount of eccentricity occurs, it will be seen that there are two extreme positions of the centre of rotation, with any number of intermediate ones when slipping of the balls with respect to both grooves occurs. As there is no simple, automatic procedure for making two identical circular grooves, an arrangement of rolling balls should not be used without consideration of the errors involved.

Body without freedom

It is often required to remove part of an instrument and to replace it in exactly the same position. A kinematic arrangement is excellent for this purpose, so long as the load imposed on the supports is moderate.

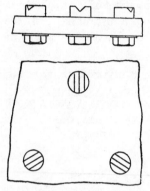

The hole, slot and plane arrangement has been often used and is quite satisfactory. It is, however, rather easier to make three vee grooves in the ends of suitable screws and arrange them as in Fig. 6.10, and this is equally good. The sides of the grooves should be smooth, but need not be flat. The part to be supported is provided with three ball-ended feet which rest in the grooves; it is of course essential that contact be made on the flat sides of each groove, not on the upper edge, which would soon become deformed in use. This would make accurate replacement impossible.

Fig. 6.10.—Accurate location of removable part obtained with vee-grooves for ball-ended feet.

It is usual to place the supporting feet at the corners of an equilateral triangle to obtain an equal distribution of weight. When, however, levelling has to be carried out, this arrangement is very inconvenient, for the adjustments of the three supports cannot be made independently. If the feet are arranged to form a right angled triangle, the supports at the acute angles may be separately adjusted, giving small rotations about two rectangular axes. Usually it is necessary to reinforce or replace the force of gravity by spring force in order to hold the parts together.

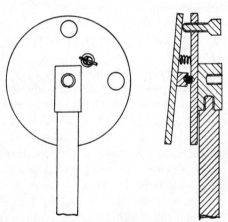

Fig. 6.11.—Adjustable mirror mount or levelling table.

Fig. 6.11 shows an application of the foregoing, designed to serve as an adjustable mirror support in the position shown, or to be unscrewed from the vertical supporting rod and replaced in a horizontal position to act as a levelling table. A strong spiral spring enables the arrangement to be used in any position without coming apart. The plate to be adjusted is supported on a steel ball and on two ball-ended adjusting screws.

Further remarks on the three point support will be found at the end of the next section.

General remarks on geometric design

In any form of geometric design in which relative motion of parts occurs, attention must be paid, not only to sufficient stiffness of the constraining surfaces, but also to the need for making the surfaces, both on the supporting and supported members, of sufficiently large radius of curvature. Unless attention is paid to these points, the motion will not be smooth, but some vibration or " chatter " will occur when sliding takes place. The mechanism of the vibration is doubtless similar to that which occurs in a bowed violin string, where the bow alternately slips and sticks.

The hardened steel balls made for ball bearings are sometimes recommended and used for geometric arrangements. They are very suitable for the case where no degrees of freedom are required, and also if they are the constraining surfaces over which other point contacts slide. But there are objections to their use in arrangements where a fixed point on such a ball slides over another constraining surface unless the latter is of hardened steel. In such a case, the constraining surface must conform to a particular shape, and alteration of this shape through wear is very undesirable. Little harm will, in many cases, result from wearing of the ball, whose surface need not have any particular shape ; there will be a slight departure from geometric conditions, as there will now be contact over a finite area instead of at a point. If desired, provision can be made for rotating one of the spherical surfaces by forming such a surface on the end of a short rod, as in Fig. 6.1. The rod may be rotated and re-clamped when the surface becomes worn so as to bring a new part of the spherical surface to bear on the constraining surfaces. In general, it would seem best to make the constraining surfaces (the ways), which must be accurate in figure, of a hard material such as steel or cast iron, and the surfaces which slide over them of a softer material, e.g., brass or gunmetal. These surfaces need only be convex, but not necessarily spherical. If the ways can be made of hardened steel, there is not much objection to the use of steel balls for the sliding surfaces, as the rate of wear will be small.

Geometric constraints are not suitable for instruments in which the sliding parts carry a heavy load, or are subject to stresses which vary considerably in magnitude, for with heavy loads unduly rapid wear will occur at the point contacts, and with varying loads the yielding of the surfaces will vary according to the reaction between them. Owing to the " point contact " which is established between the contacting plane and spherical surfaces, or other surfaces employed, very large pressures may be developed, with corresponding deformations of the surfaces.

Geometric constraints are often rather fragile and the contacting surfaces may sometimes be separated by quite small forces. To some extent this may be overcome by providing sufficiently stiff springs to hold the surfaces in contact, but there is no doubt that many cases arise in instrument design where the geometric type of constraint is unsuitable.

The " three point support " which is often used in instruments which stand on a laboratory bench may be a good or a bad application of geometric design according to the manner in which it is applied. The intention is to provide a support which can be used on an uneven surface, and this the three point support does. If, however, the points are not sufficiently widely separated, there is great danger that the instrument will be easily overturned. A fairly safe arrangement is one in which the supports are situated at the angles of a triangle of such a size that the plan of the instrument falls wholly within the triangle. A very bad arrangement, sometimes seen, is one in which the instrument is contained within a solid rectangular box (e.g., a table galvanometer or ammeter, etc.), and the supports are three small balls on the under side of the box. The arrangement is not very stable, and the user of the instrument may not be aware of the instability until pressure applied to one of the corners results in the instrument tipping over.

The accuracy of performance of a geometrically constrained mechanism

It is one of the advantages of geometrical construction that the effect produced by one or more of the surfaces being out of its true position by a known amount can readily be calculated. It is of interest to investigate the effect of small inaccuracies in the constraining surfaces due to faults in machining.

Consider a slide in which cylindrical surfaces are employed. Whether the surfaces are turned between centres and filed, or ground between centres, or turned between centres with cemented carbide tools, constancy of diameter within 0·0001 in. can be obtained and checked with a good micrometer screw gauge. Straightness to within the same limits is ensured by the method of manufacture. Each point contact as it moves along its surface is liable to departure from the true straight line. In the case of the slide shown in Fig. 6.4, this will not cause any departure from straight line motion in the horizontal plane, but in the vertical plane appreciable departure may occur, with a maximum range of 0·0001 in. At the same time, since one ball may be on a raised portion whilst another is on a depression, rotation may occur. If the distance between the centres of the two balls on one slide is b inches and the distance between centres of the cylindrical surfaces is a inches, then angular movements about the direction of motion can occur, the range in radians being $\dfrac{0 \cdot 0002}{a}$.

Similarly rotation about a horizontal axis perpendicular to the line of motion over a range of $\dfrac{0 \cdot 0002}{b}$ radians is possible. In laboratory instruments a and b might possibly be less than 6 in. ; the angular rotations corresponding to this limit (0·000033 radian) would easily be detectable with a sensitive spirit level or an auto-collinating telescope. They would make the slide quite useless for carrying the mirror of a Michelson or Fabry-Perot interferometer. In many cases, however, it may be possible so to arrange the parts of a geometric arrangement that errors caused by departure from the true shape of the surfaces is not detrimental. This is considered in a later chapter.

By using cylindrical lapped surfaces, the accuracy with which a cylindrical surface may be approached is rendered much higher ; not only is the general constancy of diameter improved, but also local irregularities are removed.

Modifications to geometric design

The unsuitability of geometric design in cases where heavy or variable loads are imposed on the sliding member has already been noted. Since it is the sliding " point " contacts which are responsible for rapid wear and deformation in such cases, a remedy may be found either by using rolling spheres or by forming the contacts so that they extend over a surface of sufficiently large area for the load to be carried. The use of rolling spheres prevents wear, but does not prevent local deformation of the surfaces on account of the large pressures developed at the " point " contacts (which are, of course, small areas in reality). The other modification, which has been discussed by Whitehead[4] under the name of " semi-kinematic design," does reduce local deformation. Consideration will now be given to some of the ways in which semi-kinematic constraints can be designed, and to consider the possibilities in relation to the means available for construction.

The most useful characteristic of geometric or kinematic design is that the conditions to be fulfilled are (in addition to ensuring that the necessary rigidity of the parts is obtained) that certain parts of the apparatus must have accuracy of form, but not necessarily accuracy of dimensions. This advantage may still be retained in some cases where semi-geometric design is employed, but more surfaces will have to be given accurate forms than in the case of pure geometric design. In some cases, accuracy of dimensions will be required also, and the design should be such that the required accuracy is easily obtained in the workshop. It is, for example, easy to produce circular holes and shafts to given diameters, but much more difficult to make two holes with their centres a given distance apart, to the same order of accuracy.

If the methods of producing motion in a straight line shown in Figs. 6.1, 6.2 and 6.3 are considered, and the point contacts are imagined expanded into contacting surfaces, it will be seen that the difficulties of manufacture are not the same in all three cases. Much the simplest semi-geometric slide to construct would be a modification of Fig. 6.3. The three co-planar areas on the one side of the sliding part could be ground flat with one setting of a surface grinder, and the two co-planar areas on the other side would similarly be produced at one operation. It is true that the angle between these sets of surfaces must be the same as that between the constraining surfaces, but no difficulty would be experienced in obtaining the necessary accuracy, especially if the angle were a right angle.

Because of the accuracy with which cylindrical surfaces can be produced, it is of interest to consider a semi-geometric modification of Fig. 6.2 ; this is shown in Fig. 6.12. The easiest way of forming the necessary surfaces would be to bore or ream out a hole of the same diameter as the cylindrical rod and then to relieve or cut away the material until four separate surfaces were left to make contact on the cylinder. It might be thought that there would be no advantage, and possibly some loss of robustness as a result of cutting away parts of the material in this way. If it were not done, a clearance or allowance would have to be left between the cylindrical rod and the hole in which it fitted, with some indefiniteness in the relative positions of the two parts, though good workmanship could reduce this to a very small amount. By making use of four separate surfaces, it is ensured that points of contact occur within each surface ; the actual situation

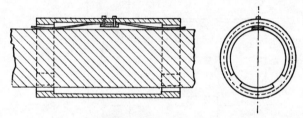

Fig. 6.12.—Semi-kinematic element, with bearing surfaces of appreciable area.

of these points is unknown, and this degree of uncertainty is in proportion to the extent of the departure from pure geometric design. The constraining or guiding surface which removes the freedom of rotation about the cylindrical surface, as well as the surface which bears on it would be preferably made flat. If these surfaces were made cylindrical, with a finite area of contact, dimensional accuracy of a kind difficult to attain would be required, and over-constraint would almost certainly result.

Semi-kinematic design is suitable for instruments which are intermediate between light, precision measuring instruments and the much heavier mechanism of the engineering workshop. The microtome used for cutting sections for the microscope is a good example. It is therefore of interest to note that semi-kinematic design is used by some manufacturers of microtomes. Fig. 6.13 shows the moving carriage or sledge of a Sartorius microtome. The resemblance to Fig. 6.2 is quite close, apart from the much heavier construction and the small areas which replace the " point contacts " of the kinematic design.

When semi-geometric modifications for motion restricted to rotation about a fixed axis are considered, it will be seen that considerable difficulty may arise in forming the surfaces which are to slide on the guides. For example, such a modification to Fig. 6.8 would present considerable practical difficulties. This is due to the fact that, although surfaces of revolution which range over a complete revolution are easily generated with the necessary accuracy, it is difficult, when only part of the complete surface is required, to obtain accuracy except by first forming the whole surface and then cutting away the part not required.

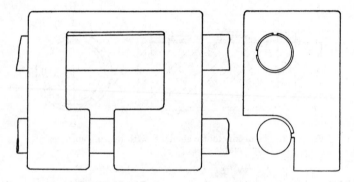

FIG. 6.13.—Semi-kinematic slide of Sartorius microtome.

If the load imposed on the constraint is considerable, or the speed of rotation is high, geometric constraint is unsuitable and it is worth while considering the use of ball bearings or of a plain journal bearing instead of a semi-geometric constraint. For many purposes ball bearings will be found good enough. For the greatest constancy of the axis of rotation under the conditions mentioned above, the best results are obtained from a plain journal bearing (a cylindrical shaft fitting in a cylindrical hole), in which both journal and bearing are made of hardened steel, lapped separately until they just fit. As lubricant, kerosene is sometimes used, but if the allowance between shaft and hole is sufficiently small, and the surfaces sufficiently perfect, air lubrication is all that is required. The degree to which friction and " play " are absent from a well constructed bearing of this kind is remarkable. Kerosene lubricated and dry bearings find some applications in machine tools.

Constrained motion employing elastic deformation

A familiar example of elastic deformation employed to control motion is afforded by the torsion wire or strip used in galvanometers. If a body is simply suspended by means of a torsion wire, it is not restricted to rotation about a fixed axis, but the forces opposing other motions (usually components of the weight of the body) can be increased out of all proportion to the forces opposing rotation about the fibre as axis, so that the motion is practically restricted to rotation. If the body is held between two stretched fibres, as in the Moll galvanometer (p. 136) the restriction to one degree of freedom is still closer.

An extensive bibliography of flexure devices is given in ref. 13.

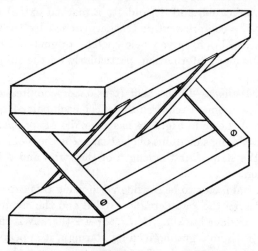

Fig. 6.14.—Strip hinge, giving rotation about a fixed axis and using elastic deformation.

The Cross-Spring Pivot or strip hinge is a constructional element now used in a variety of instruments. A simple form is illustrated in Fig. 6.14. This consists of two pairs of flat springs, usually steel, securely fastened by screws or solder, etc., to two metal blocks, one of which is to be allowed to rotate with respect to the other. The arrangement is very stiff to all forces except those which bend the strips so as to allow such rotation to take place. In consequence, it behaves like a hinge between the blocks, and may be used in place of an ordinary hinge or pivot.

The chief advantage is that as there are no sliding or rolling parts, no external frictional forces have to be overcome before a turning moment applied to one block produces appreciable rotation. There is therefore practically no hysteresis in the movement, and no backlash, neither is there any wear and consequent change in properties with repeated use. The chief disadvantages are that the arrangement is only suitable for rather small deflections, and that the reaction increases with the deflection.

The rotation of one part with respect to the other takes place around the axis of intersection of the strips, provided the deflection is small. Haringx[8] has recently investigated theoretically the behaviour of the pivot, and has compared some of his conclusions with some observations of Young[9]. Haringx's work shows that the behaviour is quite complicated, and depends to a marked extent on the load (which may be compression or tension) carried by the strips. His conclusions are briefly given below. The original work should be consulted for more information, particularly on the subject of large deflections.

Small Deflections.—If the load (tension or compression) is quite negligible, the moment required to deflect each pair of springs (note that the pivot shown in Fig. 6.14 has *two* pairs of springs) is $2 E I \psi/L$. Here E is Young's modulus of elasticity, I is the moment of inertia of area of the strip, L is the length of the strip, and ψ is the angular deflection.

The essential factor to be considered in using this expression is the relation between the load actually carried and the compression load required to produce buckling, $N L^2/4\pi^2 E I$ (here N is the load on a single strip). From a graph given by Haringx, it appears that if the compression load is 10 per cent of the buckling load, the moment for deflection of a single spring is increased approximately 50 per cent, becoming approximately $\frac{3}{2} E I \psi/L$. If a load in tension of the same magnitude is applied, the moment is reduced approximately 50 per cent to $\frac{1}{2} E I \psi/L$. For smaller loads than 10 per cent of the buckling load, the change is proportional. It will be appreciated that the load on each spring in a pair is not necessarily the same ; the total moment per pair is found by adding the moments for each component strip.

The expressions given by Haringx, from which the moment M_i of a single loaded spring may be accurately calculated for small deflections are :

$$\frac{M_i L}{E I \psi} = \frac{\frac{1}{2} q L}{tan \frac{1}{2} q L} + \frac{1}{4} q^2 L^2 \quad \text{(compression)}$$

and

$$\frac{M_i L}{E I \psi} = \frac{\frac{1}{2} q' L}{tanh \frac{1}{2} q' L} - \frac{1}{4} q'^2 L^2 \quad \text{(tension)}$$

where

$$q = \sqrt{\frac{N}{EI}}$$

and

$$q' = \sqrt{\frac{-N}{EI}}$$

It is to be noted that N is positive or negative according to whether the force is one of compression or of tension. For small deflections, the spring constant M_i is independent of the intersection angle of the springs.

For a compressed spring, M_i first increases with the load N, goes through a maximum, then falls to zero and finally becomes negative. going to infinity at the buckling load. With an increasing tension force, M_i diminishes steadily from its initial positive value, going through zero to increasing negative values.

If the restoring couple on the pivot consequent upon a deflection ψ were caused only by the elastic force of the bent strips, zero and negative values of M_i would indicate, respectively, neutral and unstable equilibrium. In many cases, however, the load on the strips produces an additional couple when the system is deflected. This may increase or diminish the stability. In Fig. 6.14, it is evident that if the upper member were fixed, the movement of the lower part is stabilised by its own weight. If, however, the lower member were fixed, the weight of the upper part would tend to produce instability. This effect is apart from and additional to the effect of the load on the elastic forces.

Though simple in character, the cross spring pivot requires accurate construction if the theoretical predictions are to be fulfilled. It is robust, and suited for use in quite large and heavy instruments (for instance, it has been used in wind tunnel balances for aerodynamic research). It readily finds application as the pivot of a lever system for magnifying small movements (see p. 110).

Effect of large deflections

When the deflections are large, the problem becomes too complicated for general treatment. If, however, the loading forces of compression or tension can be neglected, the effect of other factors can be calculated, and this has been done by Haringx.

For deflections greater than about 10 deg., the spring constant becomes appreciably greater than $2EI/L$, the increase being greater for large intersection angles of the springs. This increase is approximately 10 per cent for a deflection angle of 45 deg. when the springs intersect at 90 deg.

The centre of rotation is not fixed for large angles of deflection. Here again, the effect is somewhat greater for large intersection angles. In a pivot with 90 deg. angle of intersection, the displacement is about 1 per cent of the spring length L for a deflection of 17 deg. It is not proportional to the deflection, however. Haringx's paper may be consulted for more detailed information. The experimental results obtained by Young[9] appear to be in fairly good agreement with Haringx's formulae, but, as mentioned by the latter, there are discrepancies which are probably caused by initial distortion in fixing the springs. Because of this possibility, the theoretical results should not be relied upon to give exactly the performance of an actual pivot.

As Young has pointed out, the effect of the movement of the pivot point on the magnification produced when the cross spring pivot is used as a lever depends on the disposition of the lever arms. It is an advantage, if constant magnification is needed, to have both lever arms on the same side of the pivot, so that at least they are both altered in the same sense.

Both Haringx and Young consider that the greater stability of a pivot with 90 deg. intersection angle generally outweighs other advantages of a smaller angle (see above). Young mentions that the springs should generally be as long as considerations of stability and pivot motion allow, and that, if used as a lever, the short arm should be at least equal in length to the spring, to make the movement of the pivot point of little consequence. We may note, however, that if constant lever ratio is not important, this condition may be relaxed.

A useful investigation into the properties of cross-spring hinges has been described by Nickols and Wunsch in a paper which gives a considerable amount of quantitative information for designers.[10] The investigation was restricted to pivots consisting of two pairs of springs with their neutral axes at 90 deg., subjected to purely torsional forces.

The authors stress the need for suitable clamps for the spring strips, and describe these and also a method of assembly by means of jigs which allows the necessary accuracy of position to be obtained. Measurements of the moment required for unit angular deflection were made for strips varying in thickness up to 0·02 in. and in length up to ¾ in. These results were found to be in approximate agreement with theoretical prediction, but considerably better agreement was obtained if the measured length L was increased by a constant amount, and an empirical formula which incorporates this result is

$$M = \frac{2\,E\,I\,\psi}{L + \delta}$$

The constant δ has the value 0·035 if the other quantities are expressed in inches and pounds (ψ is in radians). If centimetres and kilograms are the units employed, δ has the value 0·089. These results are expressed graphically in Fig. 6.15, and are given for the convenience of designers.

The shift of the initial axis of rotation was also measured for the same range of spring dimensions, for rotations up to 30 deg. The results are shown in Fig. 6.16. All the results refer to springs of material with Young's modulus $27 \cdot 5 \times 10^6$ lb./in.^{2}. The measurements made by Nickols and Wunsch were made on a light-weight moving system, and the results would not apply to a heavy system (see Haringx, above).

An illustration of the cross-spring pivot used as a lever is given in Fig. 7.1. Other applications are given in ref. 15.

Strips giving parallel motion. If, instead of crossed strips, the members are connected by one or more pairs of parallel strips as in Fig. 6.17, motion is restricted to a straight line as indicated. The arrangement may be considered as a cross-strip hinge with the line of intersection, and hence the axis of rotation, at infinity.

The arrangement is useful when a small linear movement, coupled with a restoring force, is required. It has been successfully used, for instance, on the N.P.L. comparator referred to on p. 110. This comparator also uses another arrangement of flexible springs, but as this is essentially an arrangement for magnifying a small movement, rather than a method of realising constrained motion, it is described in Chapter 7.

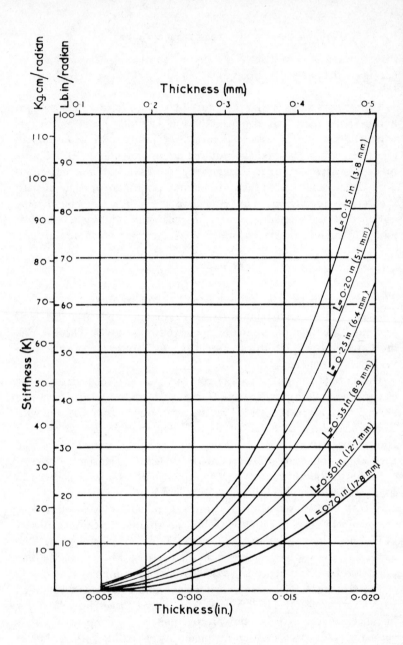

Fig. 6.15.—Stiffness of a symmetrical cross-spring pivot consisting of two pairs of spring strips intersecting at 90 deg. at their mid-points. Width of each spring = ¼ in. (Nickols and Wunsch[10].) (*Crown Copyright Reserved.*)

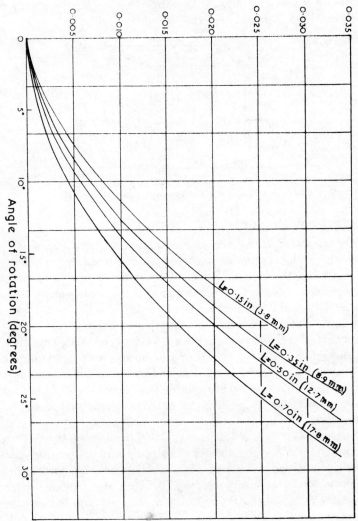

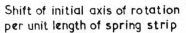

FIG. 6.16.—Shift of axis of rotation of symmetrical cross-spring pivot consisting of two pairs of spring strips intersecting at 90 deg. at their mid-points. (Nickols and Wunsch[10].)   (*Crown Copyright Reserved.*)

An investigation of the performance of flexible springs has been described by Jones[11], who concludes that they may, in certain circumstances, give more accurate linear motion than can be obtained by using kinematic slides. An interesting application, with performance data, is given in ref. 12.

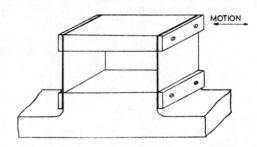

MOTION

FIG. 6.17.—Use of spring strips to give motion in a straight line (for small displacements).

Springs and clamps

The success of an instrument containing moving parts sometimes depends on the design of satisfactory springs or clamps which assist in controlling the motion. Springs are commonly used to keep working surfaces in contact, as for instance in the arrangements of geometric slides considered earlier in this chapter, and also to eliminate backlash. Clamps are required to fix the moving part relative to the fixed part of the apparatus, and a good clamp should do this without causing relative movement of the parts during clamping. Clamps can only work by producing some degree of elastic deformation, but it is usually desirable to avoid introducing large bending moments, and to endeavour as far as possible to produce simple compressions or extensions.

Springs are commonly either of the helical or of the leaf type. For keeping the working surfaces of slides in contact, the spring should have the following properties. First, it should have adequate stiffness to provide the necessary reaction between the moving surfaces. Second, any actual separation of the moving surfaces (which should remain in contact) should cause the force exerted by the spring to increase rapidly with the separation. Third, as far as possible, the action of the spring should produce only a force at right angles to the direction of motion of the slide. It is impossible to realise this completely, since unless only a very small range of motion of the slide is required, the spring will have to slip over the ways or the slide, and some friction will occur. Fourth, the spring should yield only in a direction at right angles to the motion of the slide ; yield in the direction of motion is particularly objectionable except when the range of motion is so small that no slip between slide or ways and spring need occur.

The above requirements are frequently satisfied better by a leaf spring than by a coiled helical spring. The advantages of the former may be seen by referring to Fig. 6.18. It is evident that motion of the

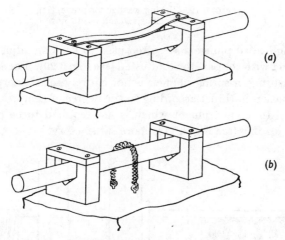

(a)

(b)

FIG. 6.18.—Good (a) and bad (b) forms of springs for holding moving parts in contact with their guides.

slide along the rod in (b) will cause the spring to extend until the component of the spring tension parallel to the rod axis is great enough to overcome static friction, when slipping of the spring over the rod will occur. The motion will be of the " slip and stick " variety instead of being smooth, and owing to the considerable movement of the slide which must take place before slipping can occur, great unevenness of motion will result. In the case of Fig. 6.18 (a), the leaf spring is very stiff to forces parallel to the rod, and very little yielding must occur before friction is overcome, hence the motion will be much smoother. The best results with leaf springs can be expected when the long dimension of the spring is parallel to the motion of the slide.

For keeping the working surfaces of screws and nuts together, so as to prevent backlash, spring washers may be employed as in Fig. 6.19. An arrangement of this kind is often fitted to micrometer heads.

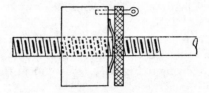

FIG. 6.19.—Spring washer for preventing backlash in screw and nut.

Spring-loaded plungers are often used to keep an adjusting screw in contact with the part to be adjusted (see Fig. 6.20). For screws used for measuring, a spring plunger is not entirely satisfactory owing to the variation in thrust according to the degree of compression of the spring. In an instrument which is not required to be portable, a gravity loading (see Fig. 6.7) is more satisfactory.

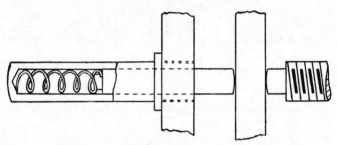

FIG. 6.20.—Spring-loaded plunger for adjusting screw.

Except for quite small micrometers it is, we believe, generally considered better to rotate the screw and prevent its translatory motion by means of a thrust block, so giving the nut a translatory motion, than to allow the screw to advance in a stationary nut. This simplifies the mechanical requirements, since the nut can " float," being prevented from rotation but not otherwise constrained. In such a case, the nut can be kept in contact with the moving part by means of a suitable spring, since there is virtually no relative movement of nut and moving part and the question of variable loading of the spring does not arise.

Clamps. In many cases where part of an instrument has to be clamped, nothing more is needed than a screw placed in a suitable position. Since, however, the point of the screw has a rotatory as well as a forward movement, there is a tendency for the clamped part to be rotated with the screw. The tendency is reduced if the screw has a ball end, but this may be objectionable on account of the " point load " and resulting local distortion produced. If the situation calls for something better than a simple screw, the arrangement shown in Fig. 6.21 may be considered. In addition to reducing the

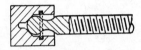

FIG. 6.21.—Self-adjusting foot for clamping screw.

tendency to rotate, and giving a distributed load owing to the large surface used, it enables surfaces not quite perpendicular to the screw axis to be clamped without distortion. The ball-ended screw is prevented from becoming disengaged from the end fitting by a single turn of spring steel wire fitting in a groove as shown.

The correct placing of the clamping screw or screws in apparatus deserves consideration, for an incorrectly placed screw may produce considerable distortion of the parts. If possible, clamping screws should be placed opposite the supports which carry the object clamped. If this is not possible, it may be an advantage to carry the clamping arrangement on a leaf spring, so that yielding of the spring in one direction prevents the setting up of large stresses in this direction. The clamping arrangement in such a case would include not only the screw shown in Fig. 6.21 but also the nut and an extension of it to which the clamped part would be pressed by the screw.

An arrangement which illustrates the use of a spring to facilitate clamping is shown in Fig. 6.22, which shows an improved form of retort stand boss. This boss was designed to allow accurate positioning on the rod of the stand, and to enable the boss to be clamped securely without change in position. The leaf spring is stiff, and by suitably adjusting the clamping screw, the spring pressure can be made sufficient to hold the boss on the rod without support. In this condition it can be slid along the rod and easily adjusted to a fraction of a millimetre. It may then be clamped to the desired extent without movement. The clamping screw does produce a slight bending of the rod on which the boss is carried, but as the vee supports on the boss are only about 1 in. apart, this bending is small. The essential feature of the design is that the clamping force is under control, as it depends on the deformation of the spring.

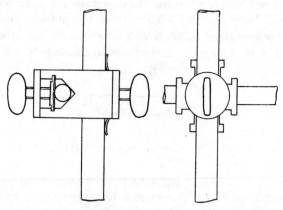

Fig. 6.22.—Retort stand boss with springs to allow regulation of clamping force.

The clamping of optical parts such as prisms, optical flats, etc., which must not be subjected to large strains (one might say they should not be subject to strains of any kind) is probably best achieved by dispensing with kinematic principles altogether, and relying on a surface support accurately made, of the most generous proportions possible. The clamping force is usually applied through a layer of cork, to distribute the load. If a single clamping screw is used, it should bear on a substantial metal plate, under which is a thin layer of cork. The arrangements for clamping prisms to the tables of small spectrometers are sometimes very bad, the cork (if any is provided) being much too small. There is something to be said for cementing prisms, etc., to a metal base with soft wax, and dispensing entirely with clamping screws, except those which are applied to the metal base, as surprisingly little force is needed to produce an appreciable loss of definition with a good prism.

Mirrors are more easily clamped than optical parts required for transmitting light, since internal strain is of much less consequence, and it is only necessary to avoid deformation of the mirror surface. Semi-geometric arrangements are quite satisfactory, and usually

106

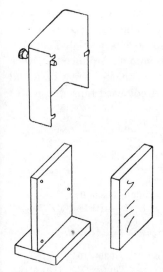

FIG. 6.23.—Clamping arrangement for plane mirror (Hilger spectrometer).

three small projections are fitted to the mounting, to make contact with the reflecting face of the mirror (see Fig. 6.23). The mirror is kept in contact with these projections by means of three *small* pieces of cork or similar yielding material cemented to a back plate, and a single screw applied to the centre of the back plate supplies the necessary pressure. This arrangement is found on some Hilger instruments. It is important that the pieces of cork should bear on the mirror at points exactly behind the projections so that no distortion of the mirror can arise. Besides the three points of support so provided, two more should be given to the base of the mirror ; friction between the mirror surface and projections will effectively provide a sixth constraint and the mirror will then be fixed relatively to its mounting.

Fig. 6.24 shows an arrangement for clamping plane mirrors in the Perkin-Elmer infra-red spectrometer. This arrangement makes use of only one spring for clamping. The mirror rests in a vee groove, and can be rotated through a small angle about a horizontal axis ; this is effected by rotating the screw near the top of the vertical support. It is also possible to displace the mirror laterally without rotation by sliding it in the vee.

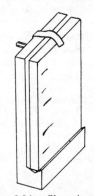

FIG. 6.24.—Clamping of plane mirror in Perkin-Elmer spectrometer.

The use of cork in clamping optical components is referred to above; the object in using cork is to introduce a material of high coefficient of friction, so that movement of the clamped part is prevented even when the clamping force is not great. For some purposes, we have found the fruiting body of *polyporus betulinus* more suitable than cork. This fungus is common in birch woods, where large specimens may be found growing on the trunks of birch trees; it is sometimes known as the razor strop fungus. Dried specimens may be cut into sheets down to paper thickness on a microtome. This material is harder and much more uniform than cork, and it has a high frictional coefficient. It is very useful for friction pads, and if introduced between the feet of an instrument and the laboratory bench, it will be found extremely effective in preventing sliding. A coloured reproduction of the fungus is given in ref. 16.

REFERENCES

[1] POLLARD, A. F. C., *The Kinematical Design of Couplings in Instrument Mechanisms* (London, Adam Hilger Ltd., 1929).

[2] ROLT, F. H., *Gauges and Fine Measurements* (London, Macmillan, 1929).

[3] SEARS, J. E., *Dictionary of Applied Physics*, Vol. III—article " Metrology " (London, Macmillan, 1922–3).

[4] WHITEHEAD, T. N., *The Design and Use of Instruments and Accurate Mechanism* (New York, The Macmillan Co., 1934).

[5] NEWMAN, A. S., and CLAY, R. S., *Journ. Sci. Inst.*, **16** (1939), 105.

[6] DARWIN, H., and MASON, C. C., *Dictionary of Applied Physics*, Vol. III—article " Design of Scientific Instruments " (London, Macmillan, 1922–3).

[7] POLLARD, A. F. C., *The Mechanical Design of Physical Instruments—Report on Progress in Physics*, Vol. X, 1944–5 (London, The Physical Society, 1946).

[8] HARINGX, J. A., *Appl. Sci. Research*, **A1** (1949), 313.

[9] YOUNG, W. E., *J. Appl. Mech.*, **11A** (1944), 113.

[10] NICKOLS, L. W., and WUNSCH, H. L., *The Engineer*, **192** (1951), 458.

[11] JONES, R. V., *J. Sci. Inst.*, **28** (1951), 38.

[12] JONES, R. V., *J. Sci. Inst.*, **33** (1956), 169.

[13] GEARY, P. J., *Flexure Devices* (British Scientific Instrument Research Association, 1954).

[14] "Discussion on Kinematic Design Applied to Instruments." *Trans. Soc. Inst. Tech.*, **6** (1954), 66.

[15] "Application of Spring Strips to Instrument Design" (National Physical Laboratory Notes on Applied Science No. 15: H.M. Stationery Office, London, 1956).

[16] RAMSBOTTOM, J., *Mushrooms and Toadstools* (London, Collins, 1953).

Chapter 7

THE MAGNIFICATION OF SMALL DISPLACEMENTS

THE problem of measuring small mechanical displacements is of frequent occurrence in scientific and industrial work. Sometimes the displacements in themselves are of interest, as when changes in the dimensions of solid bodies are measured, or they may be merely an intermediary step, as when the movements of a galvanometer coil are used in the measurement of electric current. Very frequently the displacements must be magnified before they can be compared with a scale to the desired order of accuracy. We may distinguish between two limiting cases ; the first where the force producing the displacement is so great compared with that required to keep a light mechanism in contact with the material surface moved that the displacement is not affected by such contact, and the second where the lightest conceivable contact would cause a change in the displacement. Examples of these extremes are found in the thermal expansion of a solid, and in the movement of a balance beam. The means employed for magnification in the second case must not employ any material contact, the first may. The commonest methods of obtaining magnification are mechanical, optical and electrical, of which the first requires contact with the displaced body. Often combinations of these various methods are employed.

Mechanical Methods

Mechanical methods are without doubt the oldest methods of producing magnification. They are reviewed in ref. 1. Their characteristic feature is, of course, that they usually produce a reaction on the part whose movement they magnify, and for this reason they are sometimes inappropriate. When this feature is not objectionable, they are extremely useful, being simple and reliable if properly designed and made. A typical example of the appropriate use of mechanical magnification may be seen in the comparison of steel gauge blocks, for in this case the pressure applied to the block by the measuring device is not large enough to affect the measurement. Several of the comparators designed by the National Physical Laboratory employ mechanical amplification in addition (usually) to optical methods. Although the prototypes of these comparators were designed many years ago during the first world war, they are still used for measurements of the highest accuracy (one millionth of an inch) and several of the mechanical elements they embody will be referred to in this chapter. Refs. 1 and 2 contain much useful information on mechanical amplification.

Lever magnification. There is no limit to the amount of magnification which can be obtained with a single lever, but a practical limit is soon imposed by the need for compactness. It is also easily seen that far greater flexure and attendant inaccuracy would occur in a single lever magnifying 100 $\times$ than in two levers in series, each magnifying 10 $\times$.

If accuracy is required, the lever arms should remain of constant length, and this requires suitable design of the pivot and of the ends at which movement is produced. For mechanical levers, the cross-strip pivot offers many advantages and is particularly suitable if the rotation of the lever is small, for then the axis of rotation is fixed. The characteristics of this pivot are described in Chapter 6.

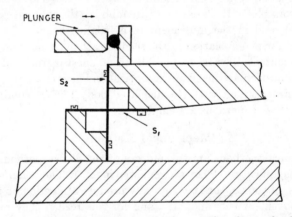

PLUNGER

S_2

S_1

Fig. 7.1.—Lever using cross-spring pivot to give rotation about a fixed point and hence to magnify plunger movement by a constant factor.

Some features of a well-designed mechanical lever are illustrated in Fig. 7.1, which shows (not, however, in accurate detail) the bell crank lever which forms part of a comparator designed by Sears at the National Physical Laboratory. The complete instrument is described in ref. 3. The movement to be magnified is applied by a plunger which terminates in a flat, hardened steel surface or anvil which is in contact with a steel ball carried by the lever. The parts are arranged so that the flat steel surface, if extended, would pass through the pivot of the hinge (formed by the strips S_1 and S_2) around which the lever turns. The consequence of this is that, for small movements, the ball rolls on the flat anvil without sliding. This eliminates sliding friction, with its attendant disadvantages. In the actual comparator, the lever operates an optical lever to obtain further magnification (see below).

The arms of the lever should generally be designed to secure adequate rigidity and lightness. Subject to adequate dimensional stability, the choice would naturally fall on a light alloy (see Chapter 3). The usual arrangements employed in cantilever construction are appropriate (H, T or channel sections, reduction in depth towards the ends, and in general any design which gives a sufficient moment of inertia of area about an axis parallel to the pivot axis).

Rolling cylinder and related methods

A well-known piece of apparatus for demonstrating the expansion of metals makes use of a very narrow cylinder resting on a plane on which it can roll, and carrying a pointer to indicate its rotation. The metal which is heated to produce expansion is in the form of a rod which rests on the cylinder, to which rotation is imparted by the movement of the expanding rod. This method of magnifying the small expansion is limited by the difficulty of making a very small cylinder, and by the fragility of such a cylinder when attached to a pointer.

A method of overcoming the difficulty was employed in a comparator made many years ago by Taylor, Taylor and Hobson Ltd. (Brit. Pat. No. 144037). The essential features are shown in Fig. 7.2. Two flexible steel bands A are wrapped half round the circumference of a roller and secured by screws to the roller and to two flat surfaces on which the roller is supported. The central part of the roller is of greater diameter than the end parts ; round it is wrapped a third band B, which is prevented from slipping by a screw. The ends of the band B are kept taut by two springs C and D, D being stronger than C. The moving part whose motions are to be magnified is attached to the end of the band near D, and is represented by a block E. When E is made to move in the direction shown by the arrow, the roller rotates about the instantaneous centre F, hence the length of the lever arm which controls the angular movement is $R_1 - R_2$ and this can be made as small as required, without loss of robustness. As the motion takes place without sliding of one surface over another, it is free from the effects of friction, and is without backlash.

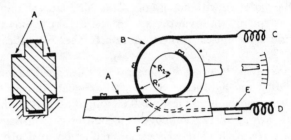

FIG. 7.2.—Differential roller mechanism.

Parallel deformable strips

The arrangement shown in Fig. 7.3 has been used in some very sensitive measuring instruments designed by the N.P.L. It consists of two flexible, parallel strips rigidly fixed to a parallel-faced spacer at one end. The other end of one strip is rigidly fastened to the body of the instrument, and that of the other strip is attached to the part whose movements are to be indicated. In the usual construction, this end is fastened rigidly to a plunger which is constrained to move in a direction parallel to the strips when they are not distorted. Such movement of the plunger bends the strips into an arc. The closer the strips are spaced (distance D), the greater is the curvature produced by a given movement of the plunger (S). The arrangement may terminate in a pointer, or may, for instance, carry a mirror whose rotation is observed optically (see

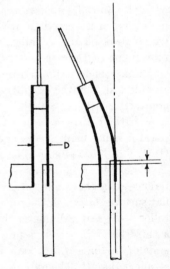

FIG. 7.3.—Magnification of movement by use of deformable parallel strips.

112

separate section below). It has the same characteristics as the cross strip pivot (page 95) as regards freedom from hysterisis and back-lash, etc., but does not produce rotation about a fixed centre.

Ratchet and toothed wheels. Dial gauges

The dial gauge is a compact instrument of high sensitivity, much used for a great variety of measurements in engineering. A plunger carrying a measuring anvil at one end is provided with a ratchet, which engages a gear wheel (see Fig. 7.4). Movement of the anvil produces thereby a rotation of this wheel, which is magnified by a

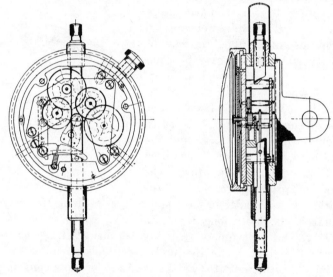

Fig. 7.4.—Dial gauge (Mercer). A similar gauge is shown in use in Fig. 11.7.

suitable train of gears, ultimately causing a pointer to rotate over a scale, from which the movement of the anvil can be read. Usually, one of the intermediate gears carries a small pointer to read whole revolutions of the measuring pointer. This is a convenience when relatively large movements have to be measured. A spring is used to keep the anvil in contact with the object whose dimensions are to be measured in such a way as to avoid backlash. Gauges fitted with jewelled bearings can be obtained.

A wide range of types is available, in English and metric scales ; scale divisions are commonly 0·001 in., 0·0005 in. or 0·0001 in. (0·01 mm., 0·002 mm.). The range of travel is up to about 1 in., depending on the type. Dial gauges should not be relied on to give accurate readings over a large range unless a check has been made.

Liquid levels. The liquid or spirit level is much used in engineering workshops for quantitative measurement, and it forms the essential element in surveying instruments.

The original form consists of a glass tube of circular bore, bent to a large radius of curvature R (Fig. 7.5) containing a liquid which fills the tube except for a small bubble of air and vapour. The centre of the bubble, when at rest, is always at the highest part of the tube, and the radius drawn from the centre of curvature to this point indicates the vertical. If the tube were rotated through an angle θ as shown, the bubble would, when again in equilibrium, have moved through an arc of length S, where $S = R\theta$.

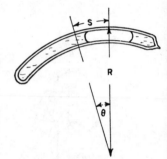

FIG. 7.5.—Principle of liquid level.

Sensitive levels, which have a large radius of curvature, cannot be satisfactorily made by bending, and are ground on a steel rod which has been bent to the required curvature. The method of grinding results in the formation of a toroidal surface, and a level made in this way can be rotated about its long horizontal axis, which is an axis of symmetry, and will function in any of the resulting positions.

The tube is divided, one division being usually about 2 mm. The sensitivity may be indicated by the radius R, or more conveniently by the tilt required to move the bubble through one division. The tilt is usually expressed in seconds of arc, or in inches per 10 in. or mm. per metre.

The highest sensitivity which may be usefully employed depends partly on the accuracy with which tubes can be ground to a constant radius, and partly on the conditions of use. As far as the first factor is concerned, tubes having radii up to 334 ft. with the necessary accuracy are commercially available. These tubes have a sensitivity of one division for 5 sec. of arc (0·00025 in. per 10 in., or 0·025 mm. per metre). It is found that the longer the bubble, the more definite is the indication, and the less is it affected by local irregularities ; for this reason sensitive levels have bubbles several centimetres long.

Conditions affecting liquid levels

Non-uniform temperature within the tube of the level will seriously affect its indications. For this reason sensitive levels are supplied with metal covers provided with glass windows. Sometimes thermally insulating finger grips are provided to minimise the effect of handling. It is undersirable to expose sensitive levels during use to sources of radiation (sun, lamps, etc.).

Accurate surveying instruments for use in the tropics should be specially constructed to reduce the effect of solar radiation. Those made by Messrs. Hilger and Watts, for instance, are painted white externally, and the level tube (which is inside the instrument) is surrounded by a copper cylinder, brightly polished inside and out. Arrangements for viewing the level are of course made.

Besides temperature irregularities, a change in temperature will generally alter the length of a bubble, because the expansion of the liquid is greater than that of the tube, hence a rise in temperature produces contraction of the bubble. This makes it desirable to read both ends of a bubble, and so always to measure the movement of the centre. The Watts Division of Messrs. Hilger and Watts Ltd. manufacture a level in which the bubble length is independent of the temperature. This was formerly done by choosing the shape of the cross section of the tube so that surface tension forces (which also change with temperature) and volume contraction together produce a constant length. The procedure now adopted is to make use of the increased vapour pressure of the spirit, together with the expansion of spirit, glass and contained air to preserve a constant bubble length in a tube of circular cross section. Because of restrictions imposed on bubble length, etc., by the requirements of compensation, such constant bubble levels are not suitable for every purpose. In a constant bubble level, only one end need be read.

Liquid levels as now made are singularly perfect instruments in respect of response to small changes, and in reproducibility. It is quite practicable to magnify the bubble movement (say by observing through a low power microscope) and so obtain greater sensitivity. It is, therefore, not always necessary to employ a tube of large radius in order to measure small changes in angle, and since greater range is obtained with a smaller radius, this may be an advantage.

Sensitive levels are made to conform to British Standard Specification No. 958, 1941 " Precision Levels for Engineering Workshops," which may be consulted for the performance of the level in the mounts suitable for workshop use. If a level tube is to be incorporated in an instrument, the manufacturers of level tubes should be consulted.

Another factor which limits the sensitivity which can be used is mechanical vibration. This should not be serious in a laboratory, but in a workshop it will probably be a limiting factor, for the bubble may never be at rest if vibration is considerable.

Mounting of levels. The less sensitive level tubes may be mounted in plaster of paris, but sensitive tubes should be kinematically mounted[13] to prevent distortion, a spring being used to keep the tube in contact with the locating surfaces. The principles of kinematic mounting are explained in Chapter 6. Sensitive levels are available in a variety of mounts and makers' catalogues may be consulted. In the most usual type of engineer's block level, the base of the mount is flat, but is relieved in the centre, and has also vee-grooves so that it can be applied to a cylindrical surface. As will appear below, this mount is not always suitable, and levels may be had in mounts whose bases are flat, lapped plates with no relieved parts. Another form is the square mount, which gives vertical as well as horizontal reference surfaces. Adjustable mounts are also made, in which the tube may be tilted with respect to the base by a calibrated micrometer movement. This increases the range of tilt which can be measured, and brings it up to a few degrees (usually 3 deg. elevation and 2 deg. depression).

Artillery clinometers giving angles up to 45° are also available.

Liquid levels for magnifying small movements

It is obvious that small mechanical movements may be made to produce a tilt in a liquid level, and that the resulting movement of the bubble can be made many times greater than that which produced it. Although the tube is comparatively light, the mount of a sensitive level, as made for engineering purposes, is quite massive, and if such mounts are used, the method is limited to cases where no appreciable error is introduced by large forces on the moving parts. An end-gauge comparator of high sensitivity was designed many years ago by A. J. C. Brookes in the National Physical Laboratory, making use of a liquid level. A description of the comparator, whose design and use illustrates some important principles, may be found in ref. 2. For measuring such quantities as the difference in height of two gauge blocks supported on a flat plate, a level should be used whose base is accurately flat, without any central portion cut away.

A general paper on levels may be found in ref. 13, and a description of some research on the properties of the liquids employed in levels, as well as of liquid levels themselves, is given in ref. 14.

Magnification by Optical Methods

Magnifying systems, varying from simple lenses to compound microscopes and telescopes, are used to render small movements more easily visible, and to measure them. The use of such aids is becoming common in many instruments, particularly those used in precision engineering. The optical aspects of such systems are described in the later chapters of this book. The optical system can of course be used to project an image on a paper or other opaque scale ; this method is flexible and easily set up from standard parts such as microscope objectives. Greater compactness, and generally speaking greater reproducibility and accuracy may be had by using a compound microscope, with the added magnification given by the eyepiece. The movements may be read off on a graticule at the focal plane of the eyepiece, tenths of a division being estimated. Alternatively, a micrometer screw fitted to the eyepiece graticule can be used to measure the fractional part. If the object whose movements are to be measured carries a suitable fiduciary mark, the micrometer screw enables high accuracy to be achieved, for the nearest (lower) scale division of the eyepiece graticule can be set on a fiduciary mark with great accuracy, and the movement of the micrometer screw required to do this gives at once the fraction of the scale division to be added to the graticule reading. If the eyepiece graticule is moved by the micrometer screw, evidently the micrometer must be read before it has been adjusted as well as after, and the calculation becomes tedious, since there is no fixed reference mark within the microscope. This objection can be overcome if the graticule carrying the scale is fixed, and the micrometer is made to operate a compensator which will displace the image of the fiduciary mark by a measured amount. Such a compensator may consist, for instance, of a tilting parallel faced glass plate. If initially set and calibrated correctly, the micrometer gives at once the amount to be added to the scale reading.

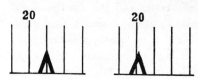

FIG. 7.6.—Fiduciary mark and scale, as used in Watts level.

The accuracy possible depends to a great extent on suitable

117

fiduciary marks. A good type, which is used in some of Messrs. Watts' surveying instruments, is shown in Fig. 7.6, and of course other equally good arrangements can be devised. (See p. 368.)

Magnification by optical lever

The commonest optical device employed for magnification is the optical lever, the principle of which is that if light is reflected from a mirror, when the mirror is rotated through an angle θ, the reflected ray is turned through an angle 2θ. The advantage of the optical lever is that the reflected light beam, whose position is read off where it falls on a scale, may be made as long as desired (subject to a restriction to be considered later) with a corresponding gain in magnification. A good and easily constructed form of optical lever for magnifying small vertical displacements, designed by D. W. Dye, is shown in Fig. 7.7. The lever, as shown, was intended for measuring

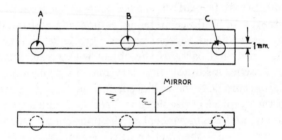

FIG. 7.7.—Optical lever for high magnification. (Dye.)

the thickness of mica sheets. It consists of a steel bar $5 \times 0.7 \times 0.2$ in. into which are let three $\frac{3}{8}$ in. steel balls. The centre of the ball B is displaced 1 mm. from the line joining the centres of the balls AC. These balls rest on gauge blocks. The lever carries a small galvanometer mirror and its deflections are read by means of a lamp and scale. The body whose thickness is to be measured is inserted between B and the block on which B normally rests, and the change in deflection on the scale read off. A magnification of about 4000 : 1 is obtained, and the stability is sufficient to allow measurements accurate to about 5 millionths of an inch to be made. It will be realised that, as the steel balls may be displaced laterally when the object whose thickness is being measured is inserted under the ball B, the surfaces on which the balls rest must be flat and co-planar to an accuracy corresponding with that which is required from the measurement. An optical flat, or a selected piece of thick plate glass may be used. It is necessary to calibrate the lever with the aid of strips of known thickness.

Observation of angular movement of light beams

In conjunction with an optical lever, or any similar device using a rotating mirror, three methods are commonly used for observing the movements of the reflected beam, and will now be considered.

Lamp and Scale.—This is by far the most widely used method of observing the deflections of a light beam. As it is not always used to best advantage, a few words may be said upon the best conditions for observations. An image of the lamp filament (Fig. 7.8) is thrown by

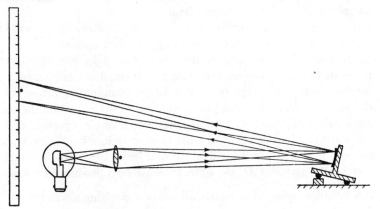

Fig. 7.8.—Lamp and scale to read deflections of optical lever.

means of the lens on the mirror attached to the rotating part ; the mirror is sometimes concave but a combination of plane mirror and lens may also be used. The mirror or mirror-lens combination forms an image of the lens aperture (across which is stretched a fibre) on the scale. Frequently the mirrors supplied for galvanometers do not give good images ; often it is impossible to read the position of the image of the crosswire to 0·1 mm., but this is quite possible with a good quality mirror. If a plane mirror and lens is used, a spectacle lens will usually suffice, as the aperture is so small that aberrations are kept low. The poor quality of mirror images is probably due to distortion of the thin glass mirror.

119

The intensity of the spot of light on the scale depends on two factors only, apart from losses of light from reflection. If the intrinsic brightness of the filament of the lamp is I (measured in ergs per sq. cm. per unit solid angle per second) and the solid angle subtended at the scale by the mirror (or such part of it as receives the image of the filament) is ω, the intensity of illumination of the scale is $I\omega$ ergs per sq. cm. per second. Hence with a given mirror at a given distance from the scale, nothing can be done to increase the scale illumination once the mirror is fully illuminated, unless an illuminant of higher intrinsic brightness is available. Actually, using a mirror of 1 cm. diameter at a distance from the scale of 1 metre, brilliant illumination is obtained with a gas-filled tungsten lamp as source. Automobile lamps (12 or 6 volts, 36 watts) are very suitable sources, for with a lens of about 9 cm. focal length the filament image can readily be made large enough to fill a mirror of 1 cm. diameter.

It is of interest to consider how great the distance from mirror to scale may usefully be made. Assuming a perfect optical system, i.e., one free from aberrations, the distribution of light intensity in the image of the crosswire on the scale is governed by diffraction. If the fiduciary mark were the image of an illuminated slit, or of a glowing filament, the image produced by the lens-mirror on the scale would be the diffraction pattern appropriate to the aperture of the lens mirror. Even if the slit or filament were infinitely narrow, the image would be of finite width. If the lens mirror had a circular aperture of diameter D, the diffraction pattern produced on a scale at a distance v would be nearly all contained within a width $2\cdot44 \dfrac{\lambda v}{D}$, λ being the wave-length of the light used. The finite width of the pattern would set a limit to the accuracy with which the eye could read off the position on the scale.

In the arrangement generally employed (see above), a wire or fibre is imaged on the scale. The distribution of light in the diffraction image on the scale is now more difficult to determine. Its form depends essentially on the ratio of the width of the " geometrical " image of the fibre to the diffraction width $2\cdot44 \dfrac{\lambda v}{D}$. If d is the fibre diameter, v the distance from scale to lens-mirror and u the distance from fibre to lens-mirror, the " geometrical " width is vd/u and the ratio of this to the diffraction width is $dD/2\cdot44u\lambda$. If it is assumed that the illumination is incoherent (that is, that no constant phase relations exist between the light passing through various parts of the condensing lens) the diffraction pattern for an opaque fibre can be found by a summation process. The results show that when the ratio $dD/2\cdot44u\lambda$ is unity the diffraction image is nearly dark at the centre, and has a half-width equal to about 0·75 of the geometrical image width. The distribution of intensity in the image is shown in Fig. 7.9 (*a*). If the fibre is now made narrower, the diffraction pattern on the scale becomes narrower too, but the intensity at the centre increases, hence the contrast in the image diminishes. The distribution when $dD/2\cdot44u\lambda$ is equal to three is shown in Fig. 7.9 (*b*).

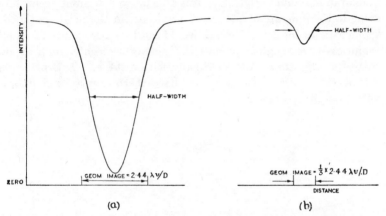

FIG. 7.9.—Contours of geometrical and of diffraction images of a narrow wire.

It is evident that there is some advantage in using a narrow fibre, but theory cannot tell us when the gain in sharpness of the image is offset by lack of contrast. The question can, however, be answered by experiment.

Some observations were carried out to decide this point, and also to determine the smallest angular movement of a light beam which could be measured, under the best conditions, when the lens-mirror had a diameter of 1 cm. and was fully illuminated. As a result, it was found that there was little advantage in increasing v beyond about 3 metres, and that a fibre diameter giving a geometrical image corresponding to one-third of $2\cdot44\lambda v/D$ gave the best conditions. (Fig. 7.9 (*b*).) The actual diameter of fibre required to satisfy this condition depends on the magnification. With v equal to 3 metres, the width of the geometrical image is 0·037 mm., and from Fig. 7.9 (*b*) the half-width is about 0·031 mm. This enables readings to be made to 0·1 mm. The corresponding angular movement of the light beam is 1/30000 radian. Hence with an optical lever with 1 mm. offset, a distance of 1/60 micron (approximately $0·6 \times 10^{-6}$ in.) should be just measurable, given stable supports and a sufficiently flat support for the optical lever.

The limit to accuracy of reading which appears to be set by the width of the crosswire image on the scale is really caused by the properties of the eye, for the centre of the image is a definite line, however wide the image may be. Being, however, the position of maximum or of minimum brightness, it is difficult to determine accurately owing to the low rate of change of brightness in the neighbourhood. A much more sensitive method would result if two points of equal brightness were sought, one on either side of the centre, in a region where the brightness changes rapidly with distance. This principle is really the basis of the very sensitive thermal relay and photovoltaic amplifier which are described later in this chapter.

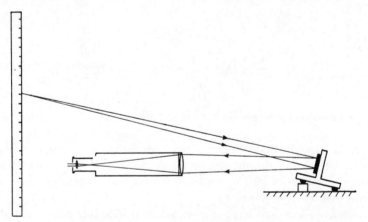

FIG. 7.10.—Observation of mirror deflection by means of telescope and scale.

Telescope and scale. Sometimes the arrangement shown in Fig. 7.10 is employed for measuring deflections of a light beam. An image of the scale is formed in the focal plane of a telescope provided with a crosswire, and the position of the crosswire on the scale image is read off by means of the eyepiece. It will be seen that a change of direction of the light beam from the mirror $\delta\theta$ causes a movement of the scale image relative to the crosswire $f\delta\theta$, f being the focal length of the objective. It is this movement $f\delta\theta$, in terms of the scale image divisions, which the eye has to estimate. Changing the distance of scale or telescope from the mirror only changes the magnitude of the scale divisions. The characteristic advantage of the optical lever, namely that the magnification can be altered at will by altering the distance from mirror to scale, when a lamp and scale is used, is not made use of here. The telescope and scale method can be used in a well lighted room, whereas formerly this was not the case when a lamp and scale was employed. As indicated in the previous section, this limitation of the lamp and scale method no longer applies. However, a telescope or reading microscope may be found useful when compactness is important, for the magnification of the eyepiece allows an objective of shorter focal length to be used than would otherwise be needed. Such an arrangement lends itself well to a self-contained unit of mirror, scale and telescope.

The Auto-collimator

The auto-collimating telescope finds many applications in measuring the rotation of a plane mirror. A simple form, containing the essential parts, is shown in Fig. 7.11. Light from a small bulb is reflected, in this case from a totally reflecting prism, past a graticule

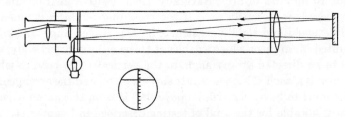

Fig. 7.11.—Auto-collimating telescope for observing mirror deflection. If no condenser is used between lamp and graticule, a frosted bulb should be used to illuminate the required field of view.

or crosswire down the tube of the telescope to the objective. The graticule or crosswire is at the principal focus of the objective, hence light from each point on the graticule leaves the objective as a parallel beam. These beams fall on the plane mirror whose rotation is to be measured, whence they are reflected back to form an image in the plane of the graticule. The plane mirror must be oriented so that this image is to one side of the reflecting prism, otherwise it would not be seen by the observer looking into the eyepiece. It is possible to replace the prism by a semi-reflecting surface (which may be unsilvered glass), and in this case the image and graticule may coincide. The image can then be seen through the semi-reflecting surface.

A small rotation of the plane mirror will displace the image relative to the lines of the graticule, which gives a method of measuring the rotation. In the simpler instruments, such as the Hilger " Angle Dekkor," there is a fixed linear scale at right angles to a similar scale which is seen after reflection. The readings on these two scales (where they intersect) enable the rotation of the mirror about axes parallel to the scales to be read off. The scale is divided to represent minutes of arc of mirror rotation, and the range of measurement is 1 deg. By estimation, readings to 6 seconds of arc may be made.

By employing a microscope for observing the reflected image, instead of an eyepiece, greater accuracy of setting is possible. In the Watts " Microptic " auto-collimater, a micrometer adjustment is used to bring a pair of parallel, closely spaced setting wires into register with the image of a single target wire. This setting can be carried out very accurately, and enables the rotation of the plane mirror to be measured to less than 1 second of arc. The range of angular movement in such a sensitive instrument is not large, it is usually about 10 minutes of arc. Naturally such sensitive instruments can only be advantageously used if the mounting of the instrument is well designed and rigidly constructed. The Hilger Angle Dekkor is mounted on an arm which enables it to be adjusted vertically, and also to be directed at any angle to the vertical. The base to which this arm is attached is an accurate surface plate, and the arrangement is designed to be as versatile as possible. It is on this account particularly suitable for the kind of testing described in Chapter 11.

It is possible to use a concave mirror instead of a lens as the objective, and by using a very long focal length ($12\frac{1}{2}$ ft.), Rank[15] has obtained an accuracy of 0·1–0·2 seconds of arc, using an eyepiece of about 1·6 in. focal length. Such an arrangement can be set up in the laboratory with few elements, but it does not compare in convenience with the usual refracting auto-collimator, which, in the form mentioned above, will give similar accuracy with an objective of only 10·8 in. focal length.

An important feature of the auto-collimator is that it indicates only rotation of the mirror about axes lying in the plane of the mirror surface, and its indications are independent of rotation around an axis normal to the mirror, and of translatory motion of mirror with respect to the telescope. It is also important that the mirror may be many feet away from the telescope without any loss in sensitivity. There is, however, a decrease in the range of angular movement measurable, since with the mirror at a great distance the returning light beam will fall outside the lens for quite small mirror rotations. This is much more marked in instruments which use a total reflection prism to send the light down the telescope tube, since the returning beam must make an appreciable angle to the telescope axis. If a semi-reflecting mirror is used, as in the Watts instrument, axial rays are used and the limiting distance at which the target mirror can be used is greatly increased. The sensitive type of instrument with micrometer adjustment reading to 0·5 seconds of arc should be usable up to about 30 ft. distance from the mirror. Auto-collimators for laboratory and workshop testing are usually from about 12–18 in. in overall length. They may, however, be built into an instrument for observing rotations of a moving part carrying a mirror, and can be made quite small, depending on the sensitivity required.

Some of the uses of the auto-collimator are described in Chapter 11.

Moiré fringes

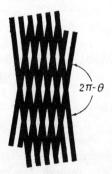

$2\pi - \theta$

FIG. 7.12.—Moiré fringes for superposed gratings.

If two identical gratings are superposed with their rulings making a small angle θ with each other as in Fig. 7.12, the system is crossed by parallel opaque bands or fringes when seen by transmitted light. These Moiré fringes, as they are called, are perpendicular to the mean direction of the grating rulings. If the shorter grating in Fig. 7.12 is moved to the right through a distance equal to the width of a grating element (that is one opaque plus one transparent bar) then the Moiré fringes will move downwards through the distance between neighbouring fringes. In this way a magnification is obtained which is $1/\theta$, and which may be made as high as we please by reducing θ. However, the greater width of the fringes at high magnification is a disadvantage, and for measuring to a high order of accuracy it is preferable to use fine gratings. With a suitable optical system and photo-cell whose output is fed into a counting circuit, the passage of fringes can be recorded at high speed, and fractions of a fringe can also be determined. The application of Moiré fringes has gone hand-in-hand with the development of processes at the National Physical Laboratory for producing accurate gratings, using the Merton nut which is briefly described in Chapter 8. Moiré fringes are finding application for controlling the movements of parts of machine tools in automatic processes. Further information is given in refs. 18–20.

Interference methods

Although Fizeau[4] employed interference fringes to measure the expansion of crystals, the possibilities of employing light waves for accurate measurements were first brought into prominence by the work of Michelson[5] and since then have been widely used for such purposes, not only in laboratories but in engineering workshops and tool-rooms, especially for measuring gauges. Interference methods of measuring small displacements are, as a rule, quite simple and do not require very expensive apparatus. They are much more accurate than methods in general use at the time when they first became known. To some extent, the idea has persisted that these methods are still the most accurate available, and while this is probably true of absolute measurements of length, there are other equally or possibly more accurate methods of measuring small differences in length, or small displacements. No other method, however, will give the same accuracy except at very greatly increased cost.

Since this chapter is concerned with the magnification of small displacements, we will consider two arrangements by means of which small movements of a glass plate are made to produce large movements of a system of interference bands. By means of the simple apparatus shown in Fig. 7.13 measurements of the displacement of plate A relative to B may easily be made with an error of less than a quarter of a wave-length of sodium light ($\lambda = 5\cdot9 \times 10^{-5}$ cm., or $2\cdot3 \times 10^{-5}$ in.); the maximum separation of the plates when light from a sodium flame is employed should not exceed about 100 wave-lengths, otherwise the fringes become diffuse owing to imperfect superposition of the two fringe systems produced by the sodium light, which is not strictly monochromatic.

If the surfaces of *A* and *B* are plane, the fringes seen by means of light reflected from the lower surface of *B* and the upper surface of *A* are straight and parallel to the line of intersection of these surfaces.

The distance between two neighbouring bright fringes is $\lambda/2\delta$ for an air film with light incident approximately normally; δ is the angle between the reflecting surfaces. If the air film between the reflecting surfaces at a given point is altered in thickness by $\lambda/2$, a fringe movement of $\lambda/2\delta$ takes place at this point, hence the ratio of a fringe movement to change in thickness of film is $1 : \delta$, or the magnification is $1/\delta$. By making δ sufficiently small, any magnification can be produced, but since the breadth of the fringes is also increased, the magnification

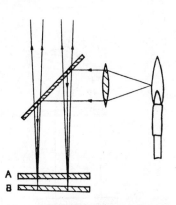

FIG. 7.13.—Arrangement for viewing interference fringes formed in *thin* air film between two semi-reflecting surfaces.

cannot usefully be increased beyond a certain point. The fringe movement may be measured relatively to a fiduciary line ruled on either of the reflecting surfaces, since for thin films the fringe system is located within the film. Measurements of the fringe shift can be made correct to half the fringe width using selected plate glass for the plates *A* and *B*, but if greater accuracy is required, optically worked surfaces should be used.

By making use of collimated incident light, and a mercury lamp to produce a highly monochromatic light source, interference fringes can be observed with quite thick air films (several centimetres), and larger displacements may be measured. The mercury lamp may be fitted with a filter transmitting only the green light of wave-length 5461 A. The arrangement needed is shown in Fig. 7.14, and it should be noted that the eye is placed at the focus of the returning light beam. The glass plates A and B should be plane parallel, or nearly so. It is an advantage to semi-silver or aluminise the reflecting surfaces bounding the air film, for then the fringe system observed by reflection will be much brighter and will, with suitable thickness of the silver film, consist of narrow dark lines separated by much broader bright lines.

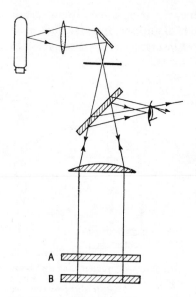

Under these conditions the position of a dark line may be estimated to a small fraction of the fringe width. A further advantage of silvering is that the fringe systems caused by interference between light beams reflected from the unsilvered surfaces cease to be troublesome.

It must be pointed out that, although a train of monochromatic light waves forms a scale of perfectly equal divisions for measurement, it is very inconvenient in having nothing to distinguish one division from another, and is not numbered. Measurements of movement by the method described above are in consequence limited to cases which allow the movement to take place sufficiently slowly for the fringes to be counted as they pass

FIG. 7.14.—Arrangement using parallel light to produce interference fringes between well-separated surfaces.

the fiduciary mark, and if the fringe shift is large there is a great risk that a mistake will be made in the count.

If observations of the fringes are made using in succession several monochromatic light sources of different and accurately known wavelengths, it is possible to determine the order of interference of a given fringe, provided that it is already known approximately. The method is used for determining in absolute measure the thickness of end gauges.

Recent work by Tolansky and others[11] has shown that in very favourable circumstances the interferometric method of measuring lengths can be made very sensitive. By using silvered plates of high reflectivity and very small path differences the fringes are made very fine compared with the space between them, as in the interferometer of Fabry and Perot. The small path difference is necessary because (unlike the Fabry-Perot interferometer) the reflecting surfaces are in general not parallel, and the multiple reflections can only coincide approximately. Tolansky claims to be able to measure displacements as small as one thousandth of a fringe. The technique has been used to examine the surface topography of various crystals, and to show the nodal pattern of a vibrating quartz crystal. These applications are made using the fringes seen by light transmitted through the silvered plates, which appear as fine bright lines on a dark ground.

The thermal relay

The use of thermo-electric effects to amplify the movements of an optical lever or galvanometer appears to have been described first by Wilson and Epps.[17] It was further developed by Moll and Burger[6] as a compact instrument for amplifying galvanometer deflections. The image of a lamp filament is projected on to the galvanometer mirror by means of a lens, to which is attached a diaphragm with a rectangular aperture. A second lens forms an image of this aperture on the cylindrical lens, which serves to concentrate the light so as to produce a narrow horizontal image of considerable intensity on a thermo-couple of special construction, shown in Fig. 7.15. This thermo-couple consists of two identical outer strips of thin foil AA joined by a strip of a different metal B. Usually manganin and constantan are the metals employed. The arrangement is contained in an evacuated glass bulb, surrounded by a metal container in the side of which is a slot through which light can enter. The image formed by the cylindrical lens is of about the same length as the distance between the junctions of AA with B. When the light falls symmetrically on these junctions, no thermo-electric current is produced, but a small deflection of the light beam causes greater heating at one junction than at the other, and a thermo-electric current is produced and measured by the galvanometer connected to the thermo-element. For small deflections, the deflection of the galvanometer is proportional to the original deflection, but may be up to about 200 times as great.

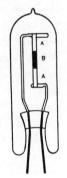

FIG. 7.15.—Thermo-couple (Moll and Burger) for thermal relay.

Photo-electric relay

The photo-electric relay is a development of the thermo-relay, in which the thermo-couple is replaced by a rectifier type photocell. The advantage of this modification is that, whereas the thermo-couple has an appreciable time lag before the full current is obtained, with the photocell an instantaneous response is obtained and the indications of the instrument are more rapid. The method has been developed by a number of workers (see refs. 7, 8, 12 and 16). Two methods will be described, suitable for small and large amplification factors, respectively.

Small amplification.—The arrangement is shown in Fig. 7.16. Light from the lamp S is concentrated on the galvanometer or optical lever mirror M by the lens L_1 which has a rectangular aperture. The

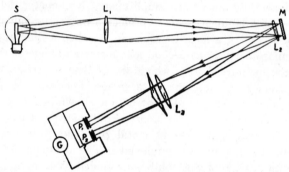

Fig. 7.16.—Arrangement of optical parts in photo-voltaic relay.

mirror, if plane, has a lens L_2 in front of it which forms an image of the aperture of L_1 on a third lens L_3 behind which is a biprism. This last lens forms two images of M on two photocells P_1 and P_2. The cells are connected in parallel but in opposition to a galvanometer G. When both cells are equally illuminated (zero position of M) the galvanometer G is undeflected. A small rotation of M will however upset the balance of the cells; the illumination of one cell will increase while that of the other cell will decrease, and the galvanometer G will deflect by a corresponding amount, proportional to the rotation of M. As the aperture of L_1 is rectangular, proportionality holds until the rotation of M becomes so large that the light falls completely outside one half of the biprism.

Arrangement giving greater amplification.—Greater amplification, using the same intensity of illumination of cell and cells of the same sensitivity, is obtained by an arrangement due to Pfund. In front of the lens L_1 is placed a coarse grating or grid A, consisting of opaque and transparent strips of equal width, and an image of this grid is formed just in front of the biprism, where a second grid A_2 is placed. The spacing of the lines of the grid A_2 is the same as that of the image of A, but A_2 has a central opaque strip of twice the normal width as shown in Fig. 7.17.

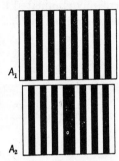

When the mirror M is in its zero position, the grid A_2 and the image of A_1 are adjusted to be as in Fig. 7.17, except that the two grids are shown separated vertically in the figure, whereas they are actually superposed ; in this position each cell receives equal illumination, but since they are opposed the galvanometer G is undeflected. A small rotation of M produces greater illumination of one cell as in the first arrangement, but a given displacement produces a photo-electric current which is $N/2$ times as great as before, N being the number of elements in the gratings employed.

Fig. 7.17.—Grids for more sensitive photo - voltaic relay.

Instead of photo-voltaic cells, it is of course possible to use photo-emissive cells, and this is sometimes done, particularly if an output sufficient to operate a pen recorder is required. The photo-emissive cell output is low, much lower than that of the photo-voltaic type, but it is much easier to apply electronic amplification to the former, on account of its higher impedance.

Preston[12] has described a photo-voltaic amplifier in which a high degree of negative feed-back is used. A small part of the output from the photocells is introduced into the primary galvanometer in a direction to reduce the deflection which resulted in the photo-current. The gain is lowered, but the stability and linearity of response are greatly improved. The gain is also not nearly so sensitive to changes in the lamp brightness. Fig. 7.18 shows the arrangement.

As a result of the feed-back, the galvanometer behaves as if the control were stiffened, and the period is reduced considerably. Galvanometers used in photo-voltaic amplifiers usually have a natural period of about two seconds ; if therefore the period of G_1 is reduced to a fraction of a second by the operation of the feed-back, there will be practically no coupling between the two galvanometers G_1 and G_2 for such disturbances as G_1 will tend to pick up from its surroundings. This contributes greatly to the stability of the arrangement. Although the gain is reduced by the feed-back, it remains quite high, and can be made great enough to show the Brownian movement of the primary galvanometer.

Preston has found that fatigue in photo-voltaic cells (which in an amplifier causes a change in gain, and drift of the zero) can be almost entirely eliminated by interposing in the light beam an infra-red absorbing filter such as Chance's " Calorex " or ON20 glass.

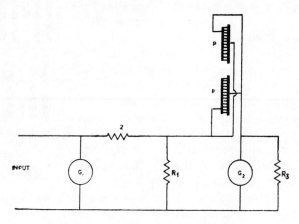

FIG. 7.18.—Photo-voltaic arrangement with feed-back (Preston) (optical arrangement not shown, but similar to Fig. 7.16).

The design of photo-electric amplifiers has been considered in detail by Jones[16] with a view to removing both short- and long-term instability. An important source of short-term instability or " noise " was found to be convection currents of air in the light-path, which produce rapid changes in the amount of light falling on the photocells. Their effects can be reduced to negligible amounts by surrounding the light paths as completely as possible by metal containers of minimal dimensions. A detailed account of the performance of the photo-electric amplifier is given by Jones, who has been able to detect a rotation of 10^{-9} radian with a mirror 5 mm. in diameter. The indication time was 1 second and the long-term drift was of the order of 10^{-8} radian/hour.

Electrical Methods

Electrical methods for measuring small displacements possess some advantages ; the apparatus can be made compact, distant reading is possible and if necessary the results can be recorded continuously on either a pen or photographic recorder.

Change of capacity and change of inductance in an oscillatory circuit, produced by the mechanical displacement, have been employed. The capacity method was successfully demonstrated by Whiddington in 1920, when electronic technique was in a very early stage of development[9]. The object whose displacement is to be measured is connected to one plate of a parallel plate capacitor, the distance between the two plates being quite small (about 0.001 in.). This capacitor is in an oscillatory circuit, and governs the frequency of oscillation therein. Displacement of the plate changes the frequency, which is detected by beats set up with another oscillatory circuit of nearly the same frequency. By means of further elaboration, displacements of about 10^{-6} cm. could be detected.

A later application of the capacitor method was made by Allsop and Lloyd[10], who used it to register movements of a diaphragm exposed to the impact of explosion waves. The circuits were chosen with a view to obtaining quick response, in order to follow transient phenomena, and the results were displayed on a cathode ray oscillograph.

The method depending on change of inductance is used in the sensitive part of gauges and comparators manufactured by Messrs. Taylor, Taylor and Hobson Ltd. Mechanical displacement of an armature produces a change in the inductance in the electrical circuit. The change is read on a microammeter which is calibrated to give directly the corresponding displacement in inches. In the most sensitive model, one division on the meter scale corresponds to a movement of 0.00002 in.

REFERENCES

[1] POLLARD, A. F. C., *J. Sci. Inst.*, **15** (1938), 37.

[2] ROLT, F. H., *Gauges and Fine Measurements*, Vol. 1 (London, Macmillan, 1929).

[3] ROLT, F. H., *A Dictionary of Applied Physics*—Article " Gauges " (London, Macmillan, 1922–3).

[4] FIZEAU, H., *Comptes Rendus*, **54** (1862), 1237.

[5] MICHELSON, A. A., *Light Waves and their Uses* (University of Chicago Press, 1907).

[6] MOLL, W. J. H., and BURGER, H. C., *Phil. Mag.*, **50** (1925), 621.

[7] MOSS, E. B., *J. Sci. Inst.*, **12** (1935), 141.

[8] TAYLOR, A. H., *Rev. Sci. Inst.*, **8** (1937), 124.

[9] WHIDDINGTON, R., *Phil. Mag.*, **40** (1920), 634.

[10] ALLSOP, G., and LLOYD, H., *A Recording Manometer having Low Inertia* (Safety in Mines Research Board, Paper No. 91 : London, H.M. Stationery Office, 1935).

[11] TOLANSKY, S., *Multiple Beam Interferometry* (Oxford, 1948).

[12] PRESTON, J. S., *J. Sci. Inst.*, **23** (1946), 173.

[13] WESTON, S., and TOWNS, V. W. H., *Proc. Optical Convention*, 1926.

[14] STARLING, S. G., *Trans Opt. Soc.*, **24** (1922–3), 261.

[15] RANK, D. H., *Rev. Sci. Inst.*, **17** (1946), 243.

[16] JONES, R. V., *Proc. Phys. Soc.* B, **64** (1951), 469.

[17] WILSON, W. H., and EPPS, T. D., *Proc. Phys. Soc.*, **32** (1920), 329.

[18] GUILD, J., *The interference systems of crossed gratings : Theory of moiré fringes* (Clarendon Press, Oxford, 1956).

[19] SAYCE, L. A., *Trans. Soc. Instrum. Techn.*, **9** (1957), 139.

[20] WILLIAMSON, D. T. N., Conference on Technology of Engineering Manufacture, paper 41 (*Inst. Mech. Engrs.*, 1958).

CHAPTER 8

SENSITIVITY AND ERRORS OF INSTRUMENTS

Sensitivity of instruments

IN the past, much stress has been laid on the need for sensitivity in instruments, which in the case of reading instruments is usually expressed as the number of scale divisions traversed by the pointer per unit change in the quantity being measured. There are, in the literature dealing with experimental technique, records of, for example, galvanometers whose sensitivity measured in this way is enormous. In many cases, however, various disturbing factors prevent a reading being taken correct to one or even several scale divisions, and the apparent high sensitivity is useless. It is now realised that the useful criterion of performance of an instrument is obtained by considering the least change in the quantity measured which can be detected by the instrument in the circumstances under which it is intended to work. Nothing is gained by making the scale divisions much smaller than correspond to this amount. It may happen that the scale divisions so made would be too small for easy reading by the eye, in which case some magnifying device may be used, or the sensitivity may be increased for example by weakening the control (torsion fibre, balancing weight, etc.). The objection to the latter course is that it results in an increased time of response of the instrument, and it may be preferable to employ magnification. There appears to be an increasing tendency in this direction in some instruments. Moll and Burger were among the first to apply this principle to the moving coil galvanometer, and their work has enormously increased the usefulness of that instrument. The thermo-amplifier which they invented (see Chapter 7) was applied to a Moll galvanometer, which is an instrument characterised by a short period and great insensitivity to mechanical disturbance. The combination gave the requisite sensitivity and at the same time preserved the desirable feature of quick response. It was so little affected by disturbing influences that the least current measureable was limited only by the Brownian movement of the galvanometer coil, as was shown by Ising[1]. A general discussion of the effect of

Brownian movements on various kinds of instruments has been given by Barnes and Silverman[2].

The question of stability becomes of great importance if the indications of an instrument are to be magnified, and it is of some interest to consider how stability is achieved in the Moll galvanometer[3]. The coil and mirror (Fig. 8.1) are made as symmetrical as possible, and are suspended between two phosphor bronze or silicon bronze wires, which are held taut by the spring as shown. The restoring couple per unit twist of the coil is not affected by the stretching force applied, hence the periodic time of torsional oscillations is also unaffected. If, however, the arrangement is made to vibrate after the manner of a stretched string (transversely) the time of vibration is decreased by increasing the stretching force. The rate at which energy is dissipated will also be increased, whilst a given disturbing force will produce a smaller displacement of the coil in a horizontal direction. The net result is that such a stretched suspension is much less sensitive to disturbances producing transverse vibrations than an unstretched system. If the system is perfectly balanced, then

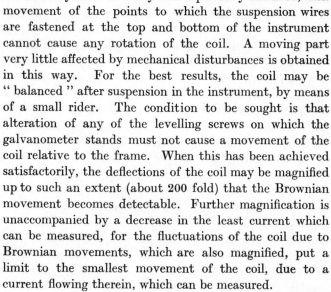

movement of the points to which the suspension wires are fastened at the top and bottom of the instrument cannot cause any rotation of the coil. A moving part very little affected by mechanical disturbances is obtained in this way. For the best results, the coil may be " balanced " after suspension in the instrument, by means of a small rider. The condition to be sought is that alteration of any of the levelling screws on which the galvanometer stands must not cause a movement of the coil relative to the frame. When this has been achieved satisfactorily, the deflections of the coil may be magnified up to such an extent (about 200 fold) that the Brownian movement becomes detectable. Further magnification is unaccompanied by a decrease in the least current which can be measured, for the fluctuations of the coil due to Brownian movements, which are also magnified, put a limit to the smallest movement of the coil, due to a current flowing therein, which can be measured.

In a critically damped moving coil galvanometer with electro-magnetic damping, the Brownian movement is

FIG. 8.1.—Suspended system of Moll galvanometer.

equivalent to a fluctuating current, the square root of whose mean square value is $\sqrt{\overline{\Delta i^2}} = \sqrt{\dfrac{\pi\,k\,T}{R\,\tau}}$, where k is Boltzmann's constant, T the absolute temperature, R the resistance of the circuit and τ the periodic time of the galvanometer on open circuit. The limit set by Brownian movements can, according to this equation, be diminished by increasing the time of vibration of the coil, but practical considerations prevent the limit being lowered much by this method.

A discussion of the fluctuations in indicating instruments will be found in ref. 13.

Errors

The subject of instrumental errors has been considered in detail by Whitehead[4] and by Pollard[10] whose work may be consulted by those requiring a more detailed treatment than the brief outline given here.

Since it is impossible to construct an instrument so that all its parts have exactly the desired shapes and dimensions, even when the best methods are employed in construction, it is of importance to consider to what extent the influence of constructional errors may be minimised by suitable design and use. Most measuring instruments employ some kind of pointer moving over a scale and the quantity measured is supposed to be related in a known manner to the movements of the pointer over the scale. The errors due to the instrument, as distinct from those due to the observer's judgment, arise on account of inaccuracies in this supposed known relation. In some cases the relation cannot readily be calculated and is determined by calibration. In such a case, apart from observer's errors made in the process of calibration and later in the use of the instrument, the only errors to be expected are what may be termed errors due to erratic behaviour of the instrument, which may be said to occur if the same instrument reading is not always obtained for a given value of the quantity to be measured. Contributory causes of erratic behaviour are external disturbing influences, unduly large frictional forces between moving parts of the instruments, leading to elastic deformation, backlash and indefiniteness of location of the parts. These causes are more commonly due to faulty design than to inferior workmanship. By applying the principles considered in Chapter 6 it should be possible to reduce erratic errors, apart from those due to external influences, below the significant level. Wherever sliding of surfaces occurs, erratic errors must be present to some extent, but need not be large ; if they are greater than can be tolerated, then rolling motion or motion depending on elastic deformation may be employed.

The investigation of the errors in an instrument (other than those of calibration, or arising from external causes) is assisted by determining the shape of the hysterisis loop (see Pollard[10]). To do this, external conditions which would affect the readings of the instrument must be kept constant. The quantity which the instrument is to measure is increased in small steps, taking readings meanwhile, then this quantity is reduced so that a complete cycle has been traversed. A plot of instrument readings against the measured quantity will show a closed loop, and this loop should be constant if the instrument is taken through several identical cycles. It is desirable to traverse a few cycles before commencing to take readings, in order that a cyclic condition may be established, when the elastically deformed parts have come into a more or less steady state. It is also important that the operation should be carried out slowly enough to prevent any periodic motion which the parts may be capable of performing, since this would of course result in other loops being traversed. If the hysterisis loop is not repeatable, the instrument is not in a proper condition for use, and should be examined. Grit, or damage to working surfaces, or defective springs may be suspected. The presence of backlash is shown by straight portions of the loop parallel to one of the axes. In addition, however, the ascending and descending parts of the graph only become straight after appreciable increments of one of the measured quantities, even after backlash has been overcome. This indicates that elastic deformation of the driving parts of the mechanism has taken place. Such an effect is always present to some extent, but it should be small. The hysterisis loop indicates the extent to which such deformation affects the readings, and allows the effect of changes in the design to be assessed quantitatively.

Systematic Errors

In instruments where the relation between measured quantity and scale reading is calculated from a knowledge of the dimensions of the instruments and not determined wholly by calibration, another class of errors appears in addition to those considered above, for now the shape and dimensions of certain parts of the apparatus are supposed known. In general it must be accepted that there are errors in the assumed values of the dimensions, due to imperfections of workmanship. The effect of these errors on the measurement depends to a considerable extent on the design, and their existence should be continually in mind when planning the arrangement of the parts of measuring apparatus. In many cases their effects can be eliminated by suitable procedure in the use of the instrument—as an example of this, the measurement of the angle of magnetic dip by means of the dip circle, familiar to readers of elementary textbooks on magnetism, will serve. It is not always, however, that the recommendation to " reverse everything " can be carried out, for readings have sometimes to be taken in the shortest possible time. In such a case the designer must do all he can to reduce the effect of errors of manufacture.

Errors due to imperfections of the constraints

In instruments in which the rectilinear motion of a sliding part relative to the frame of the instrument is measured, for example by means of a micrometer screw or a scale, or in which the motion is

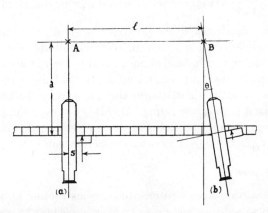

Fig. 8.2.—Illustrating errors introduced by lack of straightness of constraints.

coupled to another part of the instrument, errors will be introduced if the motion of the instrument is not truly rectilinear. It must be assumed that the ways controlling the motion will not be perfectly true, and the effect of this must be considered.

Suppose that a travelling microscope is employed as in Fig. 8.2 to measure the distance l between two points, the microscope being moved in turn from position (a) to position (b). Evidently if the microscope moves parallel to itself l is equal to the difference in the scale readings in the two positions. Suppose now that the two positions of the microscope are not exactly parallel, but that owing to lack of straightness of the ways or to some other cause there is a small angle θ (measured in the plane of the drawing) between the directions of the microscope axis in the two positions. The difference in the scale readings when the crosswire is set on the two points in turn is now $l + d \sin \theta - s(1 - \cos \theta)$, where d is the distance from the fiduciary mark to the line joining AB, and s the distance from the fiduciary mark to the microscope axis. The error is $s(1 - \cos \theta) - d \sin \theta$, or approximately $s(1 - \cos \theta) - \theta d$.

If the scale were arranged in the prolongation of AB, and the fiduciary mark, engraved on a suitable surface capable of sliding over the scale, were rigidly connected to the microscope, then d would be zero, and the error would be $s(1 - \cos \theta)$ or $2s \sin^2 \dfrac{\theta}{2}$, which is approximately $s \dfrac{\theta^2}{2}$. It is true that s would now be considerably greater than before, and perhaps several times as great as d, but the error would certainly be of a much smaller magnitude, since it would depend on the square instead of on the first power of the small angle θ. This is a most important result, and shows that the measuring scale or micrometer screw should be in the line joining the points whose distance apart is to be measured. If this is not done (and cases arise where it is impossible), much higher accuracy of the constraining ways will be required for a given accuracy of performance.

Errors of screws

Since measuring screws enter into the construction of many kinds of apparatus used in scientific work, it is important to realise that a screw and its mounting may be responsible for much larger errors than might at first sight be expected. An instructive account of methods of screw production and of errors in screws is given in refs. 5 and 6.

The most important errors of screws, from the point of view of the instrument designer, are those of pitch. Four different kinds of pitch error may occur, namely progressive error, periodic error, drunkenness and irregular error.

Progressive error is a gradual change in pitch from one end of the screw to the other. It may arise from a change in temperature during screw cutting, or from length changes during hardening, if a hardened screw is used. The effect of progressive error may be removed rather easily. If a rotating, non-translating screw is used to impart translatory motion to a nut, then clearly the nut must be prevented from rotating. This is often done, in measuring instruments, by keeping a radial arm attached to the nut in sliding contact with a guide bar which is parallel to the screw axis. If this bar is deliberately set so that it is not quite parallel to this axis, a slight rotation of the nut can be produced, and this can be made to compensate the effect of the progressive error of the screw. In principle, by making the guide bar of a suitable shape, any screw error can be allowed for.

Periodic error is a change in pitch which occurs at regular intervals, and is frequently due to errors in the lead screw or its mounting, if a screw-cutting lathe is used. Usually an error caused by faulty mounting of the lead screw produces a small to and fro movement of the screw in the direction of its axis once per revolution, and this is shown on the screw which is being cut as a periodic change in pitch. The periodicity depends on the relation between the pitches of lead screw and of the screw cut in the lathe. The way in which errors may arise from a defective thrust bearing (either in a lathe or in a measuring instrument) is made clear in Fig. 8.3. If the fixed and rotating

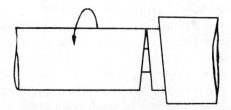

Fig. 8.3.—Plain thrust bearing in which the faces are not perpendicular to the axis of rotation.

thrust collars have faces not exactly perpendicular to the axis of rotation, a sinusoidal movement along this axis will take place. This error is very frequent when plain thrust bearings are used, and it may be eliminated by using instead the ball-ended strut (shown in Fig. 8.4 and described below) as a thrust bearing.

If the periodic error occurs at intervals equal to the pitch of the screw, it is referred to as "drunkenness." This error may be caused by a faulty thrust bearing on the lathe headstock, which gives rise to " end float," or it may occur with a faulty lead screw mounting if the pitch of the screw which is being cut is equal to that of the lead screw.

Irregular errors are due to the various causes which produce error in turning, such as uneven yielding of the parts, "built-up edge," etc.

By paying attention to these and other sources of error in screw cutting, manufacturers of micrometer screws have succeeded in grinding mass produced screws whose errors (including any errors in the mounting) are no greater than 0·0001 in. It may be said that to produce screws of this accuracy on a lathe is a somewhat formidable task. By the process of grinding screw and nut together employed by Rowland[7,8] for the screw of his ruling engine, very accurate screws can be produced but the operation is a lengthy one.

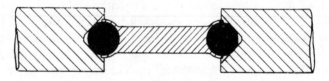

FIG. 8.4.—Ball ended strut for coupling two colinear movements.

Periodic errors in screws can be practically eliminated by an ingenious device introduced by Merton[11], and now known as the Merton nut. The principle is simple, and consists in using a long nut lined with a yielding material such as cork or elder pith, the threads in this cork engaging the screw threads. If the nut covers a sufficient number of threads, periodic errors at one point producing a deviation from the " true " or ideal translation of the nut will be balanced by an equal but opposite deviation produced elsewhere. A nut made of rigid material, fitting the screw tightly, would jam under these circumstances but a split nut of soft material may be clamped fairly tightly to the screw, the opposing thrusts caused by the periodic errors being taken up by yielding of the nut. The movement of the nut then follows the average pitch of the screw over the length of the nut. This form of nut will not remove the effect of progressive error, which can be removed as described above. The effect of errors introduced by a defective thrust bearing on the screw is of course not removed either by the use of a special nut.

The Merton nut is clearly only suitable for transmitting a very light thrust, and also does not give its best performance except when screw and nut rotate at a constant rate with respect to each other. It has been used with outstanding success in the manufacture of diffraction gratings, a development initiated by Merton and further developed at the National Physical Laboratory. The methods employed illustrate some interesting points in the design of mechanical instruments.[12]

Before leaving the subject of screw errors, reference may be made to the ball-ended connector shown in Fig. 8.4, which may be used for connecting two parts moving in approximately the same straight line. It is particularly useful when one of the components is rotating as well as advancing (screw motion). The requirements for elimination of errors are :—

(1) The holes in which the balls rest should be smooth and true surfaces of revolution, approximately conical.

(2) The balls at the ends of the strut should be good spheres. (They may be soft soldered to the strut.)

(3) The strut should be much longer than any off-axis error in the rotating part.

Subject to these conditions (which are not difficult to fulfil) the forward motion of the screw is accurately imparted by the strut to the other part. The arrangement is believed to be due to Sir Horace Darwin.

Parallax error

There is one observer's error which can be eliminated by suitable arrangements in an instrument, namely the parallax error frequently made in reading the position of a pointer with reference to a scale when the pointer does not lie in the surface of the scale. The error does not arise if the observer uses one eye situated on a line passing through the pointer, perpendicular to the surface of the scale. The usual practice is to provide a mirror with reflecting surface parallel to and in the plane of the scale, so that by taking care that the pointer covers its own image in the mirror, the observer knows that his eye is in the correct position. Observation under such conditions is somewhat tiring, however, and Forrester[9] has proposed that the image of the scale in a mirror should be observed, and the pointer arranged behind the mirror, in the plane containing the scale image. This entirely eliminates parallax error, and if necessary the pointer and scale image can be photographed. The numbers on the scale must be printed in reverse in this arrangement, but this may be avoided if the position of scale and pointer is interchanged, and the image of the pointer is observed, as in Fig. 8.5. The mirror should prefer-ably be surface reflecting, and the edge should be smooth and not chipped, as this edge separates the scale and the image of the pointer. For pointers which have a small range of motion, such as those attached to balance beams, silvered rectangular microscope cover slips are very suitable. With such thin glass it is not necessary to employ surface silvering.

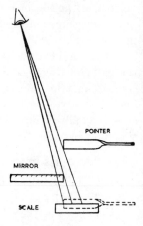

FIG. 8.5.—Use of mirror to avoid parallax error.

The measurement of distances be-tween different points on a photograph is a process carried out in many labora-tories, and is one which can be made easy or difficult according to the means employed. Detailed photographs on fine-grained plates can be measured with a travelling microscope, but there are many instances when either the grain or the photographic detail is coarse and in such cases high magnification can be a hindrance. This is often noticed, for instance, in X-ray photographs. It is usual to employ a scale or a pair of dividers to such photographs direct. This is not a very accurate method, however, for detail which is difficult to see is easily rendered invisible by such material objects. Much better results are obtained by setting the virtual image of an illuminated pinhole on the object to be measured. For instance, the optical part of a conventional travel-ling microscope may be replaced by the device shown in Fig. 8.6. On looking down through an unsilvered or half-silvered cover slip, the object to be measured is seen on the stage, and superposed on it a virtual image of the pinhole. If the distances from the object and pin-hole to the cover slip are made equal, no parallax will be seen between them, and the position of the eye is not critical. Further, any low-power magnifying lens may be used for inspecting the setting if this proves useful.

144

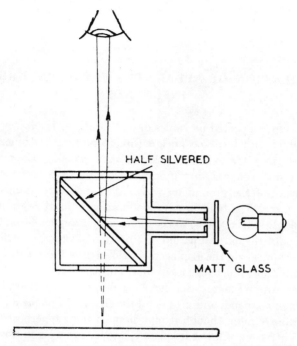

HALF SILVERED

MATT GLASS

Fig. 8.6.—Arrangement for projecting virtual image of illuminated pinhole on object to be measured, so avoiding parallax errors.

REFERENCES

[1] Ising, G., *Phil. Mag.*, **1** (1926), 827.

[2] Barnes, R. B., and Silverman, S., *Rev. Modern Physics*, **6** (1934), 162.

[3] Moll, W. J. H., *Proc. Phys. Soc.* **35** (1923), 253.

[4] Whitehead, T. N., *The Design and Use of Instruments and Accurate Mechanism* (New York, The Macmillan Co., 1934).

[5] Rolt, F. H., *Gauges and Fine Measurements*, Vol. II (London, Macmillan, 1929).

[6] Sears, J. E., *Dictionary of Applied Physics*, Vol. III—Article " Metrology " (London, Macmillan, 1922–3).

[7] Rowland, H. A., *Encyclop. Brit.*, 9th Edn. (1875)—Article " Screw."

[8] Anderson, J. A., *Dictionary of Applied Physics*, Vol. IV—Article " Diffraction Gratings, the Manufacture and Testing of " (London, Macmillan, 1922–3).

[9] Forrester, G. O., *Journ. Sci. Inst.*, **16** (1939), 268.

[10] Pollard, A. F. C., " The Mechanical Design of Physical Instruments "— *Reports on Progress in Physics*, Vol. X, 1944–5 (London, The Physical Society, 1946).

[11] Merton, Sir T., *Proc. Roy. Soc.* **A, 201** (1950), 187.

[12] "Recent Developments in Engineering Metrology at the N.P.L.," *Machinery*, 84 (1954), 36.

[13] Smith, R. A., Jones, F. E. and Chasmar, R. P., *The Detection and Measurement of Infra-red Radiation* (Oxford, 1957).

CHAPTER 9

ISOLATION OF APPARATUS FROM DISTURBING INFLUENCES

APPARATUS supported on tables or wall brackets is subject to vibrations which may be of local origin (due to running machinery, traffic, wind, etc.), or due to more distant seismic causes. The magnitudes of these disturbances vary greatly according to conditions, such as the nature of the ground on which the laboratory stands, type of building, etc. The tendency is for vibration of local origin to become increasingly severe, owing to the increase in heavy traffic on the roads.

No doubt the natural period of vibration of the wall or floor of the building appears in the displacement time curve for the disturbances, especially those due to causes of short duration, such as the footfalls of a person walking across the floor. This period is generally a small fraction of a second, and in general the frequency of the disturbances will be fairly high, though it may happen that, superposed on these vibrations, is one of lower frequency, due for example to slow running machinery. The subject of shock excitation is dealt with in ref. 10.

The local disturbances can to some extent be removed by mounting apparatus on piers which go into the ground without making direct contact with the building, but this will not eliminate seismic movements, nor the heavier disturbances due to traffic, and in any case is only practicable on the ground floor, where, however, it is often worth while.

A very good account of the theory of mechanical vibrations has been given by v. Santen (see General Reference at end of chapter). This deals with the measurement, coupling, isolation, damping etc. of vibration, and gives consideration to practical details as well as to the theory.

Effect of disturbances on instruments

A consideration of the mechanical disturbances on the indications of an instrument, and the conditions to be satisfied in order to render such effects harmless, appears to have been first published by du Bois and Rubens[1] in connection with the moving magnet galvanometer. The results apply to any freely hanging system suspended by a flexible fibre in which the rotation of the system about a vertical axis is to be measured.

Suppose a rigid body is hung from a torsion head (Fig. 9.1) by means of a light fibre OA, and let the principal inertia axis (that is, the axis about which the moment of inertia is a minimum) be I'', I'. The centre of gravity is at G, and rectangular co-ordinates OX, OY and OZ are taken through the point O, which is subject to disturbances. Evidently, if the torsion head rotates about O, the only rotation which can affect the body is that about a vertical axis, and for a light fibre the rotational coupling between O and A will be small. In consequence, small random rotational movements of O will be without appreciable effect on the body.

Translational movement of O along OZ will result in raising or lowering the suspended system, without producing rotation. Any horizontal translation of O can be resolved into two components, along OX and OY respectively. Suppose O is suddenly displaced along OX to O', and that the instantaneous position of the fibre is then AO'. The tension of the fibre along AO' and the weight of the body acting along AG will together produce a force AA', which will give rise to rotational oscillations about the principal inertia axis $I'I''$.

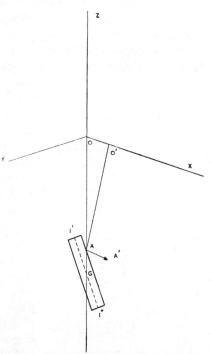

FIG. 9.1.—Rigid body suspended by single fibre.

The smaller the moment of inertia about this axis, the greater will be the amplitude of the oscillations. Only if the force AA' intersects the inertia axis will there be no oscillation produced. Besides the rotation about $I'I''$, vibrations about a horizontal axis may be set up, but they are not very objectionable if the suspended body is a galvanometer magnet and mirror since they give rise only to vertical

147

movement of the light spot on the scale. It is however, very desirable to eliminate the oscillations about $I'\ I''$, and this can be done if the point A lies on the principal inertia axis. To ensure this, the system must have complete " inertia symmetry " about the prolongation of the suspension fibre.

In addition to the effect described above, the force AA' will cause the body to make pendulum-like oscillations. These in turn may give rise to rotation of the body about a vertical axis if the resistance which the air offers to its movement is unsymmetrical about this axis. Any damping vanes on the suspended system should therefore be divided so as to present equal areas in two perpendicular planes.

In instruments in which the moving part is held between two stretched suspension fibres (e.g., the Moll galvanometer) the conditions are rather different. The problem is simplified if we consider the

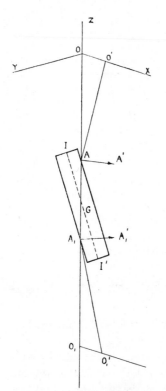

case where a body is held between equal fibres, the remote ends of the fibres being attached at O, O_1 to the frame of the instrument, and if we assume that these points simultaneously experience sudden displacements to O' and O'_1, respectively (Fig. 9.2). The body will be subject then to the horizontal components of the tension in the fibres, AA' and $A_1A'_1$ respectively. For equal displacements of O and O_1, AA' will be greater than A_1A_1' because of the weight of the body. If the tension in the stretched fibres is considerable in comparison with the weight of the body, the centre of gravity need not lie in the line OO_1, and the fibres will not be co-linear.

Since AA' and $A_1A'_1$ are very nearly parallel, they may be replaced by a single force acting through a point nearer to AA' than to $A_1A'_1$. The effect of this force will be to produce rotation about a vertical axis, unless it passes through the principal axis of inertia of the body, as well as

Fig. 9.2.—Rigid body held between stretched fibres.

to produce some rotation about a horizontal axis, if it does not pass through a point in the same horizontal plane as the centre of gravity G.

It is evidently desirable to give the suspended body as high a degree of symmetry as possible, to make OO_1 vertical and to endeavour to make the resultant of the forces AA' and $A_1A'_1$ pass through G. The last desideratum requires fibres of equal length, stretched by forces large in comparison with the weight of the body, so that AA' and $A_1A'_1$ may be as far as possible equal. If these conditions are approximately fulfilled, the most serious effect of vibration of O and O_1, namely rotation of the body about a vertical axis, can be reduced by loading the body asymmetrically in such a way as to bring G on to the line joining AA_1. This condition can be recognised by the fact that tilting the frame of the instrument to which the fibres are attached will not produce rotation of the body about a vertical axis if the centre of gravity lies on AA_1. It does not follow that the principal axis of inertia will coincide with the line AA_1, but a small inclination between these two directions can be tolerated if they intersect at a point close to the line of action of the resultant of AA' and A_1A_1'.

Means for reducing sensitiveness to disturbance

It is evident from the above considerations that symmetrical construction of the moving parts of an instrument about the axis of rotation is desirable for all kinds of instruments with suspended or pivoted rotating parts.

A further point to which attention should be paid is the need for a sufficient degree of rigidity in the frame of the instrument, as distinct from its moving part. In some cases, an improvement can be made by constructing the frame of cast iron instead of, say, mild steel. This is particularly the case when the frequency of the disturbances is high, and there is a possibility of forming standing waves in the frame. Elastic vibrations are much more quickly damped out in cast iron than in steel, and for this reason the beds of large instruments may preferably be cast. Supporting pillars of cast iron will also be less subject to vibration than steel tubing of similar size. Concrete pillars are also suitable.

There is one other method by means of which the sensitiveness to disturbance may be reduced, namely by providing adequate damping of the moving part, so that the movements caused by disturbances are quickly reduced. A simple example of this method is seen in the artificial horizon, which consists of a shallow circular flat-bottomed dish of copper, the bottom of which is amalgamated and covered with a layer of mercury about 0·1 mm. deep. Any movement of the mercury caused by vibration of the table on which the dish stands is very quickly damped out, and the surface remains practically at rest. Since it is a free surface, it maintains a horizontal position. Naturally the copper dish must be levelled so that an approximately uniform layer of mercury is formed. The effect of the damping can be realised by increasing the depth of the mercury, whose surface will then appear continually disturbed by ripples. Methods of applying damping forces are considered in Chapter 10.

Isolating apparatus from mechanical disturbances

It will be found that with sensitive instruments the necessary conditions of symmetrical construction cannot always be realised to a sufficient extent to make them independent of disturbance.

A good modern galvanometer of the Moll type, for instance, ought to be stable enough for use with a lamp and scale when supported on an ordinary wall bracket, but if the deflections are amplified with a thermal relay or other similar means it may be that the disturbance of the light spot due to wall vibrations is appreciable. It would then be necessary to mount the instrument in such a way that the vibrations, etc., are prevented from exercising a harmful effect. The ways in which this result may be approached are :—

(1) Reducing the coupling between the instrument and its surroundings.

(2) Damping out the reduced disturbances on the mounting itself.

(3) Supporting the instrument on materials which have particularly poor transmission of mechanical vibrations and waves.

The problem of isolation appears first to have been dealt with in a publication by Julius[2] who gives a very illuminating discussion of the theoretical basis of his method of isolating a galvanometer of the sensitive suspended magnet type. The so-called Julius suspension was soon widely employed, but apparently so many incorrect descriptions and examples of this suspension were in existence by the year 1905 that Julius found it necessary again to draw attention to the essential features of his mounting[3]. The following description is taken from Julius' publications.

The Julius suspension

The arrangement is shown in Fig. 9.3. A stand is made from two triangular wooden boards, connected by three stout wooden rods fastened to the corners ; the construction must be rigid. The galvanometer or other instrument is fastened securely to the lower board by screws or other suitable means. A brass rod projects from the upper board and carries an adjustable lead weight, whose purpose is to alter the position of the centre of gravity of the whole system. If the instrument is a galvanometer in which the moving part is simply hung from a torsion head, the centre of gravity is adjusted to be in the horizontal plane containing the point of suspension of the fibre, and in the same plane are situated three hooks by means of which the arrangement is hung from a cantilever, using three identical steel wires, of 2 or 3 metres length. Damping vanes are attached to each of the wooden rods in such a way that the centres of the vanes are at the same height as the hooks to which the wires are attached. The vanes dip into small beakers of oil.

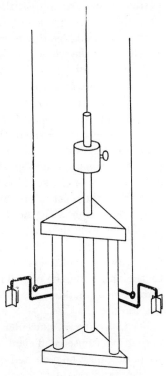

FIG. 9.3.—Julius anti-vibration suspension.

Julius states that the loading of the stand must be central, so that the tensions in the wires are equal. According to Julius, the working of the arrangement is as follows.

It is assumed that a given disturbance produces simultaneously the same displacement of the upper ends of the three wires. With displacements having a horizontal component, transverse waves will be produced in the wires, which will be in phase when they reach the lower ends. The lower ends of the wires will be slightly inclined to the vertical at this moment, and the stand will be subject momentarily to three equal horizontal components of the tension in the wires. The resultant of these forces will, since it passes through the centre of gravity of the system,

151

produce only a motion of translation, and this will be of very small extent, because the inclination of the wires is exceedingly small, hence the horizontal component of the wire tension, which produces the movement, is small also. The vanes serve to damp out movements due to air currents as well as the residual movements transmitted via the wires.

It is stated that the load on the wires should produce an appreciable extension, in order that the effect of random vertical movements may be reduced, but this, according to Müller[4], is not desirable.

The Julius suspension has been widely used with satisfactory results for instruments in which it is not necessary to isolate the system from vertical disturbances. It should be mentioned that it is desirable to provide some clamping arrangement to hold the stand firm whilst making adjustments, and that better results are obtained by shielding the whole arrangement from draughts.

Müller, in a lengthy investigation on the subject of isolation from mechanical disturbances[4] has examined the effect of various modifications to the Julius suspension, and recommends the use of soft iron wires in place of steel, for the vibrations transmitted to the stands are then considerably lessened. If this change is made, it is not so necessary that the centre of gravity of the system should lie exactly in the plane which passes through the lower ends of the wires. The need for great rigidity of the stand is emphasised.

Perhaps the most interesting and important modification, however, is in connection with the damping. It is desirable that the stand should be well damped, but heavy damping produced as in the Julius arrangement may result in the transmission of movement from the oil containers (which share in the general disturbance) to the vanes via the oil. The difficulty is overcome by a damping arrangement making use of internal motions in a fluid carried by the stand.

For this purpose, a circular metal tray of 30–40 cm. diameter, containing oil whose coefficient of viscosity is in the neighbourhood of six poises, may be mounted on the stand. Translational acceleration of the stand produces ripples on the free liquid surface and a consequent dissipation of energy. It is found that there is an optimum depth of liquid for maximum damping, and that this depth increases with increasing frequency of vibration of the Julius suspension, and also with increasing diameter of the tray. Some of the data given by Müller are reproduced in Table 9.1, which gives the optimum depth under different conditions, and also the time required to reduce the amplitude of the pendulum vibration from 10 mm. to 1 mm.

The same tray serves to damp out any rotation about a vertical axis which may be set up by air currents, etc. Acceleration about this axis causes the propagation of transverse waves from the sides of the tray through the viscous liquid, again with dissipation of energy. Unlike the damping considered above, in this case the damping increases with the depth of liquid. In practice, a number of trays is used, each being filled to the optimum depth.

TABLE 9.1—*Damping of Pendulum*

Diameter of tray	Length of pendulum					
	$l = 100$ cm.		$l = 200$ cm.		$l = 300$ cm.	
cm.	$\dfrac{d}{cm.}$	$\dfrac{t}{sec.}$	$\dfrac{d}{cm.}$	$\dfrac{t}{sec.}$	$\dfrac{d}{cm.}$	$\dfrac{t}{sec.}$
23·0	1·5	80	1·4	285	1·3	540
29·5	1·9	34	1·7	130	1·6	220
38·5	2·2	14	1·9	50	1·8	80

Note.—d is the depth of liquid for maximum damping. The time required to reduce the amplitude of the pendulum vibrations from 10 mm. to 1 mm. is indicated by t.

Müller's mounting

In the investigation referred to above, Müller has drawn attention to some disadvantages of the Julius suspension, chiefly on grounds of convenience, and has constructed and patented a mounting which has the advantage of being easily transportable. Since it does not occupy so much space as a Julius suspension, the new arrangement can be more easily enclosed to protect it from draughts.

If the natural time of vibration of the mounting and the instrument which it carries (considered as a rigid system suspended by wires, or other means) is large in comparison with the mean time of vibration of the disturbed surroundings, then the coupling between the mounting and surroundings is small and the disturbances have little effect on the mounting. The desired conditions are achieved in the Julius suspension by attaching the instrument to a long pendulum whose time of vibration is of the order of 3 seconds. Müller's arrangement provides a time of vibration of the same order by attaching a massive stand to three thin vertical rods which are supported from the floor or from a wall bracket. The essential features of the arrangement are shown in Fig. 9.4. A rigid triangular metal base is provided with three levelling screws which stand on the bracket, table, etc., and the elastic rods are held in small clamps at the corners of the metal base.

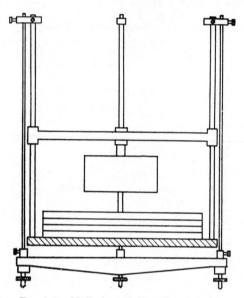

FIG. 9.4.—Müller's anti-vibration support.

To the top of each rod is clamped a stouter rod of aluminium, also in the vertical position, and the lower ends of this second set of rods are fastened to a rigid three-legged " spider " of duralumin. A similar spider, capable of adjustment in a vertical direction, is clamped near the middle of the aluminium rods, and the upper surface of this part is grooved to take the feet of the instrument which the stand is to carry. A series of four damping trays (similar to those described above) is carried by the lower spider ; these are filled with paraffin. As the apparatus is intended to be a universal one, capable of carrying various kinds of instruments, it is loaded by a metal cylinder carrying lead shot, fastened under the centre of the upper spider. The amount of lead shot is adjusted according to the mass of the instrument mounted, so that the same period for horizontal vibrations, namely 4 seconds, can be maintained under varying conditions of use. The damping is adjusted for this period of vibration. A clamping arrangement is provided (not shown in the figure) so that the lower ends of two of the aluminium rods can be temporarily clamped to the base. It will be observed that no attempt is made to isolate the instrument from vertical disturbances. According to Müller, the arrangement is as good as or better than the Julius suspension, according to circumstances.

Below are given the chief dimensions of the apparatus :

Elastic rods (brass) 45–50 cm. long, 0·4 cm. diameter.
Distance between elastic rods 44 cm.
Aluminium rods 46 cm. long, 1·2 cm. diameter.
Damping trays 38 cm. diameter, 1·2 cm. deep.
Volume of paraffin in each of the four trays 750 cc.
Total load about 5–10 kgm.

Haringx anti-vibration mounting

A general and extremely helpful treatment of the design of anti-vibration mountings is given by Haringx[7,8,] making use of the theory of coupled oscillators. The main results of his analysis are given below.

Suppose that a table of mass m is supported by a spring as shown in Fig. 9.5a. If the spring restoring force per unit displacement of the mass in a vertical direction is c, the natural frequency of oscillation of the system is $\dfrac{1}{2\pi} \sqrt{\dfrac{c}{m}}$ or for convenience we may speak of the angular frequency ω_0 which is $\sqrt{\dfrac{c}{m}}$. If the support (floor, etc.) on which the spring stands vibrates with angular frequency ω and amplitude a_0, then in the absence of damping, the mass oscillates with the angular frequency ω, but with an amplitude a such that

$$\frac{a}{a_0} = \left| \frac{c}{c - m\omega^2} \right|$$

This relation, shown graphically in Fig. 9.5b, exhibits the well-known resonance peak which occurs when the support oscillates with a frequency equal to the natural frequency of the supported system. Evidently, for a vibration-free mounting, we should choose a natural frequency much lower than the frequency with which the support oscillates. This principle is of course the basis of all anti-vibration mountings.

In addition to the possibility that the support (floor, etc.) can vibrate with a well-defined frequency we have also to consider more or less sudden disturbances which would set the mass m vibrating. In the absence of damping, such vibrations would continue. For a practical solution we must have damping to bring these vibrations to rest as quickly as possible.

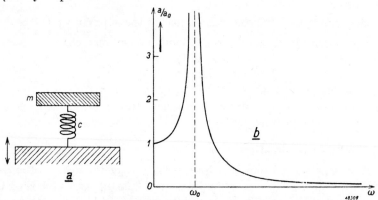

FIG. 9.5.—Diagram (a) and frequency characteristic (b) of an undamped, vibration-free system. At frequencies ω which lie far enough above the resonant frequency ω_0 the amplitudes of the forced vibrations of the mass m caused by the vibration motion of the foundation are very much reduced. The amplitude ratio is :—

$$\frac{a}{a_0} = \left| \frac{c}{c - m\omega^2} \right|$$

(*Philips Technical Review.*)

The damping may be applied as shown in Fig. 9.6 (a) by means of, say, a dash-pot containing oil carried by the support and a plunger on the mass m. If the damping force is proportional to the relative velocity of m and the support, with the constant of proportionality equal to k, the frequency characteristic becomes as shown in Fig. 9.6 (b). The resonance value of $\dfrac{a}{a_0}$,' which without damping becomes infinite, is now reduced, but in the region of frequencies which we should choose ($\omega_0 \gg \omega$) the curves are much less favourable. This is a consequence of the tighter coupling between support and mass at high frequencies, owing to the greater damping force when the relative velocity is high. Though less favourable in this respect, the damping would reduce vibrations of a transient character.

The disadvantage of " relative " damping (applied as in Fig. 9.6 (a)) must have been evident to many who have constructed anti-vibration mountings, and Müller (see above) introduced a special type of damping which did not increase the coupling between support and

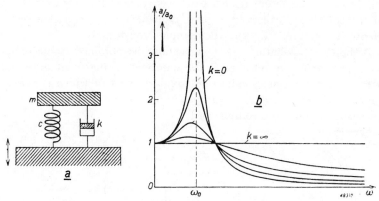

FIG. 9.6.—Diagram (a) and frequency characteristic (b) of a vibration-free system with " relative " damping. The amplitude ratio is given by the expression :—

$$\left(\frac{a}{a_0}\right)^2 = \frac{1 + q^2 \, \bar{\omega}^2}{(\bar{\omega}^2 - 1)^2 + q^2 \, \bar{\omega}^2} \quad \text{where } \bar{\omega} = \frac{\omega}{\omega_0}, \; q = \frac{k}{m \, \omega_0}$$

and $\omega_0^2 = c/m$. (*Philips Technical Review.*)

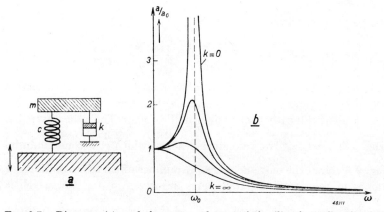

FIG. 9.7.—Diagram (a) and frequency characteristic (b) of a vibration-free system with " absolute " damping. The amplitude ratio is given by the expression :—

$$\left(\frac{a}{a_0}\right)^2 = \frac{1}{(\bar{\omega}^2 - 1)^2 + q^2 \, \bar{\omega}^2} \quad \text{where } \bar{\omega} = \frac{\omega}{\omega_0}, \; q = \frac{k}{m \, \omega_0}$$

and $\omega_0^2 = c/m$. (*Philips Technical Review.*)

mass. Haringx gives the frequency characteristic which would result if the dash-pot could be carried on a fixed support ("absolute" damping, see Fig. 9.7). Though not of course realisable in practice, this characteristic is of considerable interest. It will be observed that the height of the resonance peak is lowered, as well as the amplitude of the forced vibrations at higher frequencies, the reduction being greater for greater values of the damping constant k.

Although "absolute" damping cannot be obtained, some of its good properties are retained if the damping arrangement is placed between the main mass m and an auxiliary mass M which is loosely coupled to m by means of springs (Fig. 9.8). The frequency characteristic is now more complicated.

Writing

$$\bar{\omega} = \frac{\omega}{\omega_0} = \omega \sqrt{\frac{m + M}{c}}$$

$$p = \frac{C}{c} \frac{m + M}{M}$$

$$q = \frac{k}{M} \sqrt{\frac{m + M}{c}}$$

$$\mu = \frac{m}{m + M}$$

the frequency characteristic is

$$\left\{ \frac{a}{a_0} \right\}^2 = \frac{(\bar{\omega}^2 - p)^2 + q^2 \bar{\omega}^2}{[\mu \bar{\omega}^4 - (1 + p) \bar{\omega}^2 + p]^2 + q^2 \bar{\omega}^2 (\bar{\omega}^2 - 1)^2}$$

When the damping parameter q becomes infinite, the two masses are in effect rigidly connected and the frequency characteristic becomes identical with that shown in Fig. 9.5. The other extreme, when q is zero, has two resonance peaks at which $\frac{a}{a_0}$ becomes infinite. Fig. 9.9 shows the extreme cases. A number of curves with different values of the damping parameter q are given in Fig. 9.8, which is drawn for the case where $m = M$ and the spring ratio $\frac{C}{c} = 0 \cdot 25$.

At high frequencies

$$\left| \frac{a}{a_0} \right| \approx \frac{1}{\mu \bar{\omega}^2} = \frac{c}{m\omega^2}$$

This expression is identical with that for the arrangement of Fig. 9.5 in the high frequency region. The auxiliary mass M has therefore no influence in the region where the impressed frequency is much greater than the resonance frequency, the region in which the apparatus will function properly. The damping is, however, very effective in reducing the free vibrations of the system after accidental disturbance.

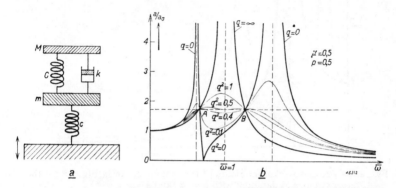

FIG. 9.8.—Vibration-free system with auxiliary mass M. The damping (k) is introduced between the main mass (m) and the auxiliary mass M. The amplitude ratio is given on p. 158. The figure is drawn for the special case $\mu = 0.5$ and $p = 0.5$ where the points of intersection A and B of all the frequency characteristics lie at the same height.
(*Philips Technical Review.*)

Haringx considers the question of the best choice of parameters, and from the rate of decay of the free vibrations deduces that the points of intersection A and B of the characteristic curves in Fig. 9.8 should be at the same height. This leads to the relation

$$p \text{ optimum } = \mu$$

The optimum value of the damping parameter q is (according to calculations of Collatz[9] quoted by Haringx)

$$q \text{ optimum } \approx \sqrt{1.5\,\mu\,(1 - \mu)}$$

As regards the choice of mass parameter, the most favourable case is when M is large compared with m. For practical reasons it is suggested however that M and m may conveniently be made equal, in which case the optimum value for q becomes 0.624. Fig. 9.10 shows frequency characteristics for an undamped system, for one with " relative " damping and for the system with auxiliary mass. The

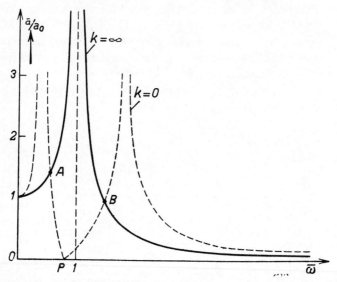

Fig. 9.9.—Frequency characteristics of the system shown in Fig. 9.8 for the two extremes of damping with $k = \infty$ and $k = 0$.

(*Philips Technical Review.*)

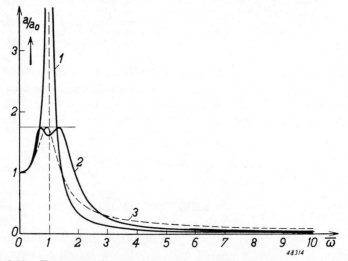

Fig. 9.10.—Frequency characteristics of an undamped system (curve 1), a system with auxiliary mass and " optimum " parameters chosen for $\mu = 0.5$ (curve 2) and a system with relative damping (curve 3). It is assumed that the total mass and also the rigidity of the spring c is the same in all three systems. Further, for curve 3 the damping was so chosen that the maximum amplitude ratio is the same as in case 2.

(*Philips Technical Review.*)

last system is clearly more efficient, on the whole, than the other two, particularly when the rapid decay of the free vibrations is considered (see Fig. 9.11). An important property of the system with auxiliary mass is that the choice of the parameters p and q is by no means critical.

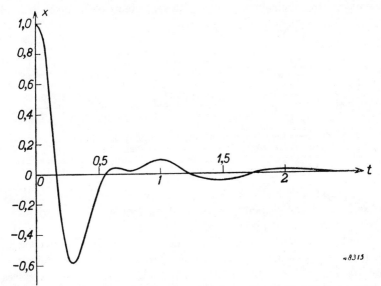

FIG. 9.11.—The decay of the free vibrations after a given initial displacement for a system according to Fig. 9.8a, with $\mu = 0{\cdot}5$ and the optimum parameters $p = 0{\cdot}5$ and $q = 0{\cdot}62$.

(*Philips Technical Review.*)

The treatment outlined above is restricted to a body having one degree of freedom. Even if the mass which serves as an anti-vibration support be considered as a rigid body, however, it has six degrees of freedom—three of translation and three of rotation. Unless certain conditions are observed, there will be coupling between the various modes of vibration, with unpredictable results. The necessary conditions are that the body should have three mutually perpendicular principal axes of elasticity passing through a point (the centre of elasticity) and coinciding in direction with the three principal axes of inertia. A principal axis of elasticity is a line along which an applied force will produce a displacement in the same direction. The necessary conditions exist if the body has three mutually perpendicular planes of symmetry (considering, of course, both the damping and the spring elements). In practice, it is not possible to have a horizontal plane of symmetry as the weight of the body introduces an asymmetrical element. It is, however, possible to arrange the springs so that the horizontal principal axes of elasticity and of inertia coincide for small displacements. Possible arrangements are shown in Fig. 9.12. To the extent to which symmetry is achieved, vibration along or around

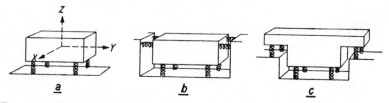

FIG. 9.12.—Three different arrangements for making an apparatus vibration-free where multi-dimensional disturbing vibrations exist. The mountings are all symmetrical with respect to two perpendicular vertical planes. (*Philips Technical Review.*)

one principal axis will not result in other vibrations. If an auxiliary mass is used the principal axes for this should coincide with the principal axes of the main mass.

For the springs, Haringx recommends using short helical steel springs and gives details for calculating their dimensions. An alternative would be one of the rubber-to-metal anti-vibration devices which are now available in variety. Fig. 9.15 shows a " Silentbloc " mounting which has been successfully used instead of steel springs in other types of anti-vibration mount. It is probable that the rubber

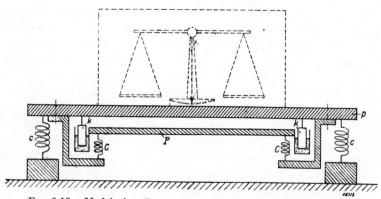

FIG. 9.13.—Model of a vibration-free mounting with auxiliary mass. (*Philips Technical Review.*)

would itself damp out harmonics of very high frequency, which might be transmitted by steel. Fig. 9.13 shows a model of a vibration-free mounting.

The damping may be applied by cups containing oil, in which other cups dip with a clearance of a few millimetres. For square damping cups, Haringx states that the damping coefficient will be equal in the vertical and horizontal directions if $H \approx 1{\cdot}45\,B$, where H is the height of the oil and B is the side of the base of the inner cup. Under these conditions

$$k \approx 18\,\frac{\eta B^4}{d^3}\,(1 + 2{\cdot}5\frac{d}{B})$$

where d is the clearance between the cup walls and η is the viscosity of the liquid.

Fig. 9.14 shows a drawing of an anti-vibration mounting which is said to bear out the predictions of the theory. The apparatus is suitable for instruments weighing up to 35 kg.

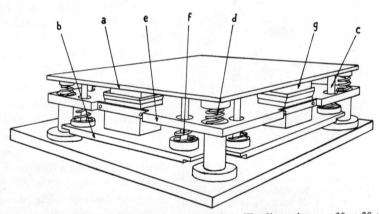

FIG. 9.14.—Example of a vibration-free mounting. The dimensions are 60 × 60 × 15 cm. ; its weight is 110 kg. The two plates a and b together form the main mass. They are connected by twelve rods c. The main mass rests upon four helical springs d. The auxiliary mass e is coupled to the main mass by eight springs f. The cup g is one of the four damping elements.

(*Philips Technical Review.*)

Methods of employing special properties of materials

A considerable degree of isolation can be obtained by mounting the apparatus on such materials as spongy rubber, or tennis balls, or on a pile consisting of alternate layers of felt and paving stones.

Such methods have the advantage over those previously considered that some isolation from vertical as well as from horizontal disturbance is obtained.

A detailed investigation of the possibilities of using air-filled cushions, etc., has been made by Gehrcke and Voigt[5,6,] who have described three different arrangements. One of these, which is particularly recommended by Gehrcke and Voigt, is illustrated in

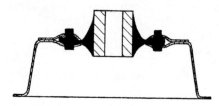

Fig. 9.16. It is intended to be used on a table, and consists of a giant balloon tyre (size 1000 × 250 mm.), on which is supported a smaller tyre (size 720 × 120 mm.), the air pressure in the tyres being about 90 mm. of mercury higher than atmospheric pressure. On the second tyre is placed a disc of wood or other suitable material, about 12 mm. thick, and the instrument is mounted on the disc. A sheet metal drum, containing 35 kgm. of lead shot and 2·5 kgm. of oil, is attached by means of bolts to the under side of the disc. In order to facilitate adjustment of the apparatus on the disc, a substantial movable platform with screw adjustment is provided. This serves also as a safety device, in case either of the tyres should become deflated. The arrangement is said to be extraordinarily free from disturbance. Some advantage is obtained by putting a layer of wax along the outer and inner circumferences of the tyres and for protection from air currents the apparatus should be surrounded by shields.

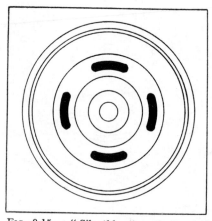

FIG. 9.15. — " Silentbloc " anti-vibration support, using rubber (shown black) bonded to metal.

It was found that the mounting described above was suitable for liquid surfaces used as reference planes in interferometric measurements, as well as for sensitive galvanometers. In connection with the latter use of the mounting, it may be mentioned that it could satis-factorily be used for a du Bois-Rubens galvanometer with a suspension weighing 16 mgm. ; this suspension could not be employed with the Julius arrangement, as the disturbances were too great.

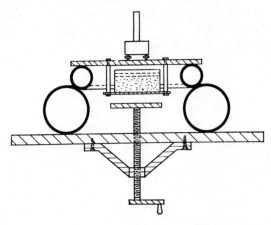

FIG. 9.16.—Anti-vibration support using inflated rubber tyres.
(*Gehrcke and Voigt.*)

Temperature variation

Temperature variation can be a very potent source of trouble and of wasted effort. If apparatus known to be sensitive to temperature changes is to be used, and the observations are to extend over an appreciable period of time, it is useless to proceed in the hope that the air temperature will remain constant. Experience shows that in general the temperature will not remain constant, and a great deal of time may be saved by realising this at the outset. Two methods, or a combination of the two, may be employed. The apparatus may be made insensitive to temperature changes, or the air temperature may be held constant. Lagging the apparatus is usually only effective if the air temperature is held constant within fairly narrow limits, and its proper function is to reduce the amplitude of temperature fluctuation inside the lagged enclosure to a fraction of the range of variation of temperature outside, as shown by Fourier's theory of heat conduction. If the mean temperature, taken over a time covering a number of the fluctuations, is not constant outside, neither will it be constant inside the enclosure.

In order to make the apparatus insensitive to temperature, it may in some cases be constructed of materials whose properties are largely independent of temperature. For instance, if temperature sensitivity is due to change in dimensions, it may be possible to employ invar or fused silica in the construction, both of these materials having low coefficients of thermal expansion. If the purpose of the instrument is the measurement of length of material objects (and in this class must be counted such measurements as the distance between lines, etc., on a photographic plate) the use of an invar scale or screw would give the true length, but only at the temperature of observation and it is sometimes simpler to use a material such as mild steel for the screw or scale, which is made correct at a stated temperature (usually 20° C. = 68° F.) and to make a correction if the absolute value of the length is required at a different temperature. Care must be used in employing a construction containing low-expansion materials as well as the ordinary metals, for in some arrangements differential expansion may set up strains which will give rise to greater distortion of the apparatus than would have been obtained by using more homogeneous material and such distortion may produce greater errors than those which it is sought to eliminate.

Compensation of effects due to temperature changes is sometimes possible, a familiar example being the balance wheel of a watch. The chief effect to be compensated is the change in elasticity of the hair spring ; the effect of this on the time of vibration is counterbalanced by the use of bimetallic strips in the rim of the balance wheel. The strips bend due to differential expansion, and it is possible to make the resulting change in the moment of inertia of the wheel just sufficient to compensate the effect of change in elasticity of the spring. A more recent construction of balance wheels employs elinvar for the hair spring. The elastic properties of this material are sufficiently independent of temperature changes to make compensation unnecessary.

Compensation is sometimes employed in sensitive instruments for measuring radiation. In the bolometer, for example, which is virtually a sensitive resistance thermometer, two fine strips of platinum, as far as possible identical, form two arms of a Wheatstone bridge. The strips are mounted close together, one being exposed to radiation whilst the other is screened from it. Changes in resistance of the strips due to temperature changes produced by fluctuations in the bridge current, or by air temperature variation, affect both strips equally and are without effect on the balance of the bridge, at least to the extent to which the strips are identical.

Frequently, too, compensating thermopiles are used. In this case, two identical thermopiles are connected in opposition and mounted close together in a common enclosure. This enclosure may be constructed of heavy metal sheet, preferably copper or aluminium because good thermal conductivity is required, the object being to produce uniform temperature conditions within the enclosure. One of the thermopiles is exposed to radiation, the other serving to produce a compensating electromotive force when temperature differences exist between the junctions of each thermopile, such as may occur during periods when the air temperature is changing.

An alternative to compensation may be used if the effect to be measured can be made to produce an intermittent signal, which in turn produces an intermittent electric potential difference in a suitable detector. Such a fluctuating potential can be fed into a tuned amplifier, which will amplify only the alternating component of the signal to which it is tuned. By tuning the amplifier to the signal frequency, the signals are amplified. Any response from the detector caused by factors such as changes in ambient temperature, which are not periodic, are not amplified. This method is much used in measuring infra-red radiation in spectrometers. The radiation is interrupted by a rotating sector whose frequency is equal to that of the tuned amplifier to which the signals are fed from the thermo-couple, bolometer, etc. This method entirely eliminates zero drift caused by changing room temperature, and renders the apparatus insensitive to all radiation except that which has been interrupted at the appropriate frequency.

In many cases it will be found advantageous to employ thermostatic control of the air temperature in the laboratory, or within an enclosure containing the sensitive apparatus. For this purpose, electrically heated elements (usually in the form of resistance mats) are disposed about the room, and a switch operated by a thermostat is arranged to cut off the heating current when the air temperature reaches a predetermined value, which should be above the highest temperature likely to be attained in the absence of the heaters.

The problem is considerably simplified if the sensitive part of the apparatus can be operated from outside the constant temperature enclosure, so that disturbance from the observer's body does not occur. Also, if the apparatus includes any generators of heat, such as lamps, resistances, motors, etc., it is desirable to isolate these, if possible, from the enclosure. In one very satisfactory arrangement which one of the authors has used for taking long exposure spectrum photographs with a spectrograph sensitive to temperature changes, the light source and the whole of the electrical apparatus required to run it was contained in one room, and the spectrograph was placed in an adjacent room, maintained at constant temperature. A small aperture in the wall served to admit light to the spectrograph.

Often the laboratory accommodation will not allow the use of two adjacent rooms for a single experiment, but a suitable enclosure, such as one of the cheap sectional buildings which are sold for garden sheds, etc., may be erected in a larger room and made into a constant temperature room. This is more economical and much more satisfactory than an arrangement in which the whole working space is thermostatically controlled. The thermal insulation of such a shed may be greatly improved by covering it inside and out with asbestos paper on both sides of which is a layer of aluminium foil. This composite material, which is supplied in rolls under such names as "·Alfol," is used for thermal insulation in buildings and can be obtained from builders' merchants.

In order to get the greatest constancy of temperature, the air in the enclosure should be thoroughly stirred up with a fan ; several fans may be required in a large room. Without such stirring, considerable local temperature variations will exist.

The thermostats which control the temperature are commonly dependent for their action either on the expansion of a liquid such as toluene or on the differential expansion of a bimetallic strip. The increasing use of thermostatic control for industrial and domestic purposes has resulted in the development of a number of convenient units capable of dealing with power of a few kilowatts. Some of these employ a bimetallic strip which controls the mains current without a relay, but usually the more sensitive type employs a toluene or mercury thermostat and in this case a relay is needed, as only a small current can be sent through the thermostat contact. With the simple form of bimetallic strip, constancy of temperature to about 1° C. may be expected. If a sensitive toluene regulator is used in conjunction with a suitable relay, temperatures may be kept constant to within about 0·1° C., though much depends on the local conditions. The toluene thermostat, for controlling air temperatures, should have a large surface in relation to its volume, and may be made from tubing bent as shown in Fig. 9.17. Spiral form toluene thermostats are also available ; these are more compact. For ease in filling, and also for altering the temperature at which the arrangement works, it is desirable to have a tap at one end, and since toluene dissolves tap-grease, a mercury column is interposed between the tap and toluene. At the other end of the apparatus is another mercury column with a platinum contact sealed through the glass, and a second platinum wire which makes contact with the mercury when the toluene expands as the result of a rise in temperature. With an arrangement of this kind, and adequate stirring of the air, the temperature can be held constant to about 0·1° C.

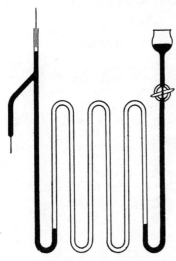

FIG. 9.17.—Toluene thermostat with large surface for air temperature control.

Thermostats of the kind described above necessarily produce a fluctuation of air temperature, and only the mean temperature is constant. In cases where this is objectionable, the sensitive part of the apparatus may be lagged with a material of low thermal conductivity, such as cork, glass wool, etc., in order to damp out the fluctuations. The fluctuations can be prevented, in the case of a thermostat with a mercury contact surface, by keeping this surface in constant vibration (for instance, by means of a small eccentrically loaded motor, which may also be used for stirring). Contact with the platinum wire is broken many times each second, and the ratio of time " on " to " off " will depend on the height of the liquid surface. The system will settle down to an almost steady state when the mean rate of heating just balances the rate of cooling. The power of the heaters must be suitably adjusted so that the current does not have to be on (or off) for too short a time. Since an electromagnetic relay will not operate sufficiently rapidly to follow the vibrations of the mercury surface, a thyrotron should be employed as relay. This system can be made to work very satisfactorily indeed.

GENERAL REFERENCE

van Santen, G. W., *Mechanical Vibration* (Philips Technical Library, Eindhoven, 1953).

REFERENCES

[1] du Bois, H. E. J. G., and Rubens, H., *Wied. Ann.*, **48** (1893), 236.

[2] Julius, W. H., *Wied. Ann.*, **56** (1895), 151.

[3] Julius, W. H., *Ann. der Physik*, **18** (1905), 206.

[4] Müller, R., *Ann. der Physik*, **1** (1929), 613.

[5] Gehrcke, E., and Voigt, B., *Zeits. f. Tech. Physik*, **12** (1931), 684.

[6] *Ibid.*, **13** (1932), 387.

[7] Haringx, J. A., *Philips Technical Review*, **9** (1947), 16.

[8] *Ibid.*, **9** (1947), 85.

[9] Collatz, L., *Ing. Arch.*, **10** (1939), 269.

[10] Manley, R. G., *Engineering*, 22nd October and 5th November, 1943.

CHAPTER 10

DAMPING

MANY measuring instruments contain a pivoted or suspended moving part, controlled by gravity or by a spring whose deflection is used to measure the force acting upon it. Such instruments are used for measuring weight, electrical current, gas pressure and many other physical quantities. In all such instruments, except ballistic ones, readings of the equilibrium position of the movement are required. When equilibrium is disturbed by a change in the force acting on the movement, the system will usually make a number of oscillations before coming to rest in the new equilibrium position. The rapidity with which the oscillations die away will depend on the rate at which the kinetic and potential energy of the movement are dissipated by resistance forces such as friction. Such forces are said to damp the oscillations.

For several reasons, it is usually desirable to adjust the damping so that the instrument will give a reading in the shortest possible time. If the damping forces are very small, the oscillations of the moving part, once started, will diminish gradually and only after many oscillations will the part be sensibly at rest. On increasing the damping, the oscillations die away more rapidly. If the forces causing damping are sufficiently great, the moving part does not pass through the equilibrium position and hence makes no oscillations. Instead, it gradually approaches the rest position asymptotically. It will readily be seen that there must be a critical value of the damping which causes equilibrium to be reached in a minimum time ; this will be considered quantitatively later. Naturally, for " equilibrium " we must accept some position within, say, $\frac{1}{2}$ per cent of the deflection from the position which would be reached after infinite time. The allowable deviation from true equilibrium will depend on the instrument and the purpose for which it is employed.

The chief reason for adjusting the damping to the critical value is to save time in reading, and also to allow continuous changes in the indicating mechanism to be followed. The second consideration is particularly important in self-recording instruments. Apart from the

171

saving of time, however, rapid indication is very desirable in order that readings may be taken before changes in the conditions of observation can occur. For instance, in many measurements a change in the ambient temperature during readings will introduce errors, hence the need for rapid indications if such errors are to be kept small.

Damping can play a useful rôle in smoothing out random fluctuations (usually referred to as " noise," in contradistinction to the " signal " which is being indicated on the instrument). Such noise may be due to mechanical vibrations in the indicating instrument, or it may be transmitted along with the signal, often as electrical impulses, to the measuring device. In either case, suitable damping will greatly increase the steadiness if the fluctuations are rapid compared with the natural period of the moving part. If critical damping will not suffice to smooth out the noise, it is probably better to increase the natural period and to re-adjust to critical damping, rather than to employ an over-damped movement.

Theoretical considerations

Suppose that the moving (rotating) part of an instrument has a moment of inertia I and experiences a restoring couple $C\theta$ when rotated through an angle θ from the zero position. For simplicity, it will be supposed that the damping couple acting on it is proportional to the angular velocity $d\theta/dt$ and is always in such a direction as to oppose the motion. This condition is approximately fulfilled by the usual damping agencies (see below). When the instrument is deflected by forces which exert a turning moment M (supposed constant), the equation of motion will be

$$I\, d^2\theta/dt^2 + p\, d\theta/dt + C\theta - M = 0$$

where $p\, d\theta/dt$ is the moment of the damping forces. Evidently, when the system is at rest, $\theta = M/C$ hence the equilibrium deflection θ is proportional to the turning moment of the deflecting forces. To study the movement before the system has come to rest, the equation is conveniently re-written

$$d^2\phi/dt^2 + k\, d\phi/dt + n^2\phi = 0$$
$$\text{where} \qquad k = p/I$$
$$n^2 = C/I$$
$$\phi = \theta - M/C$$

The details of the solution of the above equation may be found in text-books on the differential calculus. Two types of motion may be distinguished, according to whether $k^2/4$ is less than n^2 on the one hand, or equal to or greater than n^2 on the other hand.

Case (a) $k^2/4 < n^2$

In this case it may be shown that

$$\phi = a\, e^{-\frac{1}{2}kt} \cos(\omega t - \epsilon)$$

where a is a constant depending on the initial conditions and $\omega^2 = n^2 - k^2/4$. If, as is usually the case with a measuring instrument, the deflecting moment M is applied when the instrument is at rest at zero then the moving part starts from rest with $\phi = -M/C$.

In this case

$$\phi = -M/C.\sec\epsilon.\, e^{-\frac{1}{2}kt} \cos(\omega t - \epsilon)$$
$$\text{where } \epsilon = \tan^{-1}\left(\tfrac{1}{2}k/\omega\right)$$

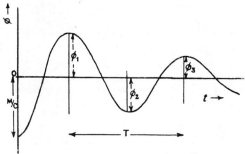

Fig. 10.1.—Damped harmonic motion.

The motion is shown in Fig. 10.1, whence it may be seen that ϕ goes through a succession of oscillations of diminishing amplitude, reaching zero after infinite time. The ratio of successive amplitudes ϕ_n/ϕ_{n+1} is constant and numerically equal to $e^{k\pi/2\omega}$.

The quantity $\lambda = k\pi/2\omega$ is known as the *logarithmic decrement.*

The periodic time T of the motion is $2\pi/\omega$ and since $\omega^2 = n^2 - \frac{1}{4}k^2$, T is equal to $2\pi/n.(1 - k^2/4n^2)^{-\frac{1}{2}}$. The periodic time T_0 if the damping were absent is, however, $2\pi/n$, hence we have for the damped motion

$$T = T_0\,(1 - k^2/4n^2)^{-\frac{1}{2}}.$$

The effect of damping is therefore to increase the periodic time. Both periodic time and logarithmic decrement may be expressed in terms of the ratio $4CI/p^2$.

If we put $\qquad 4CI/p^2 = x$

Then $\qquad T = T_0\,(1 - 1/x)^{-\frac{1}{2}}$

and $\qquad \lambda = \pi\,(x - 1)^{-\frac{1}{2}}.$

Case (b) $k^2/4 \geqslant n^2$

In this case there are no oscillations, and the moving part approaches its equilibrium position asymptotically. By making $k^2/4$ much greater than n^2, the motion is made very sluggish.

Best conditions for damping

Fig. 10.2 shows the region in the neighbourhood of the first minimum of some curves of damped motion. The practical question is usually how to arrange the damping so as to obtain a reading in the

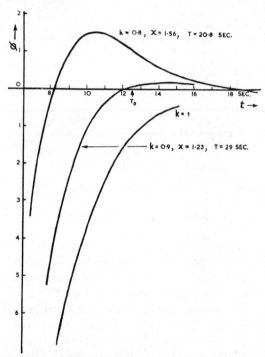

Fig. 10.2.—Damped harmonic motion in neighbourhood
of first minimum (on large scale). $n = \frac{1}{2}$.

shortest possible time. Examination of Fig. 10.2 shows that there is not a unique answer to this question, as the damping conditions depend on the permissible error allowed in making the reading. A tolerance of $1\frac{1}{2}$ per cent, for instance, would allow a reading to be made (in the particular case shown) after $7 \cdot 6$ seconds with $x = 1 \cdot 56$, whereas with $x = 1 \cdot 23$ the reading could only be made after $9 \cdot 8$

seconds. If, however, the tolerance were reduced to 0·15 per cent, the higher damping figure ($x = 1·23$) would be more favourable. Probably the most rapid indication is obtained by arranging the damping so that the amplitude after the first transit of the equilibrium position is equal to the tolerance permitted in reading. The reading is made after the instrument begins to the return to equilibrium after its first overshoot. It is a distinct advantage to be able to observe this small " overshoot," as it gives an indication when the reading can be taken.

In practice, it is usually much easier to adjust the damping while observing the extent of the " overshoot," than to attempt a solution by calculation, since exact knowledge of several of the factors involved is very difficult to obtain. A useful result deduced from Fig. 10.2 is that, with a tolerance in reading between 1 per cent and 0·2 per cent and suitable damping, the time for reading does not differ much from T_0 the time of undamped oscillation.

Methods of applying damping forces

Damping forces must always oppose the movement which calls them into being, and are therefore of the kind met with in friction, viscous resistance, and induced electric currents. Indeed, these three forces are the damping forces commonly employed.

The frictional force between solid bodies is not suitable for the damping of accurate mechanisms, as the force of static friction makes the reading of the instrument indefinite. The internal friction of fluids, whether liquid or gaseous, is not subject to this disadvantage, and is very suitable as an agency for damping. In many instruments, vanes moving in a viscous liquid such as an oil are used to bring up the damping force to the required value. In the majority of instruments there is no difficulty in producing a large enough damping force in this or in a similar way. Examples are given below. The really essential requirement is that the damping force must vanish when the instrument is at rest.

When using liquid damping, the existence of surface tension forces may lead to serious errors in delicate mechanisms, if the design is unsuitable. To avoid errors from this source, the extent of the liquid-air and liquid-solid surfaces should remain constant during the motion. There are, naturally, cases where the controlling force of the movement is so great that the effect of surface tension may be neglected.

The second point to note in connection with liquid damping is the variation of damping with temperature, owing to the great temperature coefficient of viscosity of liquids in general. The use of a suitable grade of silicone fluid in place of a plain hydrocarbon oil can reduce the temperature sensitivity of liquid damping. The high stability of silicones is an added advantage. Fig. 10.3 shows the temperature variation of viscosity for some silicone fluids and hydrocarbon oils.

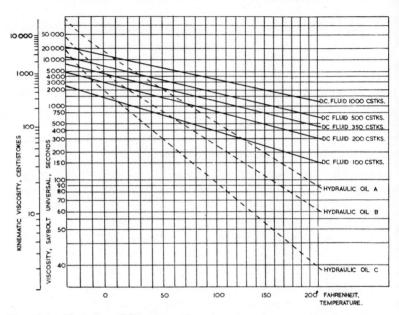

FIG. 10.3.—Variation of viscosity with temperature for some fluids suitable for damping. The full lines show curves for silicones, the broken curves refer to hydrocarbon oils. (*Dow Corning Corporation.*)

Certain kinds of liquids are unsuitable as damping fluids. Colloidal suspensions of some materials (e.g., bentonite and other clays) have viscous properties which depend on their recent history. These materials become much less viscous after stirring, and regain their viscosity after a period of rest. The phenomenon is known as " thixotropy." Some polymer solutions, too, have viscosities which are dependent on the amount of stirring to which they have been subjected. Evidently these materials should be avoided.

Fig. 10.4 shows the damping arrangement for the movement of an

Evershed-Vignoles recorder. The movement carries a pen, and is actuated by a current of 5 *mA*, with a potential difference of 500 *m.V.* The power available is therefore quite appreciable, and the liquid damping arrangement is quite satisfactory. Other examples of liquid damping are to be found in ref. 1.

When the most sensitive of mechanisms require damping, it may be impossible to reduce completely the errors due to surface tension if a liquid is used. In such cases, air damping is sometimes employed. This is often the case, for example, in precision chemical balances. The chief difficulty with air damping is to obtain adequate damping forces whilst avoiding the sliding of one surface over another.

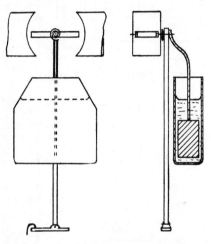

FIG. 10.4.—Oil damping for the movement of a pen recorder.

Damping applied to a sensitive chemical balance is shown in Fig. 10.5. Here the surface tension forces which would arise if a liquid were used would be much too great. The air damping is at once simple, adequate and inexpensive to produce.

In electromagnetic instruments of the moving coil type, electromagnetic damping always exists, and is usually adjusted to give the required force to produce critical damping. This may be done simply by altering the resistance in the external circuit. As a rule, in a moving coil galvanometer the instrument is greatly under-damped on open circuit, and over-damped on short circuit. If the instrument is to be critically damped, the resistance must be suitably adjusted.

This is often inconvenient, and an alternative procedure which is sometimes adopted is to alter the strength of the magnetic field. This may be done, in the case of a permanent field magnet, by shunting part of the magnetic flux through a soft iron yoke which may be slid

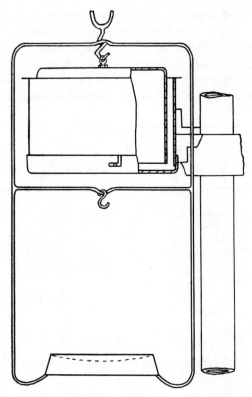

FIG. 10.5.—Air damping arrangement on a chemical balance.

along the limbs of the magnet. Naturally, there is a loss in sensitivity as a result of the reduced magnetic field in which the armature moves. It is almost always preferable to accept the lower sensitivity and to adjust for critical damping.

REFERENCE

[1] RICHTER, O., and VOSS, R. VON, *Bauelemente der Feinmechanik* (2nd Edition, revised by R. von Voss and E. Kozer, V.D.I. Verlag, Berlin, 1938).

CHAPTER 11

TESTS FOR STRAIGHTNESS, FLATNESS AND SQUARENESS

MANY methods have been developed in engineering and the gauge and tool industry for testing flat surfaces and the relation of one surface to another. These methods of testing rather than the machines or tools used to make them set the standard of accuracy attainable, and they are therefore of fundamental importance in accurate instruments and mechanisms. In Britain, the National Physical Laboratory, working in conjunction with engineering and instrument firms, has developed methods and instruments for this type of work. There is available a fairly wide choice of methods, which can be classified into those in which the test surface is compared with a standard of known accuracy, and another group in which the inclinations of different parts of the test surface are compared with one another. Methods have been selected which seemed most appropriate to instrument testing ; other methods are to be found in F. H. Rolt's work on *Gauges*[1] and E. Schlesinger's booklet on *Machine Tool Testing*[2]. Other references of interest are given at the end of this chapter.

Inclination of the surface

Two instruments are in common use for measuring the inclination of a surface—the auto-collimating telescope and the spirit level (see Chapter 7). If, using the first method, a nearly flat surface is to be examined, a small optical lever may be mounted on it, and the telescope, rigidly supported, directed at the mirror of the optical lever. Readings of the telescope scale are taken with the lever in a succession of different (preferably equally spaced) positions along a line parallel to the telescope axis. It is convenient, in the first instance, to take as reference plane the plane through the feet of the optical lever in the position at the end A of the surface (Fig. 11.1), which may be taken as the tangent plane to the surface at A. Evidently the amount of detail revealed by the test depends on how small is the portion of the surface covered by the feet of the optical lever ; we will suppose that this portion is small compared with the length of the surface irregularities to be investigated. Let A, B, C, etc. (Fig. 11.1) represent successive positions of the lever. Then the angles δ_1, δ_2, δ_3, etc., which the surface makes at these points with the reference plane are obtained by subtracting from the telescope readings at B, C, etc., the reading obtained at A. It is easily seen that the increment in perpendicular distance from the reference plane from, say B to C is equal to $S\ \dfrac{\delta_1 + \delta_2}{2}$ where S is the distance from B to C (remembering that the angles are very small). The perpendicular distance of any point above the reference plane is obtained by adding up all the preceding increments.

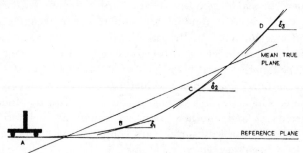

FIG. 11.1.—Use of optical lever for measuring flatness of surface.

A spirit level, mounted on a suitable stand, may be placed at A, B, C, etc., and the inclinations of the surface at these points found if the angular tilt per unit scale division of the level is known. The remaining procedure is identical with that described above.

The sensitivity of the telescope or level will naturally depend on the accuracy required. As an example, it may be mentioned that a machine bed 6 ft. long, bent into a circular arc so that the middle point is 0·0001 in. distant from the straight line joining the ends, will have an angular tilt of just over 2 seconds of arc, when one end is compared with the other. This is well within the compass of the most accurate levels or auto-collimating telescopes. In fact, the accuracy of these instruments is usually not the limiting factor in the accuracy achieved, which depends largely on the uniformity of temperature which can be maintained over the test object during the measurement. For instance, if the bed referred to in the above example were 10 in. deep, a difference of approximately 0·1° C. in temperature between the upper and lower surfaces would account for the bending. In a sense, of course, this is not an error, for the method gives the figure of the bed, whether it is deformed from temperature or from other causes. There is, however, an error peculiar to the optical method, if the telescope is used many feet away from the test mirror, for temperature gradients in the intervening air will cause angular displacements of the light beam.

Attention should be paid to the arrangement for mounting the level, or the optical lever, as the case may be. If three ball-ended feet are provided, then the full effect of any depressions in the surface under test will be obtained. In some cases, the general truth of the surface may be of greater importance than local irregularities, and in such a case it would be preferable to employ three co-planar feet, of suitable area, in place of spherical feet.

If the bed or ways of an instrument are to be tested, the same procedure as described above is followed, except that the level or the mirror of the optical lever is best mounted on the carriage belonging to the instrument. It should be pointed out that a bed may appear straight when tested by either level or telescope, and yet be subject to twist or " wind," that is the mirror or level may move along a spiral path (of very large pitch). Such a motion would rotate the mirror in its own plane or produce a sideways displacement of the level, and neither of these motions would produce a change in reading of the instrument. " Wind " may be detected by setting a level on the carriage with its long axis perpendicular to the bed of the instrument and taking readings with the carriage in various positions on the bed.

Finally it may be mentioned that, although the tangent plane to the surface or bed (as the case may be) is used as a reference plane for calculation, the results are ultimately referred to the " mean true plane " or line (see Fig. 11.1).

There is another method for testing the flatness of a surface which is independent of a standard reference surface ; it is of limited application but important because it is closely related to the methods of manufacture used in optical workshops.

If light from a small (point) source is reflected at a high angle of incidence from a spherical surface of large radius of curvature, as in Fig. 11.2, the reflected beam is astigmatic. If the reflected image (say from a distant point source) is examined through a telescope, it cannot be focused to a point, but is drawn out into a fine line ; actually there are two such focal lines, one perpendicular to the other, at different distances from the telescope objective. They may be seen,

181

one at a time, by focusing the eyepiece suitably. If the reflecting plate were flat, the image would focus to a point; the length of the focal line is related to the radius of curvature of the plate. Details of the test may be found in a published note[3]; the sensitivity allows curvature amounting to about one wave-length of green light ($5 \cdot 5 \times 10^{-5}$ cm. or $2 \cdot 2 \times 10^{-5}$ in.) in a distance of 2 in. to be observed with a small telescope.

This method of testing is not only of interest in the manufacture of polished optical components, for at an angle of incidence of about 80 deg. a finely ground glass or hard metal surface reflects sufficiently

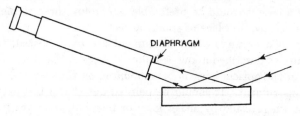

DIAPHRAGM

FIG. 11.2.—Curvature of surface revealed by astigmatism.

well. The methods of grinding used in optical shops produce accurate spherical surfaces, and it is quite easy by altering the arrangement to change a slightly convex into a slightly concave surface, and vice versa, passing through a stage when the surface is flat. By the astigmatism test it is possible to control the process and to stop at the appropriate moment.

Light beam as straightness gauge

Because of the linear propagation of light in a homogeneous medium it might appear that a beam of light would provide an ideal straight-edge against which measurements of straightness could be made. Diffraction effects, however, make it impossible to do this in a simple, straightforward way, for the width of a light beam defined by an aperture varies at different distances from the aperture, and also the intensity distribution is not constant. It would, however, be quite possible to devise suitable methods for locating accurately the centre of a beam, making use of a light detector such as a photomultiplier tube. Recently an ingenious arrangement has been described in which the reference line is the line joining the centres of two spherical mirrors, and departure from this line is shown by the movement of interference fringes. A trial arrangement with mirror centres 20 in. apart showed that the reading accuracy was of the order of 8×10^{-6} in. A brief account of the system is given in ref. 7.

Displacement from material reference surface

Under this heading come methods in which the surface under test is compared with an optically flat glass surface, or with a metal surface or with the flat surface of a liquid. In general, these methods are more convenient for testing surfaces (in two dimensions) than are the methods described in the preceding section, which are especially useful for testing rectilinear motion of (for instance) a carriage on its ways. The comparison may be made through various agencies.

Optically worked glass reference surface (interference method)

This method is the best known and one of the most extensively used of methods giving a quantitative result. The optically worked surface is laid on the surface to be tested, both surfaces having been cleaned and rendered as far as possible dust-free. Interference fringes are observed, using the arrangement shown in Fig. 7.13 and since they are (if the incident light is nearly normal to the surface, and the air film between the surfaces is thin) contour fringes, the shape of the unknown surface is readily found from the fringe pattern, provided that the worked surface is flat, to the accuracy required. Typical patterns are shown in Fig. 11.3. Straight, equidistant fringes indicate flat surfaces, but the unit in which departure from straightness is to be measured is the fringe-width, or distance between consecutive light (or dark) fringes. A departure of a fringe from straightness of one fringe width indicates a departure of the surface from flatness of half a wave-length of whatever light is employed. Green light is commonly employed, either by using a filter with white light, or from a mercury lamp, and has a wave-length of approximately $5\cdot5 \times 10^{-5}$ cm. or $2\cdot2 \times 10^{-5}$ in. In order that the method be sensitive, the fringe width should not be too small; a small fringe width is usually due to dust particles preventing the surfaces from coming into close contact—the remedy is obvious.

Handling the optical flat or test object will produce local temperature variations sufficiently large to distort the surfaces, and a sufficient time must be given after bringing the surfaces into contact to allow the temperature distribution to become uniform.

The method is really only applicable to metal surfaces which are very well finished (lapped) and is usually restricted to quite small surfaces (say up to 3 or 4 in. diameter) because of the cost of the necessary optical flat. One particular application is to the examination of razor blades for finish at the cutting edge.

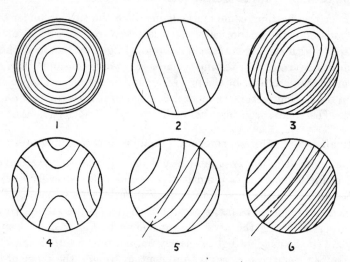

FIG. 11.3.—Interference bands formed between flat and test object. (1) Convex or concave, spherical. (2) Flat, two surfaces inclined. (3) Astigmatic—curvatures of different amounts in two directions, but both convex, or both concave. (4) Astigmatic—one curvature convex, the other concave. Note resemblance to " saddle " between hills on ordnance map contours. (5) Concave or convex (approx. one half-wavelength across the diameter). (6) Similar to (5) but surfaces more inclined. Note that fringes are straighter than in (5) though departure from flatness is the same in both cases.

Liquid reference surface

The surface of a liquid at rest is horizontal except near the edges, where surface tension causes some curvature. Lord Rayleigh used a liquid surface for testing glass plates by interference, but although this method may have been used occasionally, as far as the writer is aware it is not in regular use, possibly because of the disturbance caused by ripples on the surface. By using one of the anti-vibration mountings described in Chapter 9 this could be greatly reduced, and there is little doubt that the testing of high-class surfaces could be carried out in this way.

For many purposes, the interference method is, however, too sensitive, and it is convenient to have a method capable of measuring to about 0·0001 in. (the usual limit for a good micrometer screw gauge). It is unnecessary to use a large liquid surface, since if two vessels containing liquid are connected by rubber tubing, the free liquid surfaces will be co-planar, and may be used as a reference plane. The arrangement described below is used for testing surface plates, etc.

Two small metal vessels containing mercury are provided with micrometer heads insulated electrically from the mercury, and terminating in fine points which may be adjusted by turning the micrometer screw, so as to make contact with the mercury. Contact is indicated by a click in the telephone connected as shown in Fig. 11.4.

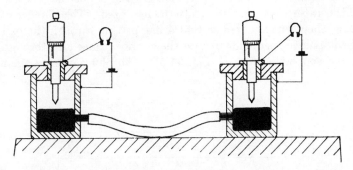

FIG. 11.4.—Method of using liquid reference surface for checking flatness of plate. The micrometer is electrically insulated from the mercury cup.

The vessels are connected by rubber tubing ; one is kept fixed at a corner of the plate to be tested, whilst the other is moved from place to place on the surface, readings of both micrometer screws when contact is made being taken for each position. The plate should previously have been levelled. It is evident that if the plate were truly plane and horizontal, the difference between the readings of the two micrometers would be constant for all positions of the movable vessel. The value of this constant difference may be ascertained by placing both vessels close together on a carefully levelled plane surface of good quality. It is then a simple matter to calculate how much any part of the surface is above or below that part of the surface on which the fixed vessel stood. As in the preceding methods, the results may be referred to the mean true plane. This method has been used for the rails of ship tanks.

Standard reference surfaces

Surface plates and straight edges are made to various degrees of accuracy, and are often used as standards with which unknown surfaces or motions, etc., may be compared. Though it is convenient if the standard can be assumed perfect (to the accuracy required) it is by no means necessary, and in fact the standard can be calibrated by internal measurements ; one method for this is given below. The actual comparison may be made in several ways, of which the method using a micrometer dial gauge is probably the most convenient, and gives readings to 0·0001 in. (p. 113). Other methods may be found in the references at the end of this chapter.

The dial gauge is mounted on a small stand supported on three feet which in turn rest on the surface to be tested. The plunger of the gauge should be situated so that a line passing through the ball end of the plunger perpendicular to the surface passes also through one of the supporting feet P (Fig. 11.5). The plunger bears against a

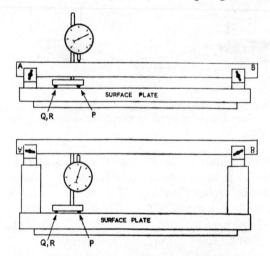

Fig. 11.5.—Checking surface plate against straight-edge by means of dial gauge.

straight-edge supported approximately parallel to the surface, and readings are taken on the dial with the plunger in a series of different positions along the length of the straight-edge. These readings are plotted against the distance of the foot P from a chosen point on the surface being tested. Since the plunger is vertically above P, it is evident that the vertical movement of P is recorded by the dial gauge, and that small elevations of the points Q and R produce negligible changes in the reading, so long as the surface under test is approximately parallel to the surface of the straight-edge on which the plunger rests.

If the straight-edge may be taken as true, the graph obtained will represent the contour of the surface to be tested, along the line traversed by the foot P. To obtain a result which is independent of the " straight-edge," the latter is turned over so that the edge which was uppermost is now the lower edge. The dial gauge is also reversed, and with the apparatus as in Fig. 11.5 (lower part), a series of readings is taken. The mean of the corresponding readings in the two series is taken and plotted against the distance of P from the chosen point on the surface under test. This curve represents the contour of the surface. It will be seen from Fig. 11.5 that, in effect, the mean dial gauge readings represent the distances from the surface to a line which is perfectly straight, because the " straight-edge " in one position is a mirror image of the other position, provided it may be assumed that the distortion caused by its own weight is negligible.

Tests for Squareness

The testing of objects for squareness is difficult to treat in a general way, since the problem varies so much with conditions. Two classes of test suffice to show the essentials of the problem (a) testing two flat surfaces for squareness (90 deg. angle between planes) and (b) testing two rectilinear movements, intended to be perpendicular to each other.

Squareness tests for two flat surfaces

The most frequent test is carried out by comparison with a try-square. One surface should rest on a flat surface plate, on which the stock of the square also rests, and the blade is applied to the other surface. The best results are obtained when the test is carried out against a uniform and fairly brightly illuminated surface ; under good conditions a gap of about 0·0001 in. between blade and surface can be detected. The result depends on the accuracy of the try-square, which should be selected according to the test requirements. This method of testing cannot always be used, as the surfaces are often inaccessible. A further objection is that errors are not quantitatively assessed.

If a measuring instrument, such as a micrometer dial gauge (p. 113) mounted on a carriage which can be traversed is available, the test may be more sensitive and at the same time quantitative. Referring to Fig. 11.6, the dial gauge is applied successively to the top and bottom parts of the surface and the difference in readings $(D_1 - D_2)$ noted. The part to be tested is replaced by a square, and the dial gauge applied to it in turn at corresponding points giving a difference $D_3 - D_4$. If the same difference in gauge readings is obtained, the object is square to the accuracy of the set square. If not, the departure from squareness is $(D_1 - D_2 - D_3 + D_4)/l$ radians where l is the distance between points. It will be noted that the traversing arrangement for the dial gauge need not be linear, but it must give reproducible settings. The use of a dial gauge allows surfaces inaccessible to the try-square to be tested.

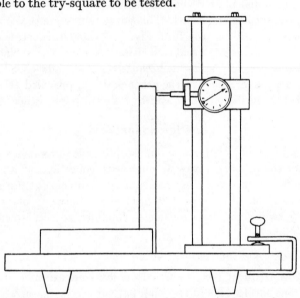

FIG. 11.6.—Standard square (to be replaced by test piece) on surface plate with dial gauge on kinematic slide.

In certain cases, a try-square is not required. If the object for testing has two parallel surfaces, rotation through 180 deg. (see Fig. 11.7) will bring the second parallel surface to the micrometer, and any error in squareness will reveal itself, the measured difference corresponding to twice the actual error. This principle is used in the construction of standard squares at the National Physical Laboratory. The square, which is of the shape shown in Fig. 11.7, is produced by

" spot grinding " (see Chapter 2) which produces accurately parallel faces, and so may be used to measure its own accuracy. If a stop is provided against which the lower part of the square can be placed, as in the figure, it is not necessary to move the dial gauge, for the change in reading when the square is reversed will be twice the error. The same arrangement could evidently be used in connection with the test illustrated in Fig. 11.6.

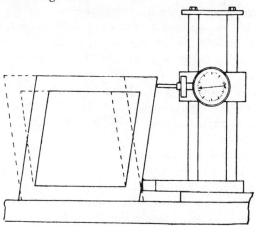

Fig. 11.7.—Checking a square whose opposite sides are known to be accurately parallel, by reversal through 180 deg.

For many purposes, an optical method based on the auto-collimator is extremely convenient. In addition to the auto-collimator, some form of 90 deg. angle gauge is needed, and also a glass plate with flat, accurately parallel faces. The angle gauge may take the form of a polished steel cube. The manufacturers of the Angle Dekkor, Messrs. Hilger and Watts Ltd., also supply a number of accessories for test purposes, among them a steel cube of 1·5 in. side, with three polished surfaces and a flat ground surface opposite each. The faces are at 90 deg. within 5 seconds of arc. An alternative to the steel cube is a polished steel angle gauge with angles of 30, 60 and 90 deg., each accurate to 2 seconds of arc. For testing angles other than 90 deg., a set of angle gauges is made having angles of 1, 3, 9 and 14 degs. These gauges may be wrung together in the same way as slip gauges, and allow any angle from 0 to 90 deg. to be made up, in steps of 1 deg., with an accuracy of a few seconds of arc.

In principle, the test for squareness is simple, though ingenuity is

189

often needed in particular cases, and sometimes special fixtures, usually quite simple in character, may be needed. Fig. 11.8 illustrates the method. For testing squareness in small components, it is very convenient to have the auto-collimator mounted on a bracket firmly attached to a flat surface plate, as in the Hilger Angle Dekkor. The standard cube or gauge is set up on the plate and the telescope is directed at the polished vertical face ; the reading of the scale seen by reflection is noted after the telescope has been firmly clamped. The gauge is now replaced by the component to be tested, one of whose test faces rests on the surface plate. To the other test face is applied a flat, parallel faced glass plate. It is sufficient for one face to be polished, the other being ground, but a plate with two polished faces is equally good. The reading from the polished plate is noted (both readings must of course be taken on a *vertical* scale), and the difference in readings gives the departure from squareness of the faces tested.

The optical method is quick and convenient, giving an accurate measure of the error. Perhaps its most valuable feature, however, is that it can be applied to surfaces which are difficult of access by other methods. More detailed examples, along with other uses of the auto-collimator, may be found in two articles by B. P. Harrold[4].

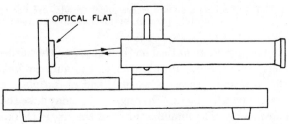

OPTICAL FLAT

Fig. 11.8.—Use of auto-collimating telescope in testing for squareness.

Testing two rectilinear motions for squareness

Measuring instruments as well as machine tools may have a table or carriage controlled by two mutually perpendicular movements or slides. Examples are instruments for measuring photographic plates so as to give Cartesian co-ordinates, and the stage micrometer fitted to many microscopes. All the machine tools of the instrument shop have some form of cross slide giving the same type of motion.

To test the squareness of the two motions, it is of course possible to examine the individual surfaces forming the " ways " and see if they are properly oriented, using the methods described above. This is satisfactory provided one is certain which are the controlling surfaces, and if they are accessible. In general, however, it is preferable to base the test on the movement of the carriage and this can readily be done with a square and a sensitive indicator such as a dial gauge (p. 113).

The square is clamped to the carriage with its edges nearly parallel to the cross motions, and the dial gauge applied to one edge. If now the carriage is run along one slide only, parallel ·to this edge, the indication of the gauge will change but little, and the square could be adjusted with one side accurately parallel to the motion. This would of course be indicated by a constant reading when the carriage was run along the slide. It is not necessary to make this adjustment accurately, however, it being only necessary that the gauge reading should change by a small amount during the run, so that the variation can be accurately measured (dial gauges cannot always be relied on over a large movement of the plunger). The change in the reading over a measured length of travel must be found, preferably by taking readings at suitable intervals and plotting a graph, so as to smooth out chance irregularities. The dial gauge is now applied to the other edge of the square, and similar measurements taken. If the same rate of change is obtained (in the appropriate sense) the motions are perpendicular, within the error of the square. A difference in rate of change gives at once (in radians) the departure from squareness.

It is not difficult to eliminate error in the square itself. Referring to Fig. 11.7, it is evident that if the square is reversed as shown, the average of the two sets of readings obtained in the direction of traverse will be identical with a single set taken with a perfect square. To ensure accurate reversal of the square, a straight edge may be clamped to the table and the square brought into contact with it.

Much useful information is contained in refs. 5 and 6.

REFERENCES

[1] ROLT, F. H., *Gauges and Fine Measurements*, Vol. 2 (London, Macmillan and Co. Ltd., 1929).
[2] SCHLESINGER, G., *Accuracy in Machine Tools : How to Measure and Maintain It* (London, Institution of Production Engineers, 1941).
[3] ELLIOTT, A., *J. Sci. Inst.*, **26** (1949).
[4] HARROLD, B. P., *Machinery*, 25th March and 8th April (1949).
[5] *Notes on Gauge Making and Measuring* (NPL-DSIR publications, May, 1946, H.M.S.O.).
[6] *Notes on Screw Gauges* (NPL-DSIR publications, August, 1944, H.M.S.O.).
[7] DYSON, J., *Nature*, **175** (1955), 559.

CHAPTER 12

GLASS

GLASS, in its many types, forms and shapes, is in constant demand in research laboratories in the form of rod, tube and sheet, as window glass, plate glass or optical glass, clear, frosted and opal, colourless, neutral and coloured. In addition there is a large range of plastics and natural and synthetic crystals in similar forms and types, but these are dealt with elsewhere.

In very general terms glass is an amorphous compound sometimes referred to as a supercooled liquid made by melting a number of oxides in carefully regulated proportions and the physical properties of the glass are largely influenced by the relative quantities and types of oxides used. Table 12.1 gives an indication of the ingredients and their proportions in a number of optical glasses. Window and plate glasses and that used for tubes, rods and vessels are normally of the silica-lime-soda variety, having a large percentage of silica and Table 12.2 gives the composition of some typical commercial glasses. The physical properties of glass depend also very largely on its after treatment, particularly in heating and cooling. When cooled slowly from a high temperature the glass tends to become homogeneous and free from strain, but if cooled rapidly very large local strains can be set up and homogeneity is destroyed. Toughened glass now used for wind-screens of motor-cars is made by deliberately introducing surface strain in glass by rapid controlled cooling.

Glass is principally used for its transparent qualities to ordinary light and, in optical instruments, for its refractive properties, but it also has important uses as an insulator of heat and electricity and being largely inert chemically it is not subject to corrosion. It is comparatively easily worked provided the correct tools and abrasives are used and it is cheap. This chapter will be devoted mainly to a description of the various types of glass and its examination for defects. The working of glass in a research laboratory is described in Chapter 14.

TABLE 12.1—*Approximate Composition of Certain Optical Glasses*

	Boro Silicate Crown	Hard Crown	Light Flint	Dense Flint	Extra Dense Flint	Double Extra Dense Flint	Medium Barium Crown	Dense Barium Crown	Special Barium Flint	Special Barium Crown
n_d	1·5099	1·5160	1·5787	1·6230	1·6530	1·7536	1·5720	1·6234	1·7170	1·6910
V.	64·2	60·8	40·6	36·0	33·6	27·7	57·7	56·2	47·9	54·8
SiO_2	70·6%	71·7%	52·8%	45·1%	40·5%	32·8%	46·5%	33·5%	15·2%	10·5%
K_2O	16·1	7·1	9·4	3·4	4·9	1·8	4·0	—	—	—
Na_2O	3·9	8·9	—	4·8	2·1	—	—	—	—	—
CaO	—	8·0	—	—	—	—	—	—	—	—
PbO	—	—	37·2	45·9	52·0	65·4	—	—	9·0	27·0
BaO	—	0·5	—	—	—	—	32·3	48·9	31·3	4·0
ZnO	—	—	—	—	—	—	8·0	5·4	2·5	—
Al_2O_3	8·8	2·1	—	—	—	—	4·1	3·7	15·4	24·3
B_2O_3	—	—	—	—	—	—	4·5	7·9	11·3	13·3
ThO_2	—	—	—	—	—	—	—	—	13·0	18·5
La_2O_3	—	—	—	—	—	—	—	—	2·5	2·0
ZrO_2	—	—	—	—	—	—	—	—	—	—
As_2O_3	0·2	1·4	0·2	0·4	0·6	—	0·6	0·4	—	—
Sb_2O_3	—	—	—	—	—	—	—	—	—	—

From *Glass* Edited J. Home Dickson (Hutchinson, 1951)

NOTE.—n_d = the refractive index for the *d* line of the spectrum.

V = the reciprocal of the dispersive power, see p. 198.

TABLE 12.2—*The General Composition of Typical Commercial Glasses*

	A Soda-Lime-Silica System			B Potash-Lead-Silica System	C Hard Borosilicate Glasses	D Soft Borosilicates	E Silica-Lime-Alumina System	F Complex Borosilicate
	Container Glasses	Sheet and Plate Glasses	Thermo-meter Glasses	Crystal Glass Glasses for Electrical Industry	Heat Resisting and Laboratory Ware. Tungsten Sealing Glasses	Ni-Fe-Co Alloy Sealing Glasses	High Softening Point Glasses	Ampoule Glasses Combustion Glasses
SiO_2	70·5-75·0	70·5-73·0	66·5-72·5	53-63	75-82	63-68	52-55	65-72
B_2O_3	0·5-3·0		0-10		10-17·5	17·5-23	0-7·5	5-11
Al_2O_3	15-17	0·5-1·5	2·5-6·0		1-3·5	0-4·0	20-23·5	4-10
Na_2O	0-0·5	12·5-16·5	13-14·0	0-9·0	3·5-4·7	5-7·5		4-10
K_2O				4·5-11·5	0-2·0	2-3·5		0-6
PbO				21-35				
CaO	4·5-9·5	8·5-12·5	0-7·0				11-14	0-6
MgO	0-3·0	0-3·0						
ZnO			0-7·0				0-3·0	0-8·5

From *Glass* Edited J. Home Dickson (Hutchinson, 1951)

1. TYPES OF GLASS

Window or sheet glass. The cheapest form of sheet glass available is ordinary window glass which can be readily obtained from local glass merchants and is very variable in quality. Its surface is uneven, the thickness uncertain and it is specified by its weight in ounces per square foot so that the average thickness is given as 12, 16, 20 or 24 oz., etc. Mirrors required only to reflect light can be obtained in this glass and it can be used for insulation and all ordinary purposes, but it cannot be used in any way for optical instruments. It can be ground or frosted and obtained with flashed coatings of coloured and opal white glass. Similar glass coloured in the substance or in pot opal form are also available. Ordinary household and the cheaper chemical glassware is made of glass of this type.

Plate glass

Originally plate glass was made by grinding and polishing sheet glass but this process was supplanted by a rolling method, first with one roller and later with two, between which the glass was rolled, followed by polishing. This process is still used to some extent, particularly for coloured glass, but it has now largely been replaced by plate glass known as twin polished plate made by drawing the molten mass from the furnace by rollers in a continuous sheet which is allowed to cool and is polished on both surfaces in its progress down the glass working shop until it is finally cut into convenient sheets.

This glass is slightly greenish in colour but is remarkably uniform in thickness and flatness, although the surface may show minute ripples which sometimes render it useless for some optical purposes. White plate can also be obtained and is actually a similar glass to which a metallic oxide has been added to remove the greenish tint without, however, increasing the mean transparency. Some white plate has also been made using iron-free sand and this has greater transparency for longer wave-lengths. The twin polished plate is mainly manufactured in $\frac{1}{4}$ in. thickness, but plate glass either white or green is obtainable in almost any thickness up to about $1\frac{1}{2}$ in., the thicker glass being generally much flatter than the thinner sheets. The refractive index of this glass is 1·523. If better quality plate glass is required it is usual to stipulate mirror quality when ordering, or to visit the glass supplier and arrange for selection according to the particular qualities required. Excellent mirrors can be made with plate glass, either of the normal type or front surface aluminised or silvered; a useful hard mirror surface is obtained with chromium and aluminium or with rhodium. The glass can also be used if carefully selected, to form windows through which optical instruments can be used, for example, for under-water photography, for weather-proof observation panels or for mounting filters.

Where flatness and freedom from defects are essential it is usual to call for " optically worked optical glass " and the name " schlieren quality " has sometimes been applied to such windows because of their application to work where the schlieren method of observation is used, e.g., in wind tunnels.

Safety glass

Safety glass for the wind-screens of motor-cars, etc., consists of a laminated sandwich having a cellulose or plastic interlayer between plate glass sheets. This type of safety glass can be manufactured in such quality that the clarity of vision is not impaired and if selected carefully it can also be used in front of optical instruments without destroying the definition or resolving power. In high pressure chambers, and in wind tunnels, for example, heavy gauge laminated safety glass known as " Multi-ply " has been used, and it has been made bullet proof for military purposes. The edges of laminated forms of safety glass require protection and the cutting and working of such glass requires expert care. The introduction of toughened forms of safety glass, made by the controlled rapid cooling of the surface, has enabled car windows to be made curved or saucer shaped, a form impossible with laminated glass. This toughened glass can be made so that vision is not impaired but its use with optical instruments of high quality is not recommended because of its inhomogeneity and it is not suitable for use in polarised light. Toughened glass cannot be worked or cut and if scratched it is liable to shatter into tiny fragments, but its strength is remarkable and it has been made bullet proof.

Fibre glass

Fibre glass is manufactured in staple form, short length fibres, by steam or air blast drawing or in continuous, virtually infinite, length by mechanical drawing and is supplied in a number of forms. Yarn, thread, woven fabric, tapes, sleeving and mats of various thicknesses are all available. Wool and mats in various forms are used for sound and heat insulation and with various resins for reinforced mouldings of great strength and light weight. Motor car and bus bodies, boats and small ships are made in fibre glass reinforced plastic (known colloquially as F.R.P.). In the laboratory models and shapes can usefully be made with this material; many firms now specialise in the manufacture of a large variety of articles. Continuous fibre yarn has been used for the transmission of optical images since each fibre is, in fact, a continuous cylinder of glass and will transmit light along its length by multiple internal reflections. In this application it is necessary to arrange the ends of the fibres in a suitable manner so that an image will be formed corresponding to the object applied at the other end. Fibre glass, with or without resin moulding, can have many uses in the laboratory and in the design of equipment and instruments. Full particulars can be obtained from the manufacturers both of the glass and of the various resins but new and novel applications of these materials are constantly being introduced. The fibre glass filaments have a very high tensile strength of up to 400,000 p.s.i. and on an equal weight basis are stronger than any other structural material. They have a high Young's Modulus of 10·5 million p.s.i. and the glass rather than the plastic carries most of the load applied to a laminate.

Chemical glass

For chemical engineering and laboratory use there are a number of proprietary brands of glassware (Pyrex, Hysil, Phoenix, etc.), principally designed to have a very low coefficient of expansion when heated and to have a high thermal endurance. These glasses contain normally a higher percentage of silica and fused silica itself may be considered as an extreme form of glass with a high thermal endurance. The applications of glass to building, architecture, decorative table-ware, electric lamps and innumerable other purposes are well known and cannot be discussed here.

Optical glass

This is manufactured with special reference to its refractive and dispersive qualities and it is essential that the refractive index and dispersion should be constant over the whole substance in any one batch or melt. The normal method of manufacture is in pots in which the ingredients are stirred in the furnace, the pot being later allowed to cool and broken up to release the mass of glass. The glass is then tested for defects and for refractive index and dispersion and is frequently stored in rough lumps as it is broken up and graded according to size. When required the appropriately sized pieces are remelted and moulded to the required shape or cast in plates or slabs which are subsequently annealed by reheating and slow cooling under rigidly controlled conditions. Optical glasses are also made in block form by pouring the molten glass direct from the pot into large iron moulds. Very recently a few commoner types are being produced in bar form by a continuous moulding process similar to the continuous plate glass process. There is almost no limit to the size and shape in which optical glass can be supplied, but usual stock sizes are 2—6 in. square or rectangular and $\frac{1}{4}$—$2\frac{1}{2}$ in. thick. Tables 12.3 and 12.4 show the refractive properties of a selection of optical glasses and it will be noticed that they are roughly divided into two classes, namely crowns and flints.

Formerly the crown glasses were characterised by low refractive index and low dispersion and the flint glasses by high refractive index and high dispersion. Reference to Table 12.1 will show that the crowns are silica glasses and the flints contain lead oxide. The glasses first introduced by the Jena glass works in 1880 and subsequent years, and now manufactured by all optical glass firms, comprise the boro-silicate and barium crowns and the barium flints in which the dispersion of crown glasses has been relatively increased and that of the flint glasses decreased. Very recently a series of new glasses in which rare earths have been used show a marked increase in refractive index without any correspondingly large increase in dispersion. Many new types of glass are constantly being produced by the manufacturers and a list of some recent glasses is given in Table 12.6. The V-value quoted against each type of glass in the tables is the reciprocal of the dispersive power, so that a low V-value corresponds to high dispersion and a high V-value to a low dispersion. The dispersive power is defined by the ratio $\dfrac{n_F - n_C}{n_d - 1}$ where n_F, n_C and n_d are the refractive indices for the wave-lengths corresponding to the F, C and d Fraunhofer lines of the spectrum, and therefore the V-value is given by $\dfrac{n_d - 1}{n_F - n_C}$. This V-value is a convenient number used in the preliminary stages of optical design where the condition of achromatism of a compound lens system is calculated. (See Chapter 15.)

TABLE 12.3—Optical Glass (Chance Bros. Ltd.)

GLASS TYPES	Refractive Index n_d	$V=\dfrac{n_d-1}{n_d-n_C}$	Mean Dispersion $C-F$	$b-C$ (7065)	$\dfrac{b-C}{C-F}$	$C-D$ (6563)	$\dfrac{C-D}{C-F}$	$C-d$ (5893)	$\dfrac{C-d}{C-F}$	$d-e$ (5875)	$\dfrac{d-e}{C-F}$	$e-F$ (5461)	$\dfrac{e-F}{C-F}$	$F-g$ (4861)	$\dfrac{F-g}{C-F}$	$g-h$ (4359)	$\dfrac{g-h}{C-F}$	n_C	n_D	$n_{G'}$	Ounces per Cubic Inch	Specific Gravity	Durability
Fluor Crown	1·49429	67·9	0·00728	0·00131	0·180	0·00219	0·301	0·00226	0·310	0·00174	0·239	0·00328	0·451	0·00385	0·529	0·00316	0·434	1·49203	1·49422	1·50332	1·39	2·41	
Borosilicate Crown	1·50970	64·4	0·00791	0·00139	0·176	0·00235	0·297	0·00243	0·307	0·00188	0·238	0·00360	0·455	0·00423	0·535	0·00348	0·440	1·50727	1·50962	1·51959	1·44	2·49	S1
Hard Crown	1·51899	60·4	0·00859	0·00149	0·173	0·00253	0·295	0·00262	0·305	0·00205	0·239	0·00392	0·456	0·00465	0·541	0·00386	0·449	1·51637	1·51890	1·52981	1·46	2·53	S1
Light Barium Crown	1·54065	59·5	0·00908	0·00158	0·174	0·00268	0·295	0·00277	0·305	0·00217	0·239	0·00414	0·456	0·00493	0·543	0·00406	0·447	1·53788	1·54056	1·55210	1·66	2·87	S2
Medium Barium Crown	1·57220	57·7	0·00991	0·00170	0·172	0·00290	0·293	0·00299	0·302	0·00237	0·239	0·00454	0·458	0·00543	0·548	0·00449	0·453	1·56921	1·57211	1·58178	1·84	3·19	S3
Dense Barium Crown	1·61452	56·2	0·01093	0·00187	0·171	0·00320	0·293	0·00331	0·303	0·00260	0·238	0·00502	0·459	0·00599	0·548	0·00500	0·457	1·61121	1·61441	1·62839	2·10	3·63	S4
Soft Crown	1·51516	57·0	0·00904	0·00165	0·182	0·00266	0·294	0·00274	0·303	0·00216	0·238	0·00414	0·458	0·00496	0·549	0·00413	0·457	1·51242	1·51508	1·52663	1·47	2·55	S3
Telescope Flint	1·53042	52·0	0·01021	0·00175	0·171	0·00301	0·295	0·00310	0·304	0·00242	0·237	0·00469	0·459	0·00561	0·549	0·00468	0·458	1·52732	1·53033	1·54339	1·49	2·58	S2
Barium Light Flint	1·57427	52·0	0·01104	0·00188	0·170	0·00321	0·291	0·00333	0·302	0·00262	0·237	0·00509	0·461	0·00614	0·556	0·00508	0·460	1·57094	1·57415	1·58319	1·86	3·21	S3
Extra Light Flint	1·54769	45·6	0·01201	0·00200	0·167	0·00346	0·288	0·00358	0·298	0·00285	0·237	0·00558	0·465	0·00679	0·565	0·00560	0·466	1·54411	1·54757	1·56319	1·71	2·95	S1
Barium Flint	1·60483	43·8	0·01380	0·00228	0·165	0·00396	0·287	0·00410	0·297	0·00327	0·237	0·00643	0·466	0·00787	0·570	0·00664	0·481	1·60073	1·60469	1·62274	2·01	3·48	S2
Light Flint	1·57860	41·1	0·01407	0·00231	0·164	0·00402	0·286	0·00416	0·296	0·00333	0·237	0·00657	0·467	0·00808	0·574	0·00684	0·486	1·57444	1·57846	1·59692	1·87	3·23	S1
Dense Flint	1·62258	36·0	0·01727	0·00278	0·161	0·00489	0·283	0·00507	0·294	0·00409	0·237	0·00811	0·470	0·01007	0·583	0·00851	0·493	1·61751	1·62240	1·64528	2·11	3·65	S4
Extra Dense Flint	1·65108	33·6	0·01940	0·00310	0·160	0·00546	0·281	0·00566	0·292	0·00459	0·237	0·00915	0·472	0·01143	0·589	0·00982	0·506	1·64542	1·65088	1·67675	2·25	3·90	S4
Double Extra Dense Flint	1·74842	27·8	0·02687	0·00422	0·157	0·00752	0·280	0·00776	0·289	0·00635	0·236	0·01276	0·475	0·01619	0·603	0·01436	0·515	1·74066	1·74818	1·78444	2·75	4·75	S6
Double Extra Dense Flint	1·92707	21·0	0·04412	0·00672	0·152	0·01206	0·273	0·01250	0·283	0·01037	0·235	0·02125	0·482	0·02768	0·627	0·02356	0·534	1·91457	1·92663	—	3·53	6·11	S6
Borate Flint	1·61200	44·9	0·01363	0·00232	0·170	0·00396	0·291	0·00410	0·301	0·00324	0·238	0·00629	0·461	0·00762	0·559	0·00646	0·474	1·60790	1·61186	1·62948	1·84	3·18	S6
Special Barium Crown	1·69100	54·8	0·01261	0·00218	0·173	0·00370	0·293	0·00383	0·304	0·00300	0·238	0·00578	0·458	0·00688	0·546	0·00571	0·453	1·68717	1·69087	1·70696	2·38	4·11	S3
Special Parium Flint	1·74400	44·7	0·01664	0·00280	0·168	0·00480	0·288	0·00497	0·299	0·00395	0·237	0·00772	0·464	0·00933	0·561	0·00792	0·476	1·73903	1·74383	1·76540	2·55	4·41	S2
Zinc Crown	**1·50759**	**61·2**	**0·00830**	**0·00147**	**0·177**	—	—	**0·00255**	**0·307**	**0·00198**	**0·239**	**0·00377**	**0·454**	**0·00446**	**0·537**	**0·00368**	**0·443**	—	—	—		**2·49**	**S1**

TABLE 12.4—*Optical Glass* (Bausch and Lomb)

No. 20—2 50—1

	Type	BSC—2	C—1	LBC—1	DBC—2	CF—1	LBF—1	LF—2	DF—3	DBF—1
	$V = \dfrac{n_d - 1}{n_F - n_C}$	64·5	58·6	59·9	55·0	51·6	53·4	41·0	36·2	38·5
K 7665	n_A'	1·51179	1·51729	1·53529	1·60905	1·52217	1·58110	1·57088	1·61066	1·60731
H 6563	n_C	1·51461	1·52036	1·53842	1·61370	1·52560	1·58479	1·57544	1·61610	1·61242
Na 5893	n_D	1·51700	1·52300	1·54110	1·61700	1·52860	1·58800	1·57950	1·62100	1·61700
He 5876	n_d	1·51707	1·52307	1·54117	1·61710	1·52869	1·58890	1·57962	1·62114	1·61714
Hg 5461	n_e	1·51899	1·52520	1·54332	1·61977	1·53112	1·59072	1·58298	1·62520	1·62093
H 4861	n_F	1·52262	1·52929	1·54746	1 62493	1 53584	1·59580	1·58957	1·63325	1·62843
Hg 4359	n_g	1·52690	1·53415	1·55236	1·63115	1·54153	1·59186	1·59767	1·64327	1·63772
H. 4341	$n_{G'}$	1·52709	1·53435	1·55257	1·63142	1·54178	1·60212	1·59802	1·64371	1·63811
Hg 4047	n_h	1·53043	1·53819	1·55645	1·63634	1·54633	1·60697	1·60459	1·65197	1·64571
F—C	$n_F - n_C$	0·00801	0·00893	0·00904	0·01122	0·01024	0·01101	0·01413	0·01715	0·01603
C—A′	$n_C - n_A'$	0·00282	0·00307	0·00313	0·00375	0·00343	0·00369	0·00456	0·00544	0·00511
C—A′/F—C	$\dfrac{n_C - n_A'}{n_F - n_C}$	0·353	0·344	0·347	0·334	0·335	0·336	0·323	0·317	0·319
D—C	$n_D - n_C$	0·00239	0·00264	0·00268	0·00330	0·00300	0·00321	0·00406	0·00490	0·00458
D—C/F—C	$\dfrac{n_D - n_C}{n_F - n_C}$	0·298	0·296	0·297	0·294	0·293	0·292	0·287	0·286	0·286
e—D	$n_e - n_D$	0·00199	0·00220	0·00222	0·00277	0·00252	0·00272	0·00348	0·00420	0·00393
e—D/F—C	$\dfrac{n_e - n_D}{n_F - n_C}$	0·248	0·247	0·246	0·247	0·246	0·246	0·246	0·245	0·245
F—e	$n_F - n_e$	0·00263	0·00409	0·00414	0·00516	0·00472	0·00508	0·00659	0·00805	0·00750
F—e/F—C	$\dfrac{n_F - n_e}{n_F - n_C}$	0·453	0·458	0·458	0·460	0·461	0·462	0·467	0·469	0·468
G′—F	$n_{G'} - n_F$	0·00447	0·00506	0·00511	0·00649	0·00594	0·00632	0·00845	0·01046	0·00968
G′—F/F—C	$\dfrac{n_{G'} - n_F}{n_F - n_C}$	0·558	0·567	0·566	0·578	0·580	0·574	0·598	0·610	0·604
h—G′	$n_h - n_{G'}$	0·00334	0·00384	0·00388	0·00492	0·00455	0·00485	0·00657	0·00826	0·00760
h—G′/F—C	$\dfrac{n_h - n_{G'}}{n_F - n_C}$	0·417	0·430	0·429	0·438	0·444	0·441	0·465	0·482	0·474
	Spec. Grav.	2·53	2·53	2·85	3·66	2·73	3·33	3·27	3·67	3·61

Optical glass manufacturers catalogue the varieties of glass with full details of the refractive index for a number of wave-lengths and, for ease of reference they also quote the dispersion, partial dispersions and relative partial dispersions, as in Tables 12.3 and 12.4. The types of glass are known by the initials of their type names, such as BSC, HC, DBC, DF, etc., and they are also given catalogue identification numbers. Chance Bros. identify their optical glasses by a six-figure number; the first three figures refer to the refractive index and the remainder to the V-value. Thus glass No. 518604 identifies a hard crown glass having a refractive index of 1·51899 and a V-value of 60·4.

TABLE 12.5—Optical Properties of Some Crystals and Plastics

MATERIAL	Refractive Index n_d	$\dfrac{n_d-1}{n_F-n_C}$ V	Mean Dispersion $C-F$	$b-C$ / $\dfrac{b-C}{C-F}$	$C-d$ / $\dfrac{C-d}{C-F}$	$d-e$ / $\dfrac{d-e}{C-F}$	$e-F$ / $\dfrac{e-F}{C-F}$	$F-g$ / $\dfrac{F-g}{C-F}$	$g-h$ / $\dfrac{g-h}{C-F}$	Limit of Transmission for 10 mm. Thickness (μ)
Lithium Fluoride	1·39225	99·1	0·00396	0·00074 / 0·187	0·00124 / 0·313	0·00095 / 0·240	0·00177 / 0·447	0·00202 / 0·510	0·00162 / 0·409	0·12–7·0
Fluorite (CaF₂)	1·43390	95·4	0·00455	0·00081 / 0·178	0·00188 / 0·303	0·00109 / 0·240	0·00208 / 0·457	0·00244 / 0·536	0·00202 / 0·444	0·18–8·5
Fused Quartz	1·45887	67·9	0·00676		0·00210 / 0·311	0·00152 / 0·225	0·00313 / 0·463	0·00357 / 0·528	0·00293 / 0·433	0·19–3·5
Magnesium Oxide	1·73764	53·5	0·01880	0·00229 / 0·166	0·00423 / 0·307	0·00326 / 0·236	0·00631 / 0·457	0·00764 / 0·554	0·00632 / 0·458	0·23–5·0
Potassium Chloride	1·49050	44·0	0·01114	0·00186 / 0·167	0·00332 / 0·298	0·00264 / 0·287	0·00518 / 0·465	0·00630 / 0·566	0·00589 / 0·484	0·20–21
Potassium Bromide	1·55998	33·4	0·01678	0·00258 / 0·154	0·00497 / 0·296	0·00395 / 0·285	0·00786 / 0·468	0·00986 / 0·587	0·00827 / 0·493	0·21–28
Perspex	1·49613	54·4	0·00912	0·00149 / 0·163	0·00269 / 0·295	0·00218 / 0·239	0·00425 / 0·466	0·00510 / 0·559	0·00432 / 0·474	0·34–2·0
Polystyrene	1·5929	30·7	0·0193		0·0056 / 0·290					0·34–2·0
Potassium Iodide	1·6655	23·4	0·0284		0·0086					0·20–35
Rocksalt (NaCl-Natural)	1·5443	42·8	0·0127		0·0036					0·20–15
Synthetic Sodium Chloride	1·5408	35·2	0·0156		0·0055					0·20–15

Wave-length table (Angstroms): b 7065, C 6563, D 5893, d 5875, e 5461, F 4861, g 4359, G′ 4841, h 4047.

1 Angstrom (A) = 10⁻⁸ cm.
1 micron (μ) = 10⁻⁴ cm.

TABLE 12.6—New Optical Glasses Available in the United States

Origin	Type	V	A'	C	D	F	G'
Corning Glass Works	8313	47·8		1·696 39	1·700 65	1·711 04	
Eastman Kodak Co.	EK-110	56·2	1·688 77	1·693 13	1·696 80	1·705 54	1·712 55
	EK-210	51·2	1·724 82	1·729 79	1·734 00	1·744 13	1·752 35
	EK-330	47·2	1·744 99	1·750 43	1·755 10	1·766 43	1·775 71
	EK-310	46·4	1·734 91	1·740 33	1·745 00	1·756 38	1·765 77
	EK-320	45·8	1·734 32	1·739 78	1·744 50	1·756 03	1·765 57
	EK-450	41·8	1·791 80	1·798 14	1·803 70	1·817 38	1·828 80
	EK-448	41·1	1·867 14	1·874 20	1·880 40	1·895 64	1·908 27
Hayward Scientific Glass Corp.	651/558	55·8		1·647 57	1·651 00	1·659 24	1·665 90
	671/520	52·0		1·667 24	1·671 00	1·680 18	1·687 72
National Bureau of Standards	610/620	62·0		1·606 7	1·609 6	1·616 5	1·622 0
	639/597	59·7		1·636 3	1·639 5	1·647 0	1·653 1
	656/582	58·2		1·652 2	1·655 5	1·663 4	1·669 8
	673/562	56·2		1·669 7	1·673 3	1·681 7	1·688 5
	682/553	55·3		1·678 2	1·681 9	1·690 6	1·697 6
	705/540	54·0		1·701 1	1·704 9	1·714 2	1·721 6
	714/531	53·1		1·710 3	1·714 3	1·723 8	1·731 5

Proceedings of the London Conference on Optical Instruments (1950).

For brevity in Tables 12.6, 12.7, A', C, D, etc., are used for $n_{A'}$, n_C, n_D, *etc.*

TABLE 12.7—Effect of Temperature on the Refraction of Plastics

Plastic Materials

Materials		V	A'	C	D	e	F	g	Transmission range
Polystyrene	15° C	31·0	1·581	1·587	1·592		1·606	1·617	
	35° C		1·578	1·584	1·589		1·603	1·614	0·34μ to 2μ
	55° C		1·575	1·581	1·586		1·600	1·612	
Polycyclohexyl- methacrylate	15° C	56·9	1·501	1·504	1·507		1·513	1·518	
	35° C		1·499	1·502	1·504		1·501	1·516	
	55° C		1·496	1·499	1·501		1·508	1·513¹	
Polymethyl- methacrylate	20° C	57·8		1·489	1·491	1·493	1·497	1·501	0·34μ to 2μ

Temperature coefficient of refractive index for above three polymers is -14×10^{-5} per °C.
Proceedings of the London Conference on Optical Instruments (1950).

TABLE 12.8—Optical Properties of Water

Refractive Index of Water at 20° C. for Various Wavelengths

Wavelength A	12560	6708	6563	6438	5893	5461	5086	4861	4800	4047	3034	2144
Refractive Index	1·3210	1·3308	1·3311	1·3314	1·3330	1·3345	1·3360	1·3371	1·3374	1·3428	1·3581	1·4032

Temperature coefficient — $8·0 \times 10^{-5}$ per °C

Bausch & Lomb in their catalogue use the identification letters of the type followed by a simple serial number, such as BSC-1, DBC-1, etc. The Jena glassworks of Schott & Gen., Mainz, use a similar classification and in their 1958 catalogue include many rare-earth glasses. They also quote the index for $1·014\mu$. The Parra-Mantois glassworks in France use an identification letter followed by a four-figure number. The letter and the first two figures give the refractive index and the last two figures the V-value. The letters are $A = 1·4, B = 1·5, C = 1·6, D = 1·7, E = 1·8$. Thus borosilicate crown glass B 1864 has a refractive index of $1·5180 \pm 0·0005$ and a V-value $64·0 \pm 0·5$. The National Bureau of Standards (N.B.S.) classify their glasses by a fractional notation, thus NBS 656/582 is a glass of index $1·656$, V-value $58·2$. Corning and Eastman Kodak use serial numbers for their new glasses. The Russian classification system is again similar to the Jena system, but the descriptive letters for the glass types are in Russian characters.

The varieties of optical glasses are necessary to enable optical systems to be made having definite properties in relation to optical aberrations, for the older types of glass imposed severe restrictions on the possible improvements in optical instruments. The introduction of the Jena glasses, which resulted from a demand by theoretical optical designers for glasses with just such properties, enabled great advances to be made in aperture and freedom from aberrations in optical instruments. The rare-earth glasses and a number of synthetic crystals have been evolved as a result of continued demands by theoretical optical workers and enable still further improvements in instruments to be made. Table 12.5 shows the refractive properties in the visible range of the spectrum of a number of crystals and other substances used for optical purposes and is placed here so that the properties can be readily compared with those of the optical glasses. Further information on natural and synthetic crystals is given in Chapter 13. Fig. 12.1 shows the relation of refractive index to V-value. This diagram is useful when selecting glass for the design of an optical instrument. When it is found, for example, that a selected pair of glasses in some instrument design do not combine well as regards the final effect on aberrations, an alternative glass can be selected by inspection of the diagram.

A glance at the partial dispersions given against each glass type in Tables 12.3, 12.4 shows that the dispersions of the various glasses do not follow any simple law, thus the dispersion of some glasses increases

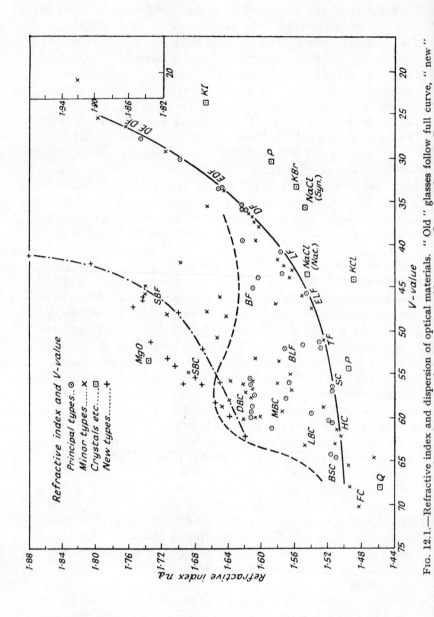

Fig. 12.1.—Refractive index and dispersion of optical materials. "Old" glasses follow full curve, "new"

more rapidly with decreasing wave-length than others. This inequality in the " run " of partial dispersion is unfortunate in that it makes it quite impossible to obtain absolute freedom from colour in optical images. It is always possible so to combine optical components that images formed by light of any two or three colours are in the same position and of the same size but the images formed in other colours are displaced. This effect, known as residual chromatism or secondary spectrum, can be made to fit any possible specification by a careful choice of glasses, but it is not possible to eliminate it entirely. It will be noted from the tables that the refractive index and partial dispersions are quoted to five places of decimals, but when ordering optical glass the works can seldom supply glass which has the exact catalogue values. Each batch or melt of glass, even of the same type, shows variations of refractive index not greater than 0·001 from the catalogue value, and it is therefore always necessary before finalising an optical design to obtain the actual glass to be used and its exact refractive properties. It may sometimes happen, where a large number of similar lenses are to be made, that more than one batch of glass has to be used and corrections become necessary in the optical design to meet the variations in the glass. It can safely be assumed, however, that any one batch of glass will be uniform in its refractive properties to two or three units in the fifth decimal place. Chapter 15 may be referred to for an elementary account of the principles of optical design requirements.

Optical plastics

The idea of using plastics for optical purposes is very attractive but there are severe limitations to their use which far outweigh the apparent advantages. Although it is theoretically possible to design achromatic doublets using Perspex or Plexiglass, Polystyrene, Transpex etc., except for their light weight these lenses have no advantages. The variety of optical glass available, its hardness, better polishing quality and the use of blooming provide great scope in design to set against the limited range of plastics, their relative softness, susceptibility to temperature and moisture, the necessity of using optical methods of polishing and the difficulty of blooming. On the other hand, very large single lenses and lenses with moulded aspheric or other surfaces, such as Fresnel lenses, required primarily as condensers, can be made more conveniently in plastics provided the working temperature is not too high. Table 12.7 shows the effect of temperature on the refractive index of some plastics. This table has been taken from the proceedings of the Optical Conference in London (1950). In the same volume H. C. Raine gives very full information on the refractive index and dispersions of a number of plastics. Information on the thermal and mechanical properties of plastics is given in Chapter 3.

Polymethyl Methacrylate (Perspex, Plexiglass) is very suitable for making large tanks for liquids in which experiments can be made and observed or photographed through the transparent sides or base. It is best to cement the joints with chloroform or some other jointing cement and to reinforce the joint with screws. Because of its transparency Perspex is useful for " piping " light to any point by multiple internal reflection. Provided the sides and edges are polished and free from scratches or matt surfaces, light from a small lamp inserted in a hole in the sheet of plastic, or a strip-light near the edge, will be transmitted to all parts. Wherever the plastic is engraved or made matt the light will be spilled and can be seen or used to illuminate a dial or other object. Any writing on the surface with a wax pencil will shine brilliantly in the colour of the pencil.

II. TRANSMISSION AND REFLECTION

The transmission or transparency of a material is usually quoted as the percentage of the incident light which emerges from the specimen. The term density is frequently used, particularly when the transmission is small, and is defined as the logarithm to the base 10 of the reciprocal of the transmission expressed as a decimal. The reciprocal of the transmission is known as the opacity.

$$\text{Thus density} = \log_{10} \frac{1}{\text{Transmission}} = \log_{10} \text{opacity}$$

and a density of 0·3 or log 2 corresponds to a transmission of 50 per cent or 0·5. Tables 12.9 and 12.10 will be found useful for the rapid conversion of transmission into density and vice versa. It should also be noted that densities can be added to obtain the total density, but transmissions and opacities must be multiplied.

The loss of light on transmission through a transparent substance can be attributed to two causes, namely reflection at the bounding surfaces and absorption in the material. In treatises on physical optics it is shown that, for normal incidence, the fraction of light

TABLE 12.9—*Transmission-Density Table*

% Transmission	Density	% Transmission	Density	% Transmission	Density	% Transmission	Density
1	2·00	26	·59	51	·29	76	·12
2	1·70	27	·57	52	·28	77	·11
3	1·52	28	·55	53	·28	78	·11
4	1·40	29	·54	54	·27	79	·10
5	1·30	30	·52	55	·26	80	·10
6	1·22	31	·51	56	·25	81	·09
7	1·16	32	·50	57	·24	82	·09
8	1·10	33	·48	58	·24	83	·08
9	1·05	34	·47	59	·23	84	·08
10	1·00	35	·46	60	·22	85	·07
11	·96	36	·44	61	·22	86	·07
12	·92	37	·43	62	·21	87	·06
13	·89	38	·42	63	·20	88	·06
14	·85	39	·41	64	·19	89	·05
15	·82	40	·40	65	·19	90	·05
16	·80	41	·39	66	·18	91	·04
17	·77	42	·38	67	·17	92	·04
18	·75	43	·37	68	·17	93	·03
19	·72	44	·36	69	·16	94	·03
20	·70	45	·35	70	·16	95	·02
21	·68	46	·34	71	·15	96	·02
22	·66	47	·33	72	·14	97	·01
23	·64	48	·32	73	·14	98	·01
24	·62	49	·31	74	·13	99	·00
25	·60	50	·30	75	·13	100	·00

TABLE 12.10—*Density—Opacity—Transmission*

Density	Opacity	Transmission %	Density	Opacity	Transmission %
0·00	1·000	100	0·75	5·623	17·78
0·02	1·047	95·5	0·80	6·310	15·85
0·04	1·095	91·2	0·85	7·079	14·13
0·06	1·148	87·1	0·90	7·943	12·59
0·08	1·202	83·18	0·95	8·913	11·22
0·10	1·259	79·43	1·00	10·00	10·00
0·15	1·413	70·79	1·25	17·78	5·623
0·20	1·585	63·10	1·50	31·62	3·162
0·25	1·778	56·23	1·75	56·23	1·778
0·30	1·995	50·12	2·00	100·00	1·000
0·35	2·239	44·67	2·25	177·8	0·5623
0·40	2·512	39·81	2·50	316·2	0·3162
0·45	2·818	35·48	2·75	575·4	0·1738
0·50	3·162	31·62	3·00	1000·0	0·100
0·55	3·548	28·18	3·5	3162·0	0·03162
0·60	3·981	25·12	4·0	10000·0	0·01
0·65	4·467	22·39	5·0	100000·0	0·001
0·70	5·012	19·95			

(1) Note the general rule :

Density	Opacity	Transmission
0·25	1·778	56·23
1·25	17·78	5·623
2·25	177·8	0·5623

$$\text{Density} = \log_{10}(\text{opacity}) = \log_{10} 1/\text{Transmission}$$

(2) Note:

$$\text{density } 3 + \text{density } 2 = \text{density } 5$$
$$\text{opacity } 1{,}000 \times \text{opacity } 100 = \text{opacity } 100{,}000$$
$$\text{transmission}\frac{0·1}{100} \times \text{transmission}\frac{1·0}{100} = \text{transmission}\frac{0·001}{100}$$
$$(0·001) \qquad (0·01) \qquad (0·00001)$$

reflected at a surface separating two media whose indices of refraction are n_1 and n_2, is given by the formula

$$\text{Fraction of light reflected} = \frac{(n_2 - n_1)^2}{(n_2 + n_1)^2} = r$$

Thus, when light passes from air into glass or glass into air the fraction of light reflected at the air-glass surface is 1/25 or 4 per cent of the incident light for glass of refractive index 1·5. In Fig. 12.2 the ordinate r is the fraction of light reflected at an air-glass surface for glass of any refractive index n given by the abscissa for values of n from 1·0–3·0.

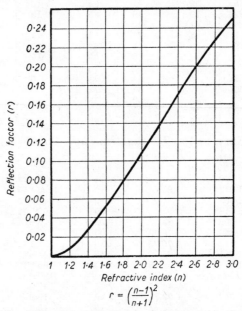

$$r = \left(\frac{n-1}{n+1}\right)^2$$

FIG. 12.2.—Fraction of light reflected at an air-glass surface for normal incidence.

When light passes through a series of plates or lenses there are of course a number of air-glass surfaces, at each of which reflection takes place, and the total light transmitted is affected by multiple internal reflections and is given by the formula

$$\text{Total light transmitted} = \frac{1 - r}{1 + (p - 1)\,r}$$

where r is the fraction of light reflected at an air-glass surface and p is the number of surfaces. If the surfaces are curved, as in lenses for example, it is obvious that the internally reflected portion of this total light emerges in any direction and does not contribute anything to the formation of the image. Hence, we can calculate the useful light transmitted as that which is free from any contributions by internal reflections and this is given by the formula

Useful light transmitted $= (1 - r)^p$.

The difference between the total light and the useful light constitutes stray light of no value to the image and it is very instructive to examine the relation between the stray light and the useful light, which, if expressed as a ratio, can be considered as the possible efficiency of an optical instrument. It is not the actual efficiency since there are other factors, such as the loss by absorption, effect of stray light on the contrast and, as an offset against all this tale of loss, the decrease in the reflection losses secured by " blooming " or the treatment of the surfaces with special films. In Fig. 12.3 curves

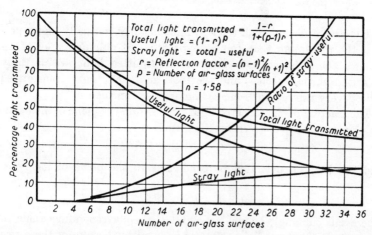

FIG. 12.3.—Stray light in optical instruments having a number of air-glass surfaces.

have been drawn for the simple case of glass for which $r = 0.05$ showing the total light and useful light transmitted through an instrument having a number of air-glass surfaces up to 36 and on the same diagram the stray light and the ratio of stray to useful light have also been drawn. Fig. 12.4 shows the useful light curves for refractive indices between 1·5 and 2·5 and it is obvious that the loss can be serious.

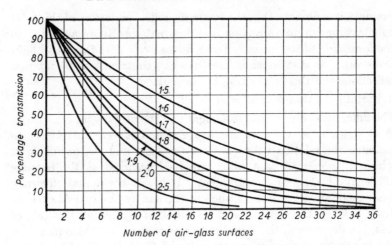

FIG. 12.4.—Percentage of useful light transmitted through a number of surfaces for various refractive indices.

The above formulae all refer to light incident normally and represent the maximum that can be expected. At oblique angles of incidence the reflected light and the transmitted light are partially polarised at the surfaces and the total and useful light transmitted fall off very rapidly with increasing angles of incidence.

The fraction of the reflected light polarised in the plane of incidence at a single surface is given by the formula :—

$$\sin^2(I - I')/\sin^2(I + I')$$

and the fraction polarised perpendicular to the plane of incidence by :—

$$\tan^2(I - I')/\tan^2(I + I')$$

where I is the angle of incidence and I' the corresponding angle of refraction. The total light reflected is equal to the sum of these two fractions. Fig. 12.5 shows how the intensities vary with angle of incidence and it is seen that, whereas for the light polarised in the plane of incidence the percentage of light reflected increases steadily with the angle of incidence (a), the percentage reflected of the light polarised perpendicular to the plane of incidence is zero when $I + I' = 90$ deg. (b).

If n is the refractive index of the glass then $\sin I = n \sin I'$ but if $I + I' = 90$ deg., $\sin I' = \cos I$; hence $\tan I = n$. This value of I for which the reflected light consists entirely of light polarised in the

210

plane of incidence is called the polarising angle. (Brewster's Law.) Light which is polarised in the plane of incidence has the electric vector in the plane at right angles to the plane of incidence.

Reflected light can be materially reduced by covering the surface with a " non-reflecting " film ; the surface is then said to be " bloomed." The effect was first noticed by H. Dennis Taylor about 1890 when he found that a lens which had apparently deteriorated by

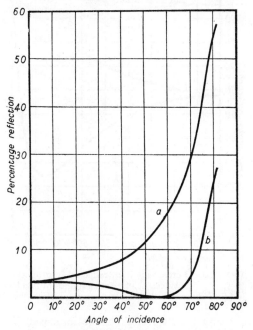

Fig. 12.5.—Percentage light reflected from a glass surface at increasing angles of incidence.
(a) Light polarised in the plane of incidence.
(b) Light polarised perpendicular to the plane of incidence.

weather and had a tarnish or " bloom " on the surface actually transmitted more light than a new clean lens. (See *The Adjustment and Testing of Telescope Objectives* by H. Dennis Taylor, 4th edition, p. 59.) Artificial methods of weathering to produce the bloom were tried but were not accepted generally and it was not until the 1930s that the application of thin films to the surfaces was introduced. For light of a given wave-length, at normal incidence, the optical thickness of the film is one quarter of the wave-length, and the refractive index of the material of the film is equal to the square root of that of the glass on which it is deposited. The efficiency of the film depends on the extent to which these conditions are fulfilled, and in practice is such that for a single surface light reflection is reduced to about 1 per cent. The material most commonly used is magnesium fluoride ($n_d = 1.390$) or cryolite.

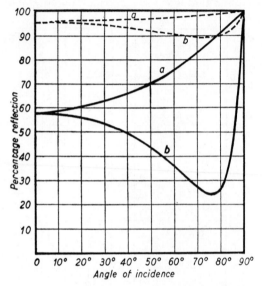

Fig. 12.6.—Percentage light reflected from metal surfaces at increasing angles of incidence. (*Full curves = steel, broken curves = silver.*)

In a similar manner reflectivity can be increased by coating the surface with a quarter wave-length film of a material of high refractive index such as zinc sulphide or titanium dioxide. Such coated surfaces are useful as beam splitters since the light absorption is low compared with that of partially metallised surfaces. Multiple layers of high and low refractive index films are also used as beam splitters and to make filters to pass very narrow bands of the spectrum. It should be noted that the transmitted and reflected light in beam splitters is frequently strongly polarised.

Table 12.11 gives particulars of semi-reflecting dielectric films; the refractive index, reflection and absorption. Table 12.12 gives the percentage reflection of light from a polished glass plate of various refractive indices for a number of angles of incidence. Figs. 12.7 and

212

TABLE 12.11

Semi-reflecting Dielectric Films on Polished Glass ($n_d = 1.52$)
Percentage Reflection and Absorption for Light of Wave-length
5400 A

Material	Refractive Index n_d	Reflection	Absorption
Beryllium Oxide	1·60	7	1
Antimony Oxide	1·85	15	0
Tellurium Oxide	1·95	18	1
Tungsten Oxide	2·00	20	0
Chromic Oxide	2·10	23	0
Cerium Oxide	2·25	30	1
Lead Oxide	2·30	32	1
Zinc Sulphide	2·40	35	0
Bismuth Oxide	2·45	36	1
Titanium Dioxide	2·60	38	1
Antimony Sulphide	2·80	47	6

TABLE 12.12

Light Reflected from Polished Glass Surfaces for Normal and
Oblique Incidence. Both Surfaces and Internal Reflections taken
into Account. Calculated for Yellow Light

Angle of Incidence	Refractive Index				
	1·5	1·55	1·60	1·65	1·70
	Percentage Reflection				
0°	7·8	8·8	10·2	11·3	12·6
10°	7·8	8·8	10·2	11·3	12·6
20°	8·0	8·9	10·3	11·4	12·7
30°	8·0	9·1	10·4	11·4	12·8
40°	8·6	9·8	11·1	12·2	13·4
50°	10·4	11·6	12·7	13·9	15·1
60°	15·2	16·3	17·4	18·4	19·4
70°	27·3	28·1	28·9	29·6	30·2

12.8 are transmission curves of some typical dielectric filters and mirrors (Barr & Stroud, Ltd.). Fig. 12.9 shows how the width of the band of wave-lengths transmitted by a dichroic filter depends on the number of layers.

One application of interference filters is for a proposed system of colour television. In this application, shown diagrammatically in Fig. 12.10, two crossing dichroic interference filters are used. One mirror r reflects red light from projector R; mirror b reflects blue light from projector B. The percentage reflections of red and blue light are high, of the order of 90% and the light lost in transmission is low, of the order of 10%. The green light from projector G passes through both filters with small transmission losses, of the order

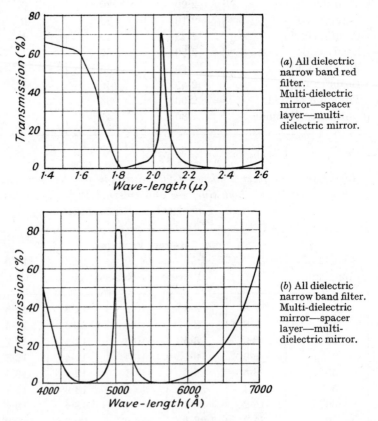

(a) All dielectric narrow band red filter.
Multi-dielectric mirror—spacer layer—multi-dielectric mirror.

(b) All dielectric narrow band filter.
Multi-dielectric mirror—spacer layer—multi-dielectric mirror.

Fig. 12.7.—Transmission curves of typical dielectric filters. (Barr & Stroud Ltd.)

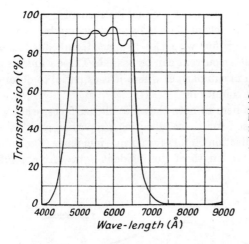

(a) Heat-resisting dichroic filter. Multi-dielectric layer, phased for maximum transmission in visible region.

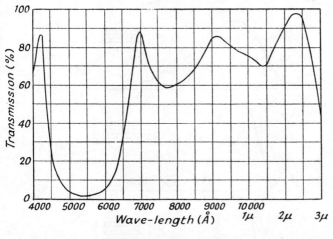

(b) Cold mirror. Multi-dielectric layer, phased for maximum reflectivity in visible region.

Fig. 12.8.—Transmission curves of typical dielectric mirrors. (Barr & Stroud Ltd.)

of 10% at each mirror, so that about 80% of each of the three colours reaches the screen. The same arrangement of mirrors can also be used at the camera end, where the camera replaces the projector.

A further application of coatings on glass is the use of cadmium to produce a thin film capable of conducting electricity from a pair of strip electrodes. By this means the temperature of a glass plate can be raised to prevent condensation of moisture and misting. Some strain is naturally induced in the glass but insufficient to cause severe loss of definition in cameras and visual instruments. Another method of making heated panels of glass is by sandwiching between a pair of plates a mesh of very fine wire, closely spaced, embedded in an epoxy resin through which a current can be passed. These windows are used in aeroplanes and in submarines where it is essential to obtain a clear view under severe conditions.

It is of interest here to note that metallic surfaces, when polished, are frequently used for their reflecting properties and Table 12.13 shows how the reflection factors for normal incidence of certain metals vary with the wave-length of the incident light. At oblique angles

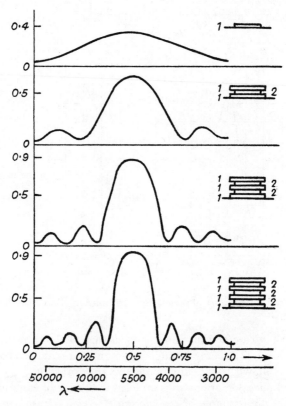

FIG. 12.9.—Dichroic Filters. Reflection coefficient R calculated for multiple layers of Zinc sulphide 1 (thickness d, index $n = 2\cdot4$) with alternate layers of Cryolite 2 (index $n = 1\cdot3$) on glass base.

Philips Tech. Rev., **19**, 63 (1957–8).

Table 12.13—Polished Metal Surfaces
Percentage Reflection for Normally Incident Light

Wavelength mμ	Aluminium	Chromium	Copper	Gold	Magnalium	Nickel	Platinum	Rhodium	Silver	Speculum metal	Steel	Tin	Zinc	Silver behind Glass	Mercury behind Glass
188		33	29	39	53	38	35		76	23	22				
200	80	36	24	34	56	43	38		76	25	27				
251	88	32	25	32	67	44	34		34	30	38				
288							39		21	40					
305		37			69		40		9	42	44				
316			25	29	77	45	41		4	51					
326			27	28	81	49	43		15						
357	84	41	29	27		50	45		75	53					
385			33	29		57	52		81						
420	86				83				87	56	50				
450	87		37	33		59	55		91	60	55			86	73
500	88		44	47		61	58		91	63	56		54	87	71
550		55	48	74	88	63	61	76	93	64	56	54	55	88	71
600			72	84		65	64		93	64	57	60	56	88	70
650	89		80	89	88	67	67		95	65	58	69	58	89	72
700	87	56	82	92		69	69	81	95	67	58	72	61	90	73
800	85	57	89	95		70	70	84	97			77	62		
1000	93	63	90			72	73	91	97	71	63	86	49		
2000		70	96	97	84	84	81	92	98	80	77	87	94		
3000			97			89	89		98	86	83		96		
4000	94	76	97	97	89	91	92	93	99	89	88		97		
5000		81	98					93		89			97		
7000	97		98			96		94		90		87	98		
9000	97	92	98				95	95	99	92	93				
11000		93	98				96		99	93					
12000	97		98	98	92		96		99	94	95		98		
14000															

of incidence there is again partial polarisation but it is found that there is no angle of incidence for which the reflected light is completely plane polarised. (See Fig. 12.6.)

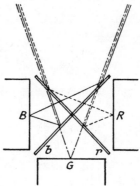

r is red-reflecting mirror.
b is blue-reflecting mirror.

FIG. 12.10.—Use of semi-reflecting dichroic mirrors for colour projection and photography.

After *Philips Tech. Rev.*, **19**, 66 (1957–8).

III. ABSORPTION

The amount of light absorbed in glass depends on the type of glass, on the wave-length of the light and on the thickness of the glass, and Table 12.14 gives the percentage absorption per inch of glass at several wave-lengths for a few typical kinds of optical glass (page 221).

Neutral glasses and filter glasses of a number of colours are manufactured for the specific purpose of absorbing and transmitting light within specified bands of wave-lengths and it should be noted that in order to obtain any definite transmission (or density) the thickness of the glass must be regulated accordingly. The manufacturer can usually state the thickness to which the glass must be worked to obtain the specified transmission characteristics.

Given the transmission T_1 of a filter glass of thickness d_1 for any given wave-length, the transmission T_2 for thickness d_2 and for the same wave-length will be given by the formula :—

$$T_2 = T_1{}^{d_2/d_1}$$

or in logarithmic form :—

$$\frac{d_2}{d_1} = \frac{\log T_2}{\log T_1}$$

If we use densities instead of transmission, and since density $=$ $\log_{10}\dfrac{1}{\text{transmission}}$, if D_2 and D_1 are the densities, at a given wavelength, for thicknesses d_2 and d_1 respectively, then $\dfrac{d_2}{d_1} = \dfrac{D_2}{D_1}$.

When using the above formulae an allowance must be made for the light lost by reflection at the air-glass surfaces of the filter, a loss which is equivalent to a density of about 0·04. As an example, if we have a filter the measured transmission of which is 40 per cent for a thickness of 2·5 mm. and we require to know the thickness for a transmission of 60 per cent the calculation is as follows. The density corresponding to a transmission of 40 per cent is 0·40 (from Table 12.9), allowing for surface reflection the true density is 0·36. For a transmission of 60 per cent the density is 0·22 and allowing again for surface reflection this is reduced to 0·18. Hence by our formula the required thickness is $\dfrac{0·18}{0·36} \times 2·5$ or 1·25 mm. The intrinsic transmission of a material corresponding to its true density, i.e., its total density less the density corresponding to reflection losses, is sometimes called the *transmittance* of the substance.

A useful set of curves connecting transmission and thickness, allowing for surface reflection, has been prepared by McLeod and is reproduced here (Fig. 12.11). Using these curves it is possible to read off directly the thickness and transmission for any filter. Using our example above, we find the point on the diagram corresponding to a thickness of 2·5 mm. and a transmission of 40 per cent and following the nearest curve to the transmission value of 60 per cent we read off directly the thickness 1·25 mm. as found above.

Not all coloured glass is suitable for optical working and care must be taken in selecting glass for optically flat filters that it is, in fact, suitable glass.

Ordinary glass absorbs ultra-violet light but, if greater protection against the harmful short wave-length radiations is required, one or other of the special glasses made for the purpose should be selected. Crookes glasses, as they are called, can be obtained almost white or very slightly tinted and may contain Cerium oxide or some of the other rare earths. Glass which transmits a larger proportion of the ultra-violet than normal can also be obtained. At the other end of the spectrum ordinary (greenish) glasses normally absorb infra-red radiations to a considerable extent and special glasses are manufactured to absorb heat and infra-red radiations but optical types of glass and iron-free white plate are more transparent in the infra-red. Such glasses transmit some radiation in the infra-red up to 4·8 μ with strong absorption bands at 2·8 μ and 3·6 μ. In optical projection equipment it is often useful to insert a sheet of heat absorbing glass to prevent too much heat from reaching the film or lantern slide and this glass is quite transparent to visible light and appears colourless. Chance's ON20 glass, containing a high proportion of P_2O_5 is very transparent to visible light while it absorbs strongly in the infra-red. As it has a low coefficient of thermal expansion it is less liable to crack with the heat and as it has practically no selective absorption in the visible range the colour values of the projected object remain unaltered on the screen. Where protection against glare is also required, for example, for welding, furnace work and in

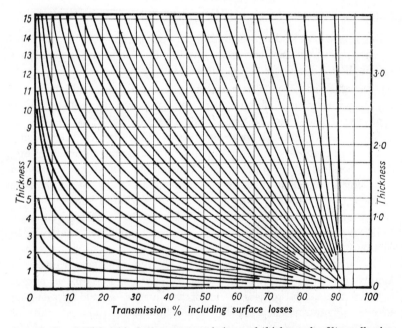

Fig. 12.11.—Relationship between transmission and thickness for filters allowing for surface reflection (McLeod *J.O.S.A.* **35** No. 2. February, 1945, p. 185). Each curve represents the transmission and corresponding thickness for a given filter glass and by following the curve any required thickness and transmission can be found.

sextants and telescopes used for observing the sun, it is important to ensure that the neutral, smoked or blue glass used also absorbs the heat and infra-red radiations.

TABLE 12.14—*Light Transmission, Chance Optical Glass*

The figures given below are extinction coefficients multiplied by 100.

Extinction coefficient $K = (\log_e I_0 - \log_e I)\,t$, where I_0 = initial light intensity, I = transmitted light intensity, t = glass thickness, inches.

Glass type	BSC	HC	MBC	DBC	LF	LBF	DF	EDF	SBC	SBF	DEDF
n_d	1·5090	1·5189	1·5682	1·6157	1·5792	1·5683	1·6230	1·6516	1·6451	1·7205	1·7525
V	64·7	59·9	55·6	55·3	41·1	55·0	36·0	33·6	57·8	47·6	27·7
Wavelength, mμ											
365	4·60	7·82	31·7	—	14·8	25·4	39·2	49·5	—	—	—
400	1·37	—	5·4	13·3	4·4	—	—	12·9	—	—	—
404·8	—	2·48	—	11·8	—	5·21	6·70	9·67	16·6	36·4	49·1
420	—	—	—	7·0	—	—	—	7·28	—	—	—
435·8	—	3·67	—	6·2	—	4·54	4·45	5·21	7·06	17·3	10·9
440	1·32	—	3·8	5·92	2·3	—	—	5·30	—	—	—
460	—	—	—	4·61	—	—	—	4·05	—	—	—
480	0·87	—	1·75	3·29	1·17	—	—	2·78	—	—	—
491·6	—	1·88	—	—	—	2·49	2·48	2·71	—	—	—
500	—	—	—	2·18	—	—	—	2·29	—	—	—
520	0·49	—	0·9	2·04	0·69	—	—	1·66	—	—	—
540	—	—	—	1·92	—	—	—	1·48	—	—	—
546	—	1·35	—	1·96	—	1·44	1·41	1·40	1·77	6·08	1·52
560	0·35	—	0·6	1·81	0·51	—	—	1·28	—	—	—
579	—	1·69	—	2·26	—	1·78	1·54	1·21	2·25	5·80	1·71
580	—	—	—	2·32	—	—	—	1·20	—	—	—
600	0·49	—	0·76	2·88	0·60	—	—	1·90	—	—	—
620	—	—	—	3·20	—	—	—	2·22	—	—	—
640	0·67	3·04	0·87	3·44	0·74	2·85	2·12	2·35	2·39	4·62	1·78
680	0·87	—	0·8	3·46	0·6	—	—	2·17	—	—	—
700	—	—	—	3·32	—	—	2·02	1·83	—	—	—

Figures supplied by kind permission of Chance Brothers Ltd.

It is interesting to note the " glass-house " effect made use of by gardeners and which can be found in buildings. Owing to the high temperature of the sun and the filtering effect of the earth's atmosphere sunshine at the earth's surface is restricted to wave-lengths in the range $0\cdot3\ \mu$ to $3\cdot0\ \mu$ for which window glass is highly transparent. The *low* temperature heat radiated by surfaces at temperatures less than 100° C. is entirely confined to long wave-lengths, beyond $5\cdot0\ \mu$ for which glass is completely opaque. As a result sunshine can pass readily through window glass to heat objects inside but the re-radiated heat from these objects cannot pass outwards through the glass. To reduce the heat of sunlight passing through skylights the simple expedient of white-washing the glass so as to reflect part of the incident light is effective. The " glass-house " effect has been used to generate power from solar energy by placing black painted boiler tubes under glass, preferably two sheets; the heat absorbed is sufficient to provide a measure of central heating in a house or to operate refrigerators. The effect is also used to condense fresh water from salt water in lifeboat water distilling equipment.

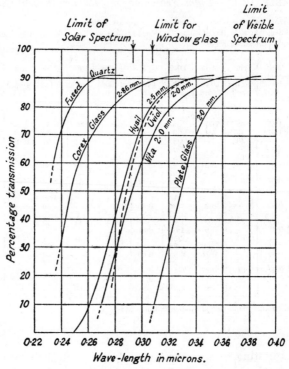

FIG. 12.12.—Ultra-violet transmission of certain glasses.

Fig. 12.12 shows the percentage transmission of ordinary window glass and of certain proprietary glasses with increased transmission in the ultra-violet region. These glasses are " Uviol " made by the Jena glassworks, " Vitaglass," made by Pilkington Bros., " Hysil," manufactured by Chance Bros. Ltd., of Birmingham, and " Corex," of the Corning Glass Works, U.S.A. Fig. 12.13 shows, in a similar manner, the transmission of certain eye-protection glasses in which the ultra-violet or infra-red transmissions are reduced.

A very large range of gelatine, cellulose acetate and other plastic filters is also available covering the whole visible wave-length range and very good neutrals are also available in gelatine. The catalogues issued by Kodak (Wratten) and by Ilford should be consulted for the absorption characteristics of these gelatine filters, but it should be noted that many of these filters may be transparent in the deep red and infra-red.

The use of " Polaroid " film has to a very large extent replaced Nicol prisms for producing and analysing polarised light but it will be found that some kinds transmit the deep violet and the deep red

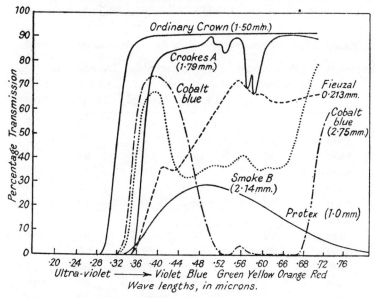

FIG. 12.13.—Transmission of certain eye protection glasses.

without polarisation so that care must be taken when using this film. The use of two pieces of polaroid, for example, to produce a neutral filter of continuously variable density is very common. Table 12.15 shows the transmission of some specimens of Polaroid but care must be taken in accepting these figures since considerable differences have been found with other specimens. The name " Polaroid " is applied to more than one kind of polarising material.

Polaroid was originally manufactured by forming crystals of an iodine-quinine salt (Herapathite) in a strong magnetic field, the crystals being deposited on a sheet of a synthetic cellulose material. More recently it has been made by heating and stretching thin sheets of certain polyvinyl derivatives to several times the original length, and subsequent staining by iodine, the sheet being then laminated with a more robust backing of plastic or with glass. The laminated plastic polaroid tends to have a higher extinction than the glass laminated specimens but in no case is it complete for any wave-length. It will usually be found advisable to obtain glass laminated discs from the manufacturer rather than attempt to cement sheet polaroid to glass. Most solvents such as are present in canada balsam and other cements tend to dissolve the sheet material partly and destroy the polarising properties in addition to causing uneven shrinkage.

TABLE 12.15—*Transmission Data for Specimens of Polaroid*

Wave-length (A)	Percentage Polarisation	Percentage Transmission			
		Film		Laminated Plate	
		Parallel	Crossed	Parallel	Crossed
3000	—	0	0	0	0
4000	70	1·5	0	22	5
4500	70	12	0·5	28	4
5000	95	13	0	32	3
5500	98	15	0	33	2·5
6000	98	16	0	33	2·5
6500	96	25	0	33	2·5
7000	91	34	2·5	32	2
8000	32	63	62	28	5
9000	9	77	77	37	29
10000	5	85	85	39	43
11000	—	85	85	41	41

NOTE.—Where the percentage transmission for crossed polaroid is shown as zero there is usually a measurable transmission which, however, is very variable in different specimens of the material.

IV. DETECTION OF DEFECTS IN GLASS

Glass, in slab or sheet form intended for use as observation windows in conjunction with optical viewing devices, shadow and Schlieren apparatus and cameras, should be as free as possible from bubbles, seed (small bubbles), scratches and sleeks. The most sensitive and revealing test for such marks, which may escape notice under ordinary methods of examination, is to illuminate the specimen through the edge. The test should be made in a darkened room, or away from bright lights and a convenient piece of test equipment is shown in Fig. 12.14. The apparatus consists simply of a flat desk, covered with black cloth or green baize on which the glass can be laid in such a manner that its edge is presented to a slit aperture which allows light from the interior of the light box to pass into the edge of the specimen. Every little defect will be seen to stand out brightly lit and unsuitable glass can be rejected or the best portions of the large sheet selected. It is not necessary to construct this apparatus, which is intended for routine examination, for isolated tests and an ordinary photographic dark-room lamp can be used to produce a slit of bright light by replacing the normal coloured screen by an opaque sheet, a sheet of cardboard for example, in which a narrow slit is cut.

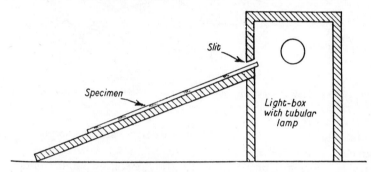

FIG. 12.14.—Light box for examination of glass plates for bubbles and surface markings.

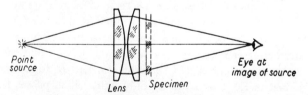

FIG. 12.15.—Testing glass for veins and striae.

Internal defects in glass not always easily visible to the naked eye are caused by " cords " or " striae " which are veins in the glass where the refractive index is not uniform. Several well-known methods exist to make these cords easily visible and possibly the simplest test is shown in Fig. 12.15. Here a point source of light (illuminated pin-hole) which should be very bright is placed in relation to a large lens in such a way that the image of the source is formed in a convenient position for observation. Although not absolutely necessary, it is convenient to arrange a screen with a hole about $\frac{1}{4}$ in. in diameter in such a way that the image is formed in the hole. An eye placed at the hole sees the whole lens filled with light (Maxwellian View). If now the specimen is interposed between the lens and the eye the veins and striae will be clearly seen as dark lines crossing the plate. An alternative method is to use a modified Schlieren system by arranging a small disc on which the image is formed and leaving an annular aperture round the disc through which the lens is observed. The arrangement is shown in Fig. 12.16

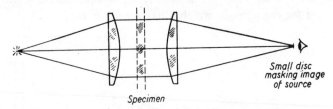

Small disc
masking image
of source

Specimen

Fig. 12.16.—Testing glass for veins and striae, a better method than that shown in Fig. 12.15.

and it will be noticed that two lenses are now used and so placed that the light between the lenses, which should be well corrected, is nearly parallel. The specimen is placed in this region of parallel light and any veins or striae are seen as bright lines crossing the semi-dark surface of the lens. Instead of direct observation by eye the image of the second lens may be thrown on a screen, or photographic plate, as in the normal Schlieren method shown in Fig. 12.17. Instead of a point source and its conjugate image formed in a circular disc it is often more convenient to use a slit as source and a knife edge at its image. It should be noted that the projector lens L_3 forms the image on the screen of the lens L_2 using only light which passes the knife

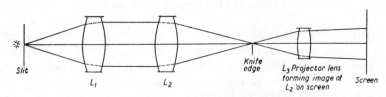

Slit
L_1
L_2
Knife
edge
L_3 Projector lens
forming image of
L_2 on screen
Screen

Fig. 12.17.—Schlieren arrangement for the examination of glass for veins. The light is parallel between lenses L_1 and L_2. Lens L_3 forms an image of L_2 on the screen using only light passing the knife edge.

edge. The adjustment should be such that the screen appears almost dark, with a very faintly luminous image of the lens L_2, mainly due to imperfections in this lens. Any slight change of refractive index in the space between L_1 and L_2 will show up on the screen. For example the hot air rising from the hand is sufficient to cause waves of light to cross the screen.

When a sheet of glass is to be used for observation or with an optical instrument, for example, as a filter in front of a photographic lens, it is not a necessary and sufficient condition that the glass should be optically flat. Veins or striae, for example, in a perfect optical flat would destroy the definition and, on the other hand, the disc may have spherical surfaces of zero power or be a very weak lens without causing loss of definition.

Hence, the method of examination of an optical flat by observing the Newton's rings formed when the disc under test is placed in contact with a standard optical flat will not necessarily imply that the disc can be used as a filter or observation panel. It is preferable to test the disc by direct observation and for this purpose a very simple test is shown in Fig. 12.18, a telescope of fairly high power

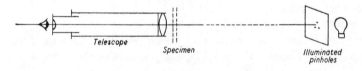

Telescope Specimen Illuminated pinholes

Fig. 12.18.—Method of testing flats and filters. The telescope is used to observe the three pin-holes and any deterioration in resolution caused by the filter can be seen.

$(30 \times$ or $40 \times)$, having an object glass whose diameter is equal to that of the instrument or camera lens with which the disc is to be used, is focused so that the observer sees the image of three pin-holes placed at a convenient distance from the telescope. The pin-holes are brightly illuminated and are at the corners of an equilateral triangle whose side is calculated according to the required resolution in the final instrument. The telescope should resolve the pin-holes easily, i.e., its resolving power should be greater than that of the final instrument. On the disc being held in front of the telescope object glass the three pin-holes should remain clearly resolved.

The test is very sensitive and it will be found that few optical flats (so called) will pass the test unless care is taken to space the pin-holes at the *practical* desired resolution limit. For example, for certain photographic cameras it was found if the pin-holes were 1 mm. apart and were placed 30 ft. or 10,000 mm. from the telescope the resolution of 1/10,000 so obtained corresponded to that obtainable with the cameras. The telescope had a 3 in. diameter object glass and a power of 30 × and the discs rejected by this test were found, on trial with the actual cameras, to cause loss of resolving power while those accepted did not. Many of the discs tested were lenticular to thirty or forty rings on both sides when tested with a standard optical flat. It should be noted that if it is allowable to re-focus the camera or instrument after the disc or filter is fitted, then it should be allowable to re-focus the testing telescope when examining the discs. In this way many discs which would be rejected owing to their being weak lenses can be accepted. On the other hand, if the instrument or camera cannot be re-focused then the test telescope must not be focused during the test and thus weak lenses would be automatically rejected. It should be noted that this test can also be used to measure any lack of parallelism in filters and discs by measuring the shift in the apparent position of the pin-holes due to the wedge. Practical limits of wedge should be accepted according to the use and purpose for which the discs are required.

Strain in glass, caused by insufficient or faulty annealing, can be detected in the usual manner by using polarised light as shown in Fig. 12.19. The use of polaroid greatly simplifies the construction of

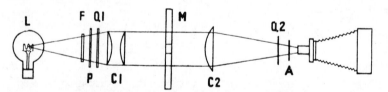

Fig. 12.19.—Detection of strain.
Light from the source L (preferably monochromatic) is polarised at P and rendered parallel by C_1. After passing lens C_2 the light is analysed at A. The eye or camera observes the lens C_2. Q_1 and Q_2 are quarter-wave plates which may be used to simplify the strain pattern. F is a filter used to obtain monochromatic light and M is the specimen being examined. (*Kodak Data Book*, C.3.)

strain detecting instruments but any source of polarised light, such as reflection at the polarising angle from black glass or from a pile of glass plates, may be used and the analyser may be a nicol prism or a small piece of polaroid.

When glass is in a state of strain it becomes birefringent, i.e., it behaves as if its refractive index depends on the direction of vibration of the light passing through it. With the polariser and analyser " crossed " the field appears dark and when a piece of strained glass is placed between them a certain amount of light passes the analyser, showing bright colours. The pattern seen indicates that strain is present. In order to measure the strain or assess its relative amount a tint plate or quarter wave plates are used. Adjusting the tint plate causes a change of colour which is easily detected and can be interpreted but the interpretation requires care and experience. The reader should consult one of the standard texts on the subject of strain analysis.

V. PHYSICAL PROPERTIES OF GLASS

The measurement, or even the definition, of the physical properties of glass is a matter of some difficulty. The properties vary with the composition and with the past physical history which is complicated by unknown and often unpredictable strain. The following information has been extracted from the *Dictionary of Applied Physics*, article " Glass " and from *Glass* (edited by) J. Home Dickson (Hutchinson, 1951).

(i) Density :—The density of glass is approximately an additive function of the composition and varies from about 2·3 in light crown glass to 6·0 for a dense flint. The density, or specific gravity, of glass is normally measured by a simple flotation method. Specimens of the glass are placed in a heavy liquid mixture, e.g., a mixture of bromoform and pentachlorethane, which is heated slowly and the temperature is noted when the specimens just begin to sink. The density can be measured in this way with an accuracy of about 0·0002 gm/cc.

TABLE 12.16—*Specific Gravity of Glass*

Common Bottle Glass ..	2·46	Dense Barium Crown ..	3·63
Plate Glass	2·49	Light Flint	3·23
Heavy Flint Tableware	3·5	Dense Flint	3·65
Borosilicate Crown ..	2·49	Extra Dense Flint ..	3·90
Hard Crown	2·53	Double Extra Dense Flint	6·11

(ii) Strength :—Very divergent values are obtained, depending largely on the annealing. The tensile strength may lie between $2\frac{1}{2}$ and 10 tons per sq. in. although very thin fibres have been made with a strength exceeding 200 tons per sq. in. The crushing strength lies between 10 and 15 tons per sq. in. The strength does not vary very much with the composition of the glass. It has been suggested, and there is a considerable body of evidence to support the hypothesis, that the variations observed in the measured strength of glass are due to very small flaws or cracks which are always present throughout the volume of the glass. The flaws become dangerous when they are on the surface where they act as stress magnifiers, the stress at the bottom of a flaw being much greater than the applied stress. The strength of glass is found to diminish with the time of loading. Toughened or bullet proof glass owes its strength to the state of compression of the outer layers. The glass will not break unless a tensile breaking stress is developed on the surface and since the initial compressive stress may be very much greater than the breaking strain the applied tension has to neutralise this before beginning to develop a tension.

(iii) Hardness :—The hardness of glass is measured by its scratching power and resistance to scratching and most glass comes between quartz and fluorspar on Moh's scale. All glass will scratch any other glass and the scratching depends largely on the temperature. The hardness of the surface of glass to shock depends very much on the annealing and heat treatment it has received. Bullet proof glass has been made by very rapid chilling of the surface, by pressing the hot glass between copper plates and by other methods.

(iv) Elasticity :—The following values are given :—

	Crown Glasses dynes/sq. cm.	Flint Glasses dynes/sq. cm.
Young's Modulus	$5\cdot9 - 7\cdot8 \times 10^{11}$	$4\cdot9 - 5\cdot9 \times 10^{11}$
Rigidity (Torsion Modulus)	$2\cdot6 - 3\cdot2 \times 10^{11}$	$2\cdot0 - 2\cdot5 \times 10^{11}$
Volume (Bulk Modulus)	$4\cdot0 - 5\cdot9 \times 10^{11}$	$3\cdot6 - 3\cdot8 \times 10^{11}$
Poisson's Ratio	$0\cdot21 - 0\cdot28$	

(v) Coefficient of Expansion :—The thermal expansion of glass is very sensitive to changes in composition, particularly to alkali content. Care must be taken when joining pieces of glass together by fusing that the total contraction of the two glasses from the temperature of fusing to room temperature is the same if strain-free joints are expected. It is usual to test glass for suitability of matching by joining them and measuring the resulting strain.

The expansion of glass is linear with temperature up to a certain temperature and then increases suddenly. The temperature at which the coefficient of expansion changes is called the transformation point.

The following values are quoted for the coefficient of thermal expansion of some glasses per degree centigrade, but the values are very variable. *Glass* (edited) by J. Home Dickson should be consulted for a good account of Glass-to-Metal seals, or for an exhaustive account the book by J. H. Partridge on *Glass to Metal Seals.*

Fused Silica	$0.4 \times 10^{-6}/°C.$
Heat-resisting glass (chemical and ovenware)	3.3×10^{-6}
Jena Laboratory glass	5.7×10^{-6}
Soda Laboratory glass	7.4×10^{-6}
Flint glass	7.8×10^{-6}

(vi) **Specific Heat :**—The specific heat is a function of the composition and rises with the temperature. Its value lies between 0·14 and 0·29.

(vii) **Thermal Conductivity :**—0·0015 — 0·0028 C.G.S. Units.

(viii) **Thermal Endurance:** —By thermal endurance is meant the capacity of glass to withstand rapid change of temperature and, in general, glass is more resistant to sudden heating than to sudden cooling. The thermal endurance is a function of the density, tensile strength, Young's Modulus, specific heat, thermal conductivity and coefficient of expansion. It can be measured by raising specimens in the form of rods successively to higher and higher temperatures and plunging into cold water until the glass cracks. Good beakers should stand about 150° C. without cracking under this test.

(ix) **Electrical Properties :**—At temperatures below about 100° C. most glasses are reasonably good insulators but surface conductivity is always present. This can be reduced by drying the glass or coating it with a water repellent such as one of the silicone liquids. The electrical conductivity of glass increases very rapidly with temperature.

The dielectric strength of glass is very variable and complex in nature, depending on its composition, thickness, humidity of the atmosphere and time of application of the electric field.

BOOKS ON GLASS

GLAZEBROOK, Sir R., *Dictionary of Applied Physics* (Macmillan, London). Articles on " Glass," " Optical Glass," etc.

MOREY, G. W., *The Properties of Glass* (Reinhold Publishing Co., New York, 1938). Deals mainly with the chemical and physical properties.

HOVESTADT, H. (translated EVERETT, J. D. and A.), *Jena Glass and its Applications* (Macmillan, London, 1902).

DICKSON, J. HOME (edited), *Glass* (Hutchinson, 1951).

STANWORTH, J. E., *Physical Properties of Glass* (Oxford U.P., 1950).

MARTIN, L. C., *Technical Optics* (Pitman, London, 1948). (New edition of Applied Optics.)

Journal of Society of Glass Technology, Sheffield.

PARTRIDGE, J. H., *Glass to Metal Seals*. (Sheffield, Society of Glass Technology.)

COKER, E. G., and FILON, L. N. G., *Photoelasticity* (Cambridge U.P., 1931).

MORGAN, P., *Glass Reinforced Plastics* (Iliffe, 1957).

SONNEBORN, R. H., *Fibreglass Reinforced Plastics* (Reinhold Publishing Co., New York).

REFERENCES

McLEOD, J. H., " Graphical Correlation of Transmittances and Thickness in Optical Filters," *J.O.S.A.*, **35** (Feb. 1945), 185.

COLEMAN, H. S., " Stray Light in Optical Systems," *J.O.S.A.*, **37** (June, 1947), 434.

GREENLAND, K. M., " Principles of the use of non-reflecting films in optical instruments," *Nature*, **152** (11th Sept., 1943), 290.

CARTWRIGHT, C. H., " The Treatment of Camera Lenses with low reflecting films," *J.O.S.A.*, **30** (March, 1940), 110.

JOHNSON, B. K., " Recent Optical Materials and Their Possible Applications," *Proc. Phys. Soc.*, **55** (1943), 291.

WHEAT, W. N., *Schott & Genossen of Jena* (C.I.O.S. report, H.M.S.O.).

ALPHEN, P. M. VAN, " Applications of the Interference of Light in thin films," *Philips Tech. Rev.*, **19**, 59 (1957/58).

VRIJER, F. W. DE, " Fundamentals of Colour Television," *Philips Tech. Rev.*, **19**, 86 (1957/58).

HOPKINS, H. H., and KAPANI, N. S., " Transparent Fibres for the Transmission of Optical Images." Problems in Contemporary Optics, Institute Nazionale di Ottica, Arcetri-Firenze (1956), 150, or *Optica Acta* **1** (4) (1955), 164, and *Nature*, **173** (1954), 39.

Handbook of Chemistry and Physics (Chemical Rubber Publishing Co., Cleveland, Ohio).

KAYE and LABY, *Physical and Chemical Constants* (Longmans Green, 11th Edition, 1956).

CHAPTER 13

NATURAL AND SYNTHETIC OPTICAL CRYSTALS

CRYSTALS have been used in optical instruments for many years; quartz, for example, for ultra-violet spectrographs and for spectacles, calcite for its double refraction and, more recently, fluorite for its transmission in the ultra-violet. With increasing practical interest in the near infra-red, particularly in the chemical industry, and for ultra-violet microscopy and spectrophotometry, crystals are becoming more important. In addition to natural crystals, quartz, calcite and rock salt, there are now many artificially produced crystals readily available on the market and these are being used more and more in scientific work.

In the following pages are given tables of the refractive index of a number of natural and synthetic crystals for a range of wave-lengths and other general tables of optical properties and some indication of sources of supply.

Crystalline quartz is only obtained from nature and is still a favourite material for use in the ultra-violet down to a wave-length at which air ceases to transmit. Crystal quartz prisms for spectrometers are cut so that the mean ray traverses the optic axis, to avoid doubling of spectral lines from bi-refringence. In addition to being bi-refringent, crystal quartz is optically active and in consequence the refractive index is different for right- and for left-handed circularly polarised light. This property would cause splitting of a monochromatic beam traversing a single prism, whatever the direction with respect to the optic axis. It is avoided in the 60° Cornu prism by making the prism from two 30° prisms, one of right-handed and the other of left-handed quartz. In spectrometers where the radiation is reflected back through the prism, the second traversal annuls the splitting and it is not necessary to use a Cornu prism. Fused-silica, also sometimes known as fused quartz, vitreous silica or quartz glass has the advantage of not being bi-refringent, but it is difficult to obtain in good optical quality. It can be obtained in prisms and lens blanks and in thin sections for microscope slides from the Thermal Syndicate, the General Electric Company and the Hanovia Chemical and Manufacturing Company. It is also obtainable under the trade

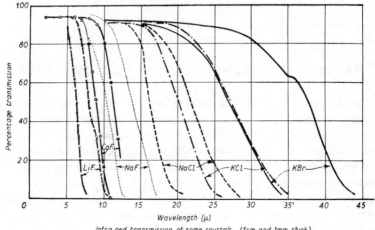

Infra red transmission of some crystals (1cm. and 1mm. thick)

FIG. 13.1.

names " Homosil " and " Ultrasil " from Heraeus Quartzschmelze, and these materials can be used for longer optical paths from 2000 A. Fig. 13.2 shows the transmission of fused quartz 10 mm. thick (after Heraeus). Similar curves are given by the Thermal Syndicate. Both firms state that they can supply cubes up to 4 inches thick and plates 9 inches in diameter, ⅝ inch thick, free from grain and optically homogeneous.

Calcium fluoride (fluorite) and lithium fluoride, when grown in

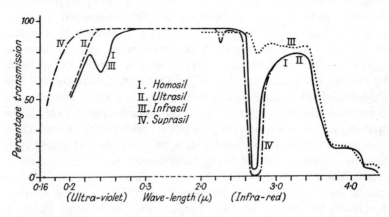

FIG. 13.2.—Transmission of fused quartz (10 mm.) (After Heraeus).

vacuum from the molten salt, using carefully purified raw materials, give UV transmissions down to 1250A and 1050A respectively, and can be used through the visible spectrum and into the near infra-red to 9 and 6 microns, respectively. Fluorite in particular is very useful in making microscope objectives for the UV and, in combination with glass elements, for making apochromatic objectives.

Sodium chloride, potassium chloride and potassium bromide also transmit in the ultra-violet down to about 2000A but are not generally used for this purpose because they are soluble in water. These crystals are, however, very largely used in infra-red spectrometers. They are readily obtainable as large ingots of about 8 in. in diameter from several sources, particularly the Harshaw Chemical Company, who also produce many other useful synthetic crystals, and also from Hilger & Watts, Ltd. Other useful materials for infra-red instruments are thallium bromide – thallium iodide (42 per cent – 58 per cent), known as " KRS-5 " which transmits up to about 40 microns. It has a high refractive index and consequently high reflection losses, and is soft and mechanically weak. These disadvantages also apply to crystalline silver chloride which transmits to 25 microns but is, in addition, extremely corrosive, even to metals, and darkens when exposed to actinic light. Caesium bromide which has lower reflection losses than KRS-5 is useful for windows, etc.

Barium fluoride, similar to calcium fluoride, transmits from well below 2000A to about 13 microns and may have applications as a substitute for sodium chloride since it is very much less soluble in water. Calcium bromide is also under development.

Some interesting materials with useful properties now being produced by the Linde Air Products Company are synthetic sapphire or corundum (Al_2O_3), spinel ($MgO. Al_2O_3$) and rutile (TiO_2). Sapphire is made in Britain by the Salford Electric Inst. Co. The outstanding properties of these substances are their extreme hardness and resistance to abrasion, their high melting point, complete insolubility in water and high chemical resistance. Their refractive indices are high, sapphire and spinel over 1·7 and rutile about 2·6 and 2·9 ; they are, of course, bi-refringent.

Ammonium dihydrogen phosphate (ADP), formerly available from the Brush Development Company, is of some optical interest. Plates up to 5 in. sq. cut perpendicular to the optic axis are available, transmit from 2000A to about 1·5 microns and are stable up to 140° C. The material is bi-refringent, with indices of refraction

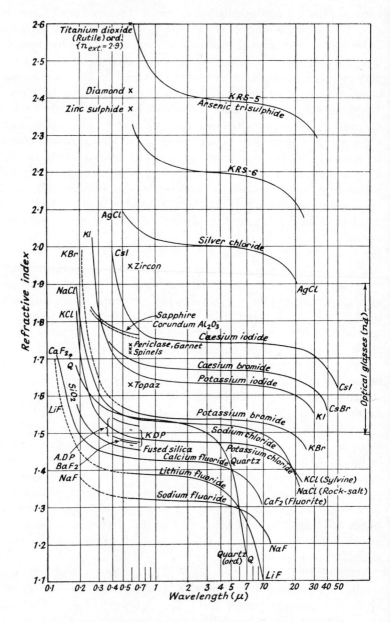

Fig. 13 3.—Refractive index of natural and synthetic crystals.

of 1·5242 for the ordinary ray and 1·4787 for the extraordinary (sodium light). Potassium dihydrogen phosphate (KDP) is similar in many respects. Both these crystals have interesting electro-optical properties. Sodium nitrate has a very large bi-refringence but is difficult to handle because of its solubility and hygroscopic tendency.

Crystalline magnesium oxide (periklase) with a refractive index of 1·74 and V-value 53·5, may have applications for achromatic lenses or prisms, possibly combined with quartz. It transmits from 2200A to about 7 microns and is hard, with a high melting point and good resistance to acids and metallic vapours. It is obtainable from the Norton Grinding Company. Periklase cleaves extremely well. It may be ground with the usual abrasives. Polishing with rouge or cerium oxide on pitch is prohibitively slow, but it may be polished on a fine-ground glass surface with very fine alumina of the kind used for polishing metallurgical specimens, with water as lubricant. In moist air, periklase surfaces become frosted. The natural cleavage surfaces are more resistant than the polished ones.

New materials for optical use and particularly for infra-red work are constantly being discovered and studied. Many of these new materials have interesting properties which make them valuable in particular applications. One such material is arsenic trisulphide glass, useful as a window and for the construction of achromatic and high aperture optical systems. It has a high refractive index, 2·42 at 2μ and 2·38 at 12μ and transmits freely between these limits. Fig. 13.4, supplied by Barr & Stroud, Ltd., shows the transmission and refractive index of arsenic trisulphide glass. It is insoluble in cold water and unaffected by atmospheric moisture, cold acetone, alcohol or ether. It is slightly attacked by hot water and organic solvents and is strongly affected by alkaline substances. Windows and lenses ranging in size from 0·08 in. diameter to 11 in. sq., 0·02 in. to 0·75 in. thick are available. The material is highly toxic especially during optical grinding operations and should be ordered in its finished size and shape. Finished optical parts can be obtained in Britain from Barr & Stroud, Ltd., and in the United States from the Servo Corporation of America, under the trade name " Servofrax."

Germanium and selenium can easily be melted and poured into moulds or otherwise shaped by hand to make lenses of low dispersion so that systems focused at 1μ are still in focus at 6μ or more.

Fig. 13.5 shows diagrammatically the method commonly used for growing crystals. The furnace is well lagged to maintain a steady

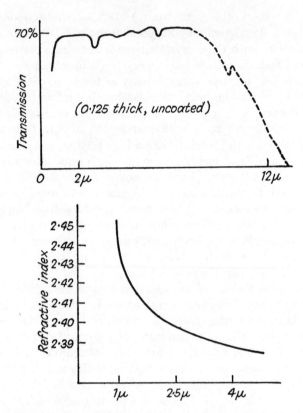

FIG. 13.4.—Transmission and refractive index of arsenic trisulphide glass. (Barr & Stroud Ltd.)

temperature gradient and arranged so that the temperature above the baffle is higher than the freezing point of the material. The temperatures quoted in the figure refer to potassium bromide. The growing crystal in its pot is lowered as growth proceeds.

Instruments

The use of optical crystals in instruments is well illustrated in monochromators used in spectroscopic analysis. Fig. 13.6 shows the general layout and diagrammatic arrangement of a simple instrument which can be used in many ways. Radiation from the entrance slit is dispersed by the first prism to form a spectrum in the plane of the central slit. The radiation which passes through this slit is further dispersed by the second prism, the dispersions of the two halves of the instrument being additive; and a partial spectrum is formed in the plane of the exit slit.

The prisms, whose refracting angles are matched within close limits, are mounted on tables which are geared together in a one-to-one ratio, and the shaft which transmits the drive to the prism tables by means of a worm gear also carries the wave-length drum. This drum is normally graduated in degrees and minutes. The drum shaft can be motor driven if required, in conjunction with a recording paper drive and there is a contactor drum to enable reference marks to be made on the recorder paper.

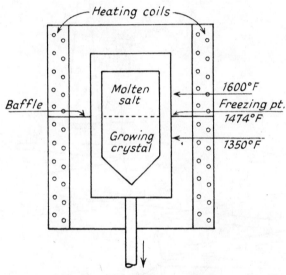

Fig. 13.5.—Crystal growing furnace. Temperatures refer to potassium bromide.

The result of the two-stage dispersion is the virtual elimination of stray radiation from the emergent beam, but in use it is often desirable to chop the radiation at a convenient frequency so that an alternating current amplifier can be used which will ignore any stray steady radiation.

The monochromator is fitted with a substantial cover and a heating system is incorporated in the instrument to protect hygroscopic prisms from damage due to the condensation of moisture on their polished surfaces.

The choice of prisms used depends on the wave-length range and dispersion required and, in the instrument described, which is manufactured by Barr & Stroud Ltd., Glasgow, the standard materials used are lithium fluoride and calcium fluoride, while quartz, rock salt and potassium bromide can also be supplied. The prism holders are fitted to the rotating tables by the hole, slot and plane method. Consequently, when the monochromator has once been

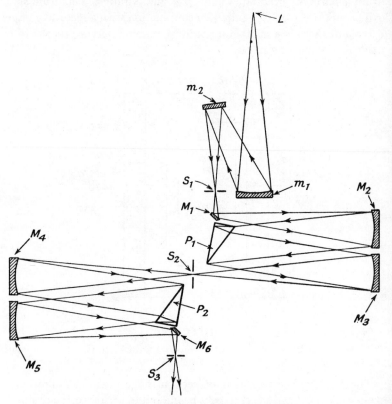

FIG. 13.6.—Diagrammatic arrangement.

M_2, M_3, M_4, M_5—Concave mirrors. 57 mm. × 55 mm. $f = 300$ mm.

M_1, M_6—Plane mirrors. 25 mm. × 27 mm.

m_1—Concave mirror. 60 mm. × 60 mm. $f = 150$ mm.

m_2—Plane mirror. 44 mm. × 48 mm. (mounted on accessory bar).

P_1, P_2—Prisms, refracting angles 30°–35° according to material, aluminised on rear face. Length of hypotenuse 70 mm.–75 mm., height 50 mm.

S_1, S_2, S_3—Straight symmetrical slits 10 mm. × 0 to 1·5 mm.

calibrated with a pair of prisms, these can be removed and replaced in their original positions with sufficient accuracy to render re-calibration unnecessary. It has been reported that, using a Nernst filament source, fluorite prisms and a Hilger-Schwartz thermopile as a detector, lines one or two wave numbers apart in the 6µ water vapour band have been resolved. Besides general-purpose mono-chromators of the kind described above, many specialised instru-ments, complete with source, detectors, amplifying and recording arrangements are available from several manufacturers.

TABLE 13.1—*Refractive Index of Sodium and Lithium Fluorides*

Wave-length (µ)	Na F. n	Li F. n	Wave-length	Na F. n
0·546	1·326	1·393		
0·80	1·323	1·388		
1·02	1·321	1·386		
1·27	1·320	1·385		
1·48	1·319	1·383		
1·67	1·318	1·381	8·90	1·258
1·83	1·318	1·380	9·10	1·255
2·00	1·318	1·378	9·30	1·252
2·20	1·317	1·376	9·50	1·249
2·40	1·316	1·374	9·70	1·245
2·60	1·316	1·372	9·90	1·242
2·80	1·315	1·369	10·10	1·238
3·10	1·313	1·365	10·30	1·235
3·30	1·313	1·362	10·50	1·231
3·50	1·312	1·358	10·70	1·227
3·70	1·310	1·354	10·90	1·223
3·90	1·309	1·351	11·26	1·21
4·10	1·308	1·347	11·74	1·20
4·50	1·305	1·338		
4·70	1·304	1·334		
4·90	1·302	1·328		
5·10	1·301	1·323	Wave-length	Li F. n
5·30	1·299	1·318		
5·50	1·298	1·312	5·78	1·31
5·70	1·296	1·305	6·70	1·26
			6·91	1·26
5·90	1·294		7·13	1·25
6·10	1·292		7·35	1·25
6·30	1·290			
6·50	1·288		7·58	1·24
6·70	1·286		7·81	1·23
			8·05	1·22
6·90	1·284		8·32	1·20
7·10	1·282		8·60	1·19
7·30	1·279			
7·50	1·277		8·88	1·17
7·70	1·275		9·18	1·16
			9·48	1·14
7·90	1·272		9·79	1·11
8·10	1·269		10·12	1·08
8·30	1·266			
8·50	1·264		10·46	1·05
8·68	1·262		10·82	1·02
			11·21	0·99
			11·62	0·95

H. W. HOHLS, *Annalen der Physik*, **29** (1937).

TABLE 13.2—*Refractive Indices, Dispersions and useful Transmission Range* (See Fig. 13.3, p. 236)

Material	n_D	V	C–F	Transmission range (μ)
Ice	1·31			
Sodium fluoride	1·3255	85·2		to 10
Lithium fluoride	1·3921	99·3	0·0037	0·105 to 6
Strontium fluoride	1·43			to 11
Calcium fluoride (fluorite)	1·4339	95·1	0·0044	0·125 to 9
Sodium aluminium sulphate (soda alum)	1·4388	57·8		
Potassium aluminium sulphate (potash alum)	1·4564	58·3		
Fused silica	1·4587	68·5	0·0067	0·19 to 3·5
Ammonium aluminium sulphate (ammonia alum)	1·4594	58·3		
Barium fluoride	1·4744	82	0·0058	0·2 to 13
Potassium chloride	1·4904	44·0	0·0111	0·2 to 21
Sodium chloride ⎰natural	1·5443	42·8	0·0127	⎱0·2 to 15
Sodium chloride ⎱synthetic	1·5498	35·2	0·0156	⎰
Cadmium fluoride	1·55			to 10
Potassium bromide	1·5599	33·4	0·0165	0·2 to 30
Topaz	1·63			
Potassium iodide	1·6674	23·2	0·0284	0·25 to 31
Caesium bromide	1·6971	34·1		to 40
Magnesium aluminium oxide: natural spinel MgO. Al_2O_3	1·715 to 1·723			
synthetic spinels ⎰MgO.3 Al_2O_3	1·7266	66·0		0·2 to 6
synthetic spinels ⎱MgO.5 Al_2O_3	1·729			
Grossularite (garnet)	1·735			
Magnesium oxide (periclase)	1·7373	53·6	0·0138	0·22 to 7
Lead fluoride	1·76			to 11
Silver chloride	2·06c.			to 25
Zinc sulphide (blende or sphalerite)	2·370	29·2		
Diamond	2·4195			
Thallium bromide-iodide (KRS 5)	2·629			0·5 to 40
Bi-refringent				
Potassium dihydrogen phosphate ⎰ord.	1·5095			
(KDP) ⎱ex.	1·4684			
Ammonium dihydrogen phosphate ⎰ord.	1·5242			0·2 to 1·5
(ADP) ⎱ex.	1·4787			
Crystalline quartz ⎰ord.	1·5443	69·7	0·0078	0·18 to 3·5
Crystalline quartz ⎱ex.	1·5534	68·3	0·0081	
Sodium nitrate ⎰ord.	1·5874			
Sodium nitrate ⎱ex.	1·3361			
Calcspar ⎰ord.	1·6584	49·2	0·0107	0·2 to 2
Calcspar ⎱ex.	1·4864	79·7		
Aluminium oxide (corundum) ⎰ord.	1·7686	71·8	0·0104	0·2 to 6
(sapphire) ⎱ex.	1·7604	73·1		
Titanium dioxide (rutile) ⎰ord.	2·6			0·48 to 6
Titanium dioxide (rutile) ⎱ex.	2·9			

TABLE 13.3—*Refractive Index of Ammonium dihydrogen phosphate* (ADP)

λ (A)	n (ord.)	n (ex.)
He 7065	1·51890	1·47489
C 6563	1·52098	1·47633
D 5893	1·52418	1·47870
F 4861	1·53098	1·48408
g 4340	1·53584	1·48810
L 4062	1·53973	1·49142

Table 13.4—*Crystals, Natural and Synthetic*
Refractive Indices at 18° C. for Various Wavelengths

Wavelength A	Calcspar ord.	Calcspar ex.	Fluorite	Quartz ord.	Quartz ex.	Fused Silica	Rock Salt	Sylvine
223000							1·3403	1·3712
94290			1·3161				1·4983	1·4587
42000			1·4078	1·4569			1·5213	1·4720
21720	1·6210	1·4746	1·4230	1·5180	1·5261		1·5262	1·4750
12560	1·6388	1·4782	1·4275	1·5316	1·5402		1·5297	1·4778
6708	1·6537	1·4843	1·4323	1·5415	1·5505	1·4561	1·5400	1·4866
6563	1·6544	1·4846	1·4325	1·5419	1·5509	1·4564	1·5407	1·4872
6438	1·6550	1·4847	1·4327	1·5423	1·5514	1·4568	1·5412	1·4877
5893	1·6584	1·4864	1·4339	1·5443	1·5534	1·4585	1·5443	1·4904
5461	1·6616	1·4879	1·4350	1·5462	1·5553	1·4602	1·5475	1·4931
5086	1·6653	1·4895	1·4362	1·5482	1·5575	1·4619	1·5509	1·4961
4861	1·6678	1·4907	1·4369	1·5497	1·5590	1·4632	1·5534	1·4983
4800	1·6686	1·4911	1·4371	1·5501	1·5594	1·4636	1·5541	1·4990
4047	1·6813	1·4969	1·4415	1·5572	1·5667	1·4697	1·5665	1·5097
3034	1·7196	1·5136	1·4534	1·5770	1·5872	1·4869	1·6085	1·5440
2144	1·8459	1·5600	1·4846	1·6305	1·6427	1·5339	1·7322	1·6618
1852			1·5099	1·6759	1·6901	1·5743	1·8933	1·8270
Temperature coefficient per °C × 10⁵	+ 0·5	+ 1·4	— 1·0	— 0·5	— 0·6	— 0·3	— 4·0	— 4·0

Temperature coefficient per °C $\times$ 10^5

TABLE 13.5—*Refractive Index of Thallium bromide-iodide* (KRS-5) *and Thallium chloride-bromide* (KRS-6)

λ (μ)	KRS-5	KRS-6	λ (μ)	KRS-5	KRS-6
0·6	2·6166	2·3294	7·0	2·3874	2·1870
0·7	2·5434	2·2892	8·0	2·3856	2·1839
0·8	2·5022	2·2660	9·0	2·3837	2·1805
0·9	2·4781	2·2510	10·0	2·3818	2·1767
1·0	2·4611	2·2404	11·0	2·3796	2·1723
1·1	2·4488	2·2321	12·0	2·3774	2·1674
1·2	2·4374	2·2255	13·0	2·3751	2·1620
1·3	2·4311	2·2211	14·0	2·3723	2·1563
1·4	2·4254	2·2176	15·0	2·3694	2·1504
1·5	2·4203	2·2148	16·0	2·3663	2·1442
1·6	2·4163	2·2124	17·0	2·3632	2·1377
1·7	2·4135	2·2103	18·0	2·3596	2·1309
1·8	2·4110	2·2086	19·0	2·3561	2·1236
1·9	2·4089	2·2071	20·0	2·3524	2·1154
2·0	2·4068	2·2059	21·0	2·3486	2·1067
2·2	2·4036	2·2039	22·0	2·3443	2·0976
2·4	2·4010	2·2024	23·0	2·3398	2·0869
2·6	2·3993	2·2016	24·0	2·3349	2·0752
2·8	2·3978	2·2001	25·0	2·3299	
3·0	2·3966	2·1990	26·0	2·3250	
3·5	2·3943	2·1972	27·0	2·3199	
4·0	2·3928	2·1956	28·0	2·3147	
4·5	2·3917	2·1942	29·0	2·3090	
5·0	2·3906	2·1928	30·0	2·3032	
6·0	2·3889	2·1900	31·0	2·2973	
			32·0	2·2914	

Hettner & Leisegang.

TABLE 13.6—*Refractive Index of Arsenic trisulphide glass*

Wave-length (μ)	Refractive index				
	A	B	C	NBS	KRS–5
0·560				2·68689	
0·580				2·65934	
0·589	2·6305	2·6265			2·628
0·600				2·63646	
0·620				2·61708	
0·640				2·60043	
0·653	2·575	2·573			
0·660				2·58594	2·577
0·680				2·57323	
0·700	2·545	2·542		2·56198	
0·800				2·52090	
0·900				2·49515	2·479
1·000	2·445	2·451	2·475	2·47773	2·461
1·200				2·45612	2·439
1·400				2·44357	2·425
1·500	2·413	2·419	2·439		2·420
1·600				2·43556	2·416
1·800				2·43009	2·411
2·000	2·402	2·406	2·427	2·42615	2·406
2·400				2·42086	2·401
2·500	2·396	2·399	2·420		
3·000	2·392	2·395	2·415	2·41608	2·397
3·400				2·41386	
3·500	2·389	2·392	2·412		2·394
4·000	2·387	2·390	2·410	2·41116	2·393
4·500	2·385	2·388	2·398		2·391
5·000				2·40725	2·390
6·000				2·40333	2·389
7·000				2·39899	2·387
8·000				2·39403	2·386
9·000				2·38827	2·384
10·000				2·38155	2·381
11·000				2·37369	2·379
12·000				2·36446	2·377

The types A, B and C refer to three fractions of the distillate into which each batch of raw material is isolated during manufacture. Values supplied by Barr & Stroud, Ltd.

Values under NBS are taken from Rodney, W. S., *et alia*, *J.O.S.A.* **48**, 634 (1958).

Values under KRS–5 are added for comparison only.

TABLE 13.7—*Refractive Index of Silver chloride*
(AgCl) at 23·9 C

λ (μ)	n	λ (μ)	n
1·0	2·02239	11·0	1·97556
1·5	2·01047	11·5	1·97297
2·0	2·00615	12·0	1·97026
2·5	2·00386	12·5	1·96742
3·0	2·00230	13·0	1·96444
3·5	2·00102	13·5	1·96133
4·0	1·99983	14·0	1·95807
4·5	1·99866	14·5	1·95467
5·0	1·99745	15·0	1·95113
5·5	1·99618	15·5	1·94743
6·0	1·99483	16·0	1·94358
6·5	1·99339	16·5	1·93958
7·0	1·99185	17·0	1·93542
7·5	1·99021	17·5	1·93109
8·0	1·99847	18·0	1·92660
8·5	1·98661	18·5	1·92194
9·0	1·98464	19·0	1·91710
9·5	1·98255	19·5	1·91208
10·0	1·98034	20·0	1·90688
10·5	1·97801	20·5	1·90149

Harshaw Chemical Co., after Tilton, L. W. E., *et. alia*, N.B.S., *J.O.S.A.*, **40**, 540 (1950).

TABLE 13.8—*Refractive Index of Caesium bromide* (CsBr)

λ (μ)	n	λ (μ)	n
0·3650	1·7514	5·344	1·6665
0·3663	1·7507	6·415	1·6661
0·4074	1·73360	9·724	1·6630
0·4359	1·72351	11·035	1·6614
0·4861	1·71169	14·29	1·6561
0·5461	1·70208	14·98	1·6549
0·5876	1·69725	15·48	1·6539
0·5893	1·69707	17·40	1·6494
0·6438	1·69221	18·16	1·6481
0·6562	1·69127	20·57	1·6420
0·6678	1·69048	21·79	1·6386
0·7065	1·68805	22·76	1·6360
0·8189	1·6832	23·92	1·6324
1·0139	1·6778	25·16	1·6284
1·1287	1·6760	25·97	1·6253
1·3622	1·6736	26·60	1·6230
1·5295	1·6725	28·33	1·6165
1·7011	1·6717	29·15	1·6131
3·3610	1·6688	29·81	1·6106
4·258	1·6681	30·69	1·6077
		33·11	1·6020
		34·48	1·5960

Rodney, W. S., and Spindler, R. J., *J.O.S.A.*, **42**, 6 (1952).

TABLE 13.9—*Refractive Index of Potassium bromide* (KBr)

λ (μ)	n	λ (μ)	n
0·7682	1·5192	12·965	1·5177
1·1786	1·5114	14·144	1·5146
1·7680	1·5385	15·912	1·5080
2·3573	1·5369	18·100	1·4983
3·5359	1·5350		
4·7146	1·5339		
5·8932	1·5325		
8·2505	1·5290		
10·0184	1·5255		
11·786	1·5209		

TABLE 13.10—*Refractive Index of Silicon and Germanium*

λ (μ)	silicon	germanium	λ (μ)	silicon	germanium
1·05	3·565		2·20	3·451	4·092
1·10	3·553		2·30		4·085
1·20	3·531		2·40	3·447	4·078
1·40	3·499		2·50		4·072
1·60	3·480		2·60	3·443	4·068
1·80	3·466	4·143			
1·85		4·135			
1·90		4·129			
2·00	3·458	4·116			
2·10		4·104			

Briggs, H. B., *Phys. Rev.*, **77**, 287 (1950).

TABLE 13.11—*Refractive Index of Potassium iodide and Barium fluoride*

λ (A)	Potassium iodide (KI)	Barium fluoride BaF_2
C 6563	1.6593	1.4727
D 5893	1.6674	1.4744
F 4861	1.6880	1.4785

TABLE 13.12.—*Refractive Index of Potassium dihydrogen phosphate* (*KDP*)

λ (A)	n (ord.)	n (ex.)
D 5893	1·5095	1·4684

TABLE 13.13—*Refractive Index of Caesium iodide* (CsI)

λ (μ)	n	λ (μ)	n
0·2967	1·98704	30·70	1·7063
1·0139	1·75681	53·12	1·6192
3·4188	1·74353		
11·035	1·7384		
20·57	1·7266		

Harshaw Chemical Co., *after Rodney, W. S.*

TABLE 13.14—*Indices of Refraction of Sapphire*

Wave-length		n (ordinary)			n (extraordinary)	
	(A)	(a)	(b)	(c)	(b)	(c)
He	7065	—	—	1·7629	—	—
H	6563 (C)	1·76487	1·7654	1·7647	1·7573	—
Na	5893 (D)	1·76804	1·7686	1·7680	1·7604	1·760
Hg	5461	—	—	1·7707	—	—
H	4861 (F)	1·77551	1·7760	1·7756	1·7677	—
H	4341 (G)	1·78135	—	—	—	—
Hg	3660	1·79354	—	—	—	—

(a) Measured by American Optical Company.
(b) Dana's System of Mineralogy.
(c) International Critical Tables.

REFERENCES

STOCKBARGER, D. D., *J.O.S.A.*, **27**, 416 (1937), **39**, 731 (1949).
BALLARD, STANLEY S., " Synthetic Optical Crystals," *Proc. Opt. Conv.* (Chapman & Hall), London, 1950.
KEBLER, RICHARD W., "Optical Properties of Synthetic Sapphire," *Proc. Inst. Soc. Amer.*, **9** (2), paper 54–3–5.
KREMERS, H. C., "Optical silver chloride," *J.O.S.A.*, **37**, 337 (1947).
Catalogues, Brochures, and Unpublished Information from:
  Harshaw Chemical Co., 1945 East 97th Street, Cleveland 6, Ohio.
  Barr & Stroud Ltd., Anniesland, Glasgow, W.3., Scotland.
  Taylor, Taylor & Hobson Ltd., Stoughton Street, Leicester, England.
  Hilger & Watts Ltd., 98 St. Pancras Way, Camden Town, London, England.
  Heraeus Quartzschmelze GMBH, Hanau, Germany.
  Optovac Company, 59 Summer Street, North Brookfield, Mass.
  Crystals S. A., Case Mont-Blanc, 281, Geneva, Switzerland, and 414 East 18th Street, New York City, 3.
  Linde Air Products Co., East Park Drive and Woodward Ave., Tonawanda, New York.
  Brush Development Co., 3405 Perkins Avenue, Cleveland 14, Ohio.
  Norton Co., Worcester, Mass., or Niagara Falls, Ontario, Canada.
  The Thermal Syndicate, Wallsend, Northumberland, England.
  General Electric Co., 150 East 42nd St., New York 17, N.Y.
  Hanovia Chemical & Manufacturing Co., Newark 5, New Jersey.
  Salford Electric Instruments, Ltd., Peel Works, Silk Street, Salford, Lancs.
  Eastman Kodak Co. (Military and Special Products Div.), 400 Plymouth Avenue, N., Rochester, 4, N.Y.
  Corning Glass Works, Corning, N.Y.
  Servo Corporation of America, 20–20, Jericho Turnpike, New Hyde Park, Long Island, N.Y.

Chapter 14

THE WORKING OF GLASS

Glass is extremely easy to work and the tools and apparatus required are of the simplest. Its comparatively low softening temperature enables glass to be bent to shape and moulded, blown and drawn, and welded or joined to other pieces of glass and suitable materials of many kinds. At normal temperatures it is easily cut, milled, ground and polished, and it can be coated with films to decrease or increase its reflecting power.

Cutting, sawing and drilling

Sheet and plate glass is usually cut to size or shape by means of a glass cutting diamond or a hardened steel wheel and both these simple tools require some practice before they can be successfully used. The pressure required is very frequently over-estimated and a beginner should practise on waste glass, starting with the very lightest of touches until cutting can be performed with certainty. For thin sheet and plate, up to about 1/16 in. thick, the cutter should not produce any audible sound of scratching and, in fact, the quality of the scratch is felt rather than heard. It becomes quite easy to judge by feel if the diamond or wheel is merely sliding over the surface or actually producing the required fine scratch. The scratch itself is visible only as a very thin line. To complete the cut the glass should be held between the forefinger and thumb and a light pressure should result in a clean fracture following the scratch exactly. If slight pressure does not cause the glass to cut, a few slight, but decided, taps on the under side, opposite the scratch, should produce a crack which can be made to advance over the whole length of the scratch by continued tapping just beyond the end of the crack. It is a mistake to exert excessive pressure in an attempt to produce a cut. Another method of producing the crack along the initial scratch is to touch the scratch with a red-hot wire. This will invariably cause the crack to commence and it can then be made to progress down the scratch by repeated application of the hot wire just beyond the end of the crack. As the thickness of the glass increases the weight of the scratch should also be increased but should never be such as to shatter the surface and produce splinters. For thick glass the cutter may be used with turpentine. The cutter must on no account be applied more than once on the same spot. If, for any reason, it has not been possible to complete the scratch in one continuous movement of the cutter, the cutter should be lifted smartly and the next cut should be made to commence exactly on the end or just beyond the end of the first scratch. In particular, in cutting circles the cutter must be lifted immediately before or exactly at the completion of the circle. Another method of completing a cut after making the scratch is to place the sheet over a lath such as the ruler used to guide the cutter and apply pressure to the glass. If, for any reason, a very small piece has to be removed or the piece to be cut off is very narrow, it will be found convenient to hold the small piece or narrow portion in the jaws of a pair of parallel nosed pliers, using a piece of blotting paper to protect the glass. For thick glass it is possible to start the cut by placing a blunt chisel over the scratch (on the opposite side) and giving a sharp tap with a light hammer.

A glass cutting diamond, and, for that matter a steel wheel cutter, should be regarded as a personal tool and not as a piece of general laboratory equipment. The exact angle at which it is held, which must be found by practice, and the weight required depend largely on the quality of the tool, and its use by someone unaccustomed to its vagaries invariably results in damage to the tool ; in addition many glass cutters use saliva to lubricate the cutter. If glass of many different thicknesses require to be cut, separate diamonds should be used for the thin and thick varieties or, better, the steel wheel used exclusively for the thicker glass. The straight edge used to guide a straight cut should be of sufficient thickness to give ample and sure support to the cutter. A useful tool for cutting photographic plates in the dark and which can be used generally is shown in Fig. 14.1 and consists of a board on which the glass plate is placed and a sliding tee-square carrying the diamond. The tee-square should be made so that its weight alone is sufficient to produce the necessary scratch and the hand should be placed only on the cross of the Tee while making a cut. A tool of this kind very soon repays the trouble taken in its construction even if the amount of cutting to be done is not large. Even when the greatest care is taken in measurement it is seldom possible to ensure perfect parallelism between edges unless this tool is used and in the dark room it is, of course, indispensable.

To cut large circles some form of turntable, on which the glass is supported, is necessary and the diamond should be given the correct pressure either by means of a spring or a small weight. Then on rotating the plate the scratch should not be allowed to go beyond the complete circle. If the circular disc is required and the outer parts are waste, cuts should then be made starting from the scratch and towards the edges of the plate to enable the outer portions to be removed piecemeal. If, on the other hand, a large circular hole in the plate is required and the central disc is waste, a cut should be made across the disc to facilitate its removal.

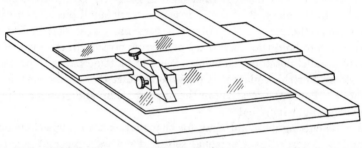

FIG. 14.1.—Glass cutting square. The diamond head is clamped to the T-square which slides along the board on which the glass is laid.

When a large disc of thick material, say for a large lens or mirror, has to be prepared, the material is frequently cut first into a square by means of sawing or slitting, then into an octagon and it may even be roughly rounded by knocking off pieces with a light hard steel hammer fitted to a cane handle. A well-known tool in glass working shops is known as the " Shanks," shaped somewhat like a large pair of nut-crackers but with cutting edges and used to break off unwanted corners. It should be remembered that when a very large number of similar lenses has to be made the glass is usually obtained from the makers in the form of mouldings, fully annealed and requiring the removal of the minimum of material in shaping. Ordinary moulding can also be carried out in a gas furnace. The piece of glass of the required weight is softened in the furnace and patted to shape with iron tools in a manner similar to that used by cooks in handling pastry. The discs must of course be annealed after this treatment by regulated cooling.

In order to drill a hole in glass the most convenient method to adopt is to use a copper, brass or soft iron tube of diameter slightly less than the required hole and a little fine emery lubricated with turpentine. It is best to fit the tube, at its upper end, with a rubber stopper or piece of rubber tubing in which the shank for the drill chuck can be fitted and the cutter should be lifted off the glass occasionally to allow the emery to come into contact with the glass. The hole should not be drilled completely through the glass but the plate should be turned over and the drilling completed from the opposite face.

Holes of any shape can be punched in glass with the Ultrasonic drill manufactured in Britain by Mullard Ltd. This instrument works on the same principle as a pneumatic road drill, but with 20,000 vibrations per second so that it can hardly be heard. The " bits " for the Ultrasonic drill are made of mild steel ; the actual cutting is done by an abrasive slurry acting between the bit and the work. Wear on the bit is slight since the abrasive

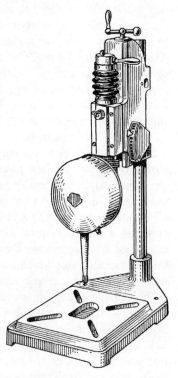

particles tend to become embedded in the surface of the bit. Only very slight pressure is required so that stresses and breakouts are minimised. No special skill is needed and there is no discomfort to the operator. The power consumption is only about 175 watts, from single phase mains, and the machine can cut holes, of any shape, from 0·006 in. to $\frac{3}{4}$ in. diameter. For slitting or cutting, thin blade tools (0·005 in.) may be used; the normal maximum depth of cut or hole is $\frac{1}{2}$ in. The abrasive used is a water slurry of silicon carbide, boron carbide or aluminium oxide. The drill can be used separately or mounted on a special precision drill stand, adjustable in height and fitted with a static load scale and depth scale graduated in 0·02 in. divisions. A slurry pump for the abrasive is also available. Fig. 14.2 is a general view of the drill mounted on the precision stand.

FIG. 14.2. Mullard Ultrasonic drill for making holes of any shape in glass.

The slitting of a glass block to form a saw cut, possibly to act as a diaphragm or stop, can easily be done by using an iron wire stretched in a hack-saw frame moistened with water, turpentine or paraffin and used with emery or carborundum. The method can be used for sawing completely through a glass block or plate but for this purpose it is probably better to use a circular soft iron disc in the periphery of which diamond dust or emery is embedded. This disc can be rotated in a lathe, lubricated with turpentine or paraffin, and the glass block mounted on the tool holder and fed into the disc. Slitting discs can easily be made and charged with diamond or carborundum.

For example, a soft iron disc, say 10 in. in diameter and 1/16 in. thick, may dip into a mud of emery or carborundum consisting of the abrasive in glycerine or syrup with some paraffin or turpentine. As the disc rotates it carries with it enough abrasive to effect the cut. Again the edge of the disc may be smeared with a paste of abrasive, diamond, emery or carborundum, in vaseline and the disc then pressed on a hard iron surface or given sharp taps with a hammer. A useful saw can be made by nicking the edge of the disc at intervals of about $\frac{1}{8}$ in., using a cold chisel, smearing with abrasive paste or setting with diamond chips and tapping with a light hammer to secure the abrasive in the nicks. Some practice is needed in making this slitting disc and it is not worth the trouble unless a considerable amount of slitting is to be done.

Small tubes of glass are very easily cut by making a small scratch with a triangular file or a glassblower's tool (from any laboratory supply house) and snapping by gentle pressure with the thumbs opposite the scratch. Large tubes or bottles should be cut by making a scratch all round the tube, using a piece of paper as a guide, and cracking by applying a heated loop of wire. A useful wire tool can be made by threading resistance wire through a wooden handle so as to form a loop of variable size which can be pulled tightly round the tube, and passing a heavy current from an accumulator to heat the wire.

When cutting large diameter thin glass tubes a very good method is to mark the cutting point with a scratch and then to wrap asbestos tape round the tube on either side of the mark leaving a gap of about half an inch. The asbestos tape is then wetted thoroughly and a fine gas jet played on the tube at the mark and all round by rotating the tube in the jet. The tube will then part easily. The moisture in the tape localises the strain and produces the cut or fracture at the required place.

Although these notes on glass manipulation are given here it is emphasised that accidents are very frequent and it is only by experience and practice that successful handling can be learnt. The beginner should lose no opportunity of practising on scrap pieces to acquire facility before attempting to work on valuable glass.

Glass blowing and working in a softened condition is an art which can only be learnt by practice, but the methods described by Strong— " Modern Physical Laboratory Practice " (Blackie) are recommended to the attention of the reader. In that book instructions will be found for all the usual manipulations, including the sealing of metals in glass. It is quite impossible within the scope of any book to replace actual practice and experience and these notes do not in any way cover all the processes which can be used ; they are intended principally as a guide.

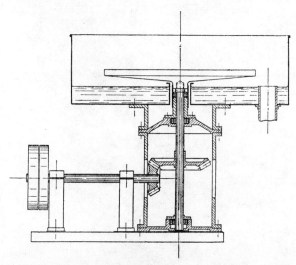

Fig. 14.3.—Roughing machine for flat work. For curved work the flat tool is replaced by one having the required radius.
(*Prism & Lens Making*, Twyman, Hilger, p. 196.)

Abrasives for glass working

A number of abrasives are used in the working of glass and these can be obtained commercially in sufficient purity for immediate use, but it is well to know the methods of purification and selection.

Grinding sands :—For rough grinding to approximate shape and size fine sand or sandstone grit, consisting of fragments of silica, mixed with water are used with the appropriate tools. For flat surfaces a large cast iron disc rotating horizontally and, for concave and convex surface, roughing tools of cast iron of the approximate radius can be used. For roughing large surfaces the work itself can be mounted in a lathe and a cast iron tool in the form of a grating applied to the surface using sand and water as the abrasives. Fig. 14.3 shows a simple roughing machine for flat work and Fig. 14.4 an Adcock and Shipley machine specially designed for roughing lenses using a diamond lap. In machines of this type rough grinding is done

FIG. 14.4.—Adcock and Shipley shaping machine. The diamond lap W has its cutting edge E exactly over the centre of the rotating table T. The lens L has a sphere generated depending on the diameter of the cutting edge and its inclination.

(*Prism & Lens Making*, Twyman, Hilger, p. 201.)

with a diamond tool of 100 grade and for fine grinding 280/320 grade and great accuracy of curvature is possible, thus largely reducing subsequent trueing and smoothing operations. The curve generated is calculated by the formulae

$$\sin A = \frac{d}{R + r} \quad \text{for convex surfaces.}$$

$$= \frac{d}{R - r} \quad \text{for concave surfaces.}$$

where
A = angle of axis of tool to perpendicular
d = $\frac{1}{2}$ diameter of tool
R = required radius of curvature
r = radius of tool edge

Fig. 14.5 shows the derivation of the formulae.

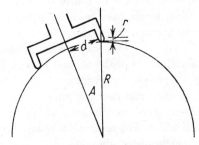

FIG. 14.5.—Derivation of formulae for grinding with diamond laps.

Emeries :—Emeries consist of grains of corundum or alumina with some impurities and are supplied graded as 000, 00 and 0 which are separated by sifting and as 1 minute, 2 minute, etc., up to 60 minutes or even 120 minutes or finer. The minute gradings are based on the elutriation process of separation in which the minutes refer to the time during which a mixture of emery and water is allowed to stand before the upper half of the liquid containing the required abrasive is drawn off. The separation can be carried out in a tall jar containing, say, some 20 pints of water and emery. The mixture is thoroughly stirred or shaken up and is then filled to overflowing to remove floating impurities. It is then allowed to stand for 2 hrs. and the upper half of the column of liquid is then drawn off, preferably by siphoning, into a clean, smooth, earthenware or glass vessel, where it is allowed to stand for several days. This liquid contains the 120 minute emery which, in time, settles and after the water has been poured off, can be dried.

The mixing vessel is again filled up with clean water, thoroughly mixed and allowed to stand for 1 hr. before the upper half, now containing 60 minute emery is siphoned off. The process can be repeated for reduced times until 1 minute emery is finally obtained.

The same process can be used for reclaiming old abrasives but greater care must be taken in the initial separation to get rid of glass chips and portions of the brass tools. By repeated stirring and withdrawal of water the glass chips can be largely removed since they are much lighter than emery, but when this process has been completed the mixture should be allowed to stand for several days and after all the water has been poured off the remaining mud should be scraped to a depth of about half an inch to remove any remaining glass chips. The mud can then be treated with dilute sulphuric or nitric acid to remove metallic chips, neutralised and the process of washing continued. It is obvious that recovery of used emery is not a laboratory process in the ordinary way but may be economically necessary in large factories. Cleanliness is of the utmost importance when dealing with abrasives and it is most important never to allow different kinds of abrasives, such as carborundum and emery, to become mixed. It is far safer to throw away any doubtful abrasive than to risk the inevitable scratches which will occur should large grains be allowed to contaminate a finer grade of abrasive.

Carborundum :—Carborundum or silicon carbide can be used for faster working when there is much material to be removed as in roughing and for charging saws and cutters or for working quartz. It is cheaper than emery and harder and is graded in the same way as emery, but since it is lighter any given grade is coarser than the corresponding grade of emery. Carborundum wheels and blocks sold commercially and used with water can be used for trueing plane or cylindrical glass surfaces in much the same way as with metals. The warning against any possibility of mixing carborundum and emery is repeated.

Pure alumina (corundum) :—Crystalline alumina, reduced to powder and graded by elutriation, can be used in place of emery, and is faster working because of its purity, but it is more expensive.

" Sira " abrasive, developed by the B.S.I.R.A. and manufactured by the United Kingdom Optical Co., Mill Hill, London, is a form of alumina produced from aluminium hydrate by special fusing processes which give a hard regular grain material suitable for smoothing glass prior to polishing. It is made in one grade only.

The Carborundum Company manufacture a brand of synthetic alumina under the trade name " Aloxite."

Diamond powder :—Commercial diamonds, of a quality unsuitable for jewellery, can be purchased by the " carat " and reduced to a dust of the required fineness by smashing in a special mortar made of hardened steel known as Abich's mortar. The use of diamond can only be justified on an industrial scale of manufacture, as its main virtue is its longevity and in the laboratory any of the cheaper abrasives are adequate. Very fine milling cutters and slitting discs can be made of iron set with diamond dust and the use of such cutters may result in a considerable saving of time when used in factories and in this way amply repay their initial cost.

Pumice stone :—Powder made from pumice stone can be ground, washed and graded in a similar manner to emery but may contain impurities which produce scratches so that care is necessary in selection, but the powder is useful for working soft crystals and metals. Powdered whetstone and lazulite can also be used for such purposes as smoothing soft materials where emery would be too harsh. Whetstone is also known as blue-stone, rotten stone or Turkey stone and it, and pumice stone, can be shaped and smoothed in suitable pieces for smoothing metal mirrors or crystals. Lazulite is a compound phosphate of several metals, blue in colour, and is used either in the piece or in powder form where a very mild smoothing agent is required.

Roughing, trueing and smoothing :—The progression from the disc, moulding or slab of glass to the finally shaped component, ready for polishing, is by way of roughing, trueing and smoothing with the abrasives so far described. Roughing can be done in many ways using coarse sandstone grit or carborundum No. 80 or No. 180 and cast iron tools or, for small convex shapes, the work may even be mounted in a lathe and roughed with an ordinary file of medium coarseness. Normally flat, concave or convex tools made of cast iron and of a radius approaching that of the final work are rotated about a vertical axis and the work, either mounted or held in the hand, is applied to the rotating surface with a quantity of carborundum and water. In mass production milling tools can of course be used and may produce the smoothed surface in one operation. During all glass grinding and polishing operations the work is given a cross motion relative to the tool so that all parts of the tool are used equally and the abrasive spread evenly over the surface. Alterations in the length of the cross strokes has an effect on the nature of the surface formed. If the work is kept stationary regular markings would of course result and the tool would be worn away at a zone. In many automatic machines the cross stroke itself produces a rotation of the work, and in hand manipulation the work is turned at the end of each stroke.

Trueing consists in reducing the work to its final shape and thickness and is normally carried out with 10 minute emery and cast iron or brass tools of the correct radius. The tools should be made in pairs, concave and convex or both flat and the counterpart of each pair is used to true the tool from time to time.

Smoothing is the final preparation before polishing and may be done with the finer grades of emery, say 30 minute and finer as the work progresses, and a tool which is definitely softer than the work, so that the grains of abrasive become embedded in the tool. The tool again requires trueing from time to time by application to its counterpart. Actual smoothing really takes place when the abrasive is truly embedded in the tool and some experience is necessary in maintaining the optimum state of pasty-dampness which produces the best surface. Fig. 14.6 shows a number of lenses mounted on a block for grinding or polishing.

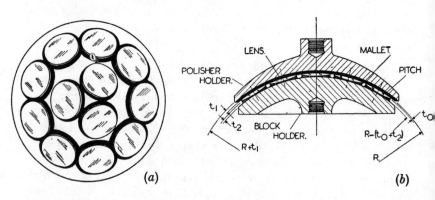

FIG. 14.6.—Plan (*a*) and elevation (*b*) of a lens block with the working tool.
(*Prism & Lens Making*, Twyman, Hilger, p. 209.)

258

Polishing powders

The process of polishing optical parts has been discussed theoretically in several places and it seems to be recognised that while the grinding process consists in actually knocking pieces off the surface by means of abrasive fragments which roll between the work and a hard tool, the polishing process is analogous to planing off the high spots by grains of abrasive embedded in a relatively soft tool. There is some evidence that in the polishing process a certain amount of flow of the glass may take place to give a uniform surface. Thus while grinding, including trueing and smoothing, is carried out mainly with cast iron tools, polishing is done with a tool of pitch or wax or with cloth or paper polishers in which the grains of the polishing powders are easily embedded. The abrasives used are graded and carefully selected by the usual elutriation processes and are used suspended in water and applied to the work by means of a soft brush. Dry polishing is carried out sometimes, particularly for hard materials and, of course, for water-soluble materials.

Rouge. By far the commonest polishing powder is common rouge (iron oxide) prepared by calcining iron sulphate. It is washed and graded as for emeries and should be finally filtered through fine muslin to remove any possible large impurities. It can be used dry or wet but more frequently wet and is biting and rapid in action. In spectacle work it is used with cloth or felt polishers and for precision optical work on pitch or wax polishers. A good quality rouge is supplied by Messrs. Hopkins & Williams Ltd. under the name " Sira."

Cerium oxide. This material is much more biting and rapid in polishing than rouge and is therefore largely used in mass production processes with automatic machinery where great accuracy is less important than speed. Because of its extreme rapidity it is not usual to polish precision work with cerium oxide.

White tripoli is a diatomaceous earth obtainable in lumps which must be broken up and very carefully washed and selected, a small quantity at a time, and tested before use. It is suitable for very hard materials and is usually used dry.

Putty powder or oxide of tin may be used for polishing soft materials such as metals and certain crystals but its use in factories is carefully controlled because of its toxic effects. It is used with soft polishers, cloth, silk or velvet, and the polisher is first prepared on waste material and then used on the work without any addition of fresh putty.

Trueing tools

The material most favoured in optical workshops for the tools used for trueing, smoothing and forming the polishers, is cast iron. A satisfactory type of iron is known as Meehanite which is iron specially treated with calcium silicide to give it a fine graphitic structure and which can be cast well and free from blow holes. Curved tools are turned to the required radius in pairs, one convex and one concave, and the pairs are then ground together until they fit exactly using trueing and then smoothing emery. The rubbing must be continued until the tools touch over nearly the whole surface, a condition which can be appreciated by removing the abrasive and rubbing the tools together fairly vigorously a few times. On examination there should not be any particularly bright patches. The tools are then measured with a spherometer to ascertain if the radius is near enough to that intended. Tools for flat work are made in sets of three which are ground together in pairs, a process which ensures that all three are flat.

Polishers

The polisher holders are similar to the trueing tools, but if deep they should have a radius of curvature greater or less than that of the trueing tools by such an amount that the polisher is of uniform thickness. Polishers are usually of pitch but felt cloth and paper are sometimes used for less precise work and some wax mixtures have certain applications. The best pitch to use is wood pitch (Swedish) filtered when hot through chiffon and then boiled until at the working temperature it can be indented readily but not too deeply by pressure of the thumb-nail. A polisher must be susceptible to a certain amount of flow so that it can be formed by application of the forming tool to give it the right shape. If it flows too easily it will rapidly go out of shape during polishing and require frequent reforming. On the other hand if it is too hard it will not form readily and moreover will be liable to cause scratches. A satisfactory substitute for wood pitch is gas pitch, obtainable from the Tar and Ammonia Products Works of the North Thames Gas Board, Beckton, East Ham, E.6, and softened if necessary by the addition of creosote. It is sometimes considered desirable to add a small quantity of beeswax to the pitch to reduce any tendency to scratch. Wax polishers, consisting of various mixtures of beeswax and black rosin with sometimes a little pitch, are used to some extent and are much less liable to cause scratches, but they are very much slower and the wax does not flow to the same extent as pitch. They have to be formed by scraping until they fit the forming tool which is then rubbed on the wax polisher with rouge until eventually a satisfactory polisher is formed which will last a considerable time.

Making a polisher

The polisher holder should be warmed just so that it is not too hot to touch and should then be stood face upwards resting on its handle as shown in Fig. 14.7. Warmed pitch is then poured on to the holder to form a layer about $\frac{1}{4}$ in. thick. The pitch should flow easily right up to the edge of the tool. The edges should then be trimmed with a knife until the pitch is flush with the edge of the tool and the polisher lifted up, inverted and pressed downwards on a cold forming tool for a few seconds. The tool is then lifted again, slightly warmed over a ring burner and again applied to the cold former, the process being

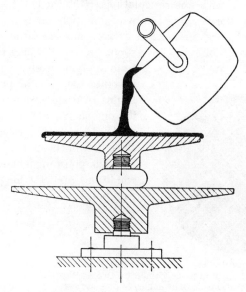

Fig. 14.7.—Making a polisher. Pouring the pitch on the tool.
(*Prism & Lens Making*, Twyman, Hilger, p. 31.)

repeated until the pitch has touched the forming tool all over its surface. A number of grooves about ⅜ in. apart are then cut using a file with a sharp three-cornered point or a special grooving tool can be used if available. This grooving tool is simply a plate having a series of ridges in parallel lines about ⅜ in. apart. The grooves are cut in the pitch in two mutually perpendicular directions so that a number of squares are formed. Figs. 14.8 and 14.9 show the grooving process and the appearance of the polisher. Rouge is now painted over the polisher and a piece of wet gauze or mosquito netting is laid taut over the surface. A forming tool is now heated

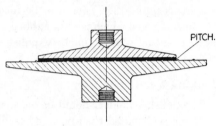

PITCH.

TOOL FOR RETICULATING POLISHER.

Fig. 14.8.—Making a polisher—grooving the surface.
(*Prism & Lens Making*, Twyman, Hilger, p. 32.)

as hot as the hand can bear, painted over with rouge and pressed firmly down on the polisher and left there for about half a minute. It is then lifted off and the gauze pulled off leaving the chequered polisher covered with fine reticulations. Rub the polisher again once or twice with the forming tool while the polisher is cooling. When in use for hand work the polisher surface must be formed again with a slightly warm tool every few " wets," a " wet " being the duration from applying fresh rouge to when it becomes too dry for polishing and begins to drag severely. In polishing one should always carry on the wet until the drag is considerable, since it is in this part of the process that the polishing is most rapid and conditions are best for producing a well polished surface.

Fig. 14.9.—Pattern of grooves formed by two applications of the grooving tool in positions at right angles to one another. The grooves may also be cut with a heated blade or with a triangular file point. The grooves are about ½ in. apart.

Centring and edging

The lens to be edged is stuck on to a tubular holder whose diameter is slightly less than that of the lens by means of a thin coating of pitch. The tubular holder should have its rim bevelled at about 60 deg. inside and outside and a small flat ground truly on the end. This holder is gently heated so that when a piece of pitch is applied to the end it melts and adheres to the tube in a viscous condition. The warmed lens is then applied to the tube and it will adhere, but can be pushed about so as to centre it. The tube is placed in a lathe chuck and when the lathe is run the reflection of a light as seen in the two lens surfaces must remain stationary, the lens being pushed as required until the images are stationary. The lens and tube are then cooled by running cold water and edging can commence. A piece of brass is pressed against the edge and carborundum mud is fed between the lens edge and the brass plate as shown in Fig. 14.10.

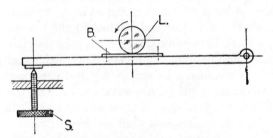

FIG. 14.10.—Lens edging and centring.
(*Prism & Lens Making*, Twyman, Hilger, p. 43.)

For the edging of spectacle lenses and for shaping thin glass plates, removing raw edges, etc., the edging machines used by spectacle makers are very useful. These consist simply of a rotating abrasive wheel, usually of carborundum, over which a stream of water is allowed to flow and the glass is held in the hand and applied to the wheel as required.

Cementing of glass parts

The components of achromatic or other lenses, prisms, etc., are most commonly cemented together with Canada Balsam which is obtainable commercially in a quality and viscosity suitable for immediate use. Other cements have been produced, and are used to some extent, but for general laboratory use Canada Balsam is the most convenient. The balsam as supplied is normally fairly " soft " and it can be hardened by careful heating to drive off volatile matter, taking care to prevent any tendency to burn. It can by suitable cooking be converted into a " medium " or " hard " consistency and the quality of the joint and the method of application and after treatment depend largely on the consistency. The actual method of applying the balsam to the surfaces to be cemented is the same for any hardness but the harder the balsam the higher the temperature to which it must be raised for use, and the subsequent finishing depends also on the hardness.

The surfaces to be joined must, of course, be carefully cleaned and free from dust. The components should be placed on a piece of white paper on top of a thick iron plate heated to a suitable temperature, and the balsam container should also be placed on the hot plate. The surfaces to be joined must then be finally brushed over with a camel hair brush and placed in contact to prevent any further dust from settling. A brass wire is then dipped in the balsam and a drop removed from the container and applied to the lower component, the upper part having been lifted off for this purpose. The upper part is then lowered into position and pressed down with a slight rotation, using a cork to spread the balsam evenly and press out all excess. The actual thickness of the balsam remaining between the surfaces is of the order of 0·00025 in. or so. The cemented parts are then allowed to cool slowly and as they cool they are pressed central with each other so that when quite cold they are in their correct relative positions. Excess balsam can now be wiped off with alcohol, petrol or benzene. The cemented articles are then placed in an oven and baked at a temperature and for a time depending on the hardness of the balsam. For soft balsam the temperature should be about 75° C. and baking should continue for 60 hrs. or more. The resulting joint is hard only at and near the edges, leaving the inner part in a viscous condition and such joints are very suitable for most work. There is no danger of the cement starting or cracking and no strain is imposed on the components. Where strain is to be avoided, therefore, soft balsam should always be used. Medium balsam should be baked at about 60° for a few hours, mainly to remove strain and for hard balsam the annealing temperature is about 40° C. for 2 hrs. Hard balsam produces very rigid joins but there is always a danger of the balsam starting or cracking, particularly if the component is subjected to mechanical shock or extreme changes of temperatures.

When prisms have to be cemented together or to other components a jig should be made up to support the cemented articles in position to prevent any possibility of movement during baking, and when mounted in instruments the method of fixing should be carefully considered to prevent any subsequent change in position.

As already stated other cements are available and have decided advantages where extremes of temperature or exposure to chemical action have to be allowed for. Canada balsam is unsuitable at very low or very high temperatures and under conditions of heavy vibration or shock. Pin markings and balsam " starts " are common faults in lenses subjected to such conditions. Araldite 103 and 101 supplied by Aero Research Ltd., Duxford, Cambridge, and Epikote resins (Epon in U.S.A.) from Shell Chemicals Ltd., Strand, London, are useful available cements with attractive properties. They may be used for hot setting or cold setting (Araldite 103). H. T. Cement (Hopkins & Williams Ltd.) or Ross No. 24 Cement are supplied ready for immediate use, are easy to apply cold and require baking for 16 to 36 hours at 75° C. These cements are not very good for lenses which are immersed in water for long periods and they are soluble in acetone. Cellulose Caprate is a thermoplastic cement and is applied to the parts at a temperature between 120° and 140° C. but no further heating is required to complete curing. It is supplied ready for use (Hopkins & Williams), is stable in storage, withstands chemicals but may break down if immersed in water at 50° C. It is soluble in benzene, toluene and acetone and since it is thermoplastic, parts can be separated by heating to over 120° C.

For temporary purposes components may be fitted together with glycerine or castor oil and in some very large lenses castor oil can be used for permanent joints, provided of course relative movement is prevented by careful design of the supporting members. The castor oil used for such lenses has to be removed and replaced from time to time as it tends to discolour slightly in time.

Cementing of glass to metals

A large number of waxes and cements are available for joining glass parts to metals and if strain is to be avoided the material used should never really harden completely but should permit of flow. A large selection of cements are fully described in *Optical Workshop Principles* by Dévé (Adam Hilger) to which the reader should refer for fuller information.

Optician's wax cement consisting of one part of pure yellow bees-wax worked into six parts of melted rosin is useful for sticking glass parts to any support and can be unstuck by slight heating. Another useful cement for fixing glass to metals consists of a small quantity of beeswax (4 grms.) mixed into rosin (200 grms.) and later incorporating with the mixture a quantity of plaster of paris (15 grms.).

Shellac in stick form, made by softening pure shellac in boiling water and pressing it into a stick, is useful for fixing small parts and when dissolved in alcohol ordinary shellac varnish has many useful applications.

A very useful cement with many uses both for optical work and in the home can be made by mixing finely powdered and washed chalk in a strong solution of water glass (sodium silicate). The powdered chalk can be replaced by a number of coloured materials to match colours, as follows :—

(a) Antimony Sulphide—black—very hard and can be polished.
(b) Powdered cast iron—dark grey.
(c) Powdered zinc—grey—when polished with agate looks like zinc.
(d) Basic copper carbonate—light green.
(e) Chromium oxide—dark green.
(f) Cobalt blue—blue.
(g) Red lead—orange.
(h) Vermilion—brilliant red.
(k) Carmine—violet.
(l) Equal parts of powdered cast iron and powdered zinc, a dark grey as hard as stone on solidification.

(*Optical Workshop Principles*, Dévé, p. 33.)

Many proprietary cements can be used but care must be taken to avoid strain if the cemented parts are to be used in instruments. Durofix and similar cellulose cements, glues of various makes and Bostick cement all have their applications, the last being very useful for sealing purposes as it never really hardens but remains flowing for a considerable time. Recently an adhesive known as " Araldite " (see p. 61) has been placed upon the market which has many useful applications. The cement is applied to heated surfaces and is hardened by baking at a fairly high temperature so that care must be taken to avoid strain at the joint particularly in optical parts.

Johnson Matthey & Co. market an alloy of tin and cerium under the name " *Cerroseal* 35 " which is not expensive and wets glass at a temperature of about 105° C. It may be used for sealing glass to glass, glass to fused silica or glass to (tinned) metal. Surfaces to be joined should be very clean, and the molten metal should be wiped on the glass, etc., with a piece of clean rag in order to wet the surface properly. If the temperature is too high the alloy will not wet the glass surfaces.

The production of graticules

A very large number of methods are available for marking glass with lines, scales or other patterns and the method to be used depends on the nature of the pattern. To describe each method fully here would be impracticable and the reader should consult the references given for fuller particulars.

Dévé in *Optical Workshop Principles* has described purely mechanical and etching methods. Specially selected diamond chips mounted in small steel rods and carefully set at the correct angle by trial and error may be used for writing and figuring or for scales and the ruling of diffraction gratings. They may be used in a dividing engine or an engraving machine and the finest lines are obtainable. Acid engraving using hydrofluoric acid vapour or in solution is more suitable for repeated work and the deep etched markings can be filled with black ink or wax for daylight use or with titanium oxide for night use with edge illumination. For etching processes the glass is covered with a resist in which the lines or marks are cut with a tracelet or fine needle and then exposed to the vapour of hydro-fluoric acid. The technique is not difficult to acquire but some practice is necessary.

A series of three articles in *The Photographic Journal* on the " Production of Graticules " (see refs. at end of chapter) describes in great detail the photo engraving methods which have proved useful. In these processes a master drawing on a greatly enlarged scale may be reduced photographically to produce a master negative of the correct size or a master may be made on a dividing engine using either the diamond or etching processes. The surface on which the pattern is to be engraved is coated with an emulsion of bichromated fish glue (process glue) and exposed in contact with the master negative to a powerful source of light, usually a naked carbon arc. After exposure the plate is washed in running water, when the unexposed portions of the bichromated glue are dissolved, leaving the light hardened portions on the plate. The remaining emulsion may then be blackened by forming a deposit of lead sulphide. One alternative method consists in coating the plate with a bichromated glue solution containing silver salts which after exposure in the usual manner and removal of the unexposed glue in water, are developed by a physical process resulting in the deposition of metallic silver. A third method of photo engraving in which the pattern is etched into the glass with hydrofluoric acid is also described. In this process the required pattern is unexposed while the clear portions are exposed, using the usual bichromated glue technique, with the result that on washing, the pattern only is in clear glass. In practice a resist is first coated on the plate, followed by the bichromated glue and the resist is removed in the pattern, after exposure and washing, using a mixture of grease and benzol. The resulting stencil is then exposed to hydrofluoric acid in glycerine. Other methods involve the use of nickel plating and further complications. In addition to these methods a process for making etched graticules in copper foil has also been perfected and is described in the paper to which reference has been made. The processes of photo engraving have been carried to great perfection by many firms and some of the methods in use are regarded as trade secrets, but sufficient has been said here to show the variety and types of processes that are available. It should not be forgotten that simple patterns can be made by removing silver from ordinary mirrors and that photographic plates of very high resolution are available on which very good graticules can be photographed directly from a master. The National Bureau of Standards Circular No. 565 describes very fully some of the difficulties and methods of graticule production.

Books

The following books may be consulted for further information on the topics mentioned in this chapter, but it should be remarked that the working of glass, and its ramifications, are all arts or techniques acquired by long experience and practice and that different methods are in general use, so that the reader is advised to consult specialists before undertaking any such work. Sufficient indication has been given, however, to enable a research worker to branch out in the development of other techniques of his own and there is room for a considerable amount of new knowledge on all these subjects, leading to improvements in the standard of instrument design.

DÉVÉ (trans. TIPPELL), *Optical Workshop Principles* 3rd Edn. (Adam Hilger, 1957).

TWYMAN, F., *Prism and Lens Making* (Adam Hilger, 2nd Edition, 1952.)

STRONG, J., *Modern Physical Laboratory Practice* (Blackie, 1940).

Dictionary of Applied Physics, Vol. IV. Article on the "Working of Glass" by Sir James French (Macmillan, 1923).

INGALLS (edited), *Amateur Telescope Making, Advanced* (Munn & Co. Inc., 1946.)

REFERENCES

STEVENS, G. W. W., " Some Optical Complications of Graticule Production,'' *Phot. J.*, **87B** (1947), 34.

BULL, A. J., and CARTWRIGHT, H. M., " The Production of Graticules I,'' *Phot. J.*, **87B** (1947), 43.

SMITH, F. H., " The Production of Graticules II,'' *Phot. J.*, **88B** (1948), 18.

COX, R. S., and HALLAM, C. D., " The Production of Graticules III,'' *Phot. J.*, **88B** (1948), 70.

National Bureau of Standards, Circular No. 565.

Chapter 15

LENSES, MIRRORS AND PRISMS

General remarks :—Lenses, mirrors and prisms find applications in many ways in the laboratory apart from their obvious uses as components in optical instruments. Many excellent books are available on the science of light, geometrical optics and optical instruments, both elementary and advanced, and the reader will obviously refer to these standard texts for detailed information. In this chapter we shall refer only to the general applications of lenses, mirrors and prisms to research problems. Some introductory matter has, however, been added to co-ordinate the subject, and various standard topics have been introduced as a pointer to more detailed study.

Thin lenses :—Simple thin lenses similar to spectacle lenses have innumerable uses in a research laboratory and they can be obtained very easily and quickly in the standard size used by the spectacle trade. The normal range of focal lengths available is from 2 in. (20 Dioptres) to 80 in. (0·5 Dioptres) and in the longer focal lengths they are made either plano-spherical or meniscus, while for shorter focal lengths bi-spherical, plano-spherical and meniscus forms are generally obtainable. (See below for the definition of Dioptre.) They are, of course, either positive (convex) or negative (concave) and if required, and at a small extra cost they can be supplied edged down to any required diameter or shape. An optician's trial case of lenses is a useful piece of equipment in any laboratory. The forms of these thin lenses are shown in Fig. 15.1 and the dotted lines in each diagram represent approximately the positions of the principal planes, for a full explanation of which the reader should consult a text book on optics. It may be mentioned here that the principal planes have little significance in thin lenses but are essential to the theory of thick lenses and combinations of lenses, and very briefly they are the planes from which object and image distances and focal lengths must be measured when using the ordinary lens formulae.

The stock lenses made for the spectacle trade in meniscus form are usually ground with one standard surface of $6D$ (i.e., about $3\frac{1}{2}$ in. (89 mm.) radius), the other surface being varied to obtain the required total power. When a cylindrical surface is required it is also

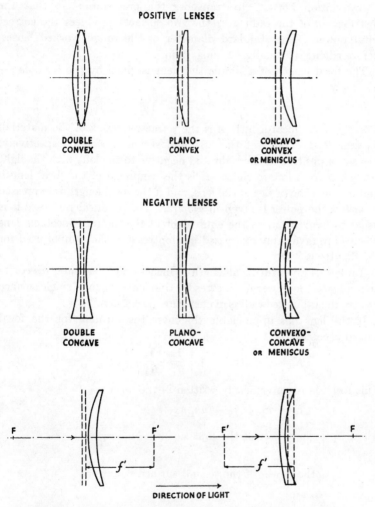

FIG. 15.1.—Forms of simple lenses. The dotted lines in each diagram are the principal planes.

worked on the second surface producing the so-called " toric " lens. The specification of a spectacle lens as supplied by an optician is based on a plano-spherical or plano-cylindrical form, the focal length being measured from the vertex of the sphere or cylinder. If the optician specifies a " toric " or meniscus type he leaves it to the " prescription house " to transpose the prescription so that the distribution of the radii over the two surfaces produces the correct total power. The standard diameter of the rough worked lenses. before edging, is usually 50 mms. (2 in.).

The focal length of a simple thin lens is given by the formula :—

$$K = \frac{1}{f} = (n - 1) \left\{ \frac{1}{R_1} - \frac{1}{R_2} \right\}$$

where f is the focal length, n is the refractive index of the material, R_1 and R_2 the radii of the first and second surfaces respectively, measured positive to the right and negative to the left, with the light travelling from left to right. K is the reciprocal of the focal length and is called the power of the lens, and if the focal length is expressed in *metres* the power is given in *dioptres*. For practical purposes it is usual to take 40 in. as the equivalent of the metre. Spectacle lens powers are invariably expressed in dioptres and the symbol used for the dioptre is " D."

Table 15.1 gives the focal length in inches and in centimetres corresponding to the power in dioptres for thin lenses or for a single surface having the tabulated radius of curvature ($n = 1 \cdot 52$).

If the lens has appreciable thickness the formula for the focal length becomes :—

$$K = \frac{1}{f} = (n - 1) \left\{ \frac{1}{R_1} - \frac{1}{R_2} + \frac{t}{n} \cdot \frac{(n - 1)}{R_1 R_2} \right\}$$

This formula is conveniently written in the form :—

$$K = k_1 + k_2 - a k_1 k_2$$

where k_1 is the power of the first surface $= \dfrac{(n - 1)}{R_1}$

k_2 is the power of the second surface $= \dfrac{1 - n}{R_2}$

and $$a = t/n$$

The use of these symbols simplifies the formulae for the positions of the principal planes which are as follows :—

The distance from the vertex of the first surface to the first principal

TABLE 15.1—*Powers in Dioptres, Focal length in inches and centimetres and radius of curvature of surface for n = 1·52*

Power D	Focal Length in.	Focal Length cm.	Radius in.	Power D	Focal Length in.	Focal Length cm.	Radius in.
0·125	320	800	166·4	5·5	7·3	18	3·78
0·25	160	400	83·2	6	6·7	16	3·47
0·375	107	267	55·5	6·5	6·1	15	3·20
0·5	80	200	41·60	7	5·7	14	2·97
0·75	53	133	27·7	7·5	5·3	13	2·78
1	40	100	20·80	8	5	12·5	2·60
1·25	32	80	16·64	9	4·5	11	2·32
1·5	27	67	13·2	10	4	10	2·08
1·75	23	57	11·9	11	3·7	9	1·898
2	20	50	10·40	12	3·3	8·3	1·740
2·25	18	44	9·25	13	3·1	7·7	1·600
2·5	16	40	8·32	14	2·8	7·1	1·486
2·75	14·5	36	7·58	15	2·7	6·7	1·386
3	13·3	33	6·95	16	2·5	6·3	1·300
3·25	12·3	31	6·40	17	2·4	5·9	1·222
3·5	11·4	29	5·92	18	2·2	5·6	1·160
3·75	10·7	27	5·55	19	2·1	5·3	1·098
4	10	25	5·20	20	2	5	1·04
4·5	9	22	4·62	30	1·3	3·3	0·696
5	8	20	4·16	40	1	2·5	0·52

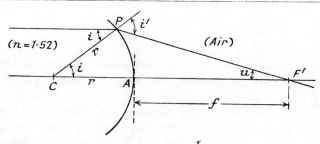

$D = 40/f$ (in.)

$\quad = 100/f$ (cm.)

Derivation of tabulated values.

$f = \dfrac{r}{n-1}$

$r = (n-1)f$

$\quad = \dfrac{40\,(n-1)}{D} = \dfrac{20\cdot8}{D}$ (in.)

$\quad = \dfrac{100\,(n-1)}{D} = \dfrac{52}{D}$ (cm.)

point or plane is given by $+ ak_2/K$ and the distance from the second vertex to the second principal plane (measured positive to the right) is $- ak_1/K$.

It must be noted that these formulae all refer to very narrow pencils of light confined to the paraxial region, i.e., the region *very* near the axis of the lens. When light rays are traced through lenses at a finite distance from the axis or making large angles with the axis the calculations must be made using the standard trigonometric ray tracing formulae, which will be found in text books on applied

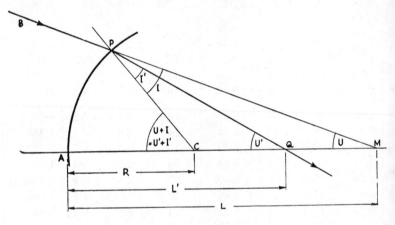

FIG. 15.2.—The standard diagram for the trigonometrical computation of a ray of light through a spherical refracting surface. The formulae used are :—

$$\text{(i)} \frac{L - R}{\sin I} = \frac{R}{\sin U} \qquad \text{(ii)} \; n \sin I = n' \sin I'$$

$$\text{(iii)} \; U' + I' = U + I \qquad \text{(iv)} \frac{L' - R}{\sin I'} = \frac{R}{\sin U'}$$

optics, but which for reference purposes are shown in Fig. 15.2 which is the standard diagram. Schedules for ray-tracing are given in an appendix.

It is superfluous to mention here the uses to which thin spectacle lenses can be put but they are extremely useful for setting up mock-up instruments before actual design work is undertaken, and it may be worth mentioning that for this purpose the simplest optical bench can consist of a piece of angle section metal supported in Vee blocks so that the lenses can rest in the trough supported by plasticine or wax. For more advanced prototypes, provided all the lenses are of the same standard diameter it is useful to mount them in a tube with separators cut from a smaller diameter tube sliding in the main tube.

From the formula for the power, or focal length, of a thick lens it will be seen that the focal length of a double convex lens increases with increasing thickness until it becomes infinite when

$$t = n \ (R_1 - R_2)/(n - 1)$$

The lens then acts like a telescope and any further increase in thickness results in a negative focal length. When one surface is plane the thickness has no effect on the focal length. In a double concave lens increasing thickness decreases the focal length.

The standard formula, given in textbooks, for the object and image distances for lenses is

$$1/v - 1/u = 1/f$$

where u is the distance from the object to the first principal point, v the distance from the second principal point to the image and f is the focal length of the lens, positive for convex lenses and negative for concave. The magnification, or size of image divided by the size of the object, is given numerically by the relation $m = v/u$. In straightforward applications of this formula to positive lenses with real images the sign convention may be ignored and the formula becomes

$$1/u + 1/v = 1/f.$$

A useful formula, derived from the above, and most convenient in use since it avoids the reciprocal quantities is the well-known Newton's formula

$$x \ x' = - f^{\,2}$$

where x is the distance from the first focal point to the object, x' the distance from the second focal point to the image, and f the focal length. Again the sign convention can be ignored for simple cases as in cameras, where x can be taken as the distance of the object and x' is then the camera extension or distance the lens must be racked out to obtain correct focus. The magnification, using Newton's formula, is simply given numerically by $m = f/x = x'/f$. Fig. 15.3 shows the various distances involved in the above formulae, all of which, of course, may be used with thin or thick lenses or combinations of

275

TABLE 15.2—*Object and Image Distances with a Lens of Unit Focal Length*

Magnifi-cation	Object Distance	Image Distance	Magnifi-cation	Object Distance	Image Distance
1·0	2·000	2·0	5·0	1·200	6·0
1·1	1·91	2·1	5·2	1·193	6·2
1·2	1·83	2·2	5·4	1·186	6·4
1·3	1·77	2·3	5·6	1·180	6·6
1·4	1·715	2·4	5·8	1·173	6·8
1·5	1·667	2·5	6·0	1·167	7·0
1·6	1·63	2·6	6·2	1·162	7·2
1·7	1·59	2·7	6·4	1·156	7·4
1·8	1·555	2·8	6·6	1·152	7·6
1·9	1·53	2·9	6·8	1·147	7·8
2·0	1·500	3·0	7·0	1·143	8·0
2·1	1·48	3·1	7·5	1·134	8·5
2·2	1·455	3·2	8·0	1·125	9·0
2·3	1·435	3·3	8·5	1·118	9·5
2·4	1·415	3·4	9·0	1·111	10·0
2·5	1·400	3·5	9·5	1·105	10·5
2·6	1·386	3·6	10·0	1·100	11·0
2·7	1·373	3·7	10·5	1·095	11·5
2·8	1·360	3·8	11·0	1·091	12·0
2·9	1·346	3·9	11·5	1·087	12·5
3·0	1·333	4·0	12·0	1·083	13·0
3·1	1·323	4·1	13·0	1·077	14·0
3·2	1·315	4·2	14·0	1·071	15·0
3·3	1·306	4·3	15·0	1·067	16·0
3·4	1·298	4·4	16·0	1·063	17·0
3·5	1·290	4·5	17·0	1·059	18·0
3·6	1·282	4·6	18·0	1·055	19·0
3·7	1·274	4·7	19·0	1·052	20·0
3·8	1·266	4·8	20·0	1·050	21·0
3·9	1·258	4·9	25·0	1·040	26·0
4·0	1·250	5·0	30·0	1·033	31·0
4·1	1·242	5·1	35·0	1·029	36·0
4·2	1·237	5·2	40·0	1·025	41·0
4·3	1·232	5·3	45·0	1·022	46·0
4·4	1·227	5·4	50·0	1·020	51·0
4·5	1·222	5·5	60·0	1·017	61·0
4·6	1·217	5·6	70·0	1·014	71·0
4·7	1·213	5·7	80·0	1·013	81·0
4·8	1·209	5·8	90·0	1·011	91·0
4·9	1·204	5·9	100·0	1·010	101·0
Minifi-cation	Image Distance	Object Distance	Minifi-cation	Image Distance	Object Distance

NOTES: $xx' = f^2$; $m = x'/f = f/x$

$x' = mf$; $x = f/m$

Object distance $= u = x + f = \dfrac{f}{m} + f = \dfrac{m+1}{m} f$

Image distance $= v = f + x' = f + mf = (m+1)f$

276

lenses, but are restricted to the paraxial conditions. It is worth noting, however, that since a camera lens is an attempt to produce a perfect image-forming instrument the above formulae can be used. Table 15.2 which gives object and image distances for a lens of unit focal length for various magnifications will be found useful.

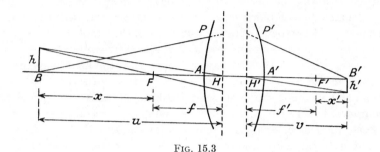

FIG. 15.3

3. Combinations of lenses. Two or more thin lenses can be used either touching or separated to construct compound lenses and instruments and, again for reference, the following formulae give the combined equivalent focal length and the positions of the principal planes.

For lenses in contact $\dfrac{1}{F} = \dfrac{1}{f_1} + \dfrac{1}{f_2} + \ldots$

or $\qquad K = k_1 + k_2 + \ldots$

where F is the combined equivalent focal length and f_1, f_2, etc., are the focal lengths of the component lenses, or K is the power of the combination of individual lenses of powers k_1, k_2, etc. If the lenses are separated by a distance a (in air) then :—

$$K = \frac{1}{F} = \frac{1}{f_1} + \frac{1}{f_2} - \frac{a}{f_1 f_2} = \frac{f_1 + f_2 - a}{f_1 f_2} = \frac{g}{f_1 f_2}$$

or $\qquad K = k_1 + k_2 - a\,k_1\,k_2 = g\,k_1\,k_2$

where $\qquad g = f_1 + f_2 - a = \dfrac{1}{k_1} + \dfrac{1}{k_2} - a = \dfrac{k_1 + k_2 - a\,k_1\,k_2}{k_1\,k_2}$

$$= \frac{K}{k_1\,k_2}$$

and the positions of the principal points are given, as before by

$$+ ak_2/K \quad \text{and} \quad - ak_1/K$$

$$\text{or} \qquad + \frac{a}{gk_1} \quad \text{and} \quad - \frac{a}{gk_2}$$

It is not always necessary, in designing optical systems, to know or to calculate the combined focal length of the system. Each lens or surface can be treated separately using any of the simple formulae to calculate the object and image positions and their sizes. Proceeding in this way through each surface or lens in turn the final image distance and size is calculated. In the early stages of serious optical design and for many simple systems graphical methods give adequate accuracy. In all such graphical work distances perpendicular to the optical axis can be exaggerated to any extent and the rays drawn according to the simple paraxial laws. At a later stage in the design the actual sizes of lenses, object, image, stops etc. must be drawn correctly to scale and " ray " and " beam " diagrams drawn. A ray should be drawn from the extreme edge of the object, through the various foci of the system, to the corresponding edge of the image. Rays should also be drawn, both from the axial point of the object, and from an extreme edge, defining the beams of light and showing how they are limited by the diaphragms, lenses or other components.

Before passing on from this short theoretical diversion it would be well to mention that a theoretically perfect image forming system, such as is assumed by the elementary paraxial discussion, cannot be realised in practice. The theoretically perfect image forming system can be defined as such that for every point, line or plane in the object space there is one and only one conjugate or corresponding point, line or plane in the image space, and the image formed on any plane perpendicular to the axis of the system must be geometrically similar to the corresponding object situated in the conjugate plane also perpendicular to the axis. This one-to-one correspondence is the basis of a number of theorems in projective geometry and the elementary optical formulae connecting object and image distances are a direct consequence of these theorems. As soon as systems of finite size are considered the laws of image formation show that no optical system can be a *perfect* image forming system.

Since light is propagated as a wave motion a point object cannot form a point image because of diffraction effects caused by the aperture through which the light has to pass, and the image is in the form of a disc surrounded by a pattern of bands of light and darkness depending on the shape and size of the aperture. For a circular aperture the disc is circular and is surrounded by dark and light rings. Airy in 1834 showed that for the image of a distant star formed in the focus of a good telescope $\rho = \dfrac{0\cdot61\lambda}{\sin U}$

where ρ is the radius of the first dark ring surrounding the Airy disc

λ is the wave-length of the image-forming light

U is the angular semi-aperture of the convergent cone from the boundary of the circular diaphragm to the centre of the image.

If D is the diameter of a telescope objective and f is its focal length then, very nearly, $D/2f = \sin u$ and the resolving power of a telescope objective is given by

$$\rho = \frac{1\cdot22\,\lambda f}{D}$$

For photographic lenses it is usual to replace f/D by A, the aperture or f-number of the lens, and the theoretical maximum resolving power becomes

$$\rho = 1\cdot22\,\lambda\,A.$$

The angular resolution is given by $\dfrac{\rho}{f}$ and its reciprocal $\dfrac{f}{\rho}$ is often used as a measure of the resolving power. Another useful formula, known as Dawe's Rule, for the resolving power of a telescope in seconds of arc is:

Angular resolving power in seconds = 5/diameter of lens in inches.

For a slit-shaped aperture the image is a bright line flanked by dark and light bands and the distance from the centre of the line to the first dark band is given by

$$\rho = \frac{0\cdot50\lambda}{\sin U}$$

As a result of this law it is assumed that two close stars will form separate images, i.e., they will be resolved, provided the images are further apart than this minimum distance ρ given by the above formula.

The distribution of light in the neighbourhood of the image is complicated by diffraction and interference effects and the assumption that the distribution can be described in terms of ray concentrations according to the rules of geometrical optics is not justified. The

279

distribution must, in fact, be calculated in terms of the path differences of the light measured in wave-lengths, and the image itself is a diffraction pattern. The formulae giving the distribution of intensity in the image are complicated and difficult to evaluate and are beyond the scope of this book.

Since optical instruments are designed by combining reflections and refractions at surfaces which are usually spherical, it soon becomes obvious, using purely geometrical rays, that as soon as finite sizes of mirrors and lenses are considered the rays do not concentrate at the points corresponding to the paraxial calculations. This wandering away of the light from the geometrical image point is called *aberration*, and for convenience several types of aberration are considered separately, but it must be remembered that in any real instrument the defects of the image are caused simply by aberration and that the divisions are purely arbitrary. Considering monochromatic light only there are five standard aberrations which can be recognised and calculated by relatively simple means.

Spherical aberration is the failure of all the light from a point object, passing axially through the system, to form a single image. In a simple converging lens the marginal rays form an image closer to the lens than the paraxial rays and the lens is said to be undercorrected or to possess positive spherical aberration measured by the distance from the marginal to the paraxial image point.

The amount of the spherical aberration of a lens depends largely on its shape, i.e., the distribution of the total curvature over the two surfaces. The mathematical process of changing the shape of a lens by altering the individual curvatures of the two surfaces while retaining the same total curvature is called " bending " the lens. In a single thin lens, consisting of one kind of glass only, it will be found that no matter how the lens is bent the spherical aberration cannot be eliminated entirely but there is a " best shape " for which the aberration is a minimum. The spherical aberration varies approximately as the square of the incident height of the ray and depends also on the distance of the object.

By combining two or more lenses, usually a positive and negative of two different types of glass, and bending the compound lens suitably it is possible to reduce the spherical aberration to zero for at least one zone of the lens and for two positions of the object. The choice of suitable glasses is very wide and is influenced by other considerations. By a suitable choice of glasses, for example, it is possible to correct the lens so as to reduce spherical aberration, coma and chromatic aberration to manageable values and at the same time to cement the two lenses together.

Coma is the name given to the defect which causes oblique images of point objects to be spread over a comet shaped blur. Coma is one of the most troublesome aberrations as its presence completely destroys definition in the image. In terms of geometrical optics it is shown that coma will be present if the focal length for marginal rays differs from the focal length for paraxial rays, i.e., the magnification of a small object does not remain constant for marginal and paraxial pencils.

In any optical system, if we confine ourselves to paraxial rays, it can be shown that the product :—

$$n \, y \, u$$

must remain constant at every refraction for a given ray throughout the system, i.e., it is an invariant. n is the refractive index of the medium in which an image of height y is formed and u is the angle at the axial image point between the axis and a paraxial ray. For a single refraction at any angle it can easily be shown that the product :—

$$n \, y \sin u$$

remains constant for that refraction, but this product is no longer an invariant for every refraction of the same ray throughout the system. It can be shown, however, that if there is no spherical aberration and the product $n \, y \sin u$ for the object space is equal to the product $n' \, y' \sin u'$ for the *final* image space for rays passing through any zone of the system then it will be free from the aberration called coma.

The condition for absence of coma states that the magnification of a small object shall be constant for all zones of the lens, i.e., y'/y must be constant for all zones. Hence we may state the *sine condition* for freedom from coma in the form.

$\dfrac{n \sin u}{n' \sin u'}$ = constant for all values of u. If the initial and final media are both air then $n/n' = 1$ and $\dfrac{\sin u}{\sin u'}$ = constant for all values of u.

If the object is at a great distance $\sin u$ will be proportional to h, the incident height, and the sine condition becomes $\dfrac{h}{\sin u'}$ = a constant (= focal length for incident height h).

It is usual in optical computation to calculate the quantity $h/\sin u'$ at the same time as the spherical aberration and the results are sometimes plotted in the same diagram. The difference between the amount of the spherical aberration and the quantity $h/\sin u'$ for the same ray is usually taken as a measure of the coma.

When an optical system is corrected for both spherical aberration and coma it is said to be *aplanatic*.

Table 15.3 taken with alterations from Hardy & Perrin's " Principles of Optics " (McGraw Hill) shows how the positions of the principal points, back focal distance, spherical aberration, departure from the sine condition, and coma vary as a simple thin lens is bent and Fig. 15.4 which is plotted from this table, shows graphically the spherical aberration, departure from the sine condition and coma.

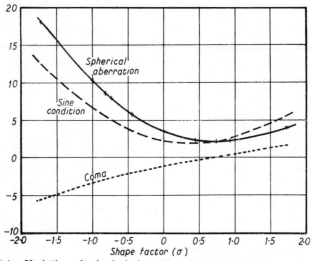

FIG. 15.4.—Variation of spherical aberration, departure from the sine condition and coma with the shape factor (σ) of a lens. Values from Table 15·3.

Astigmatism is the failure of light from a point source to form a single point (stigmatic) image. In general two images are formed as two mutually perpendicular lines separated by a finite distance known as the astigmatic difference. The best possible circular image situated between the two astigmatic lines is called the circle of least confusion.

The two images formed by a system having astigmatism are called the *tangential* and *sagittal* images respectively. The tangential images

282

TABLE 15.3—Effect of the Shape of a Simple Lens on the Spherical Aberration and Coma

Type of lens	Radii		Shape factor σ	Positions of principal points		Back focus V_2F'	Spherical aberration			Sine condition			Coma
	R_1	R_2		V_1H	$H'V_2$		10·0	12·5	15·0	10·0	12·5	15·0	15·0
Concavo-convex	− 150·0	− 40·23	− 1·73	17·0	− 4·4	104·4	7·7	12·4	18·1	5·5	8·8	12·7	− 5·4
Plano-convex	∞	− 51·77	− 1·00	13·2	0·0	100·0	4·4	6·9	10·1	2·9	4·6	6·6	− 3·5
Bi-convex	599·4	− 56·02	− 0·83	12·2	1·1	98·9	3·7	5·8	8·5	2·4	3·8	5·5	− 3·0
Bi-convex	425·2	− 58·00	− 0·74	11·8	1·6	98·4	3·5	5·4	7·9	2·2	3·5	5·1	− 2·8
Bi-convex	187·1	− 68·97	− 0·46	9·8	3·6	96·4	2·5	3·8	5·8	1·5	2·3	3·5	− 2·3
Equiconvex	100·0	− 100·0	0	6·8	6·8	93·2	1·5	2·4	3·4	0·9	1·5	2·1	− 1·3
Bi-convex	68·97	− 187·1	0·46	3·6	9·8	90·2	1·0	1·6	2·3	0·8	1·3	1·8	− 0·5
Bi-convex	58·00	− 425·2	0·74	1·6	11·8	88·2	1·0	1·5	2·2	1·0	1·5	2·2	0
Bi-convex	56·02	− 599·4	0·83	1·1	12·2	87·8	1·0	1·6	2·3	1·1	1·6	2·4	+ 0·1
Convexo-plane	51·77	∞	1·00	0·0	13·2	96·8	1·1	1·7	2·3	1·2	1·9	2·8	+ 0·5
Convexo-concave	40·23	150·0	1·73	− 4·4	17·0	83·0	1·7	2·8	4·0	2·5	3·9	5·6	+ 1·6

NOTES.— (i) Each lens has an index of refraction of 1·5177, thickness 20·00 mm. and a focal length of 100·00 mm. All values in mm.

(ii) The shape factor $\sigma = \dfrac{R_2 + R_1}{R_2 - R_1} = -1 + \dfrac{2(n-1)}{KR_1} = +1 + \dfrac{2(n-1)}{KR_2}$; $K = \dfrac{1}{f} = (n-1)\left(\dfrac{1}{R_1} - \dfrac{1}{R_2}\right)$

(iii) The position factor $\pi = \dfrac{l' + l}{l' - l} = -1 - \dfrac{2}{lK} = +1 + \dfrac{2}{l'K}$

(iv) The spherical aberration may be calculated by means of the formula :—

$$\Delta\left(\dfrac{1}{l'}\right) = \dfrac{h^2 K^3}{8}\left\{\dfrac{n+2}{n(n-1)^2}\sigma^2 + \dfrac{4(n+1)}{n(n-1)}\sigma\pi + \dfrac{3n+2}{n}\pi^2 + \dfrac{n^2}{(n-1)^2}\right\}$$

(In the above table it has been obtained by ray-tracing.)

(v) The sine condition has been obtained from ray-tracing and the coma = sine condition − spherical aberration.

(vi) H, H^1 are the principal points and V_1 and V_2 are the vertices of the lens surfaces.

are formed by rays in the meridian or tangential plane, i.e., the plane containing the axis and the incident and refracted rays (the plane of the paper in an ordinary diagram). The tangential images lie on the tangential surface. The sagittal images are formed by rays which are initially in a plane perpendicular to the tangential plane. It is usual to consider a sagittal pair of rays incident on the surface at equal distances on either side of the meridian and the sagittal images lie on the sagittal surface. The standard formulae giving the positions of the sagittal foci, s and s', and the tangential foci, t and t', along the ray, are :—

$$\frac{n'}{s'} - \frac{n}{s} = \frac{n'\cos I' - n\cos I}{r} = \frac{n'\cos^2 I'}{t'} - \frac{n\cos^2 I}{t}$$

the symbols having their usual meanings, i.e., undashed letters before and dashed letters after refraction at the surface of radius r separating media of refractive index n and n'. I and I' are the angles of incidence and refraction respectively.

Curvature is, as its name implies, the defect which causes the image of a distant plane surface to be formed on a curved surface even if there is no astigmation. In the language of geometrical optics the curved image surface is not the surface containing the circles of least confusion but the surface on which the image would be formed if there were no astigmatism present. This surface is known as the *Petzval* surface, its curvature is called the Petzval curvature and its value depends only on the radii and refractive indices of the surfaces. The Petzval sum, P, which gives the curvature of the image surface, for a series of surfaces of radii r_1, r_2, etc., separating media of refractive index n_1, n_2, etc., is given by the formula :—

$$P = \Sigma \ (n' - n)/nn' \ r$$

where the sum is taken over all the surfaces. For a thin lens, then the curvature is given by :—

$$P = (n - 1)/nr_1 + (1 - n)/nr_2 = \frac{n - 1}{n} \left(\frac{1}{r_1} - \frac{1}{r_2} \right)$$
$$= 1/fn = K/n$$

where $K = 1/f = $ the power of the lens, and for a series of thin lenses :—

$$P = K_1/n_1 + K_2/n_2 + K_3/n_3 + \text{etc.}$$

It is thus a very persistent defect in any optical system and the quality of images formed can only be improved by altering the astigmatism of the system. The astigmatic surfaces, i.e., the two surfaces on which the astigmatic images lie, are intimately related to the Petzval surface as shown in Fig. 15.5.

If there is no astigmatism the surfaces all coincide and as the amount of astigmatism, i.e., separation of the surfaces, increases in either direction, so the distances of the astigmatic surfaces from the Petzval surface increases. The quality of the final image can be controlled by arranging the astigmatic surfaces in the most suitable manner.

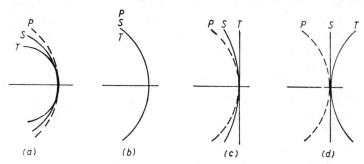

Fig. 15.5.—Relation between Petzval surface *P* and the tangential (*T*) and sagittal (*S*) surfaces.
(*a*) Under-corrected astigmatism.
(*b*) No astigmatism, the field is still curved.
(*c*) Over-corrected astigmatism with a flat tangential field, a very common form of correction.
(*d*) Over-corrected astigmatism with a flat sagittal field.
The surfaces in actual instruments are seldom simple arcs as shown but assume various shapes, depending on glass types, etc.

Distortion is a defect which causes the image of any object to become distorted from its true geometrical shape. The distortion is known as pincushion or barrel according to the appearance of the image and the defect depends in a complicated manner on all the other aberrations. No matter how narrow the pencil of rays forming the image may be made the distortion, if present, is manifest and it can usually only be changed by an axial movement of the stop or diaphragm which limits the pencil. This movement of the stop, of course, affects all the other aberrations as well (except spherical aberration) so that it becomes obvious that the question of distortion must be investigated along with all the other oblique aberrations.

The above five standard aberrations are often called the Seidel aberrations but this name really refers to the five formulae by means of which the performance of an optical system can be calculated in the early stages of design.

The five Seidel formulae are in the form of summations which must be made for all the surfaces of a centred optical system and theoretically all that is necessary in designing an optical system is to reduce each sum consecutively to zero. In practice this cannot be done because few optical systems contain a sufficient number of variables to allow the equations all to become zero simultaneously. The form of the equations is such that each is meaningless unless those preceding it have been satisfied, nor can they be solved explicitly in terms of the radii and of the surfaces. Lens designers usually trace a number of rays through the system, algebraically or trigonometrically, and estimate the performance of the instrument from the distribution of these rays. For most purposes the preliminary work is carried out in paraxial formulae and then the longitudinal spherical aberration and offence against the sine condition are found by tracing a few rays, and at the same time the chromatic aberration is corrected. Upper and lower marginal rays and a " chief " ray, i.e., one passing through the axial point of the diaphragm in an oblique direction, are then traced and enable the designer to decide the alterations required to produce the desired result.

Chromatic aberration. When we consider light of different wavelengths the above aberrations will all be found to change with the colour of the light, but if a system is so constructed that the position and size of the image for two or three given colours is the same then the best possible compromise has been found. The variation in the position of the image for light of different colours is called *longitudinal chromatic aberration* and variation in size is called lateral or *transverse chromatic aberration* or chromatic difference of magnification. The residual chromatic aberration of a system which is corrected for colour is known as *secondary spectrum* and it is obvious that this should be reduced as far as possible. The amount of the secondary spectrum depends largely on the type of glass used in the construction of the instrument.

The correction of an optical system for chromatic aberration is most frequently obtained by combining a positive lens of low dispersion glass with a negative lens of high dispersion glass to form a cemented doublet. Chromatic correction can also be obtained by using a separated pair of lenses as, for example, in the well-known Huygens and Ramsden eyepieces. When the lenses are very thick or greatly separated care must be taken that transverse chromatic aberration is not introduced causing images in the different colours to be of different sizes.

The basic formulae for the construction of an achromatic doublet consisting of two thin lenses in contact are :—

$$K = k_1 + k_2 \text{ (Power)}$$
$$k_1/V_1 + k_2/V_2 = 0 \text{ (Achromatism)}$$

where K is the power of the combination, k_1 and k_2 the powers of the components, and V_1 and V_2 the V-values or reciprocals of the dispersive powers of the two glasses. Solving for k_1 and k_2 we get :—

$$k_1 = V_1 K/(V_1 - V_2) \text{ and } K_2 = - V_2 K/(V_1 - V_2).$$

The Petzval condition for the flatness of the field is :—

$$P = k_1/n_1 + k_2/n_2 = (V_1/n_1 - V_2/n_2) K/(V_1 - V_2)$$

and to fulfil this condition $V_1/n_1 = V_2/n_2$

i.e., the V-value should be proportional to the refractive index. A reference to Chapter 12 will show that for the older glasses in the crown and flint series a low refractive index is associated with a high V-value and vice versa so that it is not possible using these glasses to find a pair which can be combined to give an achromatic doublet with a flat field. The introduction of the barium glasses was influenced by this requirement and it can be seen that by using these glasses achromatic doublets can be made in which the Petzval curvature is reduced. In the design of photographic objectives where a large flat field is essential the barium glasses are indispensable and the term " Anastigmat " as applied to photographic lenses means that by a suitable choice of glasses the astigmatism is fully corrected for one part of the field and the curvature of field and residual astigmatism in other parts of the field are nowhere very great.

It will be realised that because of the very large number of conditions which must be obeyed, many of them mutually inconsistent, it is impossible to design a lens which is completely free from all aberrations at all parts of the field and for all zones. The best that can be done is compromise and so balance the residuals of the aberrations that the resulting lens gives an acceptable performance.

In each particular design the actual use to which the lens is to be put must be the guiding factor. Thus for some telescopes, for astronomical purposes, the centre of the field only is used for exact observation and it is essential that the objective should be carefully corrected for spherical and chromatic aberrations, while coma is of secondary importance. In photographic lenses, on the other hand, coma and astigmatism are of primary importance and a considerable amount of spherical aberration can be tolerated, and is in fact frequently retained so that a better balance of the aberrations in the outer parts of the field can be obtained.

Stops, Diaphragms and Pupils. Mention has been made of the stop or diaphragm limiting the pencils of light passing through the instrument. This diaphragm is called the aperture stop and its image as seen from the side of the instrument on which the light is incident is called the entrance pupil. Thus all the light which enters the instrument must pass through the entrance pupil if it is to pass through the aperture stop. After traversing the instrument the light will again pass through another pupil, known as the exit pupil which is the image of the aperture stop in that part of the instrument which follows it. Fig. 15.6 shows the stops and pupils in telescopes of different types.

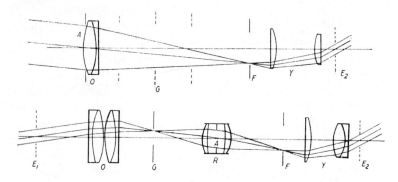

Fig. 15.6.—Stops and pupils in telescopes. Astronomical telescope (upper figure).

A is the aperture stop and coincides with the entrance pupil.

E_2 is the exit pupil and is the image of A in the system.

F is the field stop and its images are at infinity.

G are glare stops frequently used in telescopes to prevent unwanted reflections from the tube.

Y is the eyepiece consisting of a field lens and an eye lens.

One form of terrestrial telescope (lower figure). For special reasons the aperture stop has been fitted in the erector system R.

E_1 is the entrance pupil and is the image of A in all the lenses to the left of A.

E_2 is the exit pupil and is the image of A in all the lenses to its right.

F is the field stop and G is a glare stop.

Since optical instruments must of necessity only cover a certain field, i.e., a conical space within which all light entering the instrument is confined, there will almost invariably be found a diaphragm or stop associated with the instrument which is used to limit the field. Thus in a camera the photographic plate holder or film holder provides the limit and in telescopes and microscopes there is usually an internal diaphragm situated at one focal place. This diaphragm is called the field stop and its images in the preceding and following parts of the instrument are sometimes called the entrance and exit windows.

The position of the aperture stop can profoundly affect the parts of component lenses through which image forming light is allowed to pass and therefore the movement of this stop is a powerful tool in controlling the off-axis aberrations of the system. A very simple example is the use of a correctly positioned stop with a meniscus lens as in the cheaper cameras (see p. 304) to obtain a pseudo flattening of the field.

Magnifiers. The simplest form of magnifier is, of course, the single lens as used in reading glasses and for low magnification and general utility such magnifiers are adequate, but it will be noticed that they often produce considerable distortion. Recently plastic reading glasses with aspherical surfaces have been made in large quantities and these are very successful. For high power, it will be found that a plano-convex lens will give better results used plane side towards the object if the eye is at a distance and with plane towards the eye when the eye is placed close to the glass to obtain a wide field of view. The disadvantage of having to reverse the glass for these two uses can be overcome to some extent by using a triplet construction, as shown in Fig. 15.7, which shows several forms of magnifiers. The Stanhope lens is found in extremely small sizes with the object, often in the form of an advertisement for a holiday resort or a Parisian picture, on the object surface. In larger sizes the Stanhope lens still has considerable application. For high powers, as in focusing magnifiers and for measurement, magnifiers made in the form of a Ramsden or Kellner eyepiece are useful. These are frequently fitted with a scale in the focal plane which is placed in contact with the object being measured. The magnifying power of magnifiers and of microscope and telescope eyepieces is quoted as $5 \times$, $6 \times$, $8 \times$ and so on, this figure being based on the normal reading distance of 10 in. Thus a $10 \times$ magnifier or eyepiece has a focal length of 1 in. and generally 10 divided by the focal

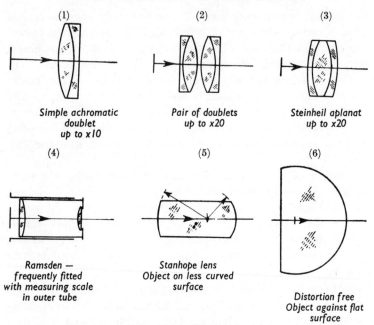

(1)

(2)

(3)

Simple achromatic
doublet
up to x10

Pair of doublets
up to x20

Steinheil aplanat
up to x20

(4)

(5)

(6)

Ramsden —
frequently fitted
with measuring scale
in outer tube

Stanhope lens
Object on less curved
surface

Distortion free
Object against flat
surface

FIG. 15.7.—Some forms of magnifiers.

1.—Simple achromatic doublet for fairly low powers up to × 10.
2.—A pair of doublets gives greater magnification.
3.—Steinheil aplanatic magnifier, reasonably high powers are possible and does not need reversing.
4.—A Ramsden eyepiece frequently fitted with a scale.
5.—Stanhope lens, the object is placed on the less curved surface.
6.—A distortion free hypersphere, object against flat surface.

length in inches is the quoted magnifying power. Another formula for the magnifying power is the power in dioptres divided by four.

It frequently happens that the use of one eye for long periods is tiring or inconvenient and binocular magnifiers may be made either in the form of strong spectacles incorporating wedges to prevent squinting or by using a large lens as shown in Fig. 15.8. With these instruments stereoscopic vision is obtained so that the objects viewed have a true solid appearance.

Eyepieces. In the following pages will be found tabulated a large number of eyepieces with their properties and particulars extracted from an article by E. Wilfred Taylor in the *Journal of Scientific Instruments* (ref. 3), and read before the Optical Group of the Physical Society. Quoting from this article the requirements of

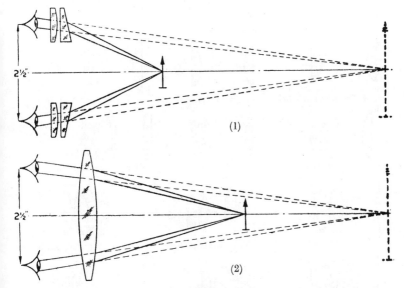

FIG. 15.8.—Binocular forms of magnifiers.
1.—Spectacle type—the prism may be incorporated in the spherical lens.
2.—Single lens type.

a good eyepiece are large well-corrected field of view, adequate eye relief and freedom from shadows, which if present, occult parts of the field of view as the eye is moved in relation to the exit pupil. If the central definition is to be good the eyepiece must be well corrected for spherical aberration and axial achromatism. If the oblique image is to be good there must be freedom from coma and the images formed by light of different wave-lengths must subtend equal angles at the eye. Distortion should not be apparent and the image must appear to lie on a plane surface.

As shown on page 284 this last condition cannot be fully realised with existing glasses because the Petzval curvature cannot be zero and even if astigmatism is absent the image will lie on a curved surface whose radius ρ is given by the formula

$$\text{Petzval curvature or Petzval sum} = \frac{1}{\rho} = \Sigma \frac{n' - n}{nn'R}$$

where n and n' are the refractive indices of the spaces separated by the surface of radius R. The most that can be done is to make use of the most favourable glasses and to introduce as much astigmatism

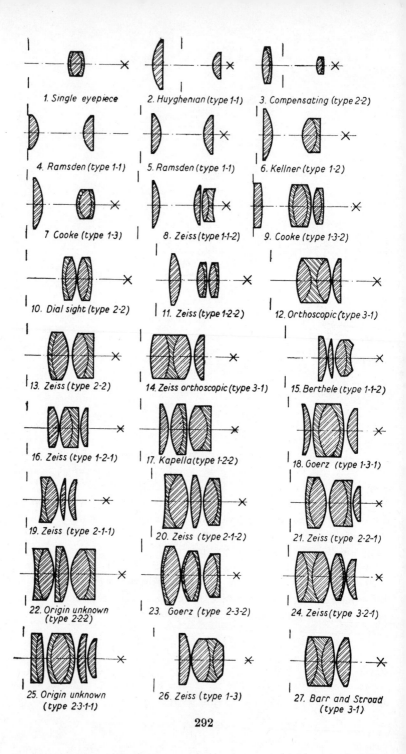

1. Single eyepiece   2. Huyghenian (type 1-1)   3. Compensating (type 2-2)

4. Ramsden (type 1-1)   5. Ramsden (type 1-1)   6. Kellner (type 1-2)

7. Cooke (type 1-3)   8. Zeiss (type 1-1-2)   9. Cooke (type 1-3-2)

10. Dial sight (type 2-2)   11. Zeiss (type 1-2-2)   12. Orthoscopic (type 3-1)

13. Zeiss (type 2-2)   14. Zeiss orthoscopic (type 3-1)   15. Berthele (type 1-1-2)

16. Zeiss (type 1-2-1)   17. Kapella (type 1-2-2)   18. Goerz (type 1-3-1)

19. Zeiss (type 2-1-1)   20. Zeiss (type 2-1-2)   21. Zeiss (type 2-2-1)

22. Origin unknown (type 2-2-2)   23. Goerz (type 2-3-2)   24. Zeiss (type 3-2-1)

25. Origin unknown (type 2-3-1-1)   26. Zeiss (type 1-3)   27. Barr and Stroud (type 3-1)

TABLE 15.4—*Particulars of Inverting Eyepieces*

Fig.	Type of eyepiece		Focal length		Focal lengths of components			Approx. field	Petzval sum Σ	Per cent eye clearance	Patent No.
			length	1	2	3	4				
1	Monocentric	1	1·0	1·0	—	—	—	30 deg.	+ 0·74	85	—
2	Huyghenian	1–1	1·0	1·75	0·70	—	—	50 deg.	+ 1·33	30	—
3	Compensating	2–2	1·0	1·33	0·76	—	—	40 deg.	+ 1·27	25	—
4	Ramsden	1–1	1·0	1·0	1·0	—	—	40 deg.	+ 1·33	25	—
5	Ramsden	1–1	1·0	1·25	1·25	—	—	40 deg.	+ 1·07	25	—
6	Kellner	1–2	1·0	1·78	0·81	—	—	40 deg.	+ 0·91	45	—
7	Cooke	1–3	1·0	1·64	1·01	—	—	50 deg.	+ 1·03	45	125,430
8	Zeiss	1–1–2	1·0	1·97	1·36	− 4·94	—	50 deg.	+ 0·82	34	188,200 (German)
9	Cooke	1–3–2	1·0	7·86	2·33	1·80	—	60 deg.	+ 0·86	69	126,837
10	Dial sight	2–2	1·0	1·76	1·76	—	—	40 deg.	+ 0·82	77	—
11	Zeiss	1–2–2	1·0	1·70	1·25	1·25	—	70 deg.	+ 1·44	32	144,321
12	Orthoscopic	3–1	1·0	2·64	1·48	—	—	80 deg.	+ 0·78	80	—
13	Zeiss	2–2	1·0	2·20	1·78	—	—	?	+ 0·67	64	509,585
14	Zeiss orthoscopic	3–1	1·0	2·77	1·51	—	—	70 deg.	+ 0·64	82	509,585
15	Berthele	1–1–2	1·0	2·62	2·29	2·96	—	?	+ 0·55	80	233,308
16	Zeiss	1–2–1	1·0	2·31	6·08	1·96	—	?	+ 0·77	67	509,990
17	Kapella	1–2–2	1·0	2·96	2·83	2·77	—	70 deg.	+ 0·69	68	409,464
18	Goerz	1–3–1	1·0	3·56	3·67	1·63	—	?	+ 0·75	59	215,337
19	Zeiss	2–1–1	1·0	6·75	2·60	2·43	—	?	+ 0·66	92	509,990
20	Zeiss	2–1–2	1·0	4·31	2·79	4·49	—	70 deg.	+ 0·64	60	145,503
21	Zeiss	2–2–1	1·0	2·05	3·44	1·86	—	70 deg.	+ 0·96	56	175,966
22	Unknown	2–2–2	1·0	6·60	3·42	1·90	—	60 deg.	+ 0·65	72	—
23	Goerz	2–3–2	1·0	2·42	2·95	2·79	—	?	+ 0·79	46	215,337
24	Zeiss	3–2–1	1·0	3·71	2·82	2·21	—	?	+ 0·77	69	509,990
25	Unknown	2–3–1–1	1·0	4·76	3·76	2·54	3·18	63 deg.	+ 0·82	70	—
26	Zeiss	1–3	1·0	3·15	1·42	—	—	?	+ 0·74	66	399,452
27	Barr and Stroud	3–1	1·0	3·91	1·19	—	—	?	+ 0·78	91	530,506

as is necessary to secure a flat field for tangential lines (page 285). The Petzval sum is therefore a most important characteristic of any eyepiece.

To revert to the requirements of good eyepieces it will be realised that the apparent field of view, diameter of eye lens and the eye clearance are closely related as shown in Fig. 15.9. For most ordinary purposes and in microscopes and astronomical telescopes a field of view of about 40 deg. is adequate. The larger fields of 60 and 70 deg., or even 90 deg., are required mainly in military telescopes of comparatively low power where large eye clearance is also desirable. Large fields of view are not always comfortable to use as rotation of the whole head of the observer is often required, whereas rotation of the eye alone is generally to be preferred.

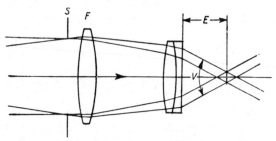

Fig. 15.9.—Field of view (*V*) and eye clearance (*E*) of an eyepiece. *S* is the field stop and *F* is the field lens. The diameter of the eye lens must be sufficient to provide the required field and eye clearance.

Microscopes and telescopes are usually fitted with Huyghenian or Ramsden eyepieces, types 2 and 5 in the table. Ramsden types are better for use with graticules or cross wires and are almost essential for measuring and moving graticules. The Kellner, No. 6, is very common in binoculars.

The Ramsden type No. 4 is the theoretical form for true achromatism but it is not used because it has no eye clearance and the focal plane lies on the surface of the field lens where any dust or defects would also be seen. Nos. 10 and 11 are frequently used where a large eye relief is necessary and No. 13 can be made in high power for astronomical telescopes. The remaining types are all examples of attempts to gain a large flat field. The image forming rays which meet at the focal plane of an eyepiece are restricted in aperture and angular divergence by the objective system, including any erector lenses and their associated diaphragms. After passing through the eyepiece the rays are rendered parallel and all pass through the exit pupil of the instrument. In most instruments considerations of magnification and overall dimensions usually restrict the diameter of the exit pupil. In high power instruments the diameter of the exit pupil may be 2 mm. or less but in binoculars and low power telescopes it may be from 5 to 8 mm. in diameter. In special cases where large eye freedom is required the exit pupil may be increased in size to 1 in. or more but it must be remembered that in such instruments the pupil of the observer's eye acts as a stop which limits the rays actually used. The question is discussed again in Chapter 16.

Telescope objectives. For a telescope objective to be of any value it must be achromatic and free from spherical aberration. Coma must also be well corrected in telescopes of low power having a large real field. In small telescopes, up to about 2 in. in diameter, these conditions can be reasonably fulfilled by cemented doublets, but where larger diameters are required the lenses are seldom cemented. Fig. 15.10 shows a few typical examples of telescope objectives.

The cemented achromat is by far the most common and such objectives are made in large quantities by all lens manufacturers. The methods of computation are very simple and are fully explained in standard text books and there are many tables specially drawn up to simplify the early stages of design. The Fraunhofer type is used in large telescopes and collimators and can usually be recognised by three small spacing pieces of tinfoil which are visible at the rim. Great care is necessary if these objectives are dismantled for cleaning that they are reassembled exactly in the same relative positions. The Gauss type is used mainly where perfect central definition is required, and in large theodolites. The Cooke Photo-Visual objective is designed to enable photographs to be taken without change of focus, i.e., it is achromatised for the $D(5890)$ and $G'(4343)$ lines of the spectrum. When the field of view is large the objective becomes more complicated and assumes the general shape and characteristics of camera lenses.

In binoculars ordinary cemented objectives are used and are corrected for use with the prisms in the system. For low power telescopes where the relative aperture is greater than the normal $f/10$, compound objectives consisting sometimes of a pair of cemented doublets are common, particularly where an advanced entrance pupil is required (see section on Telescopes in Chapter 16). The field curvature of telescope objectives can be troublesome and it is not uncommon in wide field objectives to find field flattening lenses forming part of the system. The use of a powerful negative element in the system tends to assist field flattening and for this reason tele-photo lens construction has sometimes been used.

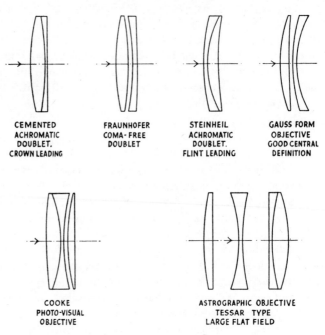

CEMENTED
ACHROMATIC
DOUBLET.
CROWN LEADING

FRAUNHOFER
COMA-FREE
DOUBLET

STEINHEIL
ACHROMATIC
DOUBLET.
FLINT LEADING

GAUSS FORM
OBJECTIVE
GOOD CENTRAL
DEFINITION

COOKE
PHOTO-VISUAL
OBJECTIVE

ASTROGRAPHIC OBJECTIVE
TESSAR TYPE
LARGE FLAT FIELD

FIG. 15.10.—Telescope objectives.

The chromatic correction of telescope objectives for visual use is obtained by combining the C(6563) and F(4861) lines of the spectrum and this correction can be used with a yellow filter and panchromatic emulsion for photography, but the lenses with this correction are quite unsuitable for photography with " ordinary " plates. The infra-red focus is of course different and can only be found by trial and error.

Microscope objectives. Microscope objectives are essenti-ally short focus lenses used to produce a magnified real image of the object which is in turn further magnified by the viewing eyepiece. Fig. 15.11 shows diagrammatically the essential features of a micro-scope and the descriptive nomenclature used in referring to the instrument and its parts. It will be seen from this figure that the

objective collects a wide angle pencil of light from each object point
and that the object size is very small relative to the lens size. The
angle of the cone of light collected by the objective is given by the
numerical aperture ($N.A.$) of the objective defined by the formula
$N.A. = n \sin U$ where n is the refractive index of the medium

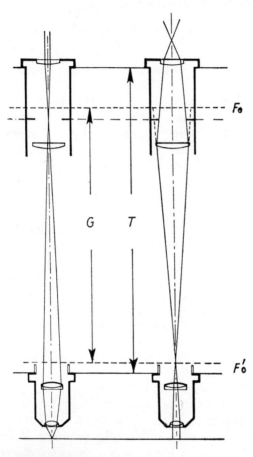

FIG. 15.11.—The microscope.

G = Optical tube length
T = Mechanical tube length
$F'o$ = Second focus of objective
Fe = First focus of eyepiece

Primary magnification = Mo = G/Focal length of objective.
Magnification by eyepiece = $M\text{E}$ = 10/Focal length of eyepiece in inches.
Magnification of complete microscope = $Mo \times Me$.

between the object and the lens and U the semi-angle of the cone of light from an axial object point. With dry lenses the greatest practical attainable *N.A.* is 0·95 (theoretically = 1). This can be increased by using immersion lenses, the resulting *N.A.* with water being 1·25, cedar wood oil 1·50 and naphthaline monobromide 1·60. The resolving power of a microscope is given theoretically by the formula :—

$$d = \frac{0 \cdot 61\lambda}{n \sin U} = \frac{0 \cdot 61\lambda}{N.A.}$$

where d is the distance between two object points seen to be separated, λ is the wave-length of the light used when observing and n is the refractive index in the object space. Thus the resolving power will be increased (d is decreased) by a decrease of wave-length or an increase of *N.A.* Having reached the limit of increase in *N.A.* it can only remain to decrease the wave-length of the light used, hence the use of ultra-violet light and eventually the electron microscope.

The other characteristic of microscope objectives is the tube length for which they are designed. The distance from the inner principal focus of the objective to the first principal focus of the eyepiece is the optical tube length. The mechanical tube length is simply the length of the actual tube of the instrument. Microscope objectives are now designed for a standard mechanical tube length of 160 mm. but some older objectives were designed for 200 or even 250 mm. The tube length is usually engraved on the mount of the objective along with the focal length and *N.A.* It should be noted that the cover glasses used to protect specimens on microscope slides should be of the standard thickness of 0·17 mm. (0·007 in.), but vary considerably in thickness. The cover glass thickness affects the spherical aberration of the system and can be compensated for by altering the tube length. It will be found that if the cover glass is thick the tube length has to be decreased and vice versa. The amount of the correction to the tube length required should be found by the observation of star images by silvering a number of cover glasses of varying thicknesses, placing them in turn on the stage silvered side down and observing the appearance of tiny pin-holes inside and outside the focus. By varying the tube length until the appearance inside and outside the focus is the same the correct tube length for each thickness of cover glass can be found. Special slides for this purpose are supplied by the principal microscope makers. Fig. 15.12 shows the appearances inside and outside the focus for correct and for under-corrected and over-corrected spherical aberration. In the following table are listed some objectives with the primary magnification corresponding to a tube length of 160 mm. and the total magnifying power with a series of eyepieces. The actual magnifications obtained with any given objective and eyepiece, as purchased, may

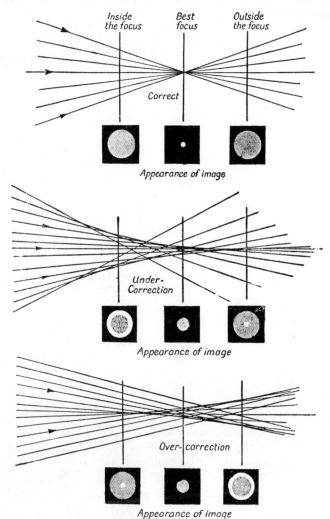

FIG. 15.12.—Diagrammatic illustration (grossly exaggerated) of the union of the rays in the image formed by the objective, in the presence of zero, under-corrected, and over-corrected spherical aberration.

vary considerably from these figures and, if accuracy is required, the magnification should be measured. The rough rule

$$\frac{\text{Tube Length}}{\text{Focal Length of Objective}} \times \text{Eyepiece Magnification}$$

can be used without much error for the higher powers, but it is necessarily only approximate.

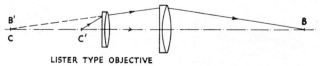

LISTER TYPE OBJECTIVE

B AND B′, C AND C′ ARE PAIRS OF POINTS FOR WHICH THE SPHERICAL ABERRATION OF THE LENSES HAS BEEN CORRECTED

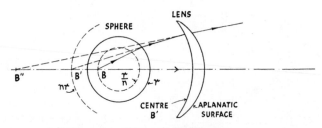

USE OF APLANATIC POINTS OF A SPHERE

B AND B′ ARE APLANATIC POINTS OF THE SPHERE OF RADIUS r
B′AND B″ ,, ,, ,, ,, ,, ,, APLANATIC SURFACE OF THE LENS

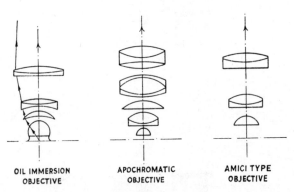

OIL IMMERSION OBJECTIVE   APOCHROMATIC OBJECTIVE   AMICI TYPE OBJECTIVE

FIG. 15.13.—Microscope objectives.

Fig. 15.13 shows a few typical objective designs and the basic principles used in objective designs. Single objectives consisting of a simple doublet or triplet are common for very low powers. The Lister principle (J. J. Lister 1830) in which two achromatised and spherically corrected lenses are used, or its later modification in which the first lens is spherically over-corrected and the back lens spherically under-corrected gives good results and is commonly used for lenses of medium power and small *N.A.* For larger *N.A.* and higher powers the Amici design consisting of two over-corrected cemented back lenses and a single thick first lens is used for the higher powers of dry objectives. Immersion types generally follow the design shown in which the principle of the Aplanatic points of a sphere is used. Much of modern objective design is based on the extensive researches of Abbe who first applied analytic methods to the work.

Care should be taken in handling microscope objectives as the small lenses in them are delicately mounted and may even be held in place by cement only. Excessive pressure when wiping immersion fluid off the surface is to be avoided.

TABLE 15.5—*Focal Length, N.A., and Magnification of some Microscopic Objectives*

Focal length of Objective		Numerical Aperture (N.A.)	Approx. Primary Mag. tube length 160 mm.	Approximate Magnification using various eyepieces				
in.	mm.			× 6	× 10	× 15	× 20	× 25
4	100	0·08	0·6	3·6	6	9	12	15
3	75	0·09	1·25	7·5	12·5	19	25	32
2	50	0·1 — 0·15	2·5	15	25	37	50	62
1½	32	0·15	4·5	27	45	67	90	112
1	25	0·15 — 0·28	6	36	60	90	120	150
2/3	16	0·17 — 0·35	9	54	90	135	180	225
1/3	8	0·36 — 0·65	20	120	200	300	400	500
1/4	6	0·85	26	156	260	390	520	670
1/6	4	0·65 — 0·95	40	240	400	600	800	1000
1/12 (O.I.)	2	1·0 — 1·4	80	480	800	1200	1600	2000

Reflecting microscope objectives

Although the principles of the reflecting microscope have been long known it is only recently that any real attempt has been made to produce or use mirror systems for microscope objectives. It is interesting to read the very extensive treatment of the subject in R. Smith's *Compleat System of Opticks* published in 1738.

C. R. Burch has designed and made several systems. The use of spherical reflecting surfaces limits the possible *N.A.* of microscope objectives to about 0·65 but the aspheric systems being used by

Burch have enabled the $N.A.$ to be increased to 0·95 for dry objectives and by immersion methods it is further increased to 1·4. Fig. 15.14 shows two types of objectives designed by Burch, the condenser systems being also in mirror form. In the system (a) the main mirrors only, and in (b) all the mirrors are aspheric. The mirrors are made of speculum metal coated with a thin layer of aluminium.

R. & J. Beck have placed on the market two reflecting microscope objectives developed on designs from the Wheatstone Laboratory and Medical Research Council Bio-physics Research Unit at King's College, London. The following particulars are given for these objectives and provision is made for centring and adjustment of the mirrors to compensate for the thickness of cover glasses. The firm recommends the use of a second reflecting objective as condenser :—

Focus	2·6 mm.	3·5 mm.
Magnification at 160 mm.	74 ×	52 ×
Numerical aperture	0·65	0·63
Central obstruction of $N.A.$	35%	42%
Central obstruction of area	12·5%	17·5%
Working distance	4·75 mm.	4·75 mm.

The principal advantages of mirror systems are the complete absence of chromatic aberration and the long working distances possible with a high value of $N.A.$ Once the instrument has been focused with light of any wave-length, or with white light, it remains in focus for all wave-lengths from the far ultra-violet to the far infra-red. The advantages of this for ultra-violet and infra-red microscopy, and micro-photography in general are obvious. By projecting an enlarged image of an object on to the slit of an ultra-violet spectrograph, for example, the entire ultra-violet and visible absorption spectrum of a microscopic object can be recorded in a single exposure. This spectro-microscopic technique can also be extended into the infra-red using the usual infra-red detectors, or with an electronic infra-red image converter the infra-red image can be seen. Good results are being obtained in this way particularly with phase contrast illumination. The possibilities of using the mirror systems for very short wave-length ultra-violet light, with the consequent increase in resolution, have still to be explored.

The long working distances possible with the mirror systems greatly facilitate micro-dissection and have many other advantages. The working distance of the system (a) is about 13 mm. and could be

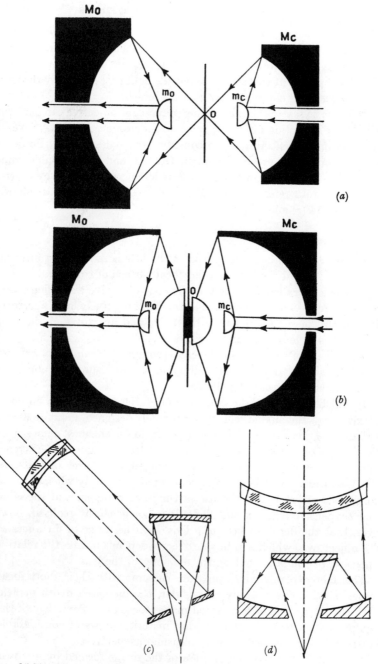

Fig. 15.14.—Mirror type microscope objectives.
    (a) Burch dry reflecting objective.
    (b) Immersion reflecting objective by Burch.
    (c) and (d) Two forms described by Bouwers.

increased without great difficulty, while for a refracting objective of the same *N.A.* the working distance would be about 1 mm. In the immersion system (*b*) the immersion lenses are hemispherical with the object placed at the centre so that the light passes radially through the surfaces and chromatic errors are avoided.

It is safe to say that the reflecting microscope objective can perform all that a refracting objective can and much more besides. Several forms of simple reflecting microscopes have been designed by Bouwers at the Oude Delft establishment in Holland and are available commercially. The review article on the reflecting microscope by Norris gives numerous references (see Refs.). Two of these forms are shown in Fig. 15.14 (*c*) and (*d*).

Camera lenses

For general photographic purposes the lens is required to form an image of external objects on a flat focal surface of considerable size. Thus the camera lens, unlike the telescope objective and microscope objective, covers a wide field and is usually of relatively large aperture. It is useful here to summarise the fields and apertures of the four main types of lenses so far described.

At the end of the chapter the construction of a number of camera lenses is shown diagrammatically and a brief summary of their characteristics is tabulated (Table 15.7).

It will be seen that the construction varies considerably in complexity from the simple meniscus, originally designed about 1820 and still used to this day in enormous numbers in the cheapest cameras, to the complex modern types striving at extreme angles and extreme apertures. For general photography the simpler forms of lenses of the Tessar and Aviar types are adequate and it is only when extreme conditions are met that the use of the more complex and therefore more expensive lenses is justified. It is not generally realised, however, that the depth of field of a lens, i.e., the range of distances of the object over which it is in sharp focus, depends not on the relative aperture, or *f-number*, but on the diameter of the lens.

This fact explains why miniature cameras with their short focus lenses of wide aperture are so popular, the increased depth of field with the advantage of high speed makes for greater flexibility of the equipment and the use of fine grain material allows of considerable enlargement and generally more pleasing perspectives.

The central or axial illumination of the image formed by a lens is

Lens Type	Field	Aperture
Eyepieces	Large, 40–60 deg. normal 60–72 deg. wide angle 72–90 deg. extra wide	Small. Image forming pencil restricted by pupil of eye, 2 mm. to 7 mm., i.e., seldom exceeds $f/4$.
Telescope Objectives	Small, less than 10 deg.	Small, usually about $f/10$.
Microscope Objectives	Small, about 6 deg.	Large N.A. varies with power from 0·3 for 1 in. to 1·4 for 1/12 in. objective (Oil immersion) ($f/1·7$ to $f/0·5$ approx.).
Camera Lenses	Large, Normal, 54 deg. Long focus, 20 deg. Wide angle, 70–180 deg.	Depends on focal length and field. Wide angle $f/22$ to $f/16$. Normal $f/11$ to $f/3·5$. Large aperture $f/3$ to $f/2$. Extra large $f/2$–$f/0·8$

proportional to the square of its diameter and inversely as the square of the focal length or, in photographic language, the brightness of the image is proportional to $1/f$-number squared and since the exposure time required is inversely proportional to the brightness of the image, the exposure time is proportional to the square of the f-number. For this reason the relative apertures of lenses are marked on the lens in definite progressions such that successively smaller stops are indicated by numbers whose squares are approximately in a geometrical series of ratio 2. The commoner f- numbers used are shown below, divided into two main sequences with their approximate squares. It will be seen, therefore, that each step from stop to stop, in any one of these sequences means doubling the exposure time—a very convenient and useful convention.

Sequence I.

f-number	1	1·4	2	2·9	4	5·6	8	11	16	22	32
(f-number)^2	1	2	4	8	16	32	64	128	256	512	1024

Sequence II.

f-number			3·5	4·5	6·3	9	12·5	18	25	36
(f-number)^2			10	20	40	80	160	320	640	1280

The largest aperture of the lens is the one used in its catalogue description and this may fall in Sequence II, but this sequence is not now common and it is usually found that the apertures of an $f/4\cdot5$ lens, for example, are marked $4\cdot5$, $5\cdot6$, 8, 11 and so on, i.e., in Sequence I.

The illumination in the outer parts of the field of a lens falls off very rapidly in proportion to $\cos^4\theta$ where θ is the angle from the axis to the point in the field. This falling off in illumination is not generally noticeable in normal photography because of the latitude of the emulsion and printing paper, but when the angle to the outer parts of the field is greater than about 30 deg. the falling off in density in the photograph can become very marked. At 45 deg., for example, the light is only one-quarter of that at the centre and in printing photographs taken with lenses of such an angular field precautions have to be taken to equalise the light. This $\cos^4\theta$ falling off in light is aggravated in most lenses by vignetting caused by the cutting off of light by the lens mount. Long lenses are more subject to vignetting than short lenses. Lens manufacturers use the vignetting as an extra degree of freedom to reduce the effect of oblique aberrations, but where it is undesirable the lens elements are made extra large to reduce vignetting to a minimum and such lenses are often described as E.M.I., the initials of the words " extra marginal illumination."

The treatment, or " blooming," of lens surfaces has very little effect on the total transmission of photographic lenses for the simple reason that there are seldom more than six or eight air glass surfaces and a reference to Chapter 12, Fig. 12.3 will show that although the light lost by reflection may be about 30 per cent, this amount is of little importance under ordinary conditions. On the other hand the light scattered in lenses can reach the photographic plate in unwanted places causing flare or overall fog and thus reducing the contrast. The treatment of the surfaces reduces this scattering and therefore increases the contrast. The contrast in a photograph can be greatly reduced if light from the sky, foreground or surrounding objects is allowed to fall on the lens. Although this light is not focused on the focal plane it is scattered by the lens surfaces or balsam and also falls on the inner sides of the camera to be again scattered. The best method of reducing the effect of this unwanted light is to fit an efficient and adequate lens hood and if possible the interior of the camera should be fitted with baffles.

Among the lenses shown are several of extreme wide angle. These lenses make use of distortion at some surface to enable the wide object to be imaged on a finite plate size and to diminish the $\cos^4$ effect which would otherwise be excessive.

If an extra wide angle lens is not available, and they are not easily obtainable, a useful device to enable wide angle photographs to be taken is to photograph the image in a spherical reflector using a normal camera, as shown in Fig. 15.15. Another unusual lens affording all-round vision is shown in Fig. 15.16 which includes a photograph of the type of image obtained with such a toroidal lens. This lens is not really intended for photographic work but for visual periscopes and with photoelectric devices.

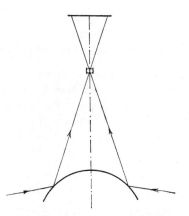

FIG. 15.15.—Wide angle photography using a spherical reflector. The camera is placed facing a convex spherical surface in which surrounding objects are seen by reflection. It is also possible to use a concave spherical surface.

In the manufacture of camera lenses great care is taken in their centring by mounting each component and cutting all the necessary threads off a single chucking thread, i.e., the first part of the mount is fitted to a mandril by means of its chucking thread, the first lens is then fitted and centred, any subsequent parts of the lens mount are then added, all without removing the lens from its mandril. When, however, lenses are dismantled for any reason and incorrectly reassembled, or more particularly, when they are fitted with inter-lens shutters, their performance very often suffers because of de-centring and this fault should be guarded against and avoided if possible.

The general performance of a camera lens as regards its optical aberrations can be measured but the information so obtained, although of interest to the designer, is no measure of its performance. A camera lens should therefore always be tested as it is going to be used and its performance judged by the results obtained. When a numerical criterion of the quality of a photographic lens is required it is usual to quote its resolving power under specified and well-defined conditions. It has been found that the resolving power depends on a large number of factors among which are the following :—

(*i*) Brightness of the object.

(*ii*) Contrast of the objects.

(*iii*) Exposure conditions.

(*iv*) Choice of focus.

(*v*) Angular distance of the object from the optical axis.

(*vi*) The aperture of the lens.

(*vii*) Characteristics of the emulsion.

Resolving power can therefore only be used as a measure of the *relative* performance of a number of lenses under identical controlled conditions of use. The resolving power is usually quoted as the

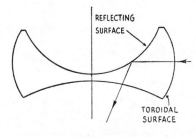

FIG. 15.16.—Toroidal lens providing an all-round view suitable for use with photo-electric devices. The accompanying photograph shows the appearance of the final image.

number of lines per millimetre on the resulting photograph and for some purposes this is a convenient measure but it does not give a true picture of the relative performance of lenses of different focal lengths. For this purpose it is better to express the resolving power as the quotient of the focal-length by the separation of two image points clearly resolved, i.e., the reciprocal of the angular resolution. For further information on this subject the reader should consult the paper by E. W. H. Selwyn and J. L. Tearle on the performance of aircraft camera lenses given in the references at the end of Chapter 18. The resolving power of camera lenses is discussed in detail in Chapter 18, p. 430.

Recently much attention has been paid to the possibility of calibrating camera lens apertures according to their true light transmitting properties. The method now in use of basing the *f*-numbers on the geometrical properties of the lens takes no account of the differences of light transmission that occur between lenses of different types, and it has been suggested that a uniform system of true apertures should be introduced. One method of achieving this standardisation would be to compare the actual light transmission of the lens at various apertures as set by the iris diaphragm with the light transmission of a series of standard holes, and engraving the iris ring accordingly. The name *T-number* has been suggested, and is used to some extent, for these *true f*-numbers. Since the *f*-number is in fact a ratio the German practice of marking their lenses in ratios, 1 : 4·5 for example, has much in its favour.

An extended uniform light source may be used in front of the lens or standard hole and a sensitive light meter placed at the principal focal plane of the lens or at a standard measured distance behind the hole. The light entering the light meter should be restricted by a small aperture (1 mm. dia.), which is actually at the focal plane or standard distance. The *f*-numbers of the standard holes are computed from the known values of the diameter of the hole and its distance from the pin-hole and a graph is drawn connecting light meter readings and *f*-numbers. The lens is then placed in position and a second graph drawn connecting light meter readings and iris settings. From these two graphs the iris settings for true *f*-numbers can be found.

Using this method of test the National Bureau of Standards, Washington, examined a number of lenses and Table 15.6 shows very clearly the differences between the marked *f*-numbers

TABLE 15.6—Measured Value of the f-number for Each Value of the Marked f-number of a Number of Lenses

(F. E. WASHER, J. Research N.B.S., $\mathbf{41}$, 301 (1948))

Nominal Focal-Length	0·5	0·5*	1·0*	1·4	1·6	2·0	2·0*	3·0	3·0*	3·0	4·0*	7·0	7·5	11·0	13·5	16·5	19·0	24·0	30·0	47·5*
1·9	2·4																			
2·2			2·09																	
2·3		2·82					2·23		2·45											
2·5				3·14		3·09					2·79										
2·7					3·14															
2·8	3·25		2·86				2·79	3·20	2·96											
3·0		3·13								3·68										
3·5										4·26										
4·0	4·42		3·92	4·33	4·10	4·36	3·95	4·48	4·07											
4·5		4·45								4·85	4·24		5·60							
5·6	5·32		5·52	5·82	5·46	6·00	5·29	6·22	5·78	6·74	5·76									
6·8		6·32								8·68		8·00	6·86							
7·5															9·72					
8·0	7·80		7·50	8·48	7·37	8·37	7·26	8·72	8·33	10·4	8·33									
9·5		8·78										9·32	9·75	10·1		12·3				
11·0	11·0		9·94	12·5	9·66	11·6	11·2	12·3	11·4	14·4	11·1	13·1	13·6	13·9	14·1	13·4	13·6			
12·5		11·8																14·3	15·6	
15·0																				16·0
16·0	15·4	17·2	13·6	16·8	12·3	16·0	15·7	17·4	17·4	21·5	15·4	18·7	18·3	19·7	19·8	19·5	19·2	19·8	19·3	17·3
22·0	21·3			24·2	16·0	21·9	20·4	24·5		33·6		25·2	24·0	28·0	28·4	26·8	25·8	28·2	26·7	23·3
32											27·6	36·7	29·5	37·0	40·0	38·0	37·6	40·9	39·2	34·7
45												49·0			56·9	52·8	50·8	59·9	53·4	48·6
64															76·0	71·8	69·6	86·8	79·0	71·1
90																100·0	98·0	117·0	99·0	97·6
128																				143·0

Lenses marked * have coated surfaces to reduce reflection losses.

and the true f-numbers corresponding to each iris setting. It will be seen that there are at times large differences suggesting that for critical work some such form of standardisation is desirable.

Condensers

In projection devices, microscopes, etc., in order to produce a bright image on the screen or to the eye as much light as possible from the source must be made to pass through the projection systems. Condensers are optical devices which are designed to collect as large a cone of light as possible from the source and divert it into the direction of the projection lens and so to the eye or screen. The brightness of a source of light is its candle-power per unit area and each element of an emitting surface appears of the same brightness whatever the angle or distance from which it is viewed. The illumination produced at any point is proportional to the brightness of the source and its apparent size as seen from the point. Thus the illumination at a point on a screen would be the same if the source consisted of a large area of low brightness or a small area of high brightness provided the product of the brightness and the area are the same. If, however, an optical device can be so placed that when viewed from the screen the size of the small bright source appears to be increased, then the illumination on the screen will be greater because the brightness of the source is greater and its apparent size has been increased.

Optical devices can alter the shape and size of a source as seen from a given direction, but they cannot make them look brighter, and the variation in intensity of illumination produced in any direction by an optical device is due to its capacity to make the source look larger or smaller. There is a limit to the intensity of illumination that can be produced by an optical device using a source of given brightness and this limit is reached when the whole aperture of the device, as seen from any given direction, is filled with the brightness of the source. This is termed a " complete flash." When only certain parts of the aperture are seen to be of the same brightness we have a " partial flash." Thus the condition for a complete flash will be realised if the rays from the eye or screen through every point of the optical system are so bent that they concentrate on the source.

The candle power of a source is the product of its area and its brightness and for a given candle power the brightness must increase as the area is decreased, and since the illumination produced depends

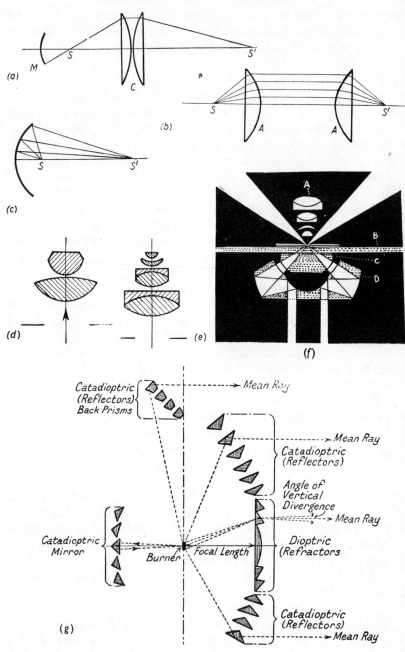

(a)

(b)

(c)

(d)

(e)

(f)

(g)

312

on the brightness and the " apparent " area as seen in the projection system it follows that the smaller the source the greater the illumination provided the candle power is constant and the projector is efficient and gives a complete flash. The illumination can in fact be said to be governed by the amount that the source appears to be increased in size and hence the smaller the source, for a given projector, the greater the brightness, always assuming we have a complete flash.

Condenser systems to be fully efficient must produce a complete flash in all the required directions. For normal projection work the simplest form of condenser, consisting of one or more simple lenses, is all that is required. Very commonly two plano-convex lenses are placed with their convex surfaces together, and this form of condenser is practically standard in enlargers and projectors of the magic lantern or cinematograph types. Where a particularly wide angle projection is required, i.e., a large screen at a small distance, it becomes necessary to ensure that the cone of light provided by the condenser is also of wide angle and the double plano-convex lens system is found to be difficult to use. Trains of three or more lenses can be employed, usually consisting of a meniscus, followed by a double convex and finally another meniscus or plano-convex lens. A good general rule in setting up a condenser system is to make all the lens surfaces share the work of bending the light as equally as possible. For still greater efficiency lenses have been produced and are available, having an aspherical convex surface and two such lenses can be made to produce an extremely wide angle cone of light with high efficiency. Mangin mirrors, paraboloidal, ellipsoidal and even hyperboloidal mirrors can all be used as condensers. Motor-car headlamps, signalling lamps and searchlights all employ such systems. The prism-mirror systems used in lighthouses are examples of condensers where the light collected from the source is probably almost as large as possible. Fig. 15.17 shows a number of condenser systems including

← Fig. 15.17.—Condenser systems.
    (a) Conventional system—two plano-convex lenses.
    (b) Wide angle system—two aspherical lenses.
    (c) Ellipsoidal mirror.
    (d) Abbe sub-stage microscope condenser.
    (e) Immersion type sub-stage condenser.
    (f) Dark ground sub-stage condenser.
    (g) Lighthouse system.
A mirror M may be used to increase the light as in (a), the centre of curvature being at the source S.

those used in microscopes for sub-stage and dark ground illumination. Notes on each system are given with the appropriate diagram to facilitate reference.

Cylindrical lenses

The uses of cylindrical lenses to produce elongated images, correct or introduce astigmatism, etc., are well known and this note will be restricted to the problem of their manufacture and supply difficulties. Low power cylindrical lenses similar to those used in spectacles, including toric surfaces, i.e., surfaces having different radii of curvature in two principal sections, are regularly manufactured by spectacle lens firms with powers up to about $12D$ positive or negative. The order of accuracy of the cylinders so produced is not very great and where critical optical definition is required these lenses will not generally serve, especially in the higher powers. It is, in fact, a matter of considerable difficulty to produce a really accurate cylindrical lens. The difficulty in producing accurate cylinders is partly caused by the fact that the tools are guided by mechanical means to generate the cylinder, whereas a spherical surface is automatically produced by the curved tool. Moreover, testing by proof plates is not easy. The centering and edging of spherical lenses is also simple but it is difficult to maintain a uniform thickness over the length of a cylindrical lens and to ensure edging parallel or perpendicular to the axis of the cylinder. These difficulties do not affect ophthalmic cylindrical surfaces where a low standard of accuracy is acceptable.

Aplanatic systems

An aplanatic system can be defined as one which forms images without aberration. Such systems in general must consist of at least two aspherical surfaces but there are several applications of the theory of aplanatism of comparatively simple form and these will be described here. It should be mentioned that the true aplanatic object and image relation involves freedom from spherical aberration *and* coma, i.e., rays from an object point must after reflection or refraction meet at a single image point for all possible ray paths, and for freedom from coma a small object perpendicular to the axis must produce a small image also perpendicular to the axis and such that the ratio of the size of object to size of image remains constant for all possible ray paths. Many so-called aplanatic systems are not free from coma but are still of considerable value. The physical condition that must

314

be satisfied for aplanatism is that the optical distance, i.e., the sum of the products of distance and refractive index, must remain constant for all ray paths.

For a single reflection the application of the condition for the constancy of the optical distance produces the equation for an ellipsoid or hyperboloid of revolution whose foci represent the positions of the object and its conjugate image. If one focus recedes to infinity the surface becomes a paraboloid of revolution.

For a single refraction the application of the condition produces the surface of revolution formed from a Cartesian oval, i.e., of the fourth degree. If one of the points recedes to infinity the surface becomes a surface of revolution of the second degree, one of its foci being the focus of the rays. The surface is a hyperboloid if the infinite point is in the optically denser medium and an ellipsoid if it is in the less dense medium. The eccentricity of the surfaces is equal to the ratio of the refractive indices of the media. In one special case the surface becomes a sphere.

Other non-spherical or figured surfaces are at times used for special purposes and these are most conveniently calculated by writing the equation to the meridian curve of the surface in terms of polar co-ordinates, in the form :—

$$R = f(\phi) = R_0 + d$$

where R_0 is the radius of curvature at the vertex and d is the radial deviation from the osculating sphere at the vertex. By expanding d in a power series of the arc $l = R_0\phi$ we may write :—

$$d = al^4 + b\,l^6 + c\,l^8 + \ldots$$

The powers are even because of symmetry and powers below the fourth do not occur because of the contact between the circle and the curve at the vertex, which is of the second order.

The coefficients a, b, c, etc., are called the coefficients of non-sphericity and may be computed from the required conditions.

(i) Ellipse :—Since in any ellipse or ellipsoid the sum of the distances of any point on the surface from the two foci is a constant, the foci are aplanatic points so far as freedom from spherical aberration is concerned. Thus an ellipsoidal mirror can be used to form an image of a point source placed at one focus, the image being formed at the other. Such ellipsoidal mirrors have an application in infra-red spectrometers to form an image of the exit slit on the thermopile. If a lens is made having one ellipsoidal surface and one concave spherical surface, and if the eccentricity of the ellipse is equal to the reciprocal of the refractive index, then rays parallel to the major axis of the ellipse and incident on the ellipsoidal surface will after refraction be directed towards the second focus. If the second surface of the lens is centred on this second focus the light is not refracted at the spherical surface and will therefore form the image at this focus. See Fig. 15.18 (a).

(ii) **Hyperbola** :—The focal properties of a hyperboloid show that rays emanating from one focus will after reflection appear to diverge from the other focus, and if a lens is constructed with a plane first surface and a hyperboloidal second surface, the eccentricity being the reciprocal of the refractive index, then rays parallel to the major axis and incident on the plane surface will be refracted to pass without spherical aberration through the remote focus. See Fig. 15.18 (b).

It should be pointed out that useful condenser and erecting systems can be imagined consisting of a pair of either ellipsoidal or hyperboloidal lenses so that the light between the lenses is parallel. Under these conditions there is also freedom from coma.

(iii) **Parabola** :—It is well known that an object placed at the focus of a paraboloidal mirror will produce parallel light by reflection and that parallel light incident parallel to the axis will form a point image. See Fig. 15.18 (c).

The paraboloid is probably the most commonly used aplanatic reflecting surface, having applications in motor-car headlamps, searchlights and astronomical telescopes. By using an off-axis position of the paraboloid useful mirrors can be made in which there is no obstruction of the beam of light. Such mirrors have applications in infra-red spectrometry. It should be noted that, contrary to general opinion, the image is not free from coma and other aberrations and the surface is therefore not truly aplanatic in the full sense of the word.

Spherical mirrors are only aplanatic for the centre of curvature, using the word aplanatic in its restricted sense of freedom from spherical aberration. The coma, is however, small when used at nearly unit magnification and astigmatism may be corrected, if necessary, by using weak cylindrical lenses. Mirrors in general are being used to a very large extent because of their freedom from any chromatic effects, particularly in infra-red and ultra-violet work. They also have applications in astronomy and recently there has been much development in mirror systems used with corrector plates (Schmidt, Maksutov, Wynne, etc.).

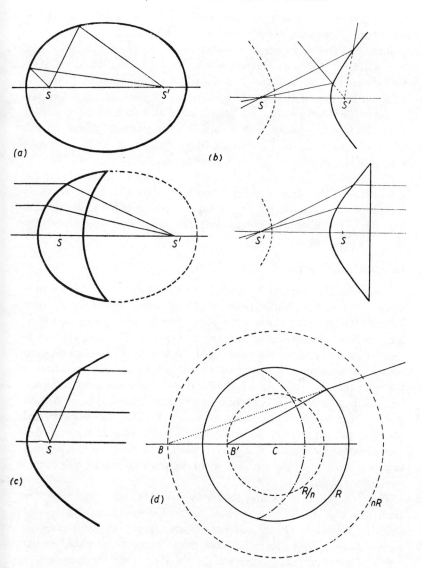

Fig. 15.18.—Aplanatic systems.
(a) Ellipsoidal mirror and lens.
(b) Hyperboloidal mirror and lens.
(c) Parabola.
(d) Aplanatic points of a sphere.

(iv) **Sphere** :—A sphere has very useful aplanatic properties which are of considerable practical utility. There is a pair of aplanatic points, also free from coma, associated with a spherical surface. In Fig. 15.18 (*d*) if R is the surface of a sphere of radius R and we draw two circles of radii nR and R/n then two points such as B and B' situated on any diameter are aplanatic. A cone of rays directed towards B will after refraction pass through B' as can be easily proved from the law of refraction, or a cone of rays emanating from B' will after refraction appear to emanate from B. This property is of considerable use in microscope objectives (*q.v.*).

It is obvious that a lens of meniscus shape can be made having for the centre of its concave surface the inner aplanatic point B'. This form is of use in lens design, but it must be remembered that since the position of the aplanatic points are functions of the refractive index they are not achromatic.

Lens-mirror systems

Reference has already been made to the Mangin mirror as a condenser system for producing a parallel beam of light from a point source. Mangin mirrors are in the form of deep meniscus lenses whose inner radius is considerably less than the outer radius, i.e., the difference of radii is greater than the axial thickness. The design of such mirrors is more or less empirical, the object being so to proportion the radii that rays of light emanating from the chosen focal point are parallel to the axis at one zone of the mirror and do not depart greatly from parallelism for all other zones. Fig. 15.19 shows a typical Mangin reflector used in signalling lamps and a lens-mirror in which coma has been reduced. Mangin mirrors if well designed can be used to produce parallel light with sufficient accuracy for use as collimators in reflector sights.

The Schmidt camera and its many variants, some of which are shown in Fig. 15.20, make use of an aspherical plate of a special shape so designed that the spherical aberration of a concave spherical mirror is completely corrected. The corrector plate is located at the centre of curvature of the mirror in the standard Schmidt camera, and in this position its rim acts as the aperture stop. Thus for all reasonable obliquities the system remains symmetrical and no oblique aberrations are introduced. Actually complete symmetry is not achieved and there is a little remnant of oblique aberration. Unfortunately the focal surface of a Schmidt system for maximum

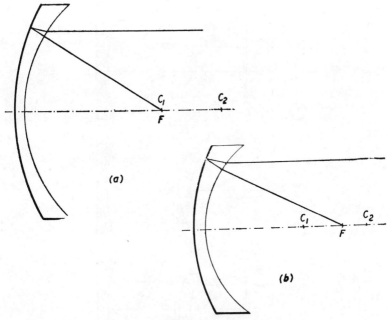

FIG. 15.19.—Mangin mirror. Two types are shown :—
   (a) Conventional Mangin.
   (b) Improved correction for coma.

efficiency must lie on a sphere concentric with the main mirror and there is always the disadvantage that the focal surface, or in other variants the secondary mirror, obstructs the incoming light. Attempts to flatten the field of Schmidt cameras invariably means a lens of some sort which immediately introduces chromatic aberration, the absence of which, except in negligible amount, in the Schmidt system is its principal asset.

In the Maksutov version of the Schmidt principle the aspherical plate is replaced by a concentric meniscus of considerable thickness which has the advantage of eliminating the troublesome and more or less empirical aspherical corrector plate. In a form developed by Wynne, two concentric meniscus lenses are used. The number of variants of these mirror-lens systems is very large and the reader should consult the references given in Appendix I for further particulars.

Some notes on a method of designing corrector plates are given in Appendix I.

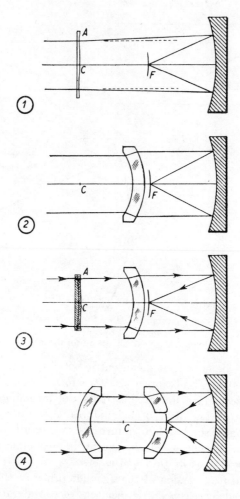

FIG. 15.20.—Systems using mirrors and correctors.

1.—Standard Schmidt system. The centre of curvature of the mirror is at C on the corrector plate.

2.—Maksutov type. The thick meniscus lens is designed to correct chromatic aberration.

3.—A Schmidt-Maksutov type using an achromatised corrector described by Hawkins and Linfoot.

4.—Double meniscus form described by Wynne.

Prisms

On pages 338–344 are shown a number of prism forms with tabulated notes on their applications. Since prisms and prism systems can be designed to fulfil almost any requirement the number of variants is very great and the table can only give examples of the principal forms. It may be as well to mention that in designing prism systems a useful artifice is to use a white rubber ball or a ping-pong ball on which to draw the directions of the light and the normals to the surfaces of the prism. Another device particularly to ascertain the length of the glass path is to develop the prism diagram by drawing the reflected images of the prism as shown in Fig. 15.21 in which several prisms have been developed to show the path of light.

An important consideration in prism design is the ratio of the glass path to the aperture which limits the angular field that the prism can

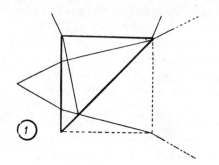

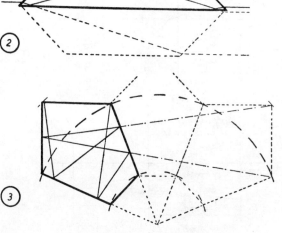

FIG. 15.21.—Development of prisms for ray tracing.
    1.—Right-angle prism is equivalent to a cube.
    2.—Dove prism is equivalent to a block of glass with parallel faces, the light being incident at an oblique angle.
    3.—The two reflections in a pentag require two developed images. The figure shows the long glass path and the extreme angular divergence which a pentag will stand.

accommodate. This ratio is given for a few of the prisms in Table 15.8 and should always be worked out, preferably by developing the prism diagram as shown in Fig. 15.21. The method of developing a simple prism is to draw the image of the actual prism in the reflecting face as shown in (1) and (2) of Fig. 15.21. The pentagonal prism has two reflecting surfaces and must therefore produce a second reflected image as shown in (3). The broken circular arcs in the figure are only construction lines to enable the two reflections to be drawn easily. The developed prism in each case is considered merely as a block of glass and the ray paths can be drawn directly through the block without considering the reflections that take place in the prism. In the diagrams in Fig. 15.21 the actual ray paths in the prisms are shown in full lines and the glass paths in the reflected images are broken lines.

Fig. 15.22 shows how the image-forming rays can be drawn through a glass block or developed prism, and the use of the equivalent air path. The figure shows that the equivalent air path is given by

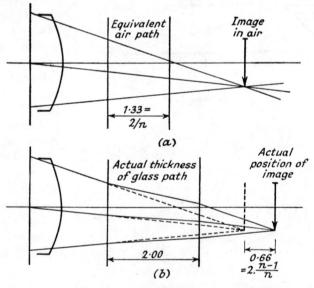

FIG. 15.22.—Effect of introducing a prism having a total glass path of 2 in. in an optical system.
(a) Ray diagram in air showing equivalent air path of prism $= 2/n$ in.($n = 1·5$)
(b) Actual ray diagram showing increase in length of system by $2(n - 1)/n$ in.

dividing the glass path by the refractive index, and the amount that the image is moved owing to the presence of the glass block is found by *multiplying* the glass path by $(n - 1)/n$. Care must be taken not to confuse these purely geometrical quantities with the physical quantity called the optical path length found by *multiplying* the path length by the refractive index to give a measure of the time taken for a disturbance to traverse the path.

Specification of optical parts

It is frequently necessary to place orders for optical parts with firms and it is essential that the information provided, or the specification of the part, should be adequate so that the firm can be expected to fulfil the requirements exactly and economically. It is a mistake to demand a higher precision than is absolutely necessary for the purpose to which the part is to be applied, and a few general rules are given below as a guide.

Plane mirrors :—Ordinary plane mirrors of sheet glass are stocked by glass firms and are easily obtainable, but are of no use for optical purposes. Plate glass mirrors, particularly in ¼-in. plate, are also easily obtained and if carefully selected can be used optically in parallel light.

Commercial glass cutters will cut sheet or plate to within plus or minus 1/16 in. in small pieces but in large pieces ⅛ in. should be allowed. They will also remove sharp edges if asked to do so, and they can grind matt or polish, flat or round, and bevel for an extra charge.

When such mirrors are ordered specially the firm should be provided with a specification of the accuracy required and some simple test should be devised for use by the firm in selecting the glass. The resolution test described in Chapter 12 can be used for selection prior to silvering (or aluminising) but after silvering some other form of test may be used. The resolution test described is applicable but it is sometimes sufficient to test the mirror by projecting an image on to a screen or the simple expedient of viewing a window obliquely by reflection in the mirror may suffice. In converging light surface or front coated mirrors must be used and here again ordinary commercial plate glass can often be used.

If an optically worked mirror surface is absolutely necessary then the firm must be told what limit of flatness is required. This is usually specified by stating the flatness in terms of the number of rings (Newton's rings) that can be tolerated and it must be realised that the greater the precision the greater the cost and the greater the thickness of the glass. The thickness of the glass should be between $\frac{1}{4}$ and $\frac{1}{8}$ of the larger dimension if the flatness is to be of the order of $\frac{1}{10}$ wave-length to $\frac{1}{4}$ wave-length. One to four rings can be fairly easily supplied and the glass need not be so thick. If necessary an interferometer test may be specified but ordinary proof-plane flatness is often adequate.

Glass windows and filters :—The same general requirements regarding flatness hold for windows and filters as for mirrors, but the parallelism must also be specified. Optically worked discs can be made to any required degree of accuracy but it cannot be too strongly emphasised that the specified limits should not be over-stated. Filters and windows are often of necessity too thin to ensure perfection and the tests used must conform to the proposed use of the filter component. The test previously described is very searching and is usually better than testing by Newton's rings. The firm must be told of the test and instructed in its use. In working such discs the two surfaces are frequently spherical but if one side is concave and the other convex within quite wide limits the disc would not cause any loss of definition or change of focus. On the other hand quite a small toroidal effect will completely destroy definition and if the disc is a weak lens a change of focus will become noticeable when it is used. Since discs are often made three or more at a time on one block, wedge effects are very common and are quite harmless in many applications. Faults to be looked for, however, are a cylindrical effect or a portion near one edge which is turned down causing excessive wedge. It is reasonable to demand a parallelism to within 2 or 3 minutes of deviation of transmitted light, but if this is not essential the firm should be informed accordingly. Deviations of less than a minute require special care in manufacture and the cost is proportionately higher.

Very thin optical flats have at times been made for special purposes using various techniques. The flats, for example may be ground on one surface and then cemented to a thick support while the thickness is reduced and the second side finished. Care has to be taken to allow for the natural spring of the glass after polishing ; it may be necessary to finish the flats slightly concave on the block so that they will spring quite flat when released.

Optical flats are essentially pieces of glass, or more frequently quartz, which are accurately flat to within 1/10 of a wave-length or less on one or both surfaces and are used mainly as proof planes so that it is a mistake to ask a firm to produce optical flats where filter or window discs are required. The term is loosely used for such discs but, if it is used to describe such a disc, the drawing or description should state the required accuracy and method of test as explained above.

Prisms. The specification of a prism should include the dimensions, angles, permitted errors, type of glass, which surfaces are to be polished and which left matt, and the sharpness or chamfers of the edges. It goes without saying that homogeneity and freedom from strain are essential and no reputable firm would deliver a prism with such faults. The dimensional accuracy is necessarily related to angular accuracy. The actual finished dimensions of a prism are seldom of great importance because prisms are usually mounted in such a way that slight adjustment is permissible and often necessary.

The angle accuracy requires very careful consideration and no greater accuracy than is essential should be demanded. Thus, in a 45 deg. right-angled prism it may be necessary to ensure that the right angle is accurate to a minute or a few seconds perhaps, but the 45 deg. angles can be allowed an error of up to 10 minutes without impairing the efficiency of the prism. On the other hand there are occasions when the 45 deg. angles must be accurately equal to each other, thus allowing some tolerance on the 90 deg. angle. A very common error in prisms is known as " prismatic " error and may require specification. In this defect the edges of the prism, instead of being truly parallel, converge towards points, i.e., the prism is slightly wedge-shaped. The tolerance on this error may be anything from 1 to 10 minutes.

Roof prisms are always difficult to make because of the necessary extreme accuracy of angle at the roof edge, usually 12 seconds or less, and because of the sharp edge which must be quite clean and free from small cracks and chips. As far as possible, therefore, roof prisms should be avoided in designing optical instruments. In a research laboratory it is seldom necessary to use a roof prism and, in fact, the use of roof prisms in general is frequently only prompted by a desire for novelty or the saving of space in construction.

The glass used for prisms is usually borosilicate crown because of its low dispersion, high transparency, durability and the ease with which it can be obtained in large pieces and well annealed. If, for

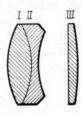

Equivalent focal length 98·7
Back focal length 85·7 ±2·0

Edges: grey & blacked
45° Chamfer grey & blacked

All dimensions in millimetres

Lens	Radius		Axial thickness	Diameter	Clear aperture	Glass	Nd	V	Axial separation
I	16·2	'vex	4·6	16·0 +0·0 −0·03	15·0	Chance B.F. 580458	1·58057	45·8	Cemented (Canada balsam) 6·2
	17·0	'vex							
II	17·0	'cave	1·1	16·0 +0·0 −0·03	15·0/13·0	Chance D.F. 623360	1·62258	36·0	
	17·0	'cave							
III	179·0	'vex	1·9	16·0 +0·0 −0·03	15·0	Chance B.F. 580458	1·58057	45·8	
	69·8	'vex							

Note: Air/glass surfaces to be 'bloomed' to secure maximum
transmission in the blue

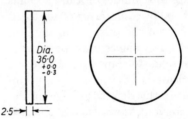

Graticule   Broken-cross pattern
Material:- Glass, Chance B.L.F. 575520
Lines to be etched and filled, not thicker than 1½ thou. inches
Length of line 10 mm.
Upper end of six o'clock line to coincide with centre of disc ±0·03 mm.
Gaps: horizontal and vertical 0·8 mm. ±0·03 mm.
Optically polished, parallel and flat

FIG. 15.23.—Examples of drawings of optical parts

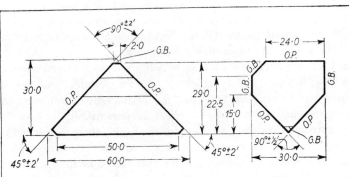

Right angle Roof-prism

Sharp edges to be removed except roof edge
Surfaces marked O.P. to be optically polished
     "   "   G.B. to be grey and then blacked
Pyramidal error not to exceed 2' of arc
All dimensions (in mms.) ±0.1
Material:- glass, Chance light flint 578407

All dimensions in mms. $\pm \frac{1}{4}$ mm.

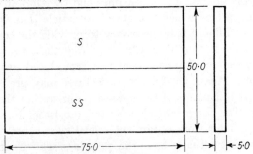

Transmitting and reflecting Plate

Material:- optical glass
Surfaces to be optically polished and parallel within $\pm\frac{1}{2}'$ of arc
    "   "   " flat to 3 fringes in mercury light
(S) One half to be fully silvered or rhodiumised
     on one side with sharp division between other half (SS) to give
     approx. 75% transmission and 25% reflection.
     Edges chamfered and grey. 2nd. surface to be 'bloomed'

prepared in suitable form for issue to a manufacturer.

some special purpose, a prism must be made in a glass of high refractive index the question of its transparency must be carefully considered as thick pieces of dense flint glasses are often tinged yellow and they are, in any case, highly absorbing.

In drawing prisms the surfaces which are to be polished should be marked with some identifying letter, " p " for example, and the matt surfaces may be marked " m " or " g," with a note of course explaining the meaning of the symbols. Glass workers usually " break " the sharp corners of prisms, i.e., they remove the sharp edges without actually bevelling or chamfering them. If the edge must be left sharp, as in roof prisms, for example, this should be indicated on the drawing. If, however, a definite bevel or chamfer is required this should be stated. Silvering, paint protection, blackening and other special finishes should also be indicated.

Lenses. When ordering lenses two courses are open to the research worker. He may provide a full specification of radii, thicknesses, glass types, edge diameters, etc., or he may ask for a lens of a given diameter having the required focal length and optical performance. Lens manufacturers usually retain a stock of tools and test plates corresponding to stock lines and therefore it is always cheaper to obtain a lens which is a standard article than to have one made specially. Should it be necessary to provide the complete computed specification it must be remembered that the catalogue values for the glass types will not necessarily be reproduced exactly in the glass available. Again the lens manufacturer may prefer to use existing tools and test plates of the nearest radius rather than make up fresh articles. The designer of a lens system must therefore quite early in the progress of his work obtain the actual glass types he intends to use, i.e., he must actually have the glass in stock. Next he should make inquiries regarding the tools and test plates available and if necessary alter his design to suit the nearest existing tools. The making of tools and test plates is often necessary and in fact it is the only way in which a manufacturer acquires his stock.

The drawing of the lens should show all the radii and a note should be added regarding the sign convention adopted. Many manufacturers call all convex surfaces positive and all concave surfaces negative, while others use the geometrical sign convention in which centre of curvature to the right is positive and to the left negative— light travelling from left to right. The thickness and edge diameters must of course be specified and any chamfers or bevels dimensioned.

Edge diameters should be shown as maximum diameters with the limits plus zero, minus (say) 5 thousandths of an inch.

When ordering standard lenses the order should state the dimensions, limits of acceptable focal lengths, limits of acceptable back focal distance, type of achromatism required, i.e., whether the C and F or the D and G' lines are to be brought to the same focus. The limits of spherical aberration may also be specified and whether the lens is to be corrected for coma. The larger lens manufacturers always have particulars of a great variety of lenses with widely varying optical qualities and can often supply a lens quickly which will fit fairly closely to some desired specification. It is therefore always advisable to consult a manufacturer before commencing the laborious work of designing a lens.

Fig. 15.23 shows a representative selection of optical parts.

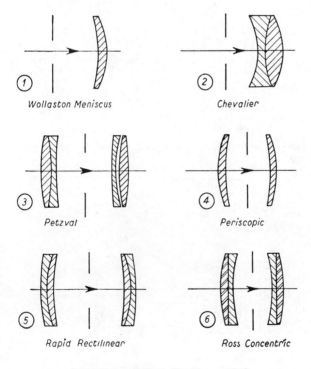

CAMERA LENSES (*See* TABLE 15.7)

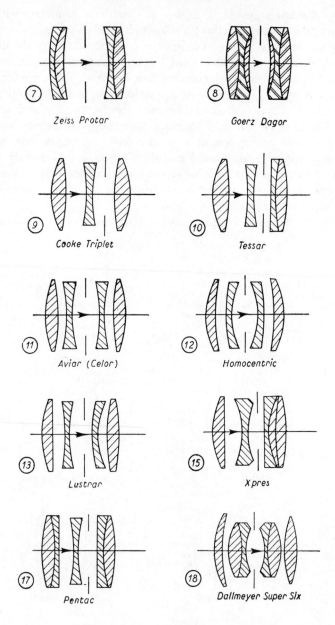

(7) Zeiss Protar

(8) Goerz Dagor

(9) Cooke Triplet

(10) Tessar

(11) Aviar (Celor)

(12) Homocentric

(13) Lustrar

(15) Xpres

(17) Pentac

(18) Dallmeyer Super Six

CAMERA LENSES (*See* TABLE 15.7)

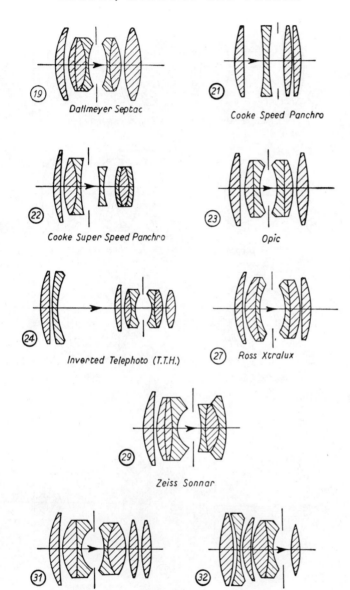

19 — Dallmeyer Septac

21 — Cooke Speed Panchro

22 — Cooke Super Speed Panchro

23 — Opic

24 — Inverted Telephoto (T.T.H.)

27 — Ross Xtralux

29 — Zeiss Sonnar

31 — T.T.H. F/1·5

32 — T.T.H. F/1·0

CAMERA LENSES (*See* TABLE 15.7)

331

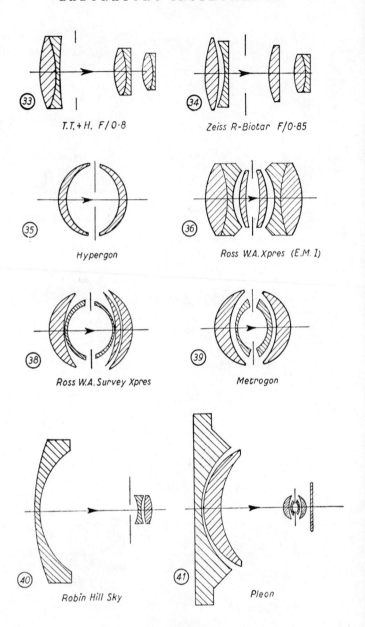

33 T.T.+H. F/0·8

34 Zeiss R-Biotar F/0·85

35 Hypergon

36 Ross W.A.Xpres (E.M.I)

38 Ross W.A.Survey Xpres

39 Metrogon

40 Robin Hill Sky

41 Pleon

CAMERA LENSES (*See* TABLE 15.7)

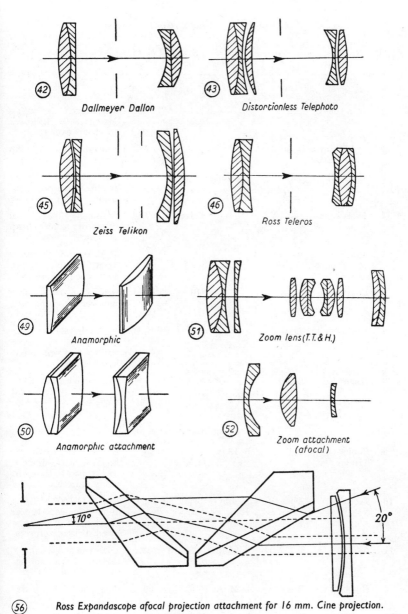

42 Dallmeyer Dallon

43 Distortionless Telephoto

45 Zeiss Telikon

46 Ross Teleros

49 Anamorphic

51 Zoom lens (T.T.& H.)

50 Anamorphic attachment

52 Zoom attachment (afocal)

56 Ross Expandascope afocal projection attachment for 16 mm. Cine projection.

CAMERA LENSES (*See* TABLE 15.7)

TABLE 15.7—*Photographic Lenses*

No.	Name	Made by	Focal Lengths	Aperture	Field deg.	Remarks
			I OLD FORMS			
1	Meniscus	All	—	*f*11–*f*16	45	Introduced by Wollaston 1812. Still used in cheap cameras.
2	Achromatic Landscape	—	—	*f*11	45	Chevalier 1821, no longer manufactured.
3	Petzval	All	Various	*f*8–*f*3	25	Petzval 1841. Many modifications and variations.
4	Periscopic	—	—	*f*11	45	Steinheil 1865. Still used in some cheap cameras.
5	Rapid Rectilinear	—	—	*f*8	45	Dallmeyer & Steinheil 1866. Still used in some cheap cameras.
6	Concentric	Ross	—	*f*16	70	Schroeder 1888 using new glasses. No longer manufactured.
7	Protar	Zeiss	—	*f*9–*f*18	Up to 100	Rudolph 1890, old and new achromats, type still used in wide angle lens designs.
8	Dagor	Goerz	—	*f*6·8, etc.	Up to 90	Von Höegh 1893. Basis of many symmetrical varieties.
			II GENERAL PURPOSE LENSES			
9	Cooke Triplet	T.T. & H.	5–18 in.	*f*5·6, *f*4·5, etc.	50	H. D. Taylor 1893. Basis of many modern lens types. Made in many varieties.
10	Tessar	Zeiss	15 mm.– 12 in. or more	*f*4·5 to *f*2·8	35–70, normal 55	Rudolph 1902. Basis of many modern types. Made in many varieties by most manufacturers.
11	Aviar	T.T. & H.	5–20 in.	*f*4·5, *f*5·6, etc.	53	Von Höegh " Celor " 1898. Basic design commonly used.
12	Homocentric	Ross	4–24 in.	*f*5·6, etc.	56	Ross 1902. Basic design in common use.
13	Lustrar	Wray	¾–15 in.	*f*6·3– *f*1·5	50	Manufactured in many varieties—a useful series.

No.	Name	Made by	Focal Lengths	Aperture	Field deg.	Remarks
14	Serrac Dalmac	Dallmeyer	1¼–18 in. 1¼–15 in.	$f4.5$ $f3.5$	53	A useful series of lenses similar in design to the Tessar.
15	Xpres	Ross		$f3.5$ $f4.5$	55	Useful series of lenses similar in design to the Tessar but with a triplet in place of the doublet of the Tessar.
16	Xpres E.M.I.	Ross	12 in. 25 in.	$f5.6$ $f6.3$	54 30	Designed to cover 9 × 9 in. specially for Air Survey Photography. Free from distortion.

III Large Aperture Lenses

No.	Name	Made by	Focal Lengths	Aperture	Field deg.	Remarks
17	Pentac	Dallmeyer	1–12 in.	$f2.9$	53	A good lens made in very large quantities for air photography by day and night.
18	Super Six	Dallmeyer	1–8 in.	$f1.9$	48	A useful series of good performance having many applications.
19	Septac	Dallmeyer	2 in.	$f1.5$		Short focus for 16 and 35 mm. motion picture photography.
20	Cooke Series x (Speedic)	T.T. & H.	6¼–9¼ in.	$f2.5$	45	A good general purpose lens of fairly long focal length.
21	Cooke Speed Panchro	T.T. & H.	24–108 mm.	$f2$	64	Lenses designed primarily for 16 and 35 mm. motion picture photography. Performance is very good.
22	Cooke Super Speed Panchro	T.T. & H.	2¼ in.	$f1.3$		
23	Cooke Series O (Opic)	T.T. & H.	1¼–5½ in.	$f2$	50	This type of lens design is being increasingly used in modern high aperture lenses.
24	Inverted Telephoto	Dallmeyer & T.T. & H.	½ in.	$f3.5$		Short focus lens with extra long back focus, for 16 mm. cine cameras.
25	Xpres	Ross	1–3 in. 1–10 in.	$f1.9$ & $f2.9$	45 53	In the shorter focal lengths for 16 and 35 mm. cine cameras
26	Ektar	Kodak	—	$f2$	54	
27	Xtralux	Ross	5, 9, 13.5 cm.	$f2$	Cover 36 × 24 mm.	Specially designed for miniature cameras.

No.	Name	Made by	Focal Lengths	Aperture	Field deg.	Remarks
28	Lustrar	Wray	25, 50 mm. $\frac{3}{4}$–2 in. 3–8 in.	$f1\cdot5$ $f2\cdot5$ $f2\cdot8$		At $f1\cdot4$–$f2$ these lenses are intended for 16 and 35 mm. motion picture photography. In the longer focal lengths at about $f2.9$ they are useful in many photographic applications.
29	Sonnar	Zeiss	25 mm. 50 mm. 10–85 mm. 50, 180 mm.	$f1\cdot4$ $f1\cdot5$ $f2$ $f2\cdot8$	27 45 27 30	
30	Biotar	Zeiss	20–70 mm. 40–80 mm.	$f1\cdot4$ $f2$	40 55	

IV RADIOGRAPHIC LENSES OF EXTREME APERTURES

No.	Name	Made by	Focal Lengths	Aperture	Field deg.	Remarks
31	—	T.T. & H.		$f1\cdot5$		These lenses are designed specifically for motion picture photography of X-ray screens on 16 and 35 mm. film.
32	—	T.T. & H.		$f1\cdot0$		
33	—	T.T. & H.		$f0\cdot8$		
34	R. Biotar	Zeiss	45, 55 mm.	$f0\cdot85$	14	

V WIDE ANGLE LENSES

No.	Name	Made by	Focal Lengths	Aperture	Field deg.	Remarks
35	Hypergon	Goerz	5–12 cm.	$f22$	140	Extreme wide angle but small aperture.
36	W.A.Xpres (E.M.I.)	Ross	2–10 in.	$f4$	70	A large aperture W.A. lens of great value. Infra-red focus coincides very nearly with visual focus.
37	W.A. Anastigmat	All	$2\frac{3}{8}$–9 in.	$f16$	90–100	All manufacturers make such lenses of various types, commonly based on the Zeiss Protar.
38	W.A. Survey Xpres	Ross	$3\frac{1}{4}$ & 6 in.	$f5\cdot5$	95	Specially designed for wide angle air survey photography.
39	Metrogen	Zeiss Bausch & Lomb	$5\frac{1}{8}$ & 6 in.	$6\cdot3$	90	Used for wide angle air photography.
40	Robin Hill Sky	R. & J. Beck	—	$f22$	180	Extreme wide angle obtained by introducing large negative distortion so that a reasonable plate size can be used and an increase in marginal illumination obtained.
41	Pleon	Zeiss	72 mm. at centre	$f8$	130	
41(a)	Aviogon	Wild	100 mm.	$f5$	90 to 125	Distortionless extra wide angle air survey photography.

No.	Name	Made by	Focal Lengths	Aperture	Field deg.	Remarks

VI TELEPHOTO LENSES

No.	Name	Made by	Focal Lengths	Aperture	Field deg.	Remarks
42	Dallon	Dallmeyer	4–60 in.	$f5\cdot6$ $f7\cdot7$ $f8$	20–30	Most lens manufacturers have made telephoto lenses since 1900 but aperture remained low until appearance of Dallon $f5\cdot6$ by Booth. T.T. & H. have made a lens at $f3\cdot5$ by Lee. The large distortion in most telephoto lenses overcome in the T.T.H. distortionless lens by Lee. The Zeiss Telikon has a relatively large negative element to give increased marginal illumination.
43	Distortionless Telephoto	T.T. & H.	—	$f5$	—	
44	{New Large {Adon	Dallmeyer	6–24 in.	$f4\cdot5$	25	
45	Telikon	Zeiss	30 in.	$f5\cdot6$	25	
46	Teleros	Ross	9 &17 in. 13 &17 in.	$f5\cdot5$ $f6\cdot3$	Up to 30	
47	Adon Grandac	Dallmeyer	Variable Focus	Variable	Variable	
48	Cine Telephoto	Dallmeyer	$1\frac{1}{2}$–12 in.	$f3\cdot5$– $f5\cdot6$	Cover cine Frame	

VII MISCELLANEOUS

No.	Name	Made by	Focal Lengths	Aperture	Field deg.	Remarks
49	Anamorphic	Special	—	—	Small	Distorted scale in two directions.
50	Anamorphic Attachment (afocal)	Special	—	—	—	Cylindrical Galilean system.
51	Zoom Lens (Warmisham & Cisski)	T.T. & H.	—	—	—	Systems of continuously variable focal length in which image is held constantly in focus by mechanical means.
52	Zoom Attachment (afocal) (Gramatzki)	—	—	—	—	
53	Zoomar "16"	Zoomar Inc., New York	1–3 in. Variable	$f2\cdot8$	—	Range 11 ft. to infinity. Coupled viewfinder. Size $4\frac{1}{2} \times 5 \times 2$ in. Weight 20 oz.
54	Reflectar	Zoomar Inc., New York	40 in. 80 in. 150 in.	$f8$ $f15$ $f25$	To cover $2\frac{1}{2}$ in. Diameter	Reflecting Objectives.
55	Varotel Zoom Lens	Taylor, Taylor & Hobson, Ltd., Leicester, England	4–20 in.	$f4\cdot5$	23–$4\frac{1}{2}$	Range 15 ft. to infinity. Overall length 29 in.
56	Expandascope	Ross	Afocal	—	—	Anamorphic attachment for wide screen projection.

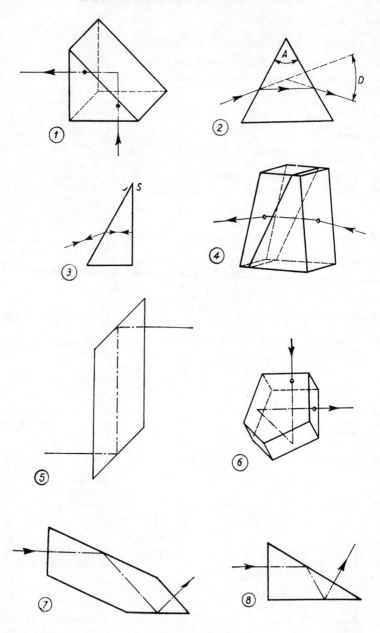

PRISMS (*See* TABLE 15.8)

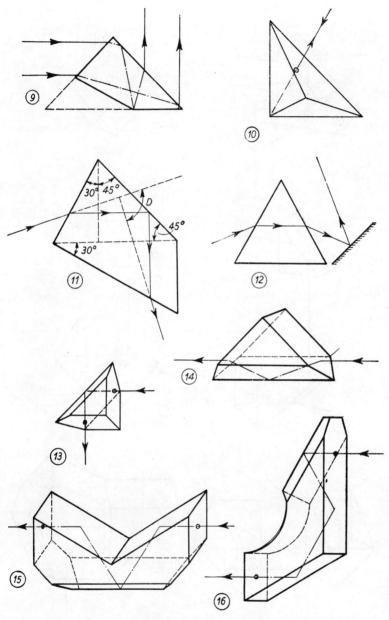

PRISMS (*See* TABLE 15.8)

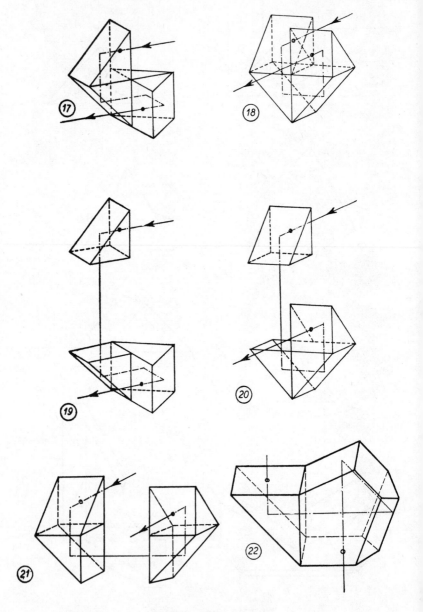

PRISMS (*See* TABLE 15.8)

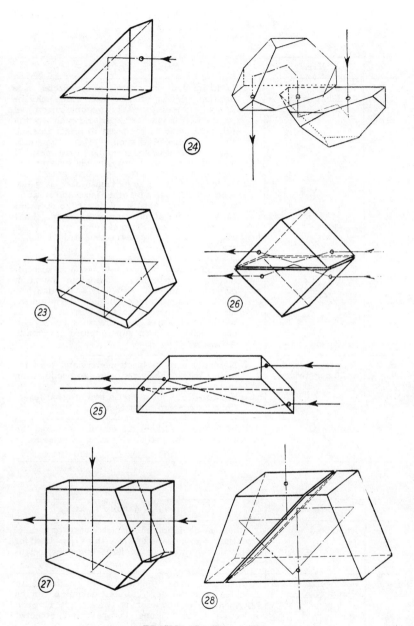

PRISMS (*See* **Table** 15.8)

TABLE 15.8—*Prism Types*

No.	Name	Properties and Uses
1	Right angle or 45 deg. prism	(*i*) Light incident on square face is reflected once internally by hypotenuse face, which may be silvered if necessary. Acts as simple mirror and rotation about an axis perpendicular to the principal plane causes beam to rotate through twice the angle of rotation of prism. In parallel light may be used for scanning (periscopes). If rotated in any other way, image also rotates. Used also in binoculars—see Porro prisms. (*ii*) Light incident on hypotenuse face is twice reflected internally by other faces and rotation of prism about axis in 90 deg. edge does not cause any deviation of reflected beam. Used in binoculars—see Porro systems. (*iii*) May be used for 90 deg. constant deviation—see No. 9.
2	Equilateral or 60 deg. prism	(*i*) Normally used in spectroscopes and spectrometers for dispersion. Minimum deviation given by formula $n = \sin \frac{1}{2}(D + A)/\sin \frac{1}{2}A$. (*ii*) Used occasionally for 60 deg. deviation as mirror. When used in this way in front of telescope objective two directions 60 deg. on either side are seen superimposed (Prismatic Astrolabe).
3	Semi equilateral or 30 deg. prism	(*i*) Normally used in spectrometers and refractometers with one silvered face—autocollimating instruments. (*ii*) See also No. 8 for use with two internal reflections for constant deviation.
4	Achromatic	Where deviation without dispersion is required the prism may be achromatised by using two glasses, as for lenses.

No.	Name	Constant Deviation Prisms
5	Rhomboid	Produces no deviation but displaces beam in parallel direction. Simple periscope is of this type. Used for interocular adjustment in large binocular instruments.
6	Pentagonal or Prandl (Pentag.)	A prism with many applications. In standard form deviates beam 90 deg. but any deviation can be obtained. The deviation is twice angle between reflecting surfaces. Long glass path and restricted field. Glass path = $3\cdot414 \times$ aperture.

No.	Name	Constant Deviation Prisms—cont.
7 8 9	45 deg. Deviation 60 deg. Deviation 90 deg. Deviation	Variations of the pentag used largely for inclined eyepieces of instruments, bent telescopes, etc.
10	Corner Cube or Tetrahedron	Causes beam to retrace its path for any angle of incidence. Secret signalling and homing devices, aiming marks. In modified form used largely in road signs.
11	Spectroscope Prism	Used in wavelength spectrometers, etc. Deviation is 90 deg. for each colour at minimum deviation angle.
12	Prism and mirror (Wadsworth)	Deviation at any constant angle at minimum deviation incidence angle. Used in spectrometers, monochromaters, etc., in a number of variations.

No.	Name	Erecting Prisms
13 14	Amici or 90 deg. Roof prism Amici	90 deg. deviation with complete erection. If used in parallel light other deviations attained by rotation as in No. 14. Glass path = 1·707 × aperture.
15	Abbé	Straight through prism frequently made in two parts. Gives complete erection. Glass path = 5·196 × aperture.
16	Sprenger or Leman	Straight through with displacement. NOTE.—All forms of roof prism are difficult to manufacture accurately and are consequently expensive. Their use in instruments should be avoided if possible. Glass path = 5·196 × aperture.

No.	Name	Erecting Combinations of Prisms
17 18 19 20 21	} Porro systems {	Known as Porro system of the first type. System of the second type. First type with periscopic extension. Second type with periscopic extension. Second type using pair of tetrahedrons.
22 23	} Hensoldt or Huet	Consists of a pentag with one roof and an added right angle prism. Used in some binoculars with periscopic extension. Glass path = 5·328 × aperture.
24	Daubresse	Two tetrahedrons with two faces in form of right angled triangles. Action similar to Porro arrangement but with added advantage that relative rotation of prisms, keeping adjacent faces parallel, does not cause any rotation of image. Of use in articulating systems.

No.	Name	Miscellaneous Types
25	Dove, Wirth or half speed prism	Essentially a truncated right angle prism used to produce rotation of the image at zero deviation. Used largely in panoramic periscopes (Dial sights) to correct rotation of image caused by rotation of top prism. Prism rotates at half the speed of the top prism, hence the name " Half speed."
26	Backed Isosceles prisms	A pair of isosceles prisms with their bases together, but not in optical contact, can be used for scanning in one plane. Accuracy in manufacture difficult to maintain.
27	Beam splitting Pentag	By cementing a half reflecting surface prism on one face a straight through vision block is obtained with a side view by reflection.
28	Schmidt	Made in several forms to produce erection and or rotation without displacement. Much discussed but seldom used.

Books

The following books should be consulted for further information on the subjects treated in Chapters 15, 16.

MARTIN, L. C., *Technical Optics*, Vols. I and II (Pitman).
TAYLOR, H. D., *A System of Applied Optics* (Macmillan) 1906. (Out of print.)
CONRADY, A. E., *Applied Optics and Optical Design* (Oxford).
JOHNSON, B. K., *Practical Optics* (Hatton Press).
GLEICHEN, A., *Modern Optical Instruments* (H.M.S.O.). (Out of print.)
JACOBS, D. H., *Optical Engineering* (McGraw Hill).
MARTIN, L. C., *Optical Measuring Instruments* (Blackie).
HABELL, K. J., & COX, A., *Engineering Optics* (Pitman).
TAYLOR, H. D., *Testing of Telescopes* (Howard Grubb).
COX, A., *Photographic Optics* (Focal Press).
HENNEY & DUDLEY, *Handbook of Photography* (McGraw Hill).
BECK, C., *The Microscope* (Beck). (Out of print.)
MARTIN, L. C., & JOHNSON, B. K., *Practical Microscopy* (Blackie).
WHITTAKER, E. T., *Theory of Optical Instruments* (Cambridge). (Out of print.)
HOPKINS, H. H., *Wave Theory of Aberrations* (Oxford), 1950.
STEWARD, G. C., *Symmetrical Optical Instruments* (Cambridge).
HARDY, A. C., & PERRIN, F. H., *The Principles of Optics* (McGraw Hill), 1932.
BOUWERS, A., *Achievements in Optics* (Elsevier, Cleaver Hume Press).
Proceedings of the Optical Convention 1926 (Physical Society).
Proceedings of the Optical Convention, 1950. Chapman & Hall (London).
VON ROHR, M., *Formation of Images in Optical Instruments* (H.M.S.O.). (O/P)
MARTIN, L. C., *Geometrical Optics* (Pitman), 1955.
HOUSTON, R. A., *Physical Optics* (Blackie), 1957.
LONGHURST, R. S., *Geometrical and Physical Optics* (Longmans, Green), 1957.

In addition to the above books there are numerous very useful articles in the volumes of the *Transactions of the Optical Society*, now merged in the *Physical Society*, and in the *Proceeding of the Physical Society*. The *Journal of the Optical Society of America* is always interesting and informative and the *Revue d'Optique* should also be consulted. It will also frequently be found that old books, long out of print, contain many devices which appear to have been forgotten.

REFERENCES

KAPRELIAN, E. K., " Recent and Unusual German Lens Designs," *J.O.S.A.*, **37** (June 1947), 466.

COX, A., and MARTIN, H. W., " The Assessment of Lenses," *J. Sci. Inst.*, **22** (Jan. 1945), 5.

TAYLOR, E. W., "The Inverting Eyepiece and its Evolution," *J. Sci. Inst.*, **22** (Mar. 1945), 43.

HOPKINS, H. H., " Light Waves and Lenses," *Phot. Jour.*, **86B** (May 1946), 73.

MARTIN, L. C., " Physical Study of Optical Images," *Phot. Jour.*, **86B** (Mar. 1946), 47.

HERZBERGER, M., " Light Distribution in Optical Images," *J.O.S.A.*, **37** (June 1947), 485.

KINGSLAKE, R., " Classification of Photographic Lens Types," *J.O.S.A.*, **36** (May 1946), 251.

KINGSLAKE, R., " Lenses for Aerial Photography," *J.O.S.A.*, **32** (March 1934), 129.

KINGSLAKE, R., " The Development of the Photographic Objective," *J.O.S.A.*, **24** (March 1934), 73.

BENNETT, A. H., " The Development of the Microscope Objective," *J.O.S.A.*, **33** (March 1943), 123.

BURCH, C. R., " Reflecting Microscopes," *Proc. Phys. Soc.*, **59** (Jan. 1947), 41.

BURCH, C. R., " Semi Aplanat Reflecting Microscopes," *Proc. Phys. Soc.*, **59** (Jan. 1947), 47.

REISS, M., "Notes on the $\cos^4$ Law of Illumination." *J.O.S.A.*, **38** (1948), 980.

FOSTER, L. V., " Microscope Optics," *J.O.S.A.*, **40** (1950), 275.

GREY, D. S., & LEE, P. H., " A New Series of Microscope Objectives," " I Catadioptric Newtonian Systems," *J.O.S.A.*, **39** (1949), 719.

GREY, D. S., " II Catadioptric Schwarzchild Systems," *J.O.S.A.*, **39** (1949), 723. " III U.V. Objectives of Intermediate Numerical Aperture," *J.O.S.A.*, **40** (1950), 283.

DYSON, J., " A Unit Magnification Optical System for the Attainment of Long Working Distance in Microscopy," *Proc. Phys. Soc.*, **62B**, 565.

BARER, R. "The Reflecting Microscope" *Lancet*, (March 1949), 533.

PAYNE, B. O., " Observations on Condensers, Objectives and Eyepieces," *J. Roy. Mic. Soc.*, **69** (1949), 200, **70** (1950), 317.

NORRIS, K. P., SEEDS, W. E. & WILKINS, M. H. F. " Reflecting Microscopes with Spherical Mirrors," *J.O.S.A.*, **41** (Feb. 1951), 111.

BLAISSE, B. S., BOUWERS, A., and BULTHUIS, "Catadioptric Microscope Objectives with Concentric Mirrors," *App. Sci. Res. Sec.B.*, **2**, p. 453 (1952).

NORRIS, K. P., "The Reflecting Microscope," *Research*, **8**, 94 (1955),

BACK, FRANK G., *A Large Range Variable Magnification Telescope, J.O.S.A.*, **43**, 1195 (1953).

WYNNE, C. G., *New Lens Systems*, Reports on Progress in Physics, **XIX**, 298 Physical Society (London) (1956).

Chapter 16

OPTICAL INSTRUMENTS

In Chapter 15 we have given an account of lenses, mirrors and prisms, all of which are optical instruments in the true sense, and here we shall describe the compound instruments of which the lenses, mirrors and prisms are the component parts. It will be assumed that the reader is already familiar with the standard optical instruments described in text books on optics and the instruments described in this chapter will be those with special applications to laboratory work or engineering requirements.

The eye

The physiological structure of the eye is described fully in many text books and we shall discuss here only its properties as an instrument and its defects and limitations. As is well known the light sensitive elements of the eye consist of rods and cones. At the fovea there are only cones, closely packed, and over the remainder of the retina the number of cones per unit area diminishes while the number of rods increases. This distribution means that distinct vision is limited to a small area round the fovea and since the cones are the only colour sensitive elements the perception of colour diminishes also as the image is formed farther away from the fovea. The cones also are more sensitive to strong light and take no part in vision under very low lighting. Under these conditions the rods only act as receptors and hence in very dim light and when fully dark adapted, objects looked at directly are invisible while objects forming images in the outer areas of the retina remain visible. Under twilight and low light conditions colours cannot be discriminated. Rod vision is called *scotopic* and cone vision *photopic*.

The eye is not equally sensitive to all colours and Fig. 16.1 shows its spectral sensitivity under bright lighting and under low lighting conditions. Tables 16.1 and 16.2 give respectively the values of the *relative visibility factor* or *relative luminous efficiency* (V_λ) for bright light (Photopic vision) and the *relative Scotopic luminous efficiency* (V_λ') for low levels of luminance from which the curves of Fig. 16.1 are drawn. These functions enable us to evaluate electromagnetic

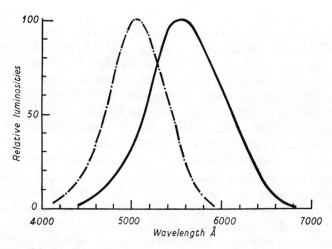

FIG. 16.1.—Luminosity curves for equal energy spectrum. The full line shows the sensitivity of the eye to bright light (photopic) and the broken line to dim light (scotopic).

TABLE 16.1—*Relative Photopic Luminous Efficiency of Monochromatic Radiation (V_λ) for Equal Energy Spectrum*

λ A.U.	0	100	200	300	400	500	600	700	800	900
4000	0·0004	0·0012	0·0040	0·0116	0·023	0·038	0·060	0·091	0·139	0·208
5000	0·323	0·503	0·710	0·862	0·954	0·995	0·995	0·952	0·870	0·757
6000	0·631	0·503	0·381	0·265	0·175	0·107	0·061	0·032	0·017	0·0082
7000	0·0041	0·0021	0·00105	0·00052	0·00025	0·00012	0·00006			

TABLE 16.2—*Relative Scotopic Luminous Efficiency of Monochromatic Radiation (V'_λ) for Equal Energy Spectrum*

λ A.U.	0	100	200	300	400	500	600	700	800	900
3000	—	—	—	—	—	—	—	—	$5·89 \times 10^{-4}$	$2·209 \times 10^{-3}$
4000	0·00929	0·03484	0·0966	0·1998	0·3281	0·455	0·567	0·676	0·793	0·904
5000	0·982	0·997	0·935	0·811	0·650	0·481	0·3288	0·2076	0·1212	0·0655
6000	0·03315	0·01593	0·00737	$3·335 \times 10^{-3}$	$1·497 \times 10^{-3}$	$6·77 \times 10^{-4}$	$3·129 \times 10^{-4}$	$1·480 \times 10^{-4}$	$7·15 \times 10^{-5}$	$3·533 \times 10^{-5}$
7000	$1·780 \times 10^{-5}$	$9·14 \times 10^{-6}$	$4·78 \times 10^{-6}$	$2·546 \times 10^{-6}$	$1·379 \times 10^{-6}$	$7·60 \times 10^{-7}$	$4·25 \times 10^{-7}$	$2·413 \times 10^{-7}$	$1·39 \times 10^{-7}$	

radiation as light. The values of the functions are the result of many experimental investigations and have been adopted by the Comité Internationale de l'Eclairage (C.I.E.) and the Comité Internationale des Poids et Mesures (C.I.P.M.). It will be seen that in bright light the maximum sensitivity occurs at about 5500A. but in very dim light the maximum occurs at about 5000A. This shift in the curve of sensitivity is known as the *Purkinje* effect. One result of this relative shift is that red light does not destroy dark adaptation and therefore people who require to remain dark adapted can safely remain in comparatively strong red light or wear red glasses.

There is a minimum quantity of light, known as the threshold quantity, which must reach the eye in order that light may be seen at all. If the source of light subtends less than about 50 minutes at the eye the threshold quantity is proportional to the candle-power of the source, i.e., the brightness multiplied by the area, or in other words the brightness required is inversely proportional to the square of the diameter. As the source increases in size, from about 1 deg. to 4 deg., the threshold brightness is approximately inversely proportional to the diameter (L. C. Martin). For still larger sizes the threshold brightness is independent of the size of the source. The threshold brightness depends on the part of the retina used and the state of adaptation of the eye. The curves in Fig. 16.2 show how the light sensitivity of the eye for bright light and for weak light vary over the retina and Fig. 16.3 shows how the threshold changes with time of dark adaptation.

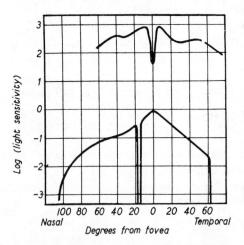

FIG. 16.2.—Variation of light sensitivity across the retina. The lower curve is for the photopic eye and the upper for the scotopic eye. Note that the scotopic eye is very much more sensitive to light particularly in the region of the retina very near the fovea (parafoveal region).

It is seen from the curves that the region of the retina just outside the fovea (the parafoveal region) is most sensitive to weak light and there is some evidence to

348

suggest that when some light falls on this para-foveal region it tends to increase the general sensitivity in the foveal region. These researches are important for the de-velopment of night-seeing instruments, the theory of which is not quite clear at present. It is a well-known fact that despite the inevitable loss of light caused by the use of an

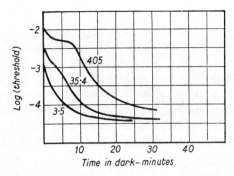

FIG. 16.3.—Variation of dark adaptation with intensity of previous stimulation (Winsor & Clark).

optical instrument objects viewed in very weak light with the use of a magnifying system appear to be brighter and are more visible. The night glass effect is apparently caused by the presentation of a larger, although less bright, image to the retina. (See p. 408.)

An important law of vision known as Fechner's Law states that the difference in brightness of two objects necessary for one to be recog-nised as brighter than the other is a constant fraction of the actual brightness. The difference is about 1 per cent but the law does not remain true either for very dim or for very bright sources.

This sets a limit to the accuracy of optical measurements. At very low intensities the Fechner fraction rises to 0·5 or more and Fig. 16.4 which shows the variation of the Fechner fraction with field bright-ness also shows that it varies with the colour of the light. The best

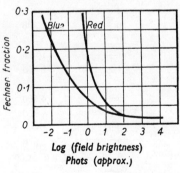

Log (field brightness) Phots (approx.)

FIG. 16.4.—Variation of the Fechner fraction with field brightness.

intensity of light contrast when using photometers, etc., is be-tween 8 and 20 millilamberts, while for reading about 30 milli-lamberts is most satisfactory. (See p. 399 for definition.)

For any actual source, the rela-tive quantity of light sensation produced by each wave-length is proportional to the product of the ordinates of the visibility curve (Fig. 16.1) and the energy distribution curve of the source for the wave-length in question (Fig. 16.5). This product is termed the *luminosity* for the wave-length.

Table 16.3 gives the brightness in candles per square centimetre of a number of sources and some energy distribution curves are shown in Fig. 16.5.

Various terms, such as candle-power, intensity, brightness have been used in this chapter and in other parts, and references have been made to radiated energy. Definitions of these terms and the relations between them are given in Chapter 17.

TABLE 16.3—*Luminance and Colour Temperature of Sources*

	Luminance cd/cm^2	Colour Temp. °K.
Zenith Sun at Earth's surface	165,000	5,400
Carbon arc, high intensity, 150 amp.	80,000	5,000–5,500
Carbon arc, crater, solid carbons	17,200	3,780
Zirconia, concentrated arc	3,000–10,000	—
Mercury Vapour:		
high pressure, compact source, 1,000 watt	40,000	—
high pressure, compact source, 250 watt	20,000	—
glass, tubular, low pressure	2·3	—
Photoflood lamp	2,500	3,250
Tungsten filament, gas-filled, 21·2 lm/watt	1,325	3,000
,, ,, ,, 18·1 ,,	1,000	2,920
,, ,, ,, 15·2 ,,	772	2,810
,, ,, ,, 12·9 ,,	597	2,740
,, ,, vacuum 7·9 ,,	125	2,400
Welsbach gas mantle, high pressure	25	—
,, ,, ,, low pressure	4·8–5·8	—
Acetylene (Kodak burner)	10·8	2,360
Sodium discharge lamp	10	—
Paraffin lamp (round wick)	1·5	1,920
,, ,, (flat wick)	1·25	2,055
Tubular fluorescent lamp, 40 watt:		
55 lm/watt, cool daylight	0·6	6,800
60 lm/watt, white	0·6	4,200
65 lm/watt, warm white	0·6	2,900
Candle	0·5	1,930
Clear blue sky	0·4	12,000–24,000
Full moon	0·25	—
CaS (Bi) Phosphor, 30 sec. after illumination	10^{-5}	—

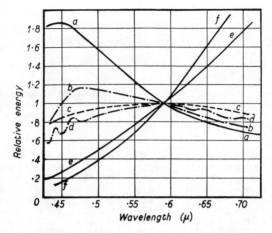

FIG. 16.5.—Energy distribution curves in the spectra of various illuminants.

(a)	Blue sky	(d)	Low sun
(b)	High sun	(e)	Gas-filled tungsten lamp
(c)	Black body at 5000° C.	(f)	Acetylene flame

The curves show relative values only and the value at wave-length 0·59μ has been taken as unity in each case.

Colour of Light

Any colour, with a few exceptions, can be reproduced by mixing a certain proportion of white light with a monochromatic light and the resulting hue may be specified by the wave-length, and the degree of saturation by the percentage of the coloured light used, but the standard method of specifying the colour of radiation is a trichromatic system adopted by the C.I.E. in 1931. The system is intended to enable the colour of a light source, or of painted or dyed surfaces, etc., to be specified without reference to a sample. The colour is specified by the relative amounts of red, green and blue light primaries, X, Y and Z respectively which when mixed will reproduce the colour required. The nature of the primaries is considered below; X, Y and Z are determined as follows.

Over the whole visible region in an equal-energy spectrum, the amounts of red, green and blue light required to match successive narrow ranges of wave-length have been determined experimentally by a number of observers. The agreed averages (for a so-called " standard observer "), are the quantities $\bar{x}$, $\bar{y}$ and $\bar{z}$ in Table 16.4. It will be seen that they tend to zero at each end of the spectrum. They are known as *tristimulus values* or *distribution coefficients*. The

351

TABLE 16.4—*Chromaticity Co-ordinates for Monochromatic Radiations and Distribution Coefficients in the C.I.E. Reference System*

Chromaticity co-ordinates			Wave-length $(m\mu)$	Distribution coefficients for monochromatic radiation of equal energy		
x	y	z		$\bar{x}$	$\bar{y}$	$\bar{z}$
0·1741	0·0050	0·8209	380	0·0014	0·0000	0·0065
0·1738	0·0049	0·8213	390	0·0042	0·0001	0·0201
0·1733	0·0048	0·8219	400	0·0143	0·0004	0·0679
0·1726	0·0048	0·8226	410	0·0435	0·0012	0·2074
0·1714	0·0051	0·8235	420	0·1344	0·0040	0·6456
0·1689	0·0069	0·8242	430	0·2839	0·0116	1·3856
0·1644	0·0109	0·8247	440	0·3483	0·0230	1·7471
0·1566	0·0177	0·8257	450	0·3362	0·0380	1·7721
0·1440	0·0297	0·8263	460	0·2908	0·0600	1·6692
0·1241	0·0578	0·8181	470	0·1954	0·0910	1·2876
0·0913	0·1327	0·7760	480	0·0956	0·1390	0·8130
0·0454	0·2950	0·6596	490	0·0320	0·2080	0·4652
0·0082	0·5384	0·4534	500	0·0049	0·3230	0·2720
0·0139	0·7502	0·2359	510	0·0093	0·5030	0·1582
0·0743	0·8338	0·0919	520	0·0633	0·7100	0·0782
0·1547	0·8059	0·0394	530	0·1655	0·8620	0·0422
0·2296	0·7543	0·0161	540	0·2904	0·9540	0·0203
0·3016	0·6923	0·0061	550	0·4334	0·9950	0·0087
0·3731	0·6245	0·0024	560	0·5945	0·9950	0·0039
0·4441	0·5547	0·0012	570	0·7621	0·9520	0·0021
0·5125	0·4866	0·0009	580	0·9163	0·8700	0·0017
0·5752	0·4242	0·0006	590	1·0263	0·7570	0·0011
0·6270	0·3725	0·0005	600	1·0622	0·6310	0·0008
0·6658	0·3340	0·0002	610	1·0026	0·5030	0·0003
0·6915	0·3083	0·0002	620	0·8544	0·3810	0·0002
0·7079	0·2920	0·0001	630	0·6424	0·2650	0·0000
0·7190	0·2809	0·0001	640	0·4479	0·1750	0·0000
0·7260	0·2740	0·0000	650	0·2835	0·1070	0·0000
0·7300	0·2700	0·0000	660	0·1649	0·0610	0·0000
0·7320	0·2680	0·0000	670	0·0874	0·0320	0·0000
0·7334	0·2666	0·0000	680	0·0468	0·0170	0·0000
0·7344	0·2656	0·0000	690	0·0227	0·0082	0·0000
0·7347	0·2653	0·0000	700	0·0114	0·0041	0·0000
0·7347	0·2653	0·0000	710	0·0058	0·0021	0·0000
0·7347	0·2653	0·0000	720	0·0029	0·0010	0·0000
0·7347	0·2653	0·0000	730	0·0014	0·0005	0·0000
0·7347	0·2653	0·0000	740	0·0007	0·0003	0·0000
0·7347	0·2653	0·0000	750	0·0003	0·0001	0·0000
0·7347	0·2653	0·0000	760	0·0002	0·0001	0·0000
0·7347	0·2653	0·0000	770	0·0001	0·0000	0·0000
0·7347	0·2653	0·0000	780	0·0000	0·0000	0·0000

Kaye & Laby, *Physical and Chemical Constants*, 11th Edition.
Wright, W. D., *The Measurement of Colour* (1958).

chromaticity coordinates x, y and z for monochromatic light are the distribution coefficients expressed as a fraction of their sum, thus at each wave-length :—

$$x = \frac{\bar{x}}{\bar{x} + \bar{y} + \bar{z}}, \, y = \frac{\bar{y}}{\bar{x} + \bar{y} + \bar{z}}, \, z = \frac{\bar{z}}{\bar{x} + \bar{y} + \bar{z}}$$

In order to determine the values of the chromaticity coordinates for a given source which radiates energy at a rate $E(\lambda) \, \delta\lambda$ between wave-lengths λ and $\lambda + \delta \, \lambda$, use is made of the expressions

$$X = \int_{-\infty}^{+\infty} E(\lambda)\bar{x}d\lambda, \; Y = \int_{-\infty}^{+\infty} E(\lambda)\bar{y}d\lambda, \; Z = \int_{-\infty}^{+\infty} E(\lambda)\bar{z}d\lambda.$$

For a discontinuous source the integral is replaced by a summation, and in either case, the summation is effectively limited by the bounds of the visible spectrum. The chromaticity coordinates are then given by :—

$$x = \frac{X}{X + Y + Z}, y = \frac{Y}{X + Y + Z}, z = \frac{Z}{X + Y + Z}.$$

There is considerable latitude in the choice of the primaries, and it is found that in fact no *real* primaries will enable a match to be made with every colour unless negative values are given to the coefficients. This is inconvenient, and so the agreed primaries are not real ones, but are so chosen that the coefficients always have positive values. The value of X (or $\bar{x}$ for monochromatic radiation) represents an amount of a reddish-purple of higher saturation (i.e., containing less white) than any real purple of this hue. The green primary Y has the hue of the spectrum colour of wave-length 5200 A but is again more saturated, as is the blue primary Z which has the hue of the spectrum colour at 4770 A. The fact that the primaries are not real is of no consequence, since they are only intermediaries which enable one colour to be related to another. The green primary of amount Y has been chosen in such a way that $\bar{y}$ (for monochromatic radiation) is equal to the visibility function V_λ given in Table 16.1. The Y value of a colour is therefore proportional to its brightness.

For reflecting surfaces the values of X, Y and Z are obtained by evaluating the expressions :—

$$X = \int_{-\infty}^{+\infty} E \, (\lambda) \, R_\lambda \, \bar{x} \, d\lambda, \text{ etc.}$$

in which as before $E \, (\lambda)$ is the relative energy of the source and R_λ the fraction reflected by the surface at wave-length λ. The values of X, Y and Z are conveniently scaled in such a way that for a perfect white surface $Y = 100$. The value of Y then gives the percentage brightness of a coloured surface on a scale in which for a black surface $Y = 0$ and for a white surface $Y = 100$.

It should be noted that the chromaticity coefficients x, y and z specify the colour of a reflecting surface for a standard observer *under given conditions of illumination,* or the colour of radiation when some agreed standard of " white " radiation is taken. Two sources

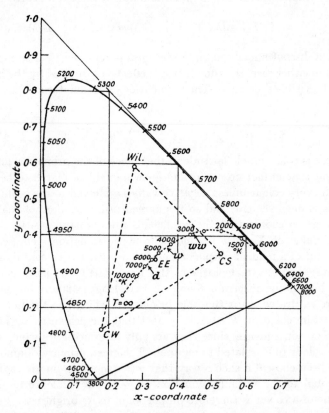

Fig. 16.6—C.I.E. diagram. The colour points of monochromatic light of various wave-lengths lie on the full curve. The colour points of a black body incandescing at various temperatures lie on the broken curve—the black body locus, calculated from Planck's formula.

    CS, CW and Wil are the colour points of three phosphors: calcium silicate, calcium tungstate, and Willemite respectively. d, w and ww correspond to the colour temperatures chosen for fluorescent lamps with colours "cool daylight", "white" and "warm white." EE is the point $x = y = z = 0.33$, the equal energy or " white " point.

or two surfaces may have identical chromaticity coefficients without being physically matched.

Since the sum of x, y and z is unity it is only necessary to specify two of them, and this enables the colour of various sources to be represented on a two-dimensional diagram. Usually x and y are specified, and Fig. 16.6 shows the C.I.E. colour diagram giving x and y for various sources, monochromatic and otherwise. It will be seen that the points $x = 1$, $y = 0$ and $x = 0$, $y = 1$, representing the pure primaries are outside the range of real colours, all of which lie within the " triangle." The colour points of monochromatic light of various wave-lengths lie on the full curve. The colour points of a black body incandescing at various temperatures lie on the inner curved lines. The black body locus is calculated from values of E (λ) given by Planck's formula (Chapter 17).

An example of the use of the chromaticity diagram may be of interest. In designing fluorescent lighting of the 40-watt mercury vapour type now commonly used for illumination, certain phosphors, such as calcium silicate, calcium tungstate and Willemite are used. Suppose that the colour points of these three phosphors, i.e., the radiation they emit when excited by the 40-watt mercury vapour discharge, are $X_1, Y_1, Z_1, X_2, Y_2, Z_2,$ and $X_3, Y_3, Z_3,$ where Y_1, Y_2, Y_3 indicate the value of the luminous flux which each phosphor supplies (see Fig. 16.6). If the three phosphors are mixed in a lamp the total luminous flux will be $aY_1 + bY_2 + cY_3$ where a, b, c are factors (and $a + b + c = 1$) determining the proportion of the three phosphors. From the mercury lamp there will also be some visible light originating directly from the mercury vapour discharge, depending on the power of the lamp. So, we have for the final colour of the lamp :—

$$\left. \begin{array}{l} X = aX_1 + bX_2 + cX_3 + X \text{ (Hg)} \\ Y = aY_1 + bY_2 + cY_3 + Y \text{ (Hg)} \\ Z = aZ_1 + bZ_2 + cZ_3 + Z \text{ (Hg)} \end{array} \right\} \quad (1)$$

$$a + b + c = 1 \qquad (2)$$

and from the required colour specification of the lamp (see Fig. 16.6)

$$x = \frac{X}{X + Y + Z} \quad y = \frac{Y}{X + Y + Z} \quad (3)$$

In these six equations we are given X_1, Y_1, Z_1 etc. for the three phosphors, X (Hg), Y (Hg), Z (Hg) for the mercury discharge and

$x, y, z\ (x + y + z = 1)$ from the specification of the required colour, hence we can solve the equations for a, b, c the proportions of the phosphors, and for X, Y, Z.

Colour rendering

So far we have only discussed colour points but have ignored the fact that sources with quite different distributions of spectral energy may have the same colour point. The radiation a (Fig. 16.7) with an equal energy spectrum has the colour point $x = y = 1/3$. The radiation b, consisting of wave-lengths 5890 and 4860, the latter having twice the energy of the former, has the same colour point and hence gives the same visual impression. The colours of objects, however,

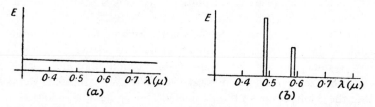

FIG. 16.7.—Colour Rendering. Sources (a) and (b) have same colour but coloured objects illuminated by these sources appear different in colour.

are in general rendered quite differently by the two lights. A red object, reflecting only red light, will appear black or dark brown by light b, but red in light a. Yellow and blue objects will approximately retain their colours in both lights. Hence when considering light sources in general it is not only necessary to know the colour point, but also the colour rendering which depends entirely on the distribution of energy in the spectrum.

An alternative method of specifying a colour on this diagram is to draw a line through it and the white point to cut the curve at the dominant wave-length, and the ratio of the distances of the point and the white point from the curve gives its purity.

Defects of the Eye

The eye suffers from very similar defects to any single lens, i.e., it has chromatic and spherical aberration and astigmatism.

The chromatic and spherical aberration can have serious consequences when making observations but the observer usually places his eye automatically in such a position that these defects are minimised. Astigmatism is caused by defects in the shape of the eye lens or cornea. The defects of vision are fully treated in many text books and will not be discussed here.

The clearness with which the eye can see detail is termed its acuity and it is found that it depends on the brightness of the object, becoming less as the brightness diminishes. Vernier acuity is the term applied to the precision with which an eye can see the lack of alignment of two lines. It is found that in good light the ordinary acuity of the eye measured by its resolving power is about 1 minute while the vernier acuity is about 10 seconds but may reach values of 2 seconds or even less under very favourable conditions. Some acuity brightness curves are shown in Fig. 16.8.

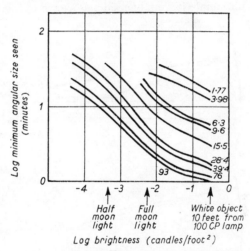

FIG. 16.8.—Variation of acuity with brightness and contrast of object for the normal eye. The figures against each curve are the percentage contrast between the test object and the background.

Telescopes

Reflecting telescopes have considerable practical value especially where large aperture and freedom from chromatic aberration are essential. In the U.V. and I.R. regions, for example, the fact that the focus is the same for visible light is a distinct advantage and it must be remembered that ordinary glass is opaque in the U.V. and has low transmission in the I.R. The coating of mirrors for use in the extremes of the spectrum, however, requires attention, for all metals are not equally good reflectors in these regions. The table given in p. 217

(Chapter 12) shows that most metals are good reflectors in the infra-red, but aluminium appears to be most suitable in the ultra-violet. Concave mirrors for reflecting telescopes may be spherical or parabolic in shape. The spherical mirror is easy to make and the reader is advised to consult "Amateur Telescope Making" for full details. All that is necessary is a slab of glass of the diameter required for the mirror and a second slab which may be smaller in diameter or the same diameter. Using the abrasives mentioned in Chapter 14 and patient grinding, smoothing and eventually polishing, a spherical surface will result. The radius of curvature of a concave spherical mirror is easily found by Foucault's test in which an illuminated pin-hole and a knife edge are used. It is usual to attach a prism behind the pinhole and illuminate it from one side, as shown in Fig. 16.9. If the

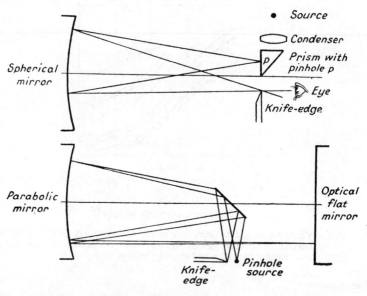

Fig. 16.9.—Knife edge (Foucault test) with spherical and parabolic mirrors.

pinhole is at the centre of curvature an eye behind the knife edge will see the mirror full of light, then on moving the knife edge a shadow should form all over the mirror surface evenly if the mirror surface is a perfect sphere. The pinhole and knife edge are mounted on a single stand and are moved together towards or away from the mirror. If the knife edge is too close to the mirror, i.e. inside the centre of curvature, the mirror will darken from the same side as the knife edge is introduced ; if too far, outside the centre of curvature, the mirror will appear to darken from the opposite side. In making parabolic mirrors it is usual to form the spherical surface first, then, using a pad of fine abrasive, to alter the curvature until the parabolic shape is achieved. Again the Foucault test is used and considerable experience is necessary to judge from the shadow formation when a parabolic shape is formed. It is possible to use a Foucault test for a parabolic mirror with the help of a good optical flat as large as the mirror. Fig. 16.9 shows the arrangement where the source of light (pinhole) is at the focus and the parallel beam reflected from the paraboloid is reflected back by the optical flat mirror and after a second reflection at the paraboloid can be analysed by the knife edge at the focus. Finally, a parabolic mirror must be tested with a star. An eyepiece or microscope is used to view the star image and by moving the eyepiece in and out of focus the characteristic rings are seen, as shown in Fig. 15.12 on p. 299.

Very large reflecting telescopes have been made and are in constant use for Astronomical work of the highest order. The famous 200-in. mirror at Mt. Palomar is an outstanding example. This mirror took many years to make, starting at some 22 tons in weight and finishing at about 14 tons ; i.e., 8 tons of glass were removed in grinding and polishing.

Reflecting telescopes are most often provided with a central hole and are used in a variety of ways. Fig. 16.10 shows the Newtonian, Herschell, Gregorian and Cassegrain methods of use. The Schmidt, and similar, cameras, described elsewhere in this book, use a spherical mirror with a corrector plate.

For most laboratory purposes the small refracting telescope has many advantages. For the reading of scales and observation of phenomena the inverting telescope is adequate and many very handy instruments are readily available. The specification of a telescope should include the following :—

(a) *Diameter of Objective.*—This determines its resolving power, but it must be remembered that the simple forms of cemented doublet usually do not exceed $f/10$ in relative aperture, i.e., their focal length is ten times the diameter. If a larger relative aperture is necessary, to combine high resolution with a short telescope for example, the objective requires more care in design, becomes complicated and expensive.

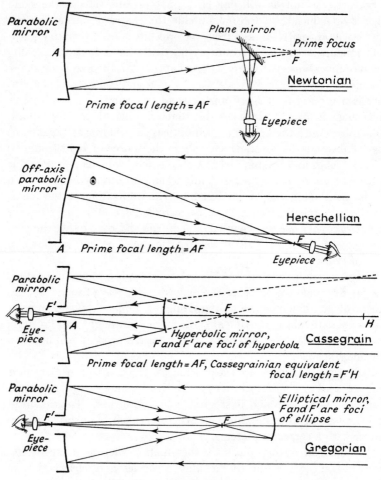

FIG. 16.10.—Reflecting telescopes.

(b) *Power of the telescope.*—In inverting telescopes the magnifying power is given by the ratio of the focal lengths of the objective and eyepiece. It must be remembered here that the ratio of the diameters of the entrance and exit pupil is also a measure of the power and if a large exit pupil is necessary either the power must be reduced or the diameter of the objective increased.

(c) *Field of View.*—The field of view of the complete instrument measured by the external angle within which objects must lie is called the real field and the angular field as seen in the eyepiece is the apparent field. The ratio of the tangents of the apparent field to the real field is equal to the magnifying power and the limit is usually set by the eyepiece (see Chapter 15). When these three main requirements have been specified and the overall length of the telescope decided upon the instrument can be designed.

Erecting telescopes can assume many forms and the erecting of the image may be performed by lenses, internal prisms or external prisms. The simplest is, of course, the Galilean in which a negative eye lens is used and this instrument, despite its restricted field of view, internal exit pupil and lack of a focal plane for a graticule, has many uses where simplicity is the keynote. In telescopes having internal erecting lenses as shown in Fig. 15.6 (p. 288), it will be seen that the diameter of the erecting lens, or a stop associated with the erector, can influence the position of the entrance pupil and diameter of the objective. By arranging an advanced entrance pupil, as shown in the figure, the diameter of the erector system can be reduced and the field of view then determines the diameter of the objective. The position of the exit pupil can also be controlled by a judicious choice of eyepiece construction and position of erector system. In erecting telescopes of the lens type the magnification can be controlled and even made variable over wide limits by changing the position of the erecting lens system. The total magnification of such a telescope is given by the ratio of the focal lengths of objective and eyepiece multiplied by the magnification introduced by the erector system. The particular advantage of advanced entrance pupils is to negotiate narrow apertures, in armour plate for example, or where a scanning prism may be required in front of the objective. Several forms of telescopes are shown in Fig. 16.11.

Prismatic forms of erection, commonly used in binocular instruments, have the advantage of decreased overall length caused by the folding up of the light path by the prisms. (See table of prisms in Chapter 15, p. 343.) The Porro system is the commonest and most easily manufactured as all the others involve the use of roof prisms which are notoriously difficult to manufacture and consequently expensive. In Porro prism systems the angles of the prisms can be maintained, in bulk production, with considerable accuracy and small errors have little effect on the performance. Definite limits are set down which are within the power of the manufacturer's tolerances. In roof prisms the angle of the roof must be accurately maintained as any error in this produces double images or overlapping images and in some cases the roof-edge must be sharp but this is only necessary if it is near a focal plane. Roof-edge prisms are, however, valuable aids in design because of the saving of space resulting from their use. External prism erectors can be used with considerable success, particularly when an internal stop is used to produce an advanced entrance pupil. The particular advantage of the external erector is in providing for scanning or for alterations of the external line of sight with a rigidly fixed telescope. (See Fig. 16.11.)

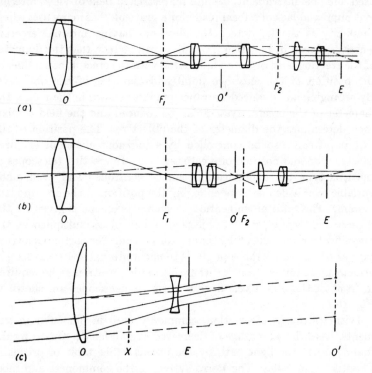

Fig. 16.11.—Telescopes.

> (a) Erecting system using separated lens and having, at O' between the erecting lenses, the first image of the object glass (entrance pupil).
>
> (b) Erecting system, with single erector lens, image O' of objective is formed outside the erector and is used to increase the eye freedom.
>
> (c) Galilean system. The true exit pupil is at X, being the image of O in the eye lens, but if E is the pupil of the eye and acts as an exit pupil the entrance pupil is virtual and is at O'.

Variations of the Porro principles are used where periscopes and cranked forms of telescope are required and a large variety of designs have been adopted. Fig. 16.12 shows forms of periscopic and cranked telescopes. The smaller angles of bending are generally more difficult

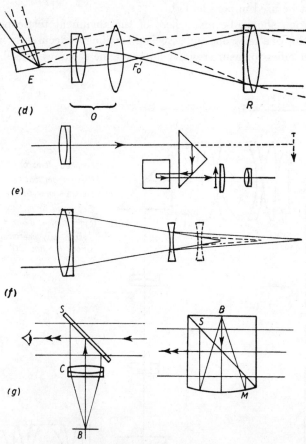

(d)

(e)

(f)

(g)

(d) Part of a periscope system. The entrance pupil is at E inside the small scanning prism, O is the objective system and R is one of the lenses in the periscope train. An oblique pencil is shown with a broken line.

(e) Porro prism system used in binoculars. The prisms used to erect the image also help to shorten the telescope.

(f) Internal focusing of telescopes. A negative or a positive lens may be used for this purpose.

(g) Two forms of reflector sights. In one the light is collimated by the lens C. In the other the spherical surface M collimates the light by reflection.

to achieve than the larger but may be necessary in certain circumstances.

In panoramic forms of periscopic telescopes it becomes necessary to keep the field of view vertical as the top prism is rotated and this effect is usually achieved by using the Dove or half-speed prism, but it must be used in parallel light.

Mention should be made here of the alignment telescope outfits consisting of a telescope and associated collimator accurately mounted in steel tubes to ensure rigidity and extreme accuracy of collimation.

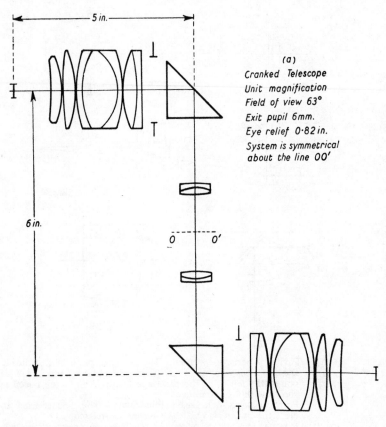

(a)
Cranked Telescope
Unit magnification
Field of view 63°
Exit pupil 6mm.
Eye relief 0·82 in.
System is symmetrical about the line OO′

FIG. 16.12.—Bent and Panoramic telescopes.

(*a*) A short unit power cranked telescope suitable for use where there is danger to an observer.

These sets of equipment have frequent applications in the laboratory for the alignment of shafts or for testing the straightness of rails, machine beds, etc. A useful outfit is supplied by Messrs. Taylor, Taylor & Hobson.

Another useful piece of laboratory equipment, for the measurement of the angles of prisms for example, is the "Angle Dekkor" of Messrs. Adam Hilger and other auto-collimating telescopes made by other optical firms (see Chapter 7).

Periscopes, introscopes and allied types of telescopes of frequent

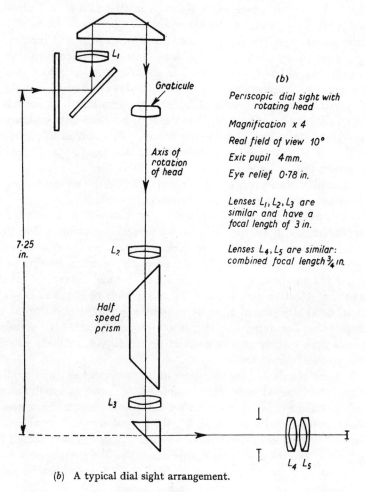

(b)

Periscopic dial sight with
rotating head

Magnification x 4

Real field of view 10°

Exit pupil 4mm.

Eye relief 0·78 in.

Lenses L_1, L_2, L_3 are
similar and have a
focal length of 3 in.

Lenses L_4, L_5 are similar:
combined focal length $\frac{3}{4}$ in.

(b) A typical dial sight arrangement.

application consist essentially of several image forming systems in series to relay the image down the tube. The same principles are used in the optical systems fitted to theodolites and levels to relay the scale readings to a convenient eyepiece.

The variety of applications of the telescope principle is almost limitless and these few examples are given here merely to remind the reader of the possibilities.

Microscopes

Essentially the principles of microscope construction are exactly the same as those used in telescopes with the fundamental difference that in telescopes a long focus objective is used to form a diminished image which is examined by the eyepiece, whereas in microscopes a short focus objective forms a magnified image which is further enlarged by the eyepiece. The standard form of the microscope is well known and will not be discussed in detail. For laboratory use, as distinct from purely microscopic uses, the lower powers of objective are generally adequate but it frequently happens that a higher power is essential in order to ensure that the N.A. is sufficient to embrace all the light from some other optical device. This applies in particular to the use of a microscope to examine the images of a star formed by a camera lens of large aperture.

Binocular microscopes with which specimens and work can be examined stereoscopically are increasingly used in laboratories and workshops and in principle these are very simple, low power instruments, frequently fitted with prismatic erecting systems and inclined at an angle of about 12 deg. to each other so that the eyes are comfortably converged as they would normally be when looking at an object placed about 10 in. from the eyes. In some instruments of this type the objective axes are inclined at an angle of about 12 deg. and an internal adjustment is made to reduce the angle to 8 deg. at the eyepiece. The binocular eyepieces frequently fitted to standard microscopes to give greater comfort in use do not normally provide true stereoscopic vision.

The use of scales in the eyepieces of microscopes has many applications. An internal scale, for example, can be used to sub-divide the scale divisions of an external scale and thus obtain extreme accuracy. These optical scales are used largely in instruments for the comparison of gauges, in spherometers and depth gauges, for Brinell impressions, and they have their applications to the reading of circular scales as in theodolites, refractometers, etc. A useful scale reading microscope made by Messrs. Taylor, Taylor & Hobson is shown in Fig. 16.13.

It frequently happens that objects have to be examined under considerable magnification but that an ordinary high-power microscope objective with its short working distance cannot be brought close enough to the object. Some means must then be adopted to attain a long working distance while retaining high powers and a reasonable N.A. Dyson has described several unit-magnification systems which can be used for this purpose and the reader should consult his paper (see ref. at end of Chapter 15). Phase-contrast microscopy and interference microscopy are subjects that would require more space than can be allotted in this book and the reader must be left to consult the very considerable literature on these most interesting applications.

Projectors

In Chapter 15, a number of condenser systems were described without direct reference to the object to be projected or the projection lens, and here the description will be extended to include the complete instrument.

The simplest arrangement where great intensity of illumination is not required is to use a large opal lamp to illuminate the object and a projector lens to produce the image. This arrangement is used in some photographic enlargers and can only be used if the object is smaller than the diameter of the lamp bulb. If the object is larger then a simple condenser can be used to form an image of the source in the entrance pupil of the projector lens, the condenser being large enough to embrace the whole object. The light source may be a large opal lamp if low intensities are sufficient or a small source of high intrinsic brightness if considerable illumination is required. In photographic enlargers the large bulb is sometimes preferred as it can be fixed in position for all degrees of enlargement while a concentrated source would have to be moved for every change in position of the projector lens, but in magic lanterns the concentrated source is necessary. Alternatively the condenser system may form an image of the source in the plane of the object being projected, but in such systems the source must be structureless, i.e., an arc or pointolite lamp must be used. If the source is a tungsten filament lamp its image would be projected on the screen along with the object. Since light sources in general emit light in every direction a mirror can usually be used to increase the total cone of light collected by the condenser. A spherical

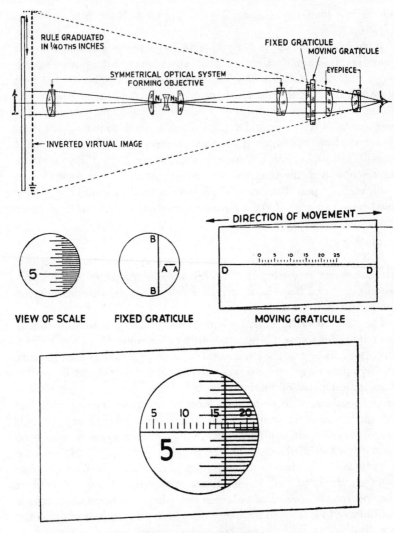

VIEW OF SCALE   FIXED GRATICULE   MOVING GRATICULE

VIEW IN EYEPIECE

READING:	SCALE	5·100″
	VERNIER	0·0166″
	TOTAL	5·1166″

Fig. 16.13.—Taylor Hobson Scale reading microscope showing the graticules and the view in the eyepiece.

mirror is frequently used with the source at its centre of curvature so that an image of the source is formed alongside the actual source, this arrangement being particularly suitable for filament types of light sources. In cinema projection systems an ellipsoidal mirror and negative lens arrangement is frequently used. Fig. 16.14 shows diagrammatically several arrangements of projection systems as described above.

The focal length of the projector lens required under given conditions can be found from the simple approximate relation :—

$$\text{Focal length of projector lens in inches} = \frac{\text{(Throw from lens to screen in feet)} \times \text{(Size of object in inches)}}{\text{(Corresponding size of image in feet)}}$$

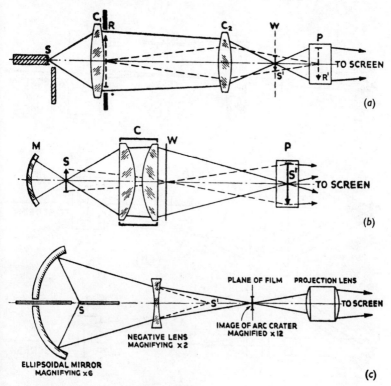

Fig. 16.14.—Projection systems.
    (a) Image of lamp formed in plane of object.
    (b) Image of lamp formed in projector lens.
    (c) Cinema projection system

For the projection of solid objects of considerable thickness, such as gauges, screw threads or other profiles, the use of convergent light in the object space is undesirable since the thickness of the object would cause deterioration of the image sharpness and distortion of its shape. It is therefore usual to place the source at the principal

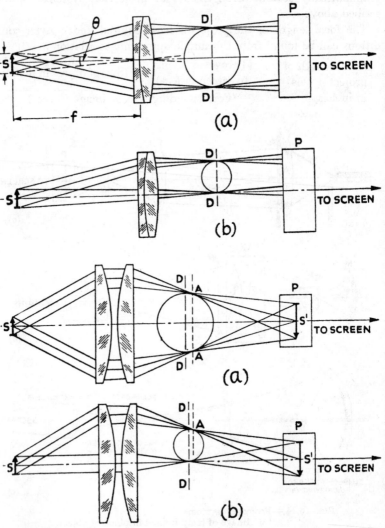

Fig. 16.15.—Profile projection. Effect of convergent and collimated light.

focus of a condenser lens so that the light emerges in parallel beams and is again collected by a field lens and so on to the screen. Fig. 16.15 shows the arrangement of typical profile projection systems and the effect of convergent light. With such systems it is easily seen that the projector lens tends to perform rather like an eyepiece, having a definite external exit pupil through which all the light passes. In specially designed profile projection lenses the field lens is sometimes included in the system and is arranged so that the image of the light source, formed by the field lens, is in the plane of the diaphragm of the projector lens.

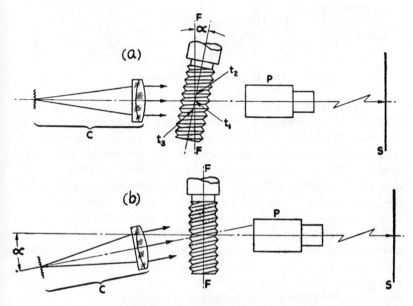

Fig. 16.16.—Screw thread projection.

For the projection of screw threads either the screw or the light beam must be raked through the helical angle of the screw as shown in Fig. 16.16, but the whole subject of screw thread projection is complicated by many factors and is outside the scope of this book. For full information the reader should refer to text books or to some of the firms which specialise in the manufacture of such projectors.

An application of the microscope for the inspection of profiles has many principles in common with profile projection devices. The light beam must again be collimated and the objective of the microscope is provided with a telecentric stop, i.e., a small hole at the principal focus of the objective. The image formed may be examined by an eyepiece or may be projected on to a screen and there is a large variety of special instruments designed for workshop and toolroom use. Fig. 16.17 shows an example but the reader is again referred to manufacturers of such instruments for further particulars as an adequate description would not be possible in the limited space of this chapter.

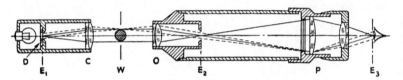

FIG. 16.17.—Profile microscope.

Mention should be made here of the modified Schmidt projection systems which are being introduced for the projection of television pictures. The brilliance of the display on the television tube cannot at present be considered as bright enough for normal projection methods. The picture is formed on a screen in the tube by fluorescence and acts as a diffuse radiator. Fig. 16.18 shows two systems which are being developed, the first for projection on to a screen possibly in a cinema theatre and the second for the home television receiver.

The production of the necessary Schmidt corrector plate at an economic cost has been overcome by the use of plastics of the Perspex and " Transpex " types, and glass corrector plates are now being manufactured in bulk at a low cost. The type of screen to obtain maximum brilliance of the picture requires careful choice. If the picture is projected on a plain white surface the light is scattered back in all directions according to Lambert's cosine law and much of it is wasted in useless directions. Several forms of beaded screens are available which are more directional but probably the best method for television projection is to use a translucent screen with the picture projected on the back surface. One type of translucent screen consists of a plastic plate which is embossed with a fine pattern of half cylinders ruled at 100 to the inch. These form cylindrical lenses which have their axes horizontal on one side of the screen and vertical on the other and spread the illumination through an angle of 80 deg. horizontally and 30 deg. vertically. One advantage of this type of screen is that stray light from the room which may fall on the screen is scattered at a wide angle and does not reduce the contrast of the image. This type of screen is obtainable from Imperial Chemical Industries.

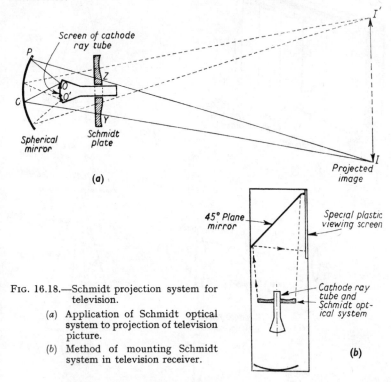

FIG. 16.18.—Schmidt projection system for television.

(a) Application of Schmidt optical system to projection of television picture.

(b) Method of mounting Schmidt system in television receiver.

Stereoscopic projection : The problem of the projection of pictures in stereoscopic relief has fascinated investigators and the public and a large number of attempts have been made to overcome the inherent difficulty of making it possible for a large audience to see the effect realistically. The simplest and so far the only really successful methods depend on the projection of the stereoscopic pair of pictures on to the screen, either in two complementary coloured lights or plane polarised in two mutually perpendicular planes, so that the audience wearing special spectacles see the right hand view with the right eye only and the left hand view with the left eye. In the coloured light method a pair of projectors is required and a stereoscopic pair of transparencies is projected through coloured

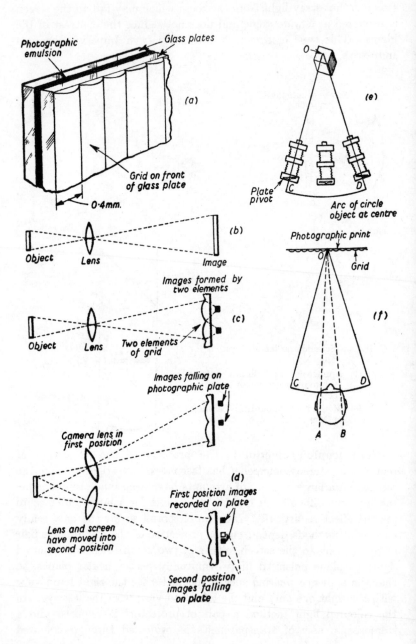

Photographic emulsion

Glass plates

(a)

Grid on front of glass plate

0·4 mm.

Object *Lens* *Image* *(b)*

Images formed by two elements

Object *Lens* *(c)*

Two elements of grid

Images falling on photographic plate

Camera lens in first position

(d)

Lens and screen have moved into second position

First position images recorded on plate

Second position images falling on plate

(e)

Plate pivot

Arc of circle object at centre

Photographic print

Grid

(f)

374

filters, usually red and green. Careful adjustment of the projectors is necessary and the pair of filters must be so chosen that when the two coloured lights are projected on the screen it appears white. The audience wear red and green spectacles and the effect, after a little education, is very good. In the polarised light process it is now possible to print on special polarising material developed by the Polaroid Corporation the pair of pictures so that when ordinary light is projected through the single transparency the two image forming beams are polarised in two mutually perpendicular planes. The screen used must not scatter light indiscriminately or it will depolarise the beams and destroy the effect, but with beaded screens the light remains polarised and if the audience wear a pair of polarising spectacles each eye sees only the appropriate image.

Many attempts have been made to obtain stereoscopic projection by means of ruled screens and lenticular surfaced screens to eliminate the necessity of wearing special spectacles, but none of these has been really successful. The well-known deep picture (see Fig. 16.19) displays are obtained by using a photographic plate having a ribbed lenticular film of transparent material over the emulsion. The photograph taken through these cylindrical lenses is obtained by swinging the camera over an arc and when the resulting photograph is viewed each eye sees only the elementary strip which the camera records from the same direction. Whether stereoscopic cinema projection will ever be a success is debatable because the psychological reactions of the audience are unpredictable. It has been found that

---

← Fig. 16.19.—Deep pictures.

    (a) Enlarged section of plastic grid in position in front of photographic plate.

    (b) Normal optical systems of a camera.

    (c) Broken image formed by grid. The two dimensional object forms a series of point images ; a solid object will produce a series of line images perpendicular to the plane of the diagram and parallel to the lines of the grid.

    (d) Two broken images formed when the lens and grid are in two different positions relative to the object.

    (e) The camera describes an arc of 32° round the object during a 2-seconds exposure; at each position a separate set of line images is formed on the plate. The photographic plate and grid remain parallel to their central position throughout the exposure.

    (f) When viewing the finished print the left eye at A sees what the camera saw when pointing along the line AO and the right eye at B sees what the camera saw when pointing along BO. Moving the head from C to D reveals all the aspects of the object seen by the camera between its extreme positions.

under certain circumstances a feeling of nausea is produced and until this can be overcome, along with the many technical difficulties, the pseudo-stereoscopic illusion produced by relative movement and difference of size probably has a more pleasing effect and is in keeping with the very small stereoscopic view normally obtained in the living theatre.

BOOKS

The subjects mentioned in this chapter cover a very wide field and there is naturally a very large number of books which can be consulted for further information and study. The books mentioned below are only a few, selected mainly because their treatment of the subject is of value to a student and because they point the way to further research.

The Eye

WRIGHT, W. D., *The Perception of Light* (Blackie), 1938.
BOWEN, E. J., *The Chemical Aspects of Light* (Oxford), 1946.
MARTIN, L. C., *Technical Optics*, Vol. I (Pitman), 1948.
MANN, I., and PIRIE, A., *The Science of Seeing* (Penguin), 1946.
WRIGHT, W. D., *Investigations in Colour Vision* (Kimpton), 1946.
PIRENNE, M. H., *Vision and The Eye* (Pilot Press), 1948.
WRIGHT, W. D., *The Measurement of Colour* (Hilger & Watts, Ltd.) 1958.
LE GRAND, YVES, *Light, Colour and Vision* (Trans.), Chapman & Hall, London, 1957.

Comprehensive Treatises on the eye in its physiological aspects are :—

HELMHOLTZ (translation SOUTHALL), *A Treatise on Physiological Optics* (Opt. Soc. Amer.), 1924.
STEWART DUKE-ELDER, W., *Text Book of Ophthalmology* (3 Vols.—Vol. I mainly) (Kimpton) 1932.

Instruments

The list given at the end of Chapter 15 includes a number of books dealing with the instruments mentioned in this chapter, and *The Dictionary of Applied Physics* is a mine of information. The two volumes on *Scientific Instruments* edited by Cooper and published by Hutchinson gives a good, more or less popular, account of a very large variety of instruments.

REFERENCES

STILES, W. S.," Current Problems in Visual Research," *Proc. Phys. Soc.*, **56** (1944), 329.
TAYLOR, A. H., "Vision at Low Brightness Levels," *Illum. Eng.*, **33** (Feb. 1943), 89.
LUCKIESH, M., and TAYLOR, A. H., " Seeing at Low Brightness Levels," *Illum. Eng.*, **38** (April 1943), 190.

CHAPTER 17

RADIATION AND PHOTOMETRY

Radiation

THE term radiation covers a very wide field of electromagnetic phenomena from the very short cosmic rays to the long radio waves used in wireless telegraphy and telephony. Fig. 17.1 shows the extent of the so-called electromagnetic spectrum. It is usual to speak of wave-length and frequency in referring to such radiation in general because the phenomena of interference, diffraction and polarisation can all be explained in terms of wave-motion. When it is necessary to consider, however, the interaction of radiation with matter it is necessary to assume that radiation is emitted in bundles of energy called quanta. The magnitude of a quantum of energy at the various wave-lengths or frequencies is also shown in Fig. 17.1 and is given by the relation $E = h\nu$ where E is the energy in one quantum, h is Planck's constant ($6 \cdot 62 \times 10^{-27}$ erg-sec.) and ν is the frequency in cycles per sec. The energy of one quantum can be expressed in many units as shown in the table of atomic and molecular constants on page 415. In this chapter we are concerned only in the band of radiation emitted by hot bodies and known as thermal radiations, i.e., from 2,000 Λ (200mμ) in the ultra-violet region to about 40 to 50 microns (μ) in the deep infra-red.

Thermal radiation

It was owing to attempts to explain the laws of thermal radiation in terms of classical thermodynamics that Planck was led to the formulation of the Quantum Theory. The distribution of energy in the spectrum of the radiation emitted by hot or incandescent bodies follows a well defined pattern, being small at wave-lengths below 3,000 A, increasing to a maximum at a wave-length depending on the temperature and decreasing more or less asymptotically to zero. Figs. 17.2 and 17.3 show the form of spectral distribution of energy curves for various temperatures of the radiating body and for the radiation from tungsten.

" Full " or " black-body " radiation has been defined as the radiation within a completely closed cavity, the walls of which are at a

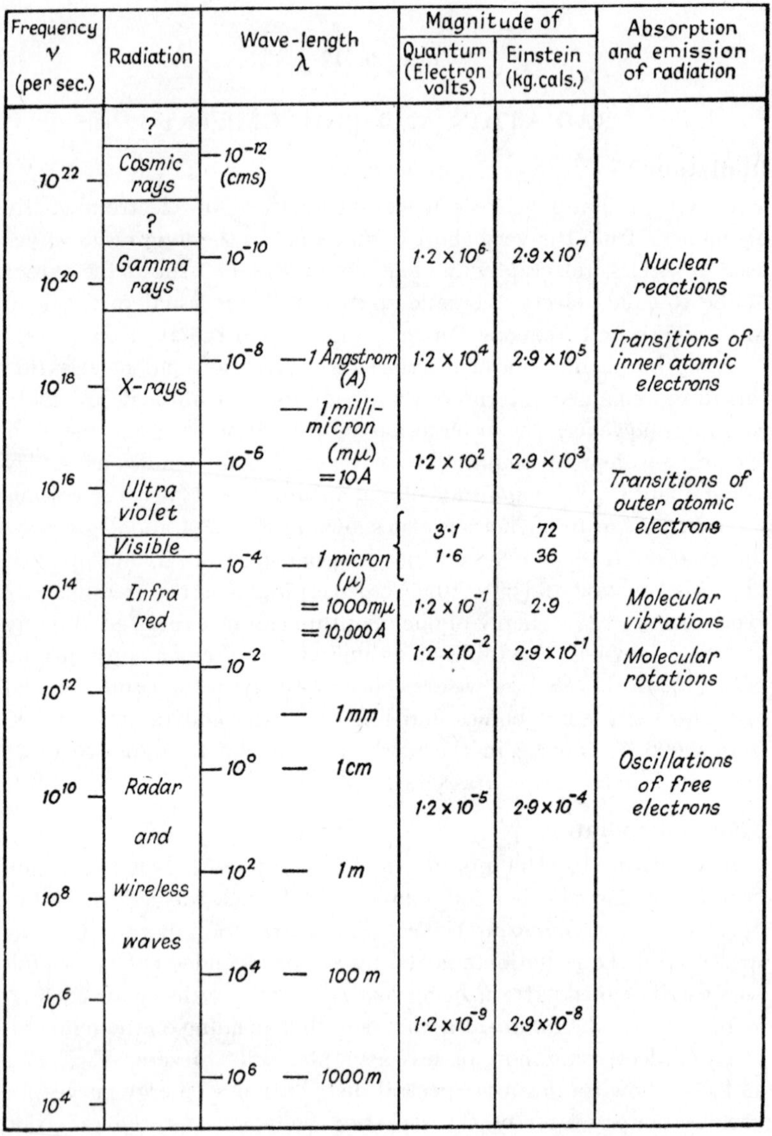

Frequency ν (per sec.)	Radiation	Wave-length λ	Magnitude of		Absorption and emission of radiation
			Quantum (Electron volts)	Einstein (kg.cals.)	
	?	10^{-12} (cms)			
10^{22}	Cosmic rays				
	?				
10^{20}	Gamma rays	10^{-10}	$1 \cdot 2 \times 10^{6}$	$2 \cdot 9 \times 10^{7}$	Nuclear reactions
10^{18}	X-rays	10^{-8} — 1 Ångstrom (A)	$1 \cdot 2 \times 10^{4}$	$2 \cdot 9 \times 10^{5}$	Transitions of inner atomic electrons
		— 1 milli-micron ($m\mu$)			
10^{16}	Ultra violet	10^{-6} =10A	$1 \cdot 2 \times 10^{2}$	$2 \cdot 9 \times 10^{3}$	Transitions of outer atomic electrons
	Visible		$3 \cdot 1$	72	
10^{14}	Infra red	10^{-4} — 1 micron (μ) = 1000$m\mu$ = 10,000A	$1 \cdot 6$	36	
			$1 \cdot 2 \times 10^{-1}$	$2 \cdot 9$	Molecular vibrations
		10^{-2}	$1 \cdot 2 \times 10^{-2}$	$2 \cdot 9 \times 10^{-1}$	Molecular rotations
10^{12}					
		— 1mm			
	Radar	10^{0} — 1cm			Oscillations of free electrons
10^{10}			$1 \cdot 2 \times 10^{-5}$	$2 \cdot 9 \times 10^{-4}$	
	and				
10^{8}	wireless	10^{2} — 1m			
	waves				
		10^{4} — 100 m			
10^{6}			$1 \cdot 2 \times 10^{-9}$	$2 \cdot 9 \times 10^{-8}$	
		10^{6} — 1000m			
10^{4}					

FIG. 17.1.—Electromagnetic spectrum.

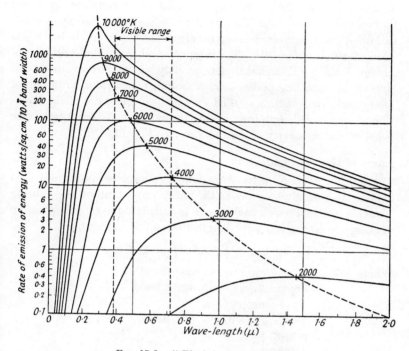

FIG. 17.2.—" Black body " radiation.

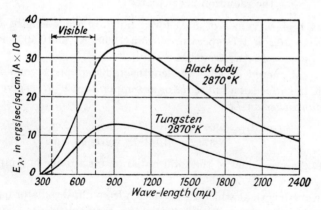

FIG. 17.3.—Radiation of energy from tungsten body compared with that from a
" black body ", at the same temperature.

(*Note* : emissivity = ratio of ordinates.)

uniform temperature. An experimental approximation to a full radiator could be a tube, closed at one end, with a small aperture at the other end to enable the radiation from the closed end to be viewed along the axis of the tube. The intensity and spectral distribution of energy from a full radiator depend only on its temperature. All normal incandescing bodies have a modified spectral distribution of energy and are sometimes called grey bodies. The ratio of the radiation at any wave-length from a body to that from an ideal black body is called the emissivity of the radiator (see Fig. 17.3).

Laws of thermal radiation

A number of more or less empirical laws have been formulated to explain radiation phenomena, the most important of these being Planck's relation, which enables one to calculate the rate of radiation of energy at any given wave-length from a full radiator.

$$E\,(\lambda) = c_1\,\lambda^{-5}\,(e^{c_2/\lambda T} - 1)^{-1}\,\delta\lambda$$

Where $E(\lambda)$ = energy radiated at wave-length λ in erg/sec./sq. cm./cm. wave band

λ = wave-length in cm.

T = temperature in absolute degrees ($^\circ$K.)

c_1 = $3 \cdot 7407 \times 10^{-5}$

c_2 = $1 \cdot 4386$.

$\delta\lambda$ = band width of wave-lengths over which the radiation is calculated.

Table 17.1 gives values of $E(\lambda)$ for a range of wave-lengths from 1,000 A to 10μ and temperatures from 1000° K. to 10,000° K. in erg./sec./sq. cm./10 Angstrom band width.

The total energy of all wave-lengths radiated per second from 1 sq. cm. of surface of a full radiator at temperature T° K. is given by the *Stefan-Boltzman Law*

$$E\,(\text{total}) = 5 \cdot 6712 \times 10^{-5} T^4 \text{ erg/sec./sq. cm.}$$
$$= 5 \cdot 6712 \times 10^{-12} T^4 \text{ watts/sq. cm.}$$

Table 17.2 gives values of the total radiation for a range of temperatures.

The wave-length at which the radiation from a full radiator has its maximum value is connected with the temperature by *Wien's Displacement Law*, namely :

$$\lambda\,(\text{max.}) \times T = \text{constant} = 0 \cdot 28975 \text{ cm.deg.}$$

Table 17.2 gives values of λ (max.) for a range of temperatures. If we insert the value of λ (max.) obtained from Wien's law in Planck's relation we obtain the value of the *maximum energy* radiated at a specific temperature—(Table 17.2).

$$E \text{ (max.)} = 1 \cdot 2870 \times 10^{-4} T^5 \text{ erg/sec./sq. cm./cm. wave band.}$$

TABLE 17.1—*Black Body Radiation*

Planck's Relation $E (\lambda) = c_1 \lambda^{-5} (e^{c_2/\lambda T} - 1)^{-1} \delta\lambda$ erg/sec./sq. cm. per cm. wave-band.

$c_1 = 3 \cdot 7407 \times 10^{-5}$; $\lambda = $ wave-length in cm. ; $c_2 = 1 \cdot 4386$; $T = $ Temperature (°K.).

Tabulated values are in watts/sq. cm./10A wave band

T°K.	1000	2000	3000	4000	5000	6000	7000	8000	9000	10000
λ (μ)										
0·1										
0·2				0·178	0·65	7·2	53	144	0·572	21
									4·2	
0·3			0·0173	0·945	10·4	51·8	155	384	392	874
									770	1280
0·4		0·00006	0·225	4·50	27·4	91·1	225	411	682	1030
0·5		0·0067	0·815	8·97	38·4	100	202	337	510	720
0·6		0·0296	1·61	12·0	40·0	89·8	163	252	361	480
0·7		0·101	2·24	13·7	37·6	75·5	124	185	254	330
0·8	0·000017	0·140	2·84	12·8	32·0	59·7	94·5	136	178	225
0·9	0·000072	0·213	3·17	11·8	27·0	47·5	72·3	99	128	160
1·0	0·00021	0·280	3·10	10·5	22·5	37·2	55·3	74	94·6	116
1·1	0·00048	0·350	3·03	9·16	18·2	29·5	42·2	56·5	71	85·7
1·2	0·00092	0·374	2·80	7·87	14·8	23·4	33·1	43	53·8	64·6
1·3	0·00169	0·415	2·56	6·83	12·4	19·1	26·2	33·9	41·7	49·6
1·4	0·00316	0·427	2·36	5·77	10·3	15·3	20·8	26·8	32·7	38·6
1·5	0·00334	0·408	2·09	4·92	8·47	12·5	16·8	21·2	25·8	30·6
1·6	0·00438	0·400	1·86	4·24	7·05	10·2	13·7	17·2	20·7	24·4
1·7	0·00538	0·385	1·67	3·60	5·98	8·53	11·2	14·0	16·9	19·7
1·8	0·00664	0·369	1·49	3·10	5·02	7·13	9·3	11·5	13·8	16·1
1·9	0·00755	0·346	1·32	2·68	4·28	5·98	7·75	9·5	11·5	13·3
2·0	0·00874	0·328	1·17	2·31	3·63	5·04	6·48	8·0	9·55	10·6
3·0	0·0128	0·154	0·39	0·66	0·95	1·26	1·58	1·87	2·20	2·5
4·0	0·0102	0·072	0·16	0·25	0·35	0·44	0·55	0·64	0·74	0·84
5·0	0·0072	0·037	0·07	0·11	0·15	0·19	0·24	0·28	0·32	0·36
10·0	0·0012	0·036	0·06	0·09	0·11	0·14	0·16	0·19	0·22	0·23

TABLE 17.2—*Radiation Formulae*

	T°K.	1000	2000	3000	4000	5000	6000	7000	8000	9000	10000
1.	E (Total) watts/sq. cm.	5·6712	90·739	459·37	1451·9	3544·5	7350·4	13616	23229	37209	56712
2.	λ (max.) (μ)	2·8975	1·4488	0·9658	0·7244	0·5795	0·4829	0·4139	0·3622	0·3219	0·2898
3.	E (max.) watts/sq. cm. per mμ	0·0128	0·4118	3·1275	13·179	40·219	100·08	216·31	421·75	760·00	1287·0

1. Stefan-Boltzmann Law.
   E (total) $= 5 \cdot 6712 \times 10^{-5} T^4$ erg/sec./sq. cm.
2. Wien's Displacement Law.
   λ (max.) $\times T = 0 \cdot 28975$ cm. deg.
3. Maximum Energy at λ (max.)
   E (max.) $= 1 \cdot 2870 \times 10^{-4} T^5$ erg/sec./sq. cm./cm. wave band.

Table 17.2 gives the values of E (max.) for a 10A band.

If we divide the energies given by any of the above relations by the energy of one quantum, i.e. by $E = h\nu$, we naturally find the *number* of quanta or photons emitted. Planck's relation gives the number of quanta (or photons) emitted at any given wave-length.

$$N (\lambda) = E (\lambda)/h\nu = 1\cdot 8836 \times 10^{11} \lambda^{-4} (e^{c_2/\lambda T} - 1)^{-1}$$

photons/sec. cm./cm. wave band

and the equation for maximum radiation gives

$$N \text{ (max.)} = 2\cdot 1020 \times 10^{11}T^4 \text{ photons/sec./sq. cm./cm. waveband}$$

and the total number of photons emitted is

$$N \text{ (total)} = 1\cdot 5210 \times 10^{11}T^3 \text{ photons/ sec./sq. cm.}$$

Colour temperature

All practical thermal radiators give emission curves over the spectrum which may be similar in shape to the black body curves, but more generally they show maxima and minima depending on the nature of the incandescent material ; i.e., they are selective, but the ordinates of the curves always lie below those of a black body at the same temperature.

The temperatures of bodies estimated from their total radiation using Stefan's Law are called *radiation temperatures*. If the temperatures are estimated from the visible brightness of the emitter as seen by the eye they are called *brightness temperatures*. If, however, the shape of the emission curve in the visible region is compared with the shape of the black body radiation curve in the same region and the best possible fit obtained they are called *colour temperatures*. Colour temperatures are usually greater, and brightness temperatures usually less, than the absolute temperature as shown in Table 17.3.

Colour temperatures are important in many applications of photography and it is usual to state the colour temperature of a source for that purpose. The colour rendering of sources depends on the colour temperature.

Standard electric lamps are available, whose spectral distribution of energy has been carefully determined and these lamps are used to calibrate simpler instruments for the determination of colour temperatures. In portable optical pyrometers, for example, the light from the hot source is brought to a focus in the same plane as a heated carbon filament. The temperature of the filament is adjusted by altering the current through it until the filament becomes invisible against the background of light from the hot source. The current-temperature relation of the carbon filament is found by calibration against a standard source. For high colour temperatures of source red filters are used to obtain the match.

TABLE 17.3

Temperature K°.			Brightness candles/cm.² (Tungsten)
Absolute	Brightness	Colour	
1000	966	1006	0·00012
1200	1149	1210	0·006
1400	1330	1414	0·11
1600	1509	1619	0·92
1800	1684	1825	5·05
2000	1857	2033	20·0
2200	2026	2242	61·3
2400	2192	2452	157·0
2600	2356	2663	347·0
2800	2516	2878	694·0
3000	2673	3095	1257
3200	2827	3311	2110
3400	2978	3533	3370
3655 (Melting point)	3165	3817	5740

Sources of infra-red radiation

Black body cavity: Not in general use as a source because of low temperature, but used as a standard at 500°K. for calibration of detectors. (McFee, R. A., *Rev.Sci.Inst.*, **23**, 52 (1952).)

Globar: Rod of silicon carbide about 6 mm. diameter heated electrically in air, low operating temperature, maximum 1400°K., about 80 per cent black from 1·5μ to 15μ. (Silverman, *J.O.S.A.*, **38**, 989.)

Welsbach Mantle: Superior to most other sources at 10μ to 15μ, emission low from 0·7μ to 6μ but approaches black body at 2000°K. at 15μ. (Sutherland, G. B. B. M., *Infra-red and Raman Spectra*, Methuen, 1935.)

Nernst Glower: Filament of Zirconium and Yttrium oxides about 3 cm. long and 1 mm. diameter, heated by A.C. or D.C. (230 volts 0·9 amp.). Requires preheating and baretta or other stabiliser because of its negative coefficient of resistance. Emission close to black body to about 15μ. (Griffiths, H. D., *Phil. Mag.*, **50**, vi, 263 (1925).)

Carbon arc: Very bright source, 3970°K., preferably D.C. with stabiliser, about 5 amp. for arc length of 5 mm. High pressure arc in inert gas at 22 atmospheres gives about 6000°K.

Carbon rod: Electrically heated, 15 volts at 40 amp., in vacuum chamber with KBr window and water cooling, about 2000°K. (Smith, L. G., *Rev. Sci. Inst.*, **13**, 63 (1942).)

Tungsten filament lamp: Commercial lamps operate at 2900°K. but glass envelope restricts emission to below 3μ. Can be used in bell jar with KBr window in inert gas. (*J.O.S.A.*, **26**, 313 (1936), and **41**, 626 (1951).)

Excited gases and vapours: At low pressures emit mainly line spectra, at high temperatures and pressures give bands. Mercury arc at low pressure has some useful lines between 1μ and 2·3μ and at about 100 atmospheres pressure gives a continuous spectrum with peaks but no correspondence to black body.

Far infra-red : " Reststrahlen " methods by selective reflection from NaCl, KCl, KBr etc. are most satisfactory.

Calibration of detectors : See Roberts, J. K., *Heat and Thermodynamics*, Blackie.

Radiation measurement

The energy of the radiation from a source over the spectrum is measured by some form of non-selective detector such as a thermopile or bolometer using a number of standard narrow band pass filters, previously calibrated for their transmission, to isolate the wave bands. The absolute measurement of radiation energy at any given wavelength, or rather over a band of wave-lengths, is not simple. In any form of monochromator used to isolate wave bands due allowance must be made for the selective reflectance of mirrors and selective transmission of the various parts, lenses, windows, prisms etc.

The sensitivity of energy or thermal detectors is independent of the wave-length of the incident radiation and they have a fairly slow response time. When connected direct to a sensitive galvanometer, they are accurate, but any form of D.C. amplification usually results in difficulty occasioned by drift and fluctuations in ambient temperature. Owing to their slow response when used with " choppers " to produce the equivalent of alternating current for amplification by tuned amplifiers, the chopping frequency must be low (about 5–15 cycles/sec).

Thermocouples depend for their action on the thermoelectric effect, i.e. the E.M.F. generated at the junction of two dissimilar metals or alloys when the temperature of that junction differs from the temperatures of the other junctions in the circuit. In the Schwartz thermocouple two junctions are made to a common gold foil, and because of its low heat capacity the response time is very short. Thermopiles are, of course, merely batteries of thermocouples. The bolometer consists of some form of metallic strip the electrical resistance of which varies with its temperature. Consequently bolometers are usually connected in some form of Wheatstone bridge circuit. Diagrammatic representations of methods of use of thermocouples and bolometers are included in Fig. 17.4 on page 386. In the D.C. operation of the bolometer a battery is of course connected across the bridge.

Another useful form of thermal detector is the pneumatic Golay cell (see Fig. 17.5) which depends for its action on the increase of pressure caused by rise of temperature of a small quantity of gas contained in a capsule. One side of the capsule is blackened to absorb the incident radiation and the other side is flexible and carries a mirror. An ingenious optical system forms an image of a grid on another grid in such a way that no light passes the second grid when the mirror is not deflected. Any deflection of the mirror causes the image of the grid to move allowing a quantity of light to pass the second grid, proportional to the deflection. The light is produced from a small bulb and is picked up after passing the grid by a light sensitive cell. The overall arrangement is such that the signal from the detector is made proportional to the energy of the incident radiation and it is, of course, independent of the wave-length.

Photo-conductive devices

There is, however, a different class of detectors, known as quantum detectors, which are very often photo-conductive devices using such materials as germanium, lead sulphide, lead selenide, lead telluride, indium antimonide. The sensitivity of these detectors is dependent on wave-length and has a long-wave useful limit which

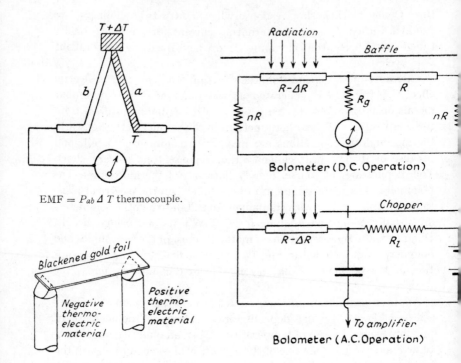

EMF $= P_{ab} \Delta T$ thermocouple.

Bolometer (D.C. Operation)

Schwartz thermocouple.

Bolometer (A.C. Operation)

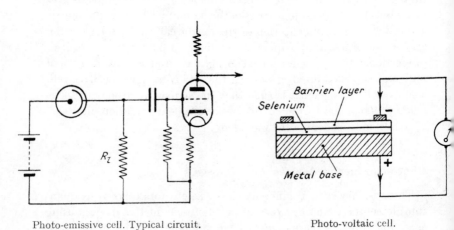

Photo-emissive cell. Typical circuit.

Photo-voltaic cell.

FIG. 17.4.

386

depends on the material of the detector; this limit can in some cases be extended by cooling the device to liquid air or even lower temperatures.

Quantum detectors are in general more sensitive over their limited wave-length range than thermal detectors and they also have very short response times which permit high frequency modulation of the

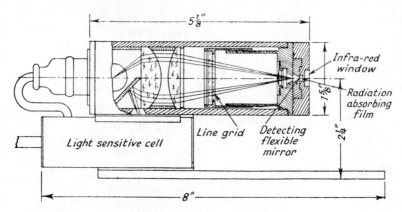

FIG. 17.5.—Golay infra-red detector.

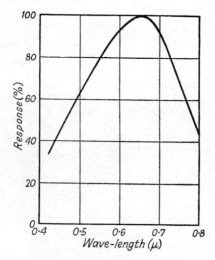

FIG. 17.6.—Spectral response of cadmium sulphide cell.

TABLE 17.4—*Materials Photo-Conductive in the Infra-Red*

Material	Form	Long Wave Limit (μ)	Temperature	Reference
Silicon	Crystal	1·0	20°C.	Pearson, G. L., and Bardeen, J., *Phys. Rev.*, **75,** 865 (1949)
Germanium	Crystal	1·7	20°C.	Haynes, J. R., and Briggs, H. B., *Phys. Rev.* **86,** 647 (1952)
Tellurium	Evaporated Layer	4·0	90°K.	Moss, T. S., *Photoconductivity in the Elements* (Butterworth, 1952)
Indium selenide	,,	1·8	20°C.	Bode, D. E., Levinstein, H., *J.O.S.A.*, **43,** 1209 (1953)
Thallium sulphide	,,	1·3	18°C.	Elliott, A., *Electronics*, (Pilot Press, 1947)
Thallium telluride	,,	2·6	90°K.	Braithwaite, J., *Proc. Phys. Soc.*, B. **64,** 274 (1951)
Mercury telluride	,,	3·9	90°K	Braithwaite, J. *Proc.Phys. Soc.*, B.**64,** 274 (1951)
Bismuth sulphide	,,	2·2	90°K.	Gibson, A. F., Moss, T. S. *Proc—Phys—Soc.*, A.**63,** 176 (1950)
Bismuth telluride	,,	4·0	90°K.	Gibson, A. F., Moss, T. S. *Proc.Phys.Soc.*, A.**63,** 176 (1950)
Lead telluride	,,	4·0	234°K.	Moss, T. S., *Proc.Phys. Soc.*, B.**62,** 741 (1949)
Lead telluride	,,	5·8	90°K.	Moss, T. S., *Proc.Phys. Soc.*, B.**62,**741 (1949)
Lead sulphide	,,	3·4	17°C.	Moss, T. S., *Proc.Phys. Soc.*, B.**62,** 741 (1949)
Lead sulphide	,,	4·3	90°K.	Moss, T. S., *Proc.Phys. Soc.*, B.**62,** 741 (1949)
Lead selenide	,,	5·4	17°C.	Gibson, A. F., Lawson, W. D., Moss, T. S., *Proc. Phys.Soc.*, A.**64,** 1054 (1951)
Lead selenide	,,	7·2	90°K.	Gibson, A. F., Lawson, W. D., Moss, T. S., *Proc. Phys.Soc.* A.**64,** 1054 (1951)
Table from *Detection and Measurement of Infra-Red Radiation*				Smith, R. A., Jones, F. E., Chasmar, R. P. (Oxford), 1957)

incoming light and the observation of transient phenomena. The internal resistance of these detectors is normally high and they can, therefore, be used in valve circuits.

The noise in these detectors is due to current and is inversely proportional to the frequency, so that by using a higher frequency modulation, better amplifiers can be used and the signal/noise ratio is increased. The indium antimonide detectors have a low internal resistance and require a matching transformer.

Table 17.4 gives information on some photo-conductive devices, and Fig. 17.6 shows a typical spectral response curve.

Photo-emissive cells

Photo-emissive cells are basically similar to photo-conductive devices in that the absorption of quanta of radiation cause electrons to be emitted from a surface. In the photo-conductive devices the effect is sometimes called " internal " since the electrons are emitted inside the crystal of the semi-conductor and cause a decrease in its resistance. In photo-emissive cells the effect is known as " external," the electrons being emitted from the surface of a metallic plate, which may be specially treated, into a space where they are collected by a second plate normally maintained at a positive potential. The flow of electrons from the emitter or cathode to the collector or anode constitutes an electric current which can be measured. As in the photo-conductive devices the energy of the photo-electron is equal to the difference between the energy of the quantum and the energy expended in surmounting the potential barrier at the surface (the work function).

Two types of photo-emissive cells are in use, namely the vacuum type and the gas-filled. In vacuum cells, the photo current reaches a saturation value which remains constant for all sufficiently positive potentials of the anode and is strictly proportional to the light flux falling on the cathode. A decreasing number of electrons continues to reach the collector even when its potential is made increasingly negative with respect to the cathode, until at some given negative potential no current flows. The value of this critical potential depends on the colour of the light, but not on its intensity. Fig. 17.7 shows the current voltage characteristics of a vacuum cell for three levels of illumination of three colours of light.

The sensitivity of photo-emissive cells can be greatly increased by

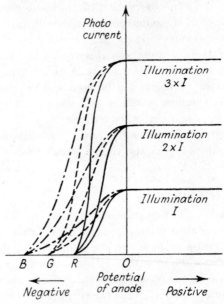

FIG. 17.7.—Characteristic of vacuum type photo-emissive cell for blue, green and red light and three levels of illumination.

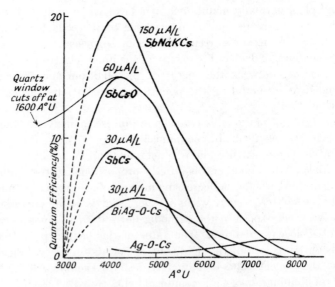

FIG. 17.8.—Spectral sensitivity of semi-transparent photo cathodes. (*Courtesy of E.M.I. Electronics Ltd.*)

introducing a small amount of an inert gas into the bulb. Depending on the pressure of the gas in the cell, the photo-electrons may, or may not, be able to ionise the gas and thus increase the flow of electrons to the collector. Over a certain range of pressures the ionising collisions increase in number with the pressure. The potential difference between the collector and cathode is also critical and has an effect on the ionisation. The characteristic curve of the cell does not show any saturation value as in vacuum cells. At low levels of illumination the current is proportional to the illumination, but when brightly illuminated, the photo-current increases more rapidly than the illumination.

Fig. 17.8 shows the relative spectral response of several types of photo-emissive cells. From these curves it is seen that the response is highly selective and it is necessary to choose a cell for each type of work. For measurements in the infra-red the silver-oxygen-caesium (Ag-O-Cs) cell is most suitable, whereas for the visible range and in the ultra-violet the antimony-caesium (Sb-Cs) is far superior.

The efficiency of a photo-cathode is often expressed in terms of its quantum yield. If every photon striking the cathode were to cause the emission of a photo-electron, the quantum yield would be 100 per cent. The energy of one quantum of green light ($\lambda = 550$ mμ) is

$$E = h\nu = 6\cdot624 \times 10^{-27} \times 3 \times 10^{10}/5\cdot5 \times 10^{-5}$$

$$= 3\cdot61 \times 10^{-12} \text{ erg.}$$

Hence, 1 watt of light at 550 mμ carries

$$\frac{10^7}{3\cdot61 \times 10^{-12}} = 2\cdot77 \times 10^{18} \text{ photons/sec.}$$

If each photon were to release 1 photo-electron, i.e., at 100 per cent quantum yield, this would correspond to a current yield:—

$$i = 0\cdot44 \text{ amp/watt.}$$

If then an actual photo-current of only 4·4 ma. is found to flow, the quantum yield would be 1 per cent. In practice the sensitivity of photo cells is usually measured in micro amperes per lumen.

Fig. 17.9 shows how the anode current in gas-filled cells depends on the anode voltage, illumination and load resistance. The much greater sensitivity of the gas-filled type is evident but they are not usually used for quantitative measurement.

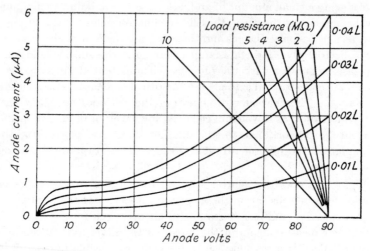

Fig. 17.9.—Characteristics of gas-filled photo-cells. (Mullard 20 CG.)

Photo-multipliers

When electrons are made to strike a target they may liberate secondary electrons from it. The photo-multiplier tubes depend on this effect. The coefficient of secondary emission, i.e., the average number of secondary electrons liberated by each primary electron, depends on several factors, particularly the target material and the angle of incidence of the primary electrons. In modern photo-multipliers the electrons emitted are accelerated by the electrostatic field in such a way as to strike a number of targets in turn.

A separate voltage of about 150 V. is applied to each stage, either by means of high tension batteries (such as are used in deaf-aid sets) or more generally from a tapped potentiometer supplied with the necessary voltage from a very well-stabilised power pack run from A.C. mains. With a suitable high tension unit, the output from a photo-multiplier tube will operate a table galvanometer without further amplification; the current taken from the tube should not exceed about 50–100µ A. for stable working, though for less quantitative purposes up to about 1 mA. may be taken. Photo-multiplier tubes are made with different numbers of stages, and with different sensitivities (by selection). Makers' values for photosensitivity vary from 10 to 50µ A. per lumen, with overall sensitivities from 5 to 30,000 A. per lumen. Photo-multipliers with quartz windows are available, but it is quite satisfactory to employ glass windows coated with a fluorescent material for detecting ultra-violet radiation, and for this purpose sodium salicylate is often used.

Photo-voltaic cells

In the photo-voltaic effect light falling on the cell produces an electromotive force at the terminals of the cell, thus causing a current to flow in an external circuit. Photo-voltaic cells are particularly useful in the visible range of the spectrum. The photo-voltaic effect occurs at the boundary between a metal and a semi-conductor and it is essential for the occurrence of the effect to have a so-called " barrier layer " of high resistance between the two materials. The barrier layer allows electrons to flow easily from the metal to the semi-conductor but not in the opposite direction. The most common available type of photo-voltaic cell is the selenium cell which is very sensitive and has a spectral response very similar to that of the human eye (see Fig. 17.10).

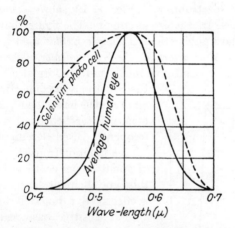

FIG. 17.10.—Spectral response of typical selenium photo-voltaic cell compared with sensitivity of human eye.

The efficiency of the cell depends on the resistance of the barrier layer which decreases rapidly with increasing illumination. In addition, if part of the surface of a cell is not illuminated it acts as a shunt for the illuminated part and thus decreases the efficiency of the cell. The size of the cell also affects the efficiency since the impedance of the cell is inversely proportional to its area.

The voltage rises at first almost linearly with the illumination on the cell, but the photo-current characteristic depends on the external resistance in the circuit. Small external resistance gives larger useful photo-current, but lower power output. Large external resistance causes the characteristic curve to deviate considerably from linearity.

Recently, selenium cells have been produced in battery form, consisting of about twenty-five separate cells connected in series. These compound cells have applications as solar batteries, particularly with modern transistor type circuits for the transmission and reception of signals by line or by wireless telegraphy or telephony.

Transistors

The study of semi-conductors has led to the development of diode and triode transistors, which in their electrical properties are similar to diode and triode thermionic valves. Many of these transistors are light-sensitive and can be used for the detection of radiation. Fig. 17.11 shows the spectral response of one type of photo-transistor to an equal energy spectrum, and Fig. 17.12 shows some methods of connecting these transistors in circuits. The figures have been taken from the Mullard publications *A Simple Explanation of Semi-conductor Devices* and *Transistors for the Experimenter*. These booklets are very well produced and give much useful information. Of the three basic methods of connecting transistors, all of which have their uses, the "common emitter" connection is the most frequently used circuit arrangement. With a junction transistor a current gain of about 50 per cent can be obtained in this type of circuit. The photo-transistor is effectively a junction transistor with a light-sensitive base region. The advantage of such a device over the photo-diode or photo-cell is that it is not only light-sensitive but is also an amplifier. This means that in practice photo-transistors can be connected in circuit directly to a relay without an intermediate amplifying stage. The books by

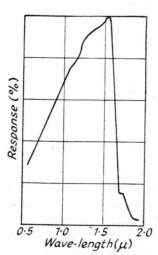

Fig. 17.11.—Spectral response of a Photo-transistor to constant energy spectrum. (Mullard OCP71).

Shea and by Krugman should be consulted for fuller information on this relatively new and fast moving subject. Transistors are not generally so suitable for the measurement of radiation as for its detection ; their response time is short and they have been much used in signal devices, such as punched tape readers.

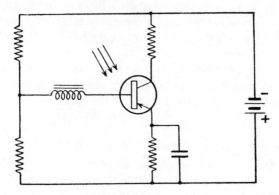

Typical photo-transistor circuit.

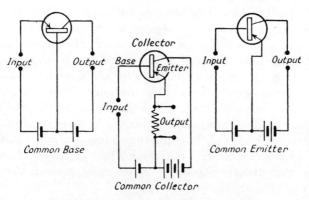

Fɪɢ. 17.12.—Junction transistor connections.

Relative sensitivity of detector with any radiator

The spectral sensitivity curves for the various detectors are based on an equal energy spectrum ; i.e., it is assumed that the energy falling on the detector is the same at all wave-lengths. All practical sources of radiation emit varying amounts of energy at each wave-length. In order to determine the relative sensitivity of a detector to any particular radiation, it is necessary to multiply the ordinates of the spectral sensitivity curve of the detector by the corresponding ordinates of the spectral distribution of energy curve of the source at each wave-length. The resulting curve shows the sensitivity of the detector to that particular radiation. If, in addition, any filters or other absorbers of energy are also used, the sensitivity curve is again calculated by multiplying the corresponding ordinates of the spectral transmission curve of the filter by the ordinates of the relative sensi-tivity curve of the combination of detector and source. This argument is of special importance in photometry where we are concerned with the effect of radiation as light visible to the eye.

Ultimate sensitivity of radiation detectors

The detailed discussion of the ultimate sensitivity of radiation receivers occupies a considerable part of a recent book by Smith, Jones and Chasmar and is outside the scope of this chapter. Never-theless, a few remarks on the subject may be made. In all the detectors, radiation is made to influence the current in an electrical circuit, and is measured by the changes in this current, after some form of amplification. When working at high amplification, it will always be found that fluctuations (noise) are present which are not related to genuine changes in the signal. Even when accidental sources of change are removed in detector and amplifier, a finite level of noise remains which may vary from one detector to another. However, by increasing the response time of the system, the level of noise may be diminished, but naturally the time required for an observation is increased. It is therefore necessary, when comparing detectors, to take account of the response time of the whole observing system; the ultimate sensitivity is inversely proportional to the square root of this time.

Comparison of detectors is further complicated by the effect of sensitive area or sensitivity. In general, higher real sensitivity is obtained by using a small sensitive area and concentrating the radia-tion on it than by using a larger target area. However, with some forms of detector this may introduce more noise, and in some optical systems it is not possible to effect high concentration of radiation. In such cases a detector sufficiently large to receive all the radiation would be chosen. Of the thermal detectors, the Golay cell is remarkable for its high target area (4 mm. diameter). (See Fig. 17.5.)

Photometry

In several parts of this book references have been made to the brightness of sources and images and to illumination and it is obvious that in any optical instrument the brightness of the image and its relation to the source of light is of importance. Owing to the very diverse nature of the general problem of illumination there have arisen a number of methods of measurement and a number of systems of units have consequently been devised to meet each requirement. The tables on p. 398, summarise the various units.

A source of light, or *luminous source*, emits radiation capable of being detected by the eye. The light from this source *illuminates* a surface and confers on it a *brightness*. This sequence leads to a series of definitions of units in which these quantities are measured.

There are thus four fundamental concepts in photometry any one of which may be considered as independent and the rest as derived. These four quantities are :—

(*i*) *Flux* (*F*) defined as the rate of flow of radiant energy and evaluated in terms of its visual effect. The unit of luminous flux is the *lumen* defined as the flux emitted in a unit solid angle by a point source of unit intensity.

(*ii*) *Intensity* (*J*) of a point source in any direction is the luminous flux per unit solid angle emitted by the source in that direction. The unit of intensity is the *candle* and intensity is often referred to as *candle-power*. The international candle is an arbitrary standard arrived at by agreement and maintained in the standardising laboratories in each country subscribing to the agreement ; in England the National Physical Laboratories and in America the National Bureau of Standards.

(*iii*) *Brightness* (*B*) of an extended source in any direction is its intensity per unit projected area in that direction. It is measured in *candles per unit area*. An illuminated surface also has brightness and is measured in the same unit.

(*iv*) *Illumination* (*E*). The illumination at a point of a surface is

TABLE 17.5—*Brightness and Illumination Conversion Tables*

BRIGHTNESS

Stilb — candles/cm²	candles/m²	candles/ft²	Lambert — lumens/cm²	millilambert	lumens/m²	equivalent foot candle — foot lambert lumens/ft²
1	10^4	929	π	$\pi \times 10^3$	$\pi \times 10^4$	$929\,\pi$
10^{-4}	1	$9 \cdot 29 \times 10^{-2}$	$\pi\,10^{-4}$	$\pi/10$	π	$9 \cdot 29\pi \times 10^{-2}$
$1 \cdot 08 \times 10^{-3}$	$10 \cdot 8$	1	$1 \cdot 08\pi \times 10^{-3}$	$1 \cdot 08\,\pi$	$10 \cdot 8\,\pi$	π
$1/\pi$	$10^4/\pi$	$929/\pi$	1	10^3	10^4	929
$1/\pi \times 10^{-3}$	$10/\pi$	$0 \cdot 929/\pi$	10^{-3}	1	10	$0 \cdot 929$
$1/\pi \times 10^{-4}$	$1/\pi$	$0 \cdot 093/\pi$	10^{-4}	$1/10$	1	$0 \cdot 093$
$1 \cdot 08/\pi \times 10^{-3}$	$10 \cdot 8/\pi$	$1/\pi$	$1 \cdot 08 \times 10^{-3}$	$1 \cdot 08$	$10 \cdot 8$	1

ILLUMINATION

lux — metre candle — lumens/m²	foot candle — lumens/ft²	phot — centimetre candle — lumens/cm²	milliphot	mile candle	kilometre candle
1	$0 \cdot 093$	10^{-4}	10^{-1}	$2 \cdot 6 \times 10^6$	10^6
$10 \cdot 8$	1	$1 \cdot 08 \times 10^{-3}$	$1 \cdot 08$	$2 \cdot 8 \times 10^7$	$1 \cdot 08 \times 10^7$
10^4	$9 \cdot 3 \times 10^2$	1	10^3	$2 \cdot 6 \times 10^{10}$	10^{10}
10	$0 \cdot 93$	10^{-3}	1	$2 \cdot 6 \times 10^7$	10^7
$3 \cdot 8 \times 10^{-7}$	$3 \cdot 5 \times 10^{-8}$	$3 \cdot 8 \times 10^{-11}$	$3 \cdot 8 \times 10^{-8}$	1	$0 \cdot 38$
10^{-6}	$9 \cdot 3 \times 10^{-8}$	10^{-10}	10^{-7}	$2 \cdot 6$	1

the surface density of luminous flux at that point, i.e., the number of lumens per unit area falling on the surface taken over a very small area including the point under consideration.

Because of the importance of a clear conception of these four quantities they are developed further below and the various derived units are discussed.

The unit of luminous flux, the *lumen*, has the same dimensions as power and has been found by experiment to be equivalent, for a normal observer, to 0·00147 watts of monochromatic green light of wave-length 5550 Angstroms, or taking the reciprocal, 1 watt of monochromatic green light is equivalent to 680 lumens. The *luminosity* of a source is therefore found by multiplying 680 by the relative visibility for each wave-length, i.e., for each wave-length we must multiply the ordinate of the spectral sensitivity curve of the eye by the ordinate of the energy distribution curve of the source for the same wave-length and find the sum of all the partial products.

The ordinates of the spectral sensitivity curve of the eye (Fig. 16.1), are given in Tables 16.1, 16.2, on p. 347. The energy distribution curve of the source has been discussed in Chapter 16 and also on p. 380; Figs. 16.5, 17.2, and 17.3 show some such curves. Thus

$$\text{Luminosity} = 680 \, \Sigma \, V_\lambda E(\lambda)\delta\lambda \quad \text{or} \quad 680 \int_0^\infty V_\lambda E(\lambda)d\lambda$$

where V_λ is the sensitivity of the eye for a given wave-length and $E(\lambda)$ is the energy emitted by the source at wave-lengths between λ and $\lambda + \delta\lambda$. Since the total power emitted by the source is $\Sigma \, E(\lambda)\delta\lambda$ or $\int_0^\infty E(\lambda)d\lambda$ the *luminous efficiency* of the source, or the number of lumens of light per watt of radiation is given by :—

$$\text{Luminous efficiency} = \frac{680 \, \Sigma \, V_\lambda E(\lambda)\delta\lambda}{\Sigma \, E(\lambda)\delta\lambda} \quad \text{or} \quad \frac{680 \int V_\lambda E(\lambda)d\lambda}{\int E(\lambda)d\lambda}$$

The formulae have been given in the summation form as it is not usually possible to carry out the integration because of the nature of the functions involved.

If the source of light is so small that it may be considered as a point source then its *luminous intensity* in any given direction is defined as *the number of lumens per unit solid angle* radiated in that direction and is called its *candle power* $J = dF/d\omega$ where $d\omega$ is an element of solid angle. Thus a point source emitting light uniformly in all directions radiates 4π lumens per candle. Also the flux radiated from a point source in any solid angle ω is given by $F = J\omega$, i.e., candle power multiplied by the solid angle.

If the source is too large to be considered as a point the quantity corresponding to luminous intensity is called *brightness* which is defined as the *candle power per unit projected area* in the direction under consideration. In symbols :—

$$B = \frac{dJ}{ds \cos \theta}$$

where dJ is the luminous intensity of an element of surface ds and θ is the angle between the normal to the surface and the given direction. The units of brightness are based on the *candle per sq. ft.* or the *candle per sq. metre*. The candle per sq. centimetre is called the *stilb*.

The brightness of a surface often depends on the direction from which it is viewed but there is a theoretical surface for which the *intensity* varies as the cosine of the angle between the normal and the direction of observation. Such a surface, since it radiates light equally in all directions, thus producing the cosine distribution of intensity, is called a diffuse radiator and is said to obey *Lambert's Law*. There are some actual surfaces which are very nearly perfectly diffusing and may be considered as obeying Lambert's Law, e.g., magnesium oxide, fresh snow, the sun's disc, an opal globe, etc.

The apparent brightness of an extended object is independent of the distance from which it is observed since the area covered by the image on the retina decreases at a rate which compensates for the smaller amount of flux entering the pupil, but a point source appears fainter as the distance is increased.

If the surface obeys Lambert's Law then it will appear equally bright from all directions.

We have defined the brightness of a surface in candles per unit projected area by means of the formula $B = dJ/ds \cos \theta$ and we can therefore say that an element of area ds of brightness B will have a normal candle power of $dJ = Bds$, and in any direction making an angle θ with the normal its candle power in that direction will be given by $dJ = Bds \cos \theta$.

We can therefore calculate the total flux in lumens emitted by an element of surface. In Fig. 17.14 ds is a small source of brightness B which radiates according to Lambert's Law. Its candle power in any direction θ is $dJ = Bds \cos\theta$ and the flux which passes through an element of area ds' on the surface of a hemisphere of radius r is $dF = dJ.ds'/r^2 = B.ds.\cos\theta.ds'/r^2$. The area of the elementary strip of the hemisphere of which ds' is a part is $2\pi r.\sin\theta.rd\theta$ and hence the total flux intercepted by this elementary strip is $(B.ds.\cos\theta/r^2) \times (2\pi r.\sin\theta.rd\theta)$ or $dF = 2\pi B.ds.\sin\theta \cos\theta \, d\theta$ and the total flux radiated into a symmetrical cone of semi angle θ is therefore :—

$$F = 2\pi \, B.ds \int_0^\theta \sin\theta \cos\theta \, d\theta$$

$$= \pi \, B.ds. \sin^2\theta$$

and the total light flux radiated into the hemisphere is :—

$$\pi \, B.ds.\sin^2 (\pi/2) = \pi \, B.ds$$

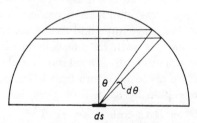

Fig. 17.14.—Luminous flux emitted by an element of surface of a perfect diffuser. The total flux in the symmetrical cone of semi-angle θ is $F = \pi \, B \, ds \, \sin^2\theta$.

When light falls on a surface the resulting *illumination* is measured by the amount of *flux incident per unit area* ($E = dF/ds$). The units of illumination are therefore based on the lumen per sq. ft. or the lumen per sq. metre. Since a point source of 1 candle power emits 4π lumens the illumination produced on the inner side of a sphere of unit radius is 1 lumen per unit area. The *lumen per sq. ft.* is also called the *foot-candle* and the *lumen per sq. metre* is called the *metre-candle* or *lux*. One lumen per sq. centimetre is called the *phot* or *cm.-candle*. Care should be taken to avoid the impression that the foot-candle and similar units are the products of distance and intensity as such units would be dimensionally incorrect, and it is always better to remember that illumination is measured in lumens per unit area.

The illumination produced by a point source of candle power J on an element of surface ds at a distance R and inclined so that the normal to the surface is at an angle θ to the direction of the source can be calculated from first principles by considering the flux. The solid angle subtended by the surface at the source is $ds.\cos\theta/R^2$ and therefore the number of lumens of flux contained in this solid angle is $J.ds.\cos\theta/R^2$, hence the illumination on the surface, in lumens per unit area, is :—

$$E = J.\cos\theta/R^2$$

This is the *fundamental law of photometry* and is used for the measurement of the intensity of sources of light, for if a surface is equally illuminated by two sources, of candle powers J_1 and J_2 placed at distances R_1 and R_2 then :—

$$J_1/J_2 = R_1{}^2/R_2{}^2$$

and if one of the sources has a known intensity the intensity of the other can be calculated.

When the source is of small but finite area ds and of brightness B (candles per unit area) the illumination produced on an element of area ds' distant r from the source and such that the normal to the surface makes an angle θ' with the line joining the elements, as in Fig. 17.15, can be calculated by considering the flux emitted by the radiating surface into the cone whose base is the receiving element. Thus the flux intercepted by ds' will be given by :—

$$dF = B.ds.\cos\theta \times ds'.\cos\theta'/r^2$$

and the illumination of ds' will be

$$dE = dF/ds' = B.ds.\cos\theta\cos\theta'/r^2$$

The symmetrical nature of these expressions should be noted. Thus it does not matter which surface is considered as the emitter and which the receiver, the illumination of either is simply given by the product of the candle power in the given direction and the solid angle subtended by the receiving surface.

When the source and the receiving surface are of considerable

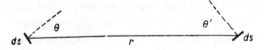

FIG. 17.15.—Illumination from an element of surface. The illumination on ds' by light from ds is given by $E = \dfrac{B.ds\cos\theta\cos\theta'}{r^2}$

extent it becomes necessary to integrate the effect over the total source and over the total receiving area, a process which can often be simplified by introducing an auxiliary surface of any shape (usually spherical) such that each element of the original source subtends the same solid angle as a corresponding element of the auxiliary surface at the point under consideration. In symbols :—

$$d\omega = ds.\ \cos\theta/r^2 = da.\ \cos\phi/R^2$$

where ds, θ and r refer to the original source and da, ϕ and R refer to the corresponding element of the auxiliary surface.

We have already shown that the light flux radiated into a symmetrical cone of semi angle θ by an element ds of brightness B is given by :—

$$F = \pi\ B.ds.\ \sin^2\theta$$

For a point source on the other hand, radiating uniformly in all directions, and of intensity J (candles) the flux radiated into a symmetrical cone of semi angle θ is given by :—

$$F = J \times \text{solid angle of the cone}$$
$$= J \times 2\pi \int_o^\theta \sin\theta\ d\theta$$
$$= 2\pi\ J(1 - \cos\theta)$$
$$= 4\pi\ J \sin^2 \frac{\theta}{2}$$

Thus the illumination due to a point source would be greater than that from a small extended source of the same normal candle power (i.e., when $J = B.ds$) owing, of course, to the fact that the point source has been assumed to radiate uniformly in all directions while the extended area radiates according to Lambert's law.

The brightness of an illuminated surface depends on its reflecting power, but if the surface obeys Lambert's law so that its brightness is the same for every angle of observation we can define a unit called the *Lambert* as the brightness of a perfectly diffusing surface emitting or reflecting 1 *lumen per sq. centimetre*. Thus the brightness of a diffusing surface in lamberts is simply the product of the illumination of the surface in lumens per sq. centimetre (Phots) and the reflecting power of the surface. The lambert is also called the equivalent centimetre-candle and the corresponding unit in the F.P.S. system is the *foot-lambert* or *equivalent foot-candle* which is the brightness of a diffusing surface illuminated with 1 foot-candle (1 lumen per sq. ft.).

It is important to notice the relation between the lambert or lumen per sq. cm. and the candle per sq. cm. We have already shown that a surface of brightness B candles per sq. cm. radiates πB lumens per sq. cm., hence 1 candle/cm.^{2} = π lamberts.

If a source of light illuminates a diffusing surface which in turn illuminates a second surface, as in an episcope for example or in the sun, moon, earth relation, we can speak of the *borrowed* brightness of the intermediate surface. In Fig. 17.16 the element ds at P of brightness B illuminates an element ds_1 of the surface Q which is assumed to be a perfect diffuser obeying Lambert's law. The quantity of light received by ds_1 from ds is :—

$$dF = B.ds. \cos\theta. ds_1. \cos\theta_1/R_1^2$$

and the illumination on ds_1 is :—

$$dF/ds_1 = B.ds. \cos\theta \cos\theta_1/R_1^2$$

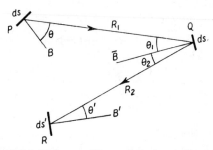

FIG. 17.16.—Borrowed brightness: The surface ds_1 at Q receives light from ds at P; the illumination of Q is $B.ds. \cos\theta. \cos\theta_1/R_1^2$. The reflectivity of Q is k and its " borrowed brightness " $\bar{B} = k/\pi \times$ (illumination of Q). The illumination on $ds' = \bar{B} ds_1 \cos\theta_2. \cos\theta'/R_2^2$.

If Q is a perfectly white surface, i.e., such that *all* the light received is re-radiated according to Lambert's law, then its brightness will be equal to the illumination (lumens per unit area) and its brightness in candles per unit area will be :—

$$B_1 = B.ds. \cos\theta \cos\theta_1/\pi R_1^2$$

We can define a factor k as the reflectivity of the surface or its co-efficient of whiteness such that it is the fraction of the incident light flux which is re-radiated. The factor k depends on the colour of the surface and would be unity for perfect whiteness, zero for perfect black, but there are many complications and it is not possible to find a single constant that would give information about the reflecting characteristics of any material. It is usual to restrict the term reflectivity to the reflecting power for monochromatic light of any particular wave-length and the term coefficient of whiteness to the integrated fraction over a range of wave-lengths. In most materials there is a variation of reflection with azimuth and with the angles of incidence and of observation, i.e., they do not obey Lambert's law. We shall therefore say that the borrowed brightness of the surface is :—

$$\bar{B} = k.B.ds.\ \cos\theta\ \cos\theta_1/R_1^2\pi$$

i.e.,
$$\bar{B} = k/\pi \times \text{(illumination of the surface)}$$

The quantity of light radiated from ds_1 to the element of surface ds' at R_2 will be given by :—

$$F' = \bar{B}.ds_1 \cos\theta_2.\ ds'\ \cos\theta'\ /R_2^2$$

where
$$\bar{B} = k/\pi \times \text{(illumination on } ds_1)$$

Photometry of Optical Instruments

It has already been shown that the flux of light emitted from an element of surface ds of brightness B into a symmetrical cone of semi angle θ is given by $F = \pi\, Bds \sin^2\theta$. In Chapter 15, p. 281, it was stated that a necessary condition for the formation of images free from aberration is that the magnification of the image of a small axial object should be constant for all zones of the lens and it was shown that this condition is fulfilled if :—

$$n\, y \sin u = n'\, y' \sin u'$$

where n and n' are the refractive indices in the object and image spaces, y and y' the heights of the small object and its (small) image and u and u' the angles made by rays from the axial object and image points to the zone of the instrument under consideration. If we square this statement of the sine condition we can write

$$n^2\, ds \sin^2 u = n'^2\, ds' \sin^2 u'$$

where ds and ds' are elements of area of the object and image.

It was also stated in Chapter 15 that all the light which passes through the entrance pupil of an instrument emerges from the instrument through the exit pupil, less, of course, losses due to internal reflections and absorption in the instrument. If we assume that a fraction k of the incident light emerges from the exit pupil so that k is the transmission factor of the instrument, then if a flux F enters through the entrance pupil a quantity kF will emerge and if the instrument is free from aberration this light will form the image.

If we now consider an optical instrument, as in Fig. 17.17 shown by its entrance and exit pupils, and if a small element ds of brightness B situated on the axis forms an image ds', then the flux which passes through the entrance pupil will be given by :—

$$F = \pi B \, ds \, \sin^2 U$$

where U is the angle at the axial object point formed by the extreme ray to the rim of the entrance pupil. The light which emerges from the exit pupil is kF if k is the transmission factor and since $n^2 \, ds \, \sin^2 U = n'^2 \, ds' \, \sin^2 U'$ we can write :—

$$kF = k\pi B \, ds' \, \sin^2 U' \times \left(\frac{n'}{n}\right)^2$$

and the *illumination* of the image, i.e., kF/ds' is given by :

$$E' = k\pi B \left(\frac{n'}{n}\right)^2 \sin^2 U'.$$

If, as frequently happens, the instrument is bounded by air on both sides $n'/n = 1$ and :—

$$E' = k\pi B \sin^2 U'$$

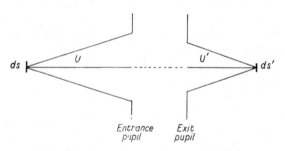

FIG. 17.17.—Photometry of an optical instrument.

Thus the illumination of a small axial image formed by an optical instrument simply depends on the brightness of the source and the size of the pencil of rays converging at the image.

This result is of fundamental importance and its application to a number of representative instruments is given below.

We have so far assumed that the object is of finite but small size and that its image is sufficiently large as not to be affected by diffraction. If the source is a distant star, i.e., a point source, of candle power J then the quantity of light entering the instrument will be given by

$$F = \frac{J}{R^2} \times \text{(area of the entrance pupil)}$$

and the image will be in the form of a diffraction pattern, the Airy disc, the radius of which is given by :—

$$\rho = \frac{0\cdot61\lambda}{n'\sin U'} \quad \text{(See Chapter 15, p. 279.)}$$

and about 84 per cent of the flux will be concentrated in the central diffraction disc.

On the other hand if the source is of very great area it becomes necessary to consider the distribution of the illumination over the large extended image by considering small elements of area and their respective images. The illumination on the axis has been derived above and the illumination of the image at extra axial points cannot be simply derived but, as an approximation, it is sufficient to assume that the projected area of the exit pupil in the direction of the extra axial image point will control the light flux. Assuming that there is no vignetting the projected area of the exit pupil in a direction making an angle θ with the axis will be proportioned to $\cos\theta$ and the increased distance from the pupil to the image, due to obliquity, will reduce the light by a further factor of $\cos^2\theta$ (inverse square law). Finally since the light is falling obliquely on the image its illumination will again be reduced by a factor of $\cos\theta$. Thus the illumination of extra axial image points will be reduced by a final factor of $\cos^4\theta$.

It is interesting to note that for a circular exit pupil the solid angle ω' within the cone whose semi plane angle is θ' is given by :—

$$\omega' = 2\pi\,(1\,-\,\cos\theta')$$

and if θ' is small, as it frequently is in many optical systems, $2\,(1\,-\,\cos\theta')$ is approximately equal to $\sin^2\theta'$ so that we can write :—

$$E = B\,\omega'$$

i.e., the illumination of the image is proportional to the solid angle subtended at the image by the exit pupil of the instrument. This result can be used where the shape of the exit pupil does not permit of a simple integration.

If the object is very small the illumination falling per unit area on the entrance pupil of the instrument would, of course, be given by :—

$$E = \frac{J}{R^2}$$

where J is the candle power of the source and R is its distance, and the total light entering the instrument would be given by $F = E \times$ (area of the entrance pupil). This total flux would be reduced by the transmission factor k in passing through the instrument.

The transmission factor k of an instrument can be very simply measured by using some form of brightness photometer. The instrument is set up before an opal glass illuminated from behind by a lamp and the brightness of the opal as seen through the instrument is measured. The instrument is then removed and the brightness of the surface measured directly. Since the apparent brightness of a surface is the same from whatever distance it is measured the position of the photometer in relation to the surface is immaterial.

Some important particular cases of the brightness of optical images require further consideration and are summarised below :—

(a) The unaided eye

Here the pupil diameter decides the value of U'. Clearly extended objects will appear equally bright at all distances, except for light attenuation by the atmosphere.

(b) Telescopes or field glasses ; night glasses

The value of U' in a telescope may be set by the exit pupil of the instrument or by the eye pupil, whichever is the smaller. Hence a telescope cannot increase the apparent brightness of an extended object ; it must always reduce it by a factor k or by an even greater factor if the exit pupil is small.

Instruments intended for use under conditions of low illumination (" night glasses ") have exit pupils large enough to fill the dark-adapted eye with light (7 mm.). Using such instruments at night it is difficult not to believe that even extended objects are rendered brighter by the glasses. This is not the case : The effect (first explained by Lord Rayleigh) is caused by the properties of the eye at low intensities of illumination. The magnification is of advantage in seeing faint objects. (See also p. 349.)

For point objects, such as stars, the illumination varies as the square of the effective diameter of the object-glass and therefore a greater number of stars become visible when using a telescope, while the background is less bright.

(c) Simple lens or Camera lens (extended object).

$$E = k\pi B \sin^2 U'$$

E = illumination on plate in foot candles
B = brightness of object in candles per sq. ft.
k = transmission factor of lens
U' = semi angle of image forming cone.

If d is the diameter of the lens and f its focal length, and if the object is at a great distance, then $\sin U'$ is equal approximately to

$$d/2f \text{ so that } E = k \, \pi \, B \, \frac{d^2}{4f^2}$$

or writing A for $\frac{f}{d}$ where A is the f-number or relative aperture.

$$E = \frac{k \, \pi \, B}{4A^2}$$

A simple and easy rule to remember is that at $f/8$ and assuming a value of 80 per cent for k as a reasonable average

$$E = B/100$$

If the object is not at a great distance then $\sin U' = \dfrac{d}{2f(m+1)}$ where m is the magnification (numerically) and :—

$$E = \frac{k \, \pi \, B}{(m+1)^2 \, 4 \, A^2}$$

(d) *Simple or Camera lens* (point source)

The quantity of light falling on the entrance pupil will be given by :—

$$F = \frac{J}{R^2} \times \text{(area of entrance pupil)}$$

where J is the candle power of the point source and R is its distance. The image will be in the form of a diffraction pattern the size of which will depend on the relative aperture of the lens, the quantity of light in the pattern is proportional to the area of the entrance pupil, and the distribution of light will depend on the position of the focus and the aberrations of the system.

(e) *Optical Lantern*

$$E = \frac{k_1 \, k_2, \text{ etc.} \times \text{(utilised area of projection lens)}}{\text{square of distance from lens to screen}}$$

k_1 = transmission of condenser system

k_2 = transmission of lens system, etc.

It is of interest to consider the actual transmission of the various parts of an actual cinematograph projector as shown in the following table (taken from Martin—*Technical Optics*, Vol. II, p. 245).

APPROXIMATE PERCENTAGE TRANSMISSIONS

Condenser	Gate	Film	Projector	Shutter	Combined
70	50	75	60	50	7·8

Thus the average efficiency of projector systems is very low; only about 8 per cent of the light entering the condenser reaches the screen. The losses in the condenser are caused by reflection (about 4 per cent at each surface) and absorption in the thick glass. In the gate, owing to aberrations and obstruction, a large amount of light is lost. The loss in the film depends on the density and the figure of 75 per cent transmission corresponds approximately to fog level in the clearest portions. The projector lens may have six or eight air-glass surfaces, and even if treated with non-reflecting film (bloomed or coated) the transmission seldom exceeds the figure given. The shutter, of course, in a cinema projector is open for only half the time and thus cuts off at least 50 per cent and usually more. Hence the combined efficiency is $0·7 \times 0·5 \times 0·75 \times 0·6 \times 0·5 = 0·078$.

(ƒ) Episcopes

No simple formula exists for the complete system.

The lens projects the image directly and the camera lens formula holds for this portion, but we have to consider the illumination of the object and its reflectance. It is instructive to consider an example which has been taken with some alterations from Martin's *Technical Optics*, Vol. II, p. 246.

A 2,000 candle-power lamp placed 6 in. from the object surface may be expected to produce an illumination of 8,000 lumens per sq. ft. The total radiation is πB lumens per sq. ft., hence $B = 8,000/\pi$. The candle power of an element of area ds is therefore $8,000ds/\pi$ and the total light radiated into the cone of semi angle θ will be :—

$$\pi \sin^2\theta \; ds. \; 8,000/\pi$$

If the lens is working at a relative aperture of $f/2$, $\sin \theta$ is approximately $\frac{1}{4}$ and $\sin^2 \theta = 1/16$, hence the amount of light is $500 \; ds$ lumens. This light is distributed over the magnified image at a linear magnification of, say, 18 times, giving an area magnification of 324. Taking the transmission of the lens at 80 per cent we have $0·8 \times 500$ ds lumens distributed over an area of $324 \; ds$ so that the illumination of the screen will be 400/324 or 1·23 foot candles. No allowance has been made for other light losses caused by the reflection factor of the object.

(g) *Searchlight*, etc.

The illumination of the target is given by the formula :—

$$E = \frac{Bk \times (\text{Area of Projector})}{(\text{Range})^2} \times (\text{atmospheric transmission})$$

Effective candle power $= Bk \times (\text{area of projector})$

Assuming a 3-ft. mirror (radius 18 in.) and a carbon arc of brightness 100,000 candles per sq. in., a complete flash would give a gross candle power of $\pi \times 18^2 \times 10^5 = 10^8$ candles (approx.). Allowance must be made for optical imperfections which would prevent a complete flash being obtained, the obstruction of the carbons and the protective cover glass.

The searchlight affords an interesting example of the importance of the conditions of use. The effect of moderate atmospheric scatter on the target illumination is considerable, but the reduction in the visibility of the target owing to the brightness of the beam of scattered light is devastating. The increase of range to be obtained by doubling the beam candle power of a large searchlight is trivial under ordinary conditions in Great Britain.

Photometric instruments

(a) Lamp standards :

In all photometric measurements the quantity to be measured must be ultimately compared with a standard quantity and this can only be provided by some form of standard lamp. The legal standard sources are not usually convenient for laboratory or practical use and secondary standards are therefore generally set up and used. The legal standards are of several forms and are described fully in the *Dictionary of Applied Physics* to which the reader is referred for full information. The sub-standards are usually electric filament lamps carefully aged and calibrated and run off a constant voltage supply or with constant current consumption. The candle power of such lamps varies as the fourth power of the current or sixth power of the voltage, so that accurate measurement of the latter is essential and in portable photometric apparatus it is usual to fit a good voltmeter or to place the lamp in an arm of a wheatstone network and use the null indication of a micro-ammeter to ensure a constant current.

(b) *Instruments :*

The comparison of light sources is always made by comparing the brightness of surfaces illuminated by the sources. In the instruments used for the direct comparison of sources, or the measurement of candle power, the problem is reduced to the design of the photometric head which consists essentially of two surfaces whose brightnesses when illuminated by the standard and unknown sources are compared by eye. In instruments used for the measurement of illumination a standard white surface is placed in the position where the illumination is to be measured and its brightness compared with that of a surface contained in the instrument which is given a variable illumination until a match is obtained. Photo-electric cell photometers are now available in large numbers and are very convenient and portable instruments for the measurement of illumination.

The Lummer-Brodhun photometer head is generally considered to be the most accurate instrument for the comparison of light sources, but many variations are in use and the reader should consult a text book on Photometry, such as that by Walsh, for details.

Among the instruments which do not use the eye for the actual comparison there are the selenium cell types, photo-electric cells and thermopiles, all of which can be considered as instruments for direct measurement, but null methods are frequently employed where the cell is exposed in turn to the two sources of light or illumination and a balance obtained by a variety of means. One drawback to the use of these physical methods of comparison is that the sensitivity of these instruments as discussed on p. 391 does not always conform to that of the eye and care must therefore be taken in their use and in the interpretation of the results.

In the earlier types of selenium cells, in which a layer of crystallised annealed selenium was crossed by a number of pairs of conductors, the effect of illumination on the conductivity of the selenium was measured. This type of cell had many disadvantages, including high resistance, sensitiveness to humidity and temperature and particularly a hysteresis lag. The newer cells, known as the barrier layer types, are photo-emissive and are used directly connected to a micro-ammeter. An average performance may be 0·5 micro amperes per sq. cm. of cell per foot candle and where additional sensitivity to very low light intensities is required several cells may be used in parallel to increase the effective area. Many instruments have been made incorporating photo-emissive barrier layer cells, the photographic exposure meter type being perhaps the best known. They have been used successfully in such instruments as the Hilger recording photo-electric micro-photometer. Unfortunately the response of these cells is not necessarily proportional to the quantity of light nor equal for all wave-lengths. Nevertheless, when used with due precaution they are very useful laboratory tools and the spectral response is not greatly different from that of the human eye.

Radiation meters of the bolometer, radiometer and thermopile types have the great advantage that their response is truly linear and equal for all wave-lengths. They may be used to measure the total radiation from any source. In the radio micrometer a thermopile is mounted directly to the moving system of a galvanometer and a mirror so that there are no outside leads. In the bolometer the variation in resistance of a black metal strip is measured. The radio-meter consists frequently of a black vane carrying a mirror and mounted with a torsion spring in an almost evacuated envelope. When radiation falls on the black surface the rise of temperature of that surface causes an increase in the velocity of recoil of molecules of gas which collide with it so that there is a deflection balanced by the torque of the suspension. There is a considerable volume of literature on the subject and the reader interested in such applications may consult the book on the *Detection and Measurement of Infra-Red Radiation* by Smith, Jones and Chasmar and Strong's *Physical Laboratory Practice* which gives a full list of references.

The applications of photometric methods in the laboratory are too numerous to attempt to describe but a few examples are instructive. Selenium cells are used in the Spekker Absorptiometer manu-factured by Adam Hilger and shown in Fig. 17.18. In this instrument a central lamp, either of the filament or mercury vapour type, pro-vides light in one direction through a filter and carefully calibrated iris diaphragm to a lens which renders the beam parallel during its passage through the material under test. A second lens forms an image of the light source on one selenium cell. In the other direction the light passes through a filter, iris and compensating cell to a second selenium cell. The two cells are connected in opposition in circuit with a sensitive galvanometer and adjustments to the iris diaphragms are made until there is no deflection. The areas of the diaphragms are calibrated and provide the data for the measurement. Similar cells are used in recording and non-recording types of micro-photo-meters and in spectro photometers.

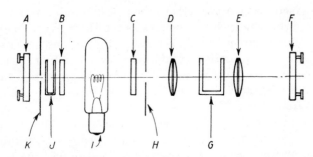

Fig. 17.18.—Optical system of Spekker Absorptiometer (Hilger). Light from the lamp is made parallel by lens D, passes through the specimen in the cell G and lens E forms an image of the lamp on photo cell F. H is a calibrated variable aperture which varies the quantity of light falling on F. A compensating photo cell A also receives light from the lamp, the quantity being varied by the iris diaphragm K. J is a protective water cell and B and C are filters. The photo cells are connected in opposition to a galvanometer which reads zero when the photo-electric currents are equal.

The use of thermo-couples is illustrated in the infra-red spectrometer shown in Fig. 17.19, also manufactured by Adam Hilger. The introduction of the Hilger-Schwarz rapid response thermo-couple used in this instrument has been of great benefit to infra-red spectrometry.

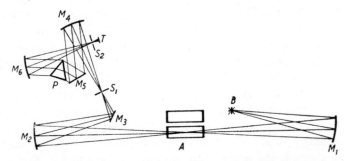

Fig. 17.19.—Diagrammatic lay-out of the Hilger Industrial non-recording infra-red spectrometer. The source B is a Nernst filament in a water-cooled housing. Radiation from B is focused by mirrors M_1, M_2 and M_3 to form an image of the filament on the slit S_1 of the monochromator. The two cells at A carry the absorbing substance and a blank. The monochromator has interchangeable prisms and the drum is calibrated in wave-lengths. The light is collimated by aluminised concave mirrors. T is a Schwarz thermopile.

Light from the source, which is a Nernst filament, is reflected by means of aluminised mirrors through the material under test in the tubes A and is again reflected into the slit of the monochromator system, after which the light is concentrated, often by elliptical mirrors, on the thermopile. This thermopile has a sensitivity of 18 micro volts per micro watt of incident energy and a response time better than 0·4 seconds.

The number and variety of instruments for the measurement of illumination is very great and only a few can be mentioned here. In one form, known as the Macbeth Illuminometer, a surface is illuminated by the outside source and its brightness compared in a photometer head with that of a second surface which is illuminated by a sliding lamp. The position of the lamp is adjusted until a balance is obtained and the illumination calculated by means of the inverse square law. Actually the scale of the instrument is calibrated directly and the indicator is attached to the lamp adjusting mechanism. In another form the comparison surface is illuminated through a variable filter and the position of this filter calibrated directly. In the " Lumeter " the intensity of the light used to illuminate the comparison surface is varied by means of a rotating wedge-shaped diaphragm or by a step diaphragm the rotation of which is used to indicate the brightness of the comparison surface. The test surface is a white sheet of material placed in the required position and viewed through a central clear hole in the comparison surface. The range of the instrument can be varied by inserting filters.

Some atomic and molecular constants

Volume of gram-molecular weight of an ideal gas at 0° C. and 760 mm. pressure (N.T.P.) = 22·1412 litres.

Number of molecules per gram-molecular weight

Avogadro's number $\qquad N = 6\cdot023 \times 10^{23}$

Number of molecules per cc. at N.T.P. $= 2\cdot7048 \times 10^{19}$.

The gas constant $R = PV/T = 8\cdot315 \times 10^7$ ergs/deg.

$\qquad\qquad = 1\cdot987$ cal./deg.

Boltzmann's Constant $= k = R/N = 1\cdot372 \times 10^{-16}$ erg/deg.

Velocity of light	c	$= 2\cdot9979 \times 10^{10}$ cm./sec.
Charge on electron	e	$= 1\cdot602 \times 10^{-20}$ e.m.u.
Mass of electron	m	$= 8\cdot995 \times 10^{-28}$ gm.
Ratio of Charge: mass	e/m	$= 1\cdot769 \times 10^7$ e.m.u./gm.
Planck's Constant	h	$= 6\cdot6242 \times 10^{-27}$ erg/sec.

1 electron volt $= 1\cdot6019 \times 10^{-12}$ ergs.

1 calorie	$= 4\cdot19$ Joules	$= 4\cdot19 \times 10^7$ ergs.
1 lumen at $5550A$		$= 0\cdot00147$ watt.
		$= 0\cdot000385$ gm. cal./sec.
1 watt of light at $5550A$		$= 680$ lumens.

Example: Consider light of wave-length 3000A. $= 3 \times 10^{-5}$ cm.

Frequency $= 10^{15}$ per sec.

Energy of one quantum of light of wave-length 3000A.

$$E = \quad = 6 \cdot 62 \times 10^{-27} \times 10^{15} = 6 \cdot 62 \times 10^{-12} \text{ ergs.}$$

$$= 6 \cdot 62 \times 10^{-12}/4 \cdot 19 \times 10^{7} = 1 \cdot 584 \times 10^{-19} \text{ cal.}$$

$$= 1 \cdot 584 \times 10^{-19} \times 10^{-3} \times 6 \cdot 023 \times 10^{23} = 95 \cdot 27 \text{ Kg./cals.}$$
mole.

$$= 6 \cdot 62 \times 10^{-12} \div 1 \cdot 602 \times 10^{12} = 4 \cdot 11 \text{ electron volts.}$$

BOOKS

SMITH, R. A., JONES, F. E., and CHASMAR, R. P., *The Detection and Measurement of Infra-Red Radiation*, Oxford, 1957.

SHEA, *Principles of Transistor Circuits*, Chapman & Hall. (Wiley, N.Y.)

SHEA, *Transistor Audio Amplifiers*, Chapman & Hall. (Wiley, N.Y.)

KRUGMAN, *Fundamentals of Transistors*, Chapman & Hall. (Rider, N.Y.)

RCA LABORATORIES, *Transistors I.*

MULLARD, *Transistors for the Experimenter*, and *A Simple Explanation of Transistors.*

ZWORYKIN, V. K., WILSON, E. D., *Photocells and Their Application*, Chapman & Hall, (Wiley, N.Y.), 1930.

HEAVENS, O. S., *Optical Properties of Thin Solid Films* (Butterworth), 1955.

Photometry

WALSH, J. W. T., *Photometry* (Constable), 1926.

WALSH, J. W. T., *Text Book of Illuminating Engineering* (Pitman), 1947.

BOAST, *Illuminating Engineering* (McGraw Hill).

JOLLEY, WALDRAM and WILSON, *Theory and Design of Illuminating, Engineering Equipment* (Chapman & Hall), 1930.

REFERENCES

RING, J., and WILCOCK, W. L., *Nature, Lond.*, **171**, 648.

SUTHERLAND, G. B. B. M., and LEE, E., *Report on Progress in Physics*, 1946–7, XI 144.

GOLAY, M. J. E., *Rev. Sci. Instrum.*, **18**, 347 (1947), **18**, 357 (1947).

HILSUM, C., OLIVER, D. J., and RICKAYZEN, G., *J. Electronics* **1**, 134 (1955).

ROBERTS, D. H., *Chemistry and Industry* (April 1957), p. 482.

PLESSEY Co. Ltd., Advance Information (August 1957). Infra-Red Detector type PC 21.

ELLIOTT, A., " Photo Cells for the Infra Red," *Electronics*, edited Lovell, London. Pilot Press, 1947.

MARTIN, L. C., *D.S.I.R. Bulletin No. 3*, H.M.S.O.

WALSH, J. W. T., " The Measurement of Light," *Phot. J.* (A), **92A** (1952), p. 178.

Catalogues, Brochures and Date Sheets on radiation detectors:—

The British Thomson-Houston Co. Ltd., Rugby, England.

Cintel, Ltd., Worsley Bridge Road, London, S.E.26.

20th Century Electronics, Ltd., King Henry's Drive, New Addington, Surrey.

Eastman Kodak, Rochester, N.Y.

E.M.I. Electronics, Ltd., Hayes, Middlesex.

Evans Electroselenium, Ltd., Harlow, Essex.

General Electric Co. Ltd., Kingsway, London, W.C.2.

Hilger & Watts, Ltd., 98 St. Pancras Way, London, N.W.1.

Mullard, Ltd., Torrington Place, London, W.C.1.

Megatron, Ltd., 115a, Fonthill Road, London, N.4.

Plessey Company Ltd., Ilford, Essex.

Radio Corporation of America, RCA International Div., 30 Rockefeller Plaza, N.Y. 20, and RCA Gt. Britain Ltd., Lincoln Way, Windmill Road, Sunbury-on-Thames, Middlesex.

Standard Telephones & Cables, Ltd., Harlow, Essex,

The Eppley Laboratory, Inc., Newport, R.I., U.S.A.

Unicam Instruments, Ltd., Cambridge, England.

Chapter 18

PHOTOGRAPHY IN RESEARCH

The applications of photographic processes to research work are so diverse and specialised that it would be impossible to give anything more than an outline in a short chapter and it cannot be too strongly emphasised that before a photographic process is contemplated the advice of one of the large photographic firms should be obtained. The range of materials and processes is so great that only by seeking advice at the source can full use be made of photography. It very frequently happens that through over-confidence in the knowledge and ability of an expert amateur photographer the results obtained are disappointing and a useful method abandoned.

The emulsion

Generally speaking photography is a recording process depending on the sensitivity to light of a chemical substance which requires subsequent *processing* to develop the image and render it permanent. The essential material is therefore the sensitive emulsion which is available in very many forms coated on glass, film or paper. The emulsions can be graded according to their speed, colour sensitivity, contrast and resolving power so far as monochrome processes are concerned and there are in addition a number of materials for direct colour reproduction.

In many cases commercially available plates, film or paper will be found quite suitable, but the manufacturers are able to supply materials specially suited for specific scientific purposes. The special scientific types of emulsion can be either what is known as " unsensitised " or sensitised by the addition of dyes for a particular range of wave-lengths and may be of high speed with medium contrast, medium speed with high contrast or low speed with very high contrast. The " unsensitised " type is sensitive from about 2000 A in the ultra-violet up to about 5,000 A. The emulsion corresponding to the " Chrome " types commercially available are sensitised to the blue-green and have increased sensitivity at about 5,000 A. Panchromatic materials of the slower types are sensitive up to about 6,200 A and the faster types to 6,600 A or 6,900 A. Then follow a range of emulsions suitable for infra-red work with sensitivities ranging in steps from 6,400 A up to 12,000 A. The makers can always supply spectrograms (examples of which are shown in Fig. 18.1) for all their emulsions. These wedge spectrograms show very clearly the range of wave-lengths for which the particular emulsion is sensitive. Owing to the type of apparatus used for obtaining wedge spectrograms

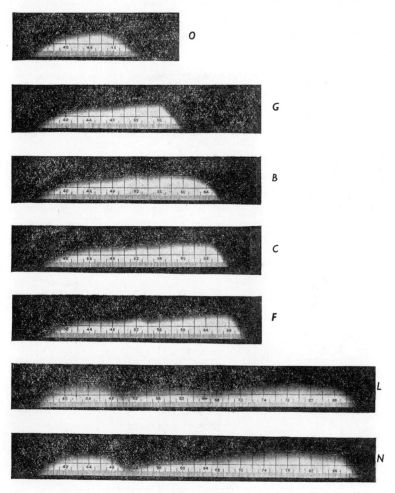

FIG. 18.1.—Representative wedge spectrograms of seven types of emulsion. The letters refer to the sensitising classification used by Kodak Ltd. O is unsensitised, G is orthochromatic, B, C and F are panchromatic of varying red-sensitivity. L and N are infra-red types.

the response is not uniform over the whole spectrum, especially in the ultra-violet region where the curve appears to end, though in actual fact *all* sensitised materials have some sensitivity in the ultra-violet down to about 2100 A. The curves are however quite consistent and therefore it is permissible to use them to compare the colour sensitivities of the different materials. Spectral sensitivity curves obtained from the wedge spectrograms are usually adjusted to a standard height at a certain wave-length and are purely relative. They cannot be used, in this form, to compare the overall speeds of different materials.

Characteristic curve

The blackening of the exposed and developed emulsion is measured by its density which is defined as the logarithm of the ratio of the amount of light falling on it to the amount which emerges (see p. 206), i.e., density $= \log. \dfrac{1}{\text{transmission}}$. If the emulsion is given a series of exposures increasing in geometrical progression the density will at first be found to increase slowly, then more rapidly and again more slowly to a maximum value and if it is greatly over-exposed the density obtained will be found to fall again, but this gross over-exposure is not generally utilised in photography. When a curve is drawn as in Fig. 18.2 with log exposure as abscissa and density as

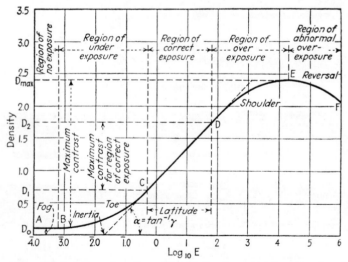

FIG. 18.2.—Typical $D - \log_{10}E$, or H. and D. characteristic curve for photographic materials with important regions specified.

ordinate it is known as the characteristic or H. and D. curve of the emulsion, after Hurter and Driffield who first introduced this method of measurement, and shows (1) the speed, given by the position of curve along the log exposure axis (2) the gamma or contrast, measured by the gradient of the middle part, and (3) the maximum density. The shape and position of this curve depend on the type of development, i.e., the constitution of the developer, its temperature and time of development, on the colour of the light and on whether the steps of exposure were obtained by varying the intensity I of the light or the time during which it reached the emulsion.

The type of developer used has an effect on the speed which is sometimes measured by the point on the log exposure axis where the tangent to the middle portion of the curve cuts it (H. & D. speed). The measurement of speed is still somewhat controversial as is exemplified by the various markings (Scheiner, DIN, etc.) and the systems of measurement are not accurately related to each other, because of the different methods of sensitometry, but Tables 18.1 and 18.2 give approximate corresponding values and the speeds of some common materials respectively, and Fig. 18.3 indicates the basis of the various systems of speed rating. The British and American agreed speed standard is now based on the exposure E corresponding

TABLE 18.1—*Film Speed Systems Compared*

| Relative Speed | Ilford Group | Exposure Index | | European Scheiner | General Electric Weston | DIN | British H. & D. | American or Weston Scheiner | Wellcome Calculator (up to 1950) |
		A.S.A.	B.S.I.						
2	B	6	19°	20°	8	9/10	200	15°	1/4
		8	20°	21°	10	10/10	250	16°	—
4	C	10	21°	22°	12	11/10	320	17°	1/6
		12	22°	23°	16	12/10	400	18°	1/8
		16	23°	24°	20	13/10	500	19°	—
8	D	20	24°	25°	24	14/10	640	20°	1/12
		25	25°	26°	32	15/10	800	21°	1/16
		32	26°	27°	40	16/10	1000	22°	—
16	E	40	27°	28°	50	17/10	1300	23°	1/24
		50	28°	29°	64	18/10	1600	24°	1/32
		64	29°	30°	80	19/10	2000	25°	—
32	F	80	30°	31°	100	20/10	2500	26°	1/48
		100	31°	32°	125	21/10	3200	27°	1/64
		125	32°	33°	160	22/10	4000	28°	—
64	G	160	33°	34°	200	23/10	5000	29°	1/96
		200	34°	35°	250	25/10	6400	30°	1/128
		250	35°	36°	320	26/10	8000	31°	—
128	H	320	36°	37°	400		10000	32°	1/192
		400	37°	38°	500		12800	33°	1/256
		500	38°	39°	640		16000	34°	—

to the density where the gradient of the curve is 0·3 of the average gradient over a log E range of 1·5 or, in Fig. 18.4, $PQ = 0·3 \times PR$.

In Table 18.1, where speeds are marked in degrees, and in the DIN rating, it will be noticed that the markings are in a natural series of numbers. An increase of three units in any of these series corresponds to a doubling of the speed. In the other ratings, H. and D., Weston, A.S.A. etc., the numbers are in geometrical progression so that a

TABLE 18.2—*Film Speeds*

| | Exposure Index | | | |
| | A.S.A. | | B.S.I. | |
Material	*Daylight*	*Tungsten*	*Daylight*	*Tungsten*
35 mm. Film			*degrees*	*degrees*
Gevaert Microgran	32	20	27	25
Gevaert Panchromosa	125	80	33	31
Ilford Pan. F.	16	8	24	21
Ilford F.P.3	32	20	27	25
Ilford H.P.3	125	80	33	31
Ilford H.P.S.	400	320	37	36
Kodak Panatomic-X	25	20	25	24
Kodak Quick Finish Pan.	40	32	27	26
Kodak Plus-X	80	64	30	29
Kodak Tri-X	200	160	34	33
Roll Film				
Ensign Finegrain Pan	16	10	24	22
Ensign Ultrachrome	32	10	27	22
Gevaert Microgran	32	20	27	25
Gevaert Panchromosa	125	80	33	31
Ilford Selochrome	64	20	30	25
Ilford F.P.3	32	20	27	25
Ilford H.P.3	125	80	33	31
Ilford H.P.S.	400	320	37	36
Kodak Verichrome Pan.	80	64	30	29
Kodak Panatomic-X	25	20	25	24
Kodak Tri-X	200	160	34	33
Cut Film				
Gevaert Microgran Pan.	32	20	27	25
Gevaert Superchrom.	64	20	30	25
Gevaert Panchromosa	125	80	33	31
Ilford Commercial Ortho	32	10	27	22
Ilford Selochrome	64	20	30	25
Ilford Hyperchromatic	125	80	33	31
Ilford H.P.3	125	80	33	31
Kodak Commercial F.G.	20	4	24	17
Kodak Commercial Ortho	25	8	25	20
Kodak Panatomic-X	32	20	27	25
Kodak Plus-X	80	64	30	29
Kodak Ortho-X	125	64	32	29
Kodak Super-XX	100	80	31	30
Kodak Panchro Royal	200	160	34	33

doubling of a number corresponds to a doubling of speed; i.e., the relative speeds are proportional to their speed numbers as given in the table. The first column in the table shows the relative speeds and the second column the former Ilford grading in which the letters A to H are used. In this grading each letter corresponds to a doubling of the speed.

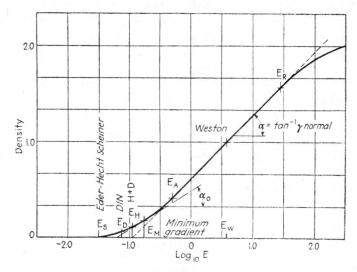

Fig. 18.3.—$D - \log_{10} E$ characteristic and the exposure values from which a number of well-known speed systems are determined.

E_S = Threshold speed—basis of Scheiner rating.
E_D = Exposure corresponding to a density of 0·1—basis of DIN (Deutsche Industrial Normal) system.
E_H = Inertia speed—basis of H. & D. (Hurter & Driffield) rating.
E_M = Exposure corresponding to minimum useful gradient, a_0 basis of Kodak rating. (See Fig. 18.4.)
E_W = Exposure where $\log_{10}E = Y$ (numerically)—basis of Weston system.

In most ordinary practical applications a change of 2 : 1 in speed is of minor importance because the latitude of the emulsion is sufficient to cover a far greater variation in exposure. It is only in critical circumstances that careful calculation of exposure is necessary. An old adage :—" Expose for the shadows and let the highlights look after themselves " is often forgotten.

Speed ratings are not published for high contrast materials such as those used in the graphic arts or for micro-copying, nor for special materials, for astronomical plates, recording films etc.

The type of developer and to a larger extent the time and temperature affect the gamma or slope of the curve, increase of development time causing in general an increase of contrast as expressed by the tangent of the angle which the middle portion of the curve makes with the exposure axis.

There is of course a maximum gamma or slope for each type of emulsion and developer and any increase in development time after this maximum has been attained leads only to general fog, i.e., an overall density where there has been no exposure. For the best results development should be arranged so that the gamma obtained is about 80 per cent of the maximum.

The maximum density depends largely on the exposure but can be affected by the developer used and its temperature.

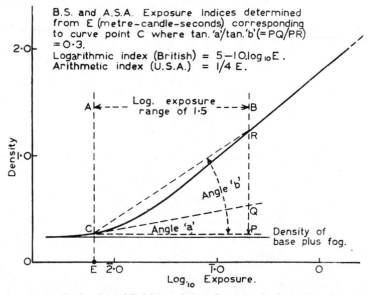

FIG. 18.4.—Derivation of British and American standard exposure indices.

Colour film

Exposure is more critical with reversal colour film than with black and white negative material. Owing to the variations which exist between different camera shutters, lenses and individual exposure meters, any published ratings can serve only as a guide for practical tests, which should be carried out as carefully as possible. For consistent results with colour film the "highlight" or "white card" method of using a meter is strongly recommended. Instructions are issued with the meters.

There are no B.S.I. or A.S.A. standards for the speeds of colour film but the manufacturers supply a speed index for colour materials which is based on the same arithmetic and logarithmic series. Table 18.3 shows some of the speeds given by the manufacturers.

TABLE 18.3

	B.S.I.	A.S.A.
Reversal (*Daylight*)		
Agfacolor Type CT.18	28°	50
Ferraniacolor	24°	20
Gevacolor R.5	25°	25
Ilford Colour	21°	10
Kodachrome	21°	10
Ektachrome	20°	8
Ektachrome E.2	26°	32
Anscochrome	26°	32
Anscocolor	21°	10
Raycolor Rev.	24°	20
Reversal (*Artificial Light*)		
Agfacolor Type K	24°	20
Ilford Colour A	23°	16
Kodachrome A	23°	16
Ektachrome B	21°	10
Ektachrome Type F	25°	25
Anscocolor Type A	22°	12
Raycolor Type A	24°	20
Negative (*Daylight*)		
Agfa Type T	21°	10
Gevacolor N.5	25°	25
Kodacolor	25°	25
Pakolor Type D	20°	8
Negative *Artificial Light*		
Agfa Type K	23°	16
Pakolor Type A	20°	8

As a general indication of the effect of artificial light on exposure the following factors show by how much the exposure should be increased when using artificial light as against daylight.

Ordinary, non colour sensitive material $\times$ 4

Orthochromatic $\times$ 2

Normal Panchromatic $\times$ $1\frac{1}{2}$

Hypersensitive Panchromatic $\times$ $1\frac{1}{4}$

These factors arise from the fact that artificial light generally contains much more red light than blue light and the panchromatic materials are of course more sensitive to red than the ortho or ordinary emulsions.

For really accurate colour rendering with colour film it is advisable to find out the colour temperature of the light for which the film is designed. The whole question of the viewing of colour as well as colour photography is complicated by the spectral distribution and colour temperature of light as explained on p. 382.

Exposure

The exposure is calculated as the product of the intensity I and the time of exposure t, but these two are not reciprocal quantities, i.e., the same curve is not obtained by increasing intensity and by increasing time. If the log exposure (log It) required to obtain a given density is plotted against the logarithm of the intensity (log I) as in Fig. 18.5 a curve showing a minimum and known as the *reciprocity failure curve* is obtained. The range of exposure time over

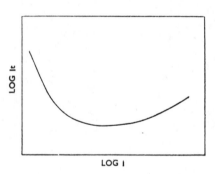

FIG. 18.5.—Log It—log I or reciprocity failure curve.

which the reciprocity failure is small is considerable and may be from 1/100 second to 1 second beyond which limits the effective speed of the emulsion diminishes. For very long exposures, minutes to hours, the curve is nearly straight and the effective exposure is given as $I\ t^p$ where p is a constant. This is Schwartzchild's law which has an application in astronomical photography. Table 18.4, is taken from *The British Journal Photographic Almanac*, after Wallis and Beatt, and gives some data on reciprocity failure in the form of corrected exposure times. It is intended for non-reversal material. Somewhat less correction is needed for reversal materials.

When log It is plotted against the logarithm of the exposure time (log t) as in Fig. 18.6 the curves obtained are of the same shape but displaced vertically for different wave-lengths of the incident light. Thus the ratios of the light of different colours necessary to produce a given density is independent of the time of exposure provided this time is the same for all colours. This fact enables photographs of spectra to be calibrated for intensity without the necessity of ensuring that every spectrum measured has received the same exposure time. For example, if a blue line produces twice the density produced by a red line at any given exposure time, then for any other exposure time the blue line will remain twice as dense as the red line.

Methods of obtaining increased speed

When the exposure given to a material is of very short duration, as in high speed flash photography and the recording of high speed

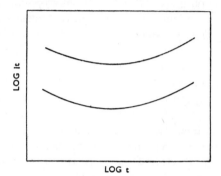

Fig. 18.6.—Log It—log t. Each curve corresponds to light of a particular wave-length.

TABLE 18.4.—*Reciprocity Failure*

Indicated Exposure	Corrected Exposure	Per cent Increase	Indicated Exposure	Corrected Exposure		Per cent Increase
sec.	sec.	%	min.	min.	sec.	%
200 μ sec. 1/5000	1/1500	230	1	2	30	250
400 μ sec. 1/2500	1/930	170	1½	5	50	265
1 m. sec. 1/1000	1/470	113	2	8	33	325
2 m. sec. 1/500	1/280	80	3	14	31	385
1/300	1/210	60	4	20	45	420
5 m. sec. 1/200	1/140	43	5	27	30	550
1/150	1/110	38	10	68	22	680
10 m. sec. 1/100	1/80	25	—	—		—
1/50	1/45	10	—	—		—
1/30 ⎫ 1/3 ⎬	No correction					
1	1¼	25	—	—		—
2	2¾	38	—	—		—
4	6½	63	—	—		—
8	16	100	—	—		—
15	35	133	—	—		—
30	85	183	—	—		—

Note. For short exposures the correctness of the shutter indicated speeds should be verified. Many shutters, at high speeds, are inefficient.

(Table from the *British Journal Photographic Almanac*, after Wallis and Beatt.)

cathode ray traces, a very useful increase in speed can be obtained simply by prolonged development, which also tends to increase the contrast. High energy MQ developers, such as are used for X-ray material, are particularly suitable but tend to increase the fog level and grain. The Ilford " Microphen " developer, however, is claimed to permit very considerable increase in development time, with increase of speed and without increase in fog or grain. This developer is one of a series containing Phenidone which has been produced by Ilford. Similar increases in speed are also obtained with this developer when the light level has been low and adequate time for full exposures is impossible.

A certain amount of speed increase can be obtained by a mercury vapour treatment. All that is necessary is to place the material, in its normal wrapping, in a tin containing a few drops of mercury. Twenty-four to thirty hours' treatment at room temperature for plates and cut film and about a week for 1,000-ft. rolls of cine film have been quoted and apparently this method is more effective where long duration exposures to weak light are used. Another method of presensitisation for subsequent long exposures is by giving a uniform fogging exposure to light before the camera exposure. The pre-exposure should be *short*, about 1/25 sec., to light just enough to cause a perceptible increase in fog. The method is of no value if the camera exposure is short.

Latensification, or the treatment of the latent image between camera exposure and processing offers a wide choice of method. One method is to bathe the material, after exposure, in a solution of 0·5 per cent potassium metabisulphite and 0·85 per cent sodium sulphite with a wetting agent and allowing to dry before developing in the normal way. Sulphur dioxide, mercury vapour and the fumes of formic and acetic acids have been shown to give increased speeds but the methods are difficult to control and reproduce.

Where the camera exposure is of short duration, 1/25 second or less, the effective speed of many materials may be increased by giving a *long* uniform fogging exposure to a weak light. The fogging times quoted are between 30 and 60 minutes at 6 feet from a safelight and the development times must be kept short or loss of speed will result. Negative intensification by normal well-known methods, Quinone thiosulphate, Kodak IN 6, or Uranium intensifiers are probably safer methods of obtaining increased speed.

Grain

It is a fairly general rule that the faster the emulsion the more grainy it is so that its resolving power is low, and that the so-called fine grain developers can do no more than prevent the excessive growth of grain, usually at the expense of some part of the effective speed. Thus, there is very little advantage to be gained by using a very fast material with a fine grain developer since the effective speed may be reduced by as much as 40 per cent and a slower material with a normal developer would probably give better results. Where maximum resolution is important a fine grain emulsion should be selected and every endeavour made to increase the effective illumination either by using a larger aperture lens or increasing the light to compensate for the lower speed of the emulsion. It should be noted that the effect of grain depends largely on its distribution in the emulsion. Some large grain emulsions (Schumann plates) give better resolution because there is no sideways spread of light.

A few general rules regarding graininess may be summarised as follows :—

(i) Fast emulsions are more grainy than slow emulsions.

(ii) Fast working developers tend to give more grain than slow working developers containing a relatively high concentration of sulphite.

(iii) Over-development increases grain.

(iv) Differences in temperature of various solutions tend to cause reticulation which looks like increased grain, and high temperature developers tend to cause more grain.

If the photographs are to be printed on paper, then contrasty papers enhance the appearance of grain and the best results can generally be obtained by using a normal paper.

The grainy quality of the emulsion has an effect during exposure of scattering the incident light so that strong spectrum lines appear wider than they should be and the photographic images of bright stars are larger than the true optical images. This quality is used in astronomical work to measure the relative brightness of stars since the brighter the star is the larger its image ; on the other hand the spreading of a bright spectrum line image can mask nearby fine images.

Another effect of grain is known as halation which is caused by the internal reflection on the back of the film or base plate of the light scattered back by the grains of the emulsion, and appears as a ring of light surrounding the image of a bright object. Halation can be considerably reduced by using so-called " backed " films or plates, the backing tending to absorb the scattered light.

Resolution

The resolving power of an emulsion can be measured by direct contact printing from a master negative using directed light from a condenser or a distant point source. The resolving power of a lens may be measured visually or photographically, but it is ultimately the resolving power of the combination of lens and emulsion under its normal condition of use that really matters. There is a general relation between the resolutions obtained given by the formula

$$1/R_C = 1/R_L + 1/R_E$$

where R_C is the resolving power of the combination of lens and emulsion, R_L is the resolution of the lens measured in some standard manner which requires specification, and R_E is the resolution of the emulsion. This relationship is not a firmly established physical law but is an adequate basis for estimation and comparison in a relative manner.

The theoretical limit of the resolution of a lens considered as a perfect image forming optical instrument and based on the distribution of light in the image caused by diffraction and the wave-length of light is given by Airy's formula (see p. 279). For a photographic lens this takes the form $\rho = 1 \cdot 22 \lambda A$ where ρ is the distance between two image points, λ the wave-length of the light measured in the same units and A is the relative aperture or f-number of the lens (focal length/diameter). This may be written in the form

R = resolving power of lens in lines/mm. $= \dfrac{1,000}{1 \cdot 22 \lambda A}$ where λ is the

wave-length in *microns*.

Few, if any, photographic lenses ever attain this perfection. In cameras in general it is usual to quote the *angular resolution*, i.e., the distance between two resolved image points divided by the focal length of the lens, or, which is the same thing, the distance between two object points divided by the object distance. The reciprocal of the angular resolution is called the *field resolution* and is often quoted in logarithmic form.

The resolving power of the lens-film combination depends on a number of variables as shown in Fig. 18.7 (*a*) to (*g*). (Cook, *Phot.J.*)

(a) *The test object.* Various types of test object are shown in Fig. 18.8. Different results are often obtained with different objects and the test object selected should be as nearly as possible similar to the type of work required.

(b) *Contrast.* The curves show very clearly that contrast has a profound influence on the resolution. Loss of contrast may be due to the actual shades of the object itself or to intervening atmosphere or haze, or to stray light from the lens or within the camera by reflection from surfaces. The blooming of the lens, use of lens shields, internal baffles in the camera all tend to improve contrast.

(c) *Emulsion.* The emulsion itself may be of low contrast or it may be grainy. High resolution emulsions are available and these work at maximum contrast, i.e., black and white only with no half-tones.

(d) and (e) *Development.* The necessity for correct development is clearly shown by the curves. Different developers can also cause changes in resolution and the remarks on fine-grain development should be noted.

(f) *Position of Focus.* The results shown by the curves do not tell the whole story. Normally in cameras there is a choice of focus and two distinct and easily differentiated positions can be described (i) the " maximum resolution " position in which the image shows high resolution but often of very low contrast caused by colour or an overlaid haze. This position of focus gives best results with high contrast objects and very contrasty emulsions which do not record the half-tones. (ii) The " minimum fringe " position in which the edge of a large object appears free from fringe and the overall contrast appears to be a maximum. In this position there is usually some loss of resolution of fine detail but it is the best position of focus for low contrast objects and normal films. It is the position of focus normally selected by the naked eye or a low power focusing magnifier on ground glass. The high resolution position is often only seen under a high magnification and is frequently selected if no ground glass is used or the ground glass is too transparent.

(g) *Aperture.* Most camera lenses are designed for use at their full aperture and the lens aberrations, particularly spherical aberrations, are balanced over the full aperture. Consequently, on stopping down, there is often a decrease of resolution. This can often be corrected by selecting a new position of focus (see p. 461).

The curves (a) to (g) also show very clearly how the resolution falls off over the field covered by the lens. Although these curves were

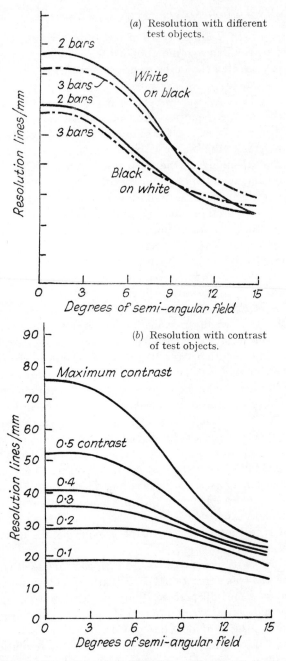

FIG. 18.7 (a)–(g) Resolving power of lens-film combination (Cook, *Phot.J.*)

432

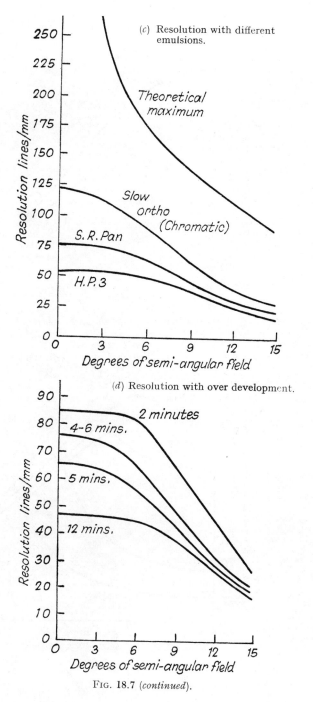

(c) Resolution with different emulsions.

Theoretical maximum

Slow ortho (Chromatic)

S. R. Pan

H.P. 3

Resolution lines/mm

Degrees of semi-angular field

(d) Resolution with over development.

2 minutes

4-6 mins.

5 mins.

12 mins.

Resolution lines/mm

Degrees of semi-angular field

Fig. 18.7 (continued).

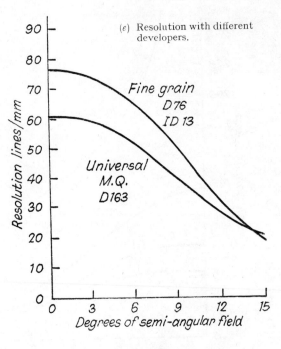

(e) Resolution with different developers.

Fine grain
D 76
ID 13

Universal
M.Q.
D 163

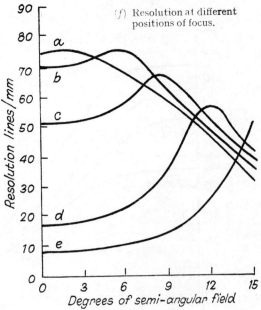

(f) Resolution at different positions of focus.

a

b

c

d

e

Fig. 18.7 (continued).

434

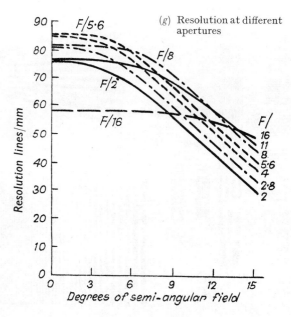

FIG. 18.7 *(continued)*.

all obtained with one lens type they are fairly typical. The figures, of course, refer to average resolution but on most lenses there is a considerable difference of resolution between radial lines and transverse or tangential lines in the outer parts of the field caused by astigmatism which is invariably present.

Processing

A properly equipped darkroom is an essential to successful photography and attempts at makeshifts invariably result in waste of valuable time. The room should have light coloured walls and, needless to say, it should be so dark when closed that nothing can be seen even when fully dark-adapted. A good large porcelain sink with running hot and cold water, the taps being well separated and with different handles for ease of identification in the dark, and a large number of shelves and lockers are very convenient. The safelights should be arranged so that the maximum of *safe* illumination can be obtained and it is worth while making sure that the main white light switch is not anywhere near the other switches in the room. Great

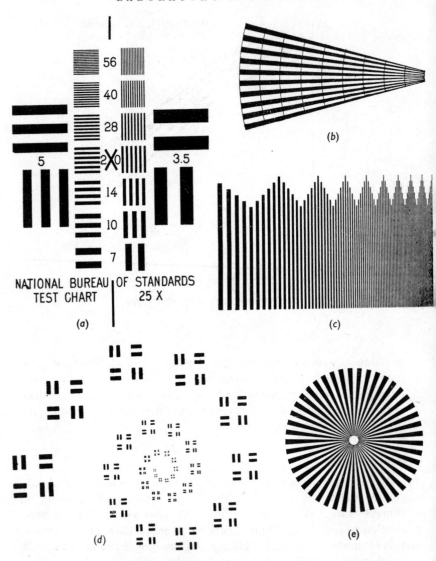

FIG. 18.8.—Resolution test objects.
(a) National Bureau of Standards.
(b) Ross (*Physics of the Developed Photographic Image*, p. 146).
(c) Sayce, *Photographic Journal*, 80, p. 454 (1049). See Appendix 4.
(d) Cobb, *Amer. Jour. Physiology*, **36,** p. 335 (1915).
(e) Wheel-type.

NOTE.—Selwyn (*Phot. J.* **88B**) used a sine wave test object which cannot be illustrated but has theoretical advantages.

care must be taken to prevent the possibility of electric shock with wet hands. The standard safelights obtainable from the photographic manufacturers should always be used and their instructions regarding installation followed. Racks should be provided for dishes so that they can drip safely without fear of contaminating other solutions or materials in use or in storage. Films, plates, photographic paper, etc., should be kept in good tight drawers in a dry part of the room.

Chemicals for development, fixing and for all the operations of processing are now obtainable made up in tins or packets and these should generally be used. Much time can be spent in weighing out chemicals' and the cost of the made-up supplies is so small as hardly to warrant using chemicals in bulk. It does not appear to be generally realised that developing and fixing solutions can be made up in tanks, ready for immediate use, and will last for a month or more. Tank processing is much more convenient, cleaner and quicker in the long run than dish development, besides being very much more economical. If the tanks are in continuous use the solutions can be maintained at an efficient strength by the addition of a replenishing solution. The tanks themselves should preferably be made of hard rubber and are readily obtainable from the photographic manufacturers. A floating lid in the developing tank prevents excessive oxidation of the solution and the covers are such that when films or plates, in their proper hangers, are put into the tank and covered up with the lid the main light can be turned on and other work completed while waiting. A darkroom alarm clock to indicate the correct length of development is almost essential. Fig. 18.9 shows a type of tank with lids and hangers supplied by Messrs. Kodak Ltd. The tanks can very conveniently be installed in a recessed table with a hinged lid which can be lowered over the installation to give more table space when printing or enlarging is being done.

For the development of short lengths of film similar to the amateur film ranges, including 35 and 16 mm. film a very useful small tank is supplied by Messrs. Johnson Ltd. Moderately long lengths of 16 mm. or 35 mm. film are best processed in tanks provided with wooden frames, four or five of which, each holding about 100 ft. of 35 mm. film or 200 ft. of 16 mm. film, can be inserted at once. The tanks are supplied in sets and equipment for winding the film on to the frames and for drying is also available. Where long lengths of film have to be processed it is advisable to make use of the services of one or other of the firms who specialise in this work. Film can be processed and

Fig. 18.9.—Kodak developing tank with film hangers, floating lid and cover.

returned within twenty-four hours by these firms but if the expense is warranted and a very considerable volume of work is anticipated it is almost necessary to install automatic continuous processing plant.

Several types of automatic plant for film processing are available, which are suitable for use in research establishments where only moderate quantities of film are used at irregular intervals. Great care is necessary to maintain any such plant in a scrupulously clean condition to be always ready for immediate use. One type, the " Aiglonne," manufactured by André Debrie in Paris (France), is housed in a light tight box into which 16 or 35 mm. films can be fed direct from a camera casette or magazine. A short leader is first inserted and clipped on to the film which is drawn through the machine by rollers. The film passes through a series of loops or coils of tubing, is developed, rinsed, fixed, washed and delivered dry on to a take-up spool. The dry processed film begins to appear from 5 to 15 minutes from the time of entry, depending on the type of film being processed. In this machine fresh chemicals are constantly delivered to the tubes and the spent solutions are carried away with the exhaust water. The whole system is thermostatically controlled and entirely automatic. Any length of film from a few inches to several hundred feet can be accommodated and the leader used may only be a few feet long ; no trailer is required.

In other machines a leader length of film is left in the machine at the end of a run for use when next required. The film to be processed is clipped to the leader and is dragged along by rollers in and out of a series of tanks containing the solutions and washing water. These machines are miniatures of the large commercial plants and must usually be installed in darkrooms.

Films of other widths, in long lengths, such as 70 mm., $5\frac{1}{2}$ in. or $9\frac{1}{2}$ in. or larger widths, in lengths up to some 60 ft. are most conveniently handled in tanks provided with a pair of drums on which the film is wound from one drum to the other while the processing proceeds.

Plates, in quantities, should be provided with metal racks which can be inserted in tanks for development, but where density measurements are to be made tank development is not suitable because of the tendency for unequal development to take place. Where particular care must be taken with plates, dish development is essential and even development should be ensured by brushing the surface of the plate with a soft brush, wider than the plate, during development.

The washing arrangements require just as much care and design as developing and fixing and the special tanks on the market should be used wherever possible.

The materials used for tanks, dishes, measures, etc., require careful consideration if their construction is contemplated. Hard rubber is probably the best material for developing and fixing tanks and stainless steel for washing and for racks, measures, funnels and other equipment. Porcelain dishes are good but fragile, as are glass measures and funnels. Enamel ware is apt to crack and discolour and plated metal is often unsuitable because chemical reactions are set up and local galvanic action can occur where the plating is scratched or damaged. Solutions should never be left in metal containers for any length of time. Polythene funnels are now generally available and polythene coated metal tanks can also be obtained which are acid resistant and are very suitable for photographic work. The Telegraphic Construction and Maintenance Co. Ltd. provide a service for coating metals with polythene.

Drying arrangements should not be forgotten when designing photographic processing lay-outs. Cupboards with warm filtered air intakes and similar drying cabinets are available on the market and for long lengths of film drying drums rotated by electric motor are convenient. Freedom from dust where plates and films are drying is of the utmost importance. For plates and films quick drying by methylated spirit or alcohol may be resorted to and has the advantage of preventing the possible deposition of dust.

Finally, it cannot be too strongly emphasised that in all photographic work the utmost cleanliness and tidiness are essentials to success and well ventilated and carefully arranged and lit darkrooms of adequate size, with correct equipment, are economies, the initial cost of which is amply repaid. The services of the research laboratories of the large manufacturers (Messrs. Kodak and Messrs. Ilford) or of a good firm of consultants are always available and it should be remembered that the normal photographic dealers have little or no knowledge of scientific photography.

Light sources

The photographic effect of light in producing the required density in the developed plate depends on a number of factors some of which have been discussed above (Characteristic Curve). The remaining factors are associated with the light source in combination with the photographic emulsion and therefore depend on the spectral energy distribution of the light source and the spectral sensitivity of the photographic material. The effect of filters, which will be discussed later (pp. 447–449), is to modify the spectral energy distribution of the light which is allowed to reach the emulsion.

Fig. 18.10 shows in graphical form the relative spectral sensitivity of typical photographic materials. Curve A represents the sensitivity of an average panchromatic material, B that of an orthochromatic and C a non-colour sensitive emulsion. These curves have been drawn from the indications of the wedge spectrograms shown in Fig. 18.1 corrected for equal energy of each wave-length.

Fig. 18.11 in a similar manner shows the relative spectral intensity curves of three sources of light much used in photography. Curve (1) refers to a tungsten lamp at 2360° K. colour temperature (2) to a photo-flash bulb and (3) to sunlight.

The colour temperature of 2360° K. for the tungsten lamp refers to a vacuum type specially run at this temperature for photographic sensitometry. Gas-filled tungsten lamps with coiled filaments as generally used for household purposes have colour temperatures ranging from 2700–2900° K. or in some special lamps as high as 3400° K. (Photoflood).

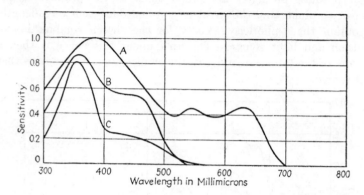

Fig. 18.10.—Relative spectral sensitivity of typical photographic materials. Curve *A* represents the sensitivity of panchromatic material; Curve *B*, orthochromatic materials; and curve *C*, non-colour-sensitive materials.

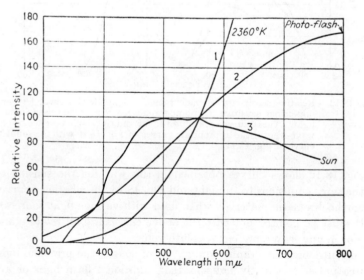

Fig. 18.11.—Spectral-intensity curves of common light sources used in photography plotted relative to the energy at 5600 *A*.

The actual light effect on the emulsion at any one wave-length can be assumed to be given by the product of the light intensity at that wave-length and the sensitivity, and this product has been called the " photicity " (Henney & Dudley) of the emulsion. If then we draw a curve whose ordinates are proportional to the product of the intensity ordinate and the sensitivity ordinate for each wave-length, we obtain the " photicity " curve for the chosen combination of emulsion and light source. The area under this curve is then a measure of the total sensitivity of the emulsion when used with that light source.

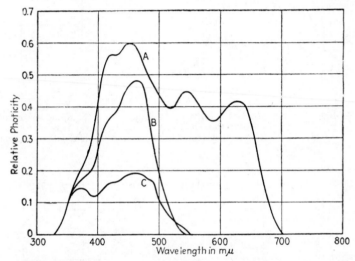

FIG. 18.12.—Relative sensitivity of panchromatic (A), orthochromatic (B), and non-colour sensitive (C) photographic materials when used in sunlight. These curves are obtained by multiplying, wave-length by wave-length, the appropriate curves of Fig. 18.10 with the sunlight curve of Fig. 18.11.

Fig. 18.12 shows curves obtained in this way for the sensitivity of the three emulsions to sunlight and Fig. 18.13 the photicity curves for orthochromatic materials when used with various light sources.

It must be pointed out that the above curves are all relative and do not in any way represent absolute values.

For outdoor photography sunlight is, of course, the principal light source but it frequently happens that additional flash light or arc light can be used with advantage. The intensity of daylight varies with the time of the year, the altitude of the sun above the horizon, i.e., the latitude and time of the day and the weather conditions. For the early morning and late evening or when the sun is low on the horizon the sunlight contains a larger proportion of longer wave-lengths (red light) than at other times, due to the absorption of the shorter wave-lengths by the atmosphere. As a consequence of this variation the exposure required to obtain a photograph must be increased but the increase in exposure would be smaller if panchromatic materials were used than with orthochromatic emulsions, and it would be safe to say that non-colour sensitive emulsion would require so great an increase in exposure as to be useless.

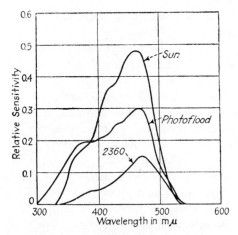

Fig. 18.13.—Relative sensitivity curves for orthochromatic materia︰when used with various light sources. These curves are obtained by multiplying, wave-length by wave-length, the orthochromatic curve of Fig. 18.10 with the appropriate curves of Fig. 18.11.

Some of the factors involved in the combination of light source, emulsion used, relative speed and use of filters are frequently over-looked. For example, fast panchromatic materials are often selected, purely because of their rated speed, to photograph cathode ray tube traces in which the light is restricted to blue or green. Obviously, a blue sensitive or orthochromatic emulsion is indicated and will usually be found to give greater speed, higher contrast and less grain. A glaring example of this lack of knowledge or forethought led to an experimenter using a panchromatic film with a blue filter to prevent red light reaching the film ; he was amazed at the results he later obtained with a blue sensitive ordinary emulsion.

Cathode ray tube photography plays an increasingly important part in research of all kinds and film manufacturers have developed special films to meet the requirement. The factors involved are the colour of the phosphor used in the tube, its response and delay time, the speed of the moving spot and the final writing speed required, i.e., the speed at which the film is required to move. In some applications of the C.R.O. the pattern on the tube face remains static and a relatively long exposure with stationary film is possible. In other uses the pattern may be transient and moving film is required to analyse the spot movement. Only trial and error can show ultimately the limits of speed attainable.

Spark, flame and electronic flashes are also much used and here some care is necessary to obtain the best types of emulsion with a small reciprocity failure to very short durations of exposure.

Artificial sources of light in many varieties are available and in general use. For the copying of black and white articles or pictures and print, as in press work and what is known as " process " photography, where non-colour-sensitive materials are used, carbon arc lamps and mercury-vapour arcs are most suitable. These lamps are rich in the shorter wave-lengths to which the emulsions are most sensitive and therefore are most efficient. The use of tungsten filament lamps, although very convenient in many ways, is unnecessary and the long wave-length light and heat emitted by these lamps is so much wasted energy. If, however, colour work is being done or coloured objects being photographed then tungsten lamps must be used, but they can be supplemented by mercury or carbon arcs to level out the spectral distribution of intensity. This expedient can be dangerous as there is a danger of one source illuminating the shadows cast by the other. Recently a series of high intensity discharge lamps have been developed having an almost complete colour correction designed specifically for colour cinematography. The large lamp manufacturers may be consulted for full details of lamps and Mole-Richardson Ltd. who specialise in the illumination problems of film studios have developed suitable control apparatus for use with these lamps.

Flash bulbs are very convenient for portable installations or where short exposures are required and there are now on the market several types of discharge lamps, of very high actinic value, operated by the discharge of condensers. Extremely short exposures, of the order of a few micro seconds, can be obtained with discharge tubes and repeated exposures, possibly on moving film, can be made by varying the time constant of the condenser circuit. The large electric lamp manufacturers and others supply the discharge tubes and all the equipment necessary for their operation and portable condenser discharge flash light instruments are readily available both for single flashes or for stroboscopic purposes. The reader should consult *Discharge Lamps for Photography and Projection* by E. K. Bourne (Chapman & Hall, 1948) for full information on the subject of light sources.

Exposure meters

Many guides to exposure values are available. The manufacturers of photographic materials, and others, issue comprehensive tables and instructions which are always reliable and it is a good practice to retain the printed sheets of instructions usually packed with every batch of material. In addition there are a number of exposure calculators, and exposure meters of various kinds. The chief types of exposure meters can be divided into classes. Actinic or photographic types of exposure indicators usually consist of a small portion of a sensitive material which darkens to a standard tint when exposed to light. By noting the time taken to reach this standard tint and referring to tables supplied with the instrument the basic light value can be found. Photo-electric exposure meters measure the same quantity directly by the indications of a pointer on a dial. Both these instruments measure total light value or general level of illumination and there is always an element of doubt when they are used as to whether they should be held near the camera lens and facing the object being photographed, or near the object and facing the source of illumination. It does not matter which convention is used provided it is understood that the indications are relative and if they are always used in the same way their indications, if correctly interpreted, can be relied upon as a guide to the basic exposure. It is still necessary to allow for the emulsion, the light source, the filter, the light and shade and contrast of the objects being photographed and so on.

A third, and important, class of exposure measurers may be called the photometric type. The simplest of these is of the extinction type in which a number of figures are marked on a screen which is viewed through an eyepiece and the largest or smallest figure visible is taken as an indication of the light level. The chief disadvantage of this type of meter lies in its dependence on the eye of the observer. Thus under bright conditions when the pupil of the eye is small the light may be grossly under-estimated because the fainter figures will not be visible, and if the observer continues to look into the instrument his eye will become dark adapted and he may over-estimate the light. A better class of photometric instrument contains a lamp and a comparison surface such that by varying the intensity of the internal lighting a match can be obtained between the comparison surface and any particular part of the object whose brightness is to be measured. This type of instrument is, in fact, a true photometer and its indications can be read in absolute units if the scales are calibrated. Fig. 18.14 shows a typical photometric exposure meter.

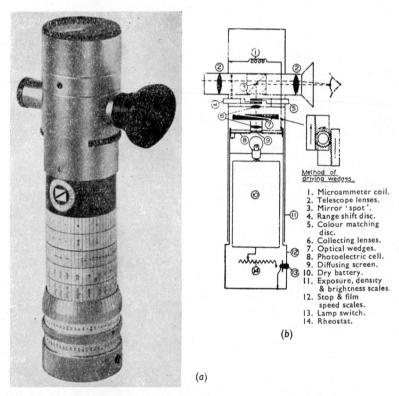

Method of driving wedges.

1. Microammeter coil.
2. Telescope lenses.
3. Mirror 'spot'.
4. Range shift disc.
5. Colour matching disc.
6. Collecting lenses.
7. Optical wedges.
8. Photoelectric cell.
9. Diffusing screen.
10. Dry battery.
11. Exposure, density & brightness scales.
12. Stop & film speed scales.
13. Lamp switch.
14. Rheostat.

(b)

(a)

FIG. 18.14.—Photometric exposure meter.
(a) General view of exposure photometer. It is 7 in. high, 1½ in. diameter and weighs 1¼ lb. It contains a photo-electric self calibrating device and is independent of dry-cell voltage or lamp efficiency.
(b) Diagram of exposure photometer. Rotation of 12 relative to 11 slides wedges 7 over each other and controls brightness of spot 3.

The advantage of using a true photometric instrument, which is a scientific instrument of the tele-photometer class, is that the actual brightnesses of the various parts of the object to be photographed can be accurately measured and the exposure calculated for the particular result required. For example, where shadow detail is required the exposure must be increased and where high light detail is wanted the toe of the characteristic curve must be used or the exposure cut short. The indications of the photometric instruments would give these brightnesses directly for it is obvious that the user would measure the brightness of just those objects in which the detail is required. The photo-electric and actinic meters, on the other hand, would give identical readings and leave to the photographer the duty of calculating the correct exposure for the required conditions and result.

Filters

It has already been mentioned that filters are used to modify the spectral intensity of the light which is allowed to reach the sensitive material. Filters may take the form of solutions of salts and dye-stuffs, glass discs or gelatine film either alone or cemented between glass discs. A very large range of filters is obtainable in the dyed gelatine form and for all ordinary purposes their convenience, reasonable constancy and their relative cheapness are distinct advantages. Their transmission does not remain constant over long periods, particularly if they are exposed to strong light and in their plain form they are delicate and easily marked, but they can be easily replaced and can be inserted in lenses without much trouble or alteration of focus. When cemented between glass plates they are less liable to damage although they still fade, and the cemented parts tend to separate, particularly near the edges, and may cause loss of definition in the photograph.

Coloured glass discs are more reliable where constancy of transmission over a period of time, general robustness and convenience as an accessory are desirable. Unfortunately the range of colours available is not very great and reproducibility is often difficult, different batches of ostensibly the same glass having totally different transmission characteristics. The optical qualities of glass discs, whether coloured or used for sandwich filters, should not be taken for granted and really perfect discs are difficult to obtain and expensive. Filter discs should be examined and tested as described in Chapter 12 (Fig. 12.18).

Filters in the form of solutions of salts and dyes contained in parallel sided glass vessels are very commonly used in spectrometric work and have many advantages where an almost infinite variability of transmission is required, but they are hardly portable.

The effect of filters on the photograph can be calculated in exactly the same manner as the effect of the light source on the emulsion as described on page 442. Fig. 18.15 shows how by multiplying the ordinates of the light intensity curve, the sensitivity curve and the filter transmission curve the photicity curve can be obtained and the filter factor calculated. The curves in the lowest figure show (*A*) the relative sensitivity of the panchromatic emulsion when used with daylight and (*B*) the effect on the same film and source of the addition of the filter. The filter factor is given by the ratio of the area under the curve *B* to the area under *A*. The curve *C* shows the relative sensi-

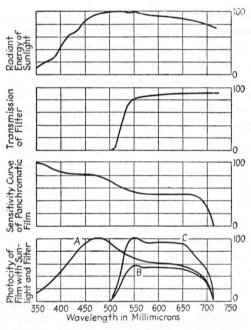

Fig. 18.15.—Spectral curves of sunlight (top), a yellow filter (second) and panchromatic material (third). The effect of exposing the panchromatic film to light of daylight quality is shown in curve *A* (bottom graph), whereas if a yellow filter is used, the effect is represented by curve *B*. The area under curve *A*, compared with the area under *B* gives an indication of the filter factor required. If the exposure with the filter is increased by the filter factor, curve *C* results.

tivity when the exposure has been increased by the correct filter factor and shows very clearly how the maximum density of the developed emulsion has been relatively moved along the wave-length axis towards the red. This means that orange coloured objects will receive relatively more exposure than blue objects when the filter is used, while blue objects received greater relative exposure without the filter. The use of the orange filter is thus to increase the detail recorded in orange coloured objects and to suppress blue objects. If a blue filter had been used the opposite effect would have been obtained, i.e., increased detail in blue objects and a suppression of all orange and red.

Fig. 18.16 shows a selection of transmission curves of filters and it should be remembered that the makers of emulsions will always supply details of filter factors and frequently publish such data in the leaflets enclosed in packages of materials. Messrs. Kodak Ltd. and Ilford Ltd. both publish very comprehensive booklets giving transmission data for gelatine filters. For glass filters Messrs. Chance Brothers catalogue of optical glass gives the transmission data or *Glass* (edited) J. Home Dickson (Hutchinson, 1951) has a chapter on the subject and a series of transmission curves. Tables 18.5 and 18.6 give details of stock solutions and their uses for isolating certain lines in the mercury spectrum. For the isolation of narrow bands of the spectrum use can be made of the interference filters based on the principle of the Fabry-Perot etalons. In some types there is very little absorption of light, all light which is not transmitted is reflected so that the spectral distributions of the transmitted and reflected portions are complementary. Beam splitters of this kind can also be made and are highly efficient, either having complementary colours in the two portions or nearly neutral in both. Messrs. Barr & Stroud Ltd. of Glasgow have done much work on this subject and can give full information.

Shutters

The shutters used in commercial cameras fall generally into two groups : the inter-lens type in which one or more blades situated between the lens elements are opened and closed by means of springs and the focal plane type which consists essentially of a roller blind with a slit which travels across the camera as near as possible to the sensitive emulsion surface. A third type of shutter used considerably in scientific and air cameras is known as the *louvre* type and consists

K-1 Partial Correction

Filter factor	Daylight	Tungsten
Panchromatic	1½	1½
Orthochromatic	2	1½
Slow Ortho	3½	2½

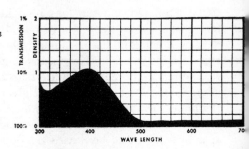

K-2 Full Correction, Contrast, Haze Penetration

Filter factor	Daylight	Tungsten
Panchromatic	2	1½
Orthochromatic	2½	1½
Slow Ortho	8	4

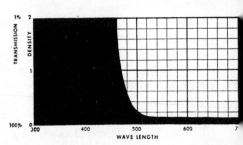

G Over-correction, Contrast, Haze Penetration

Filter factor	Daylight	Tungsten
Panchromatic	2·5	2
Orthochromatic	3·5	2·5

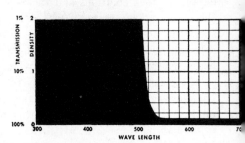

X-1 Correction Filter for Panchromatic Materials in Tungsten Light

Filter factor	Daylight	Tungsten
Panchromatic	4	3

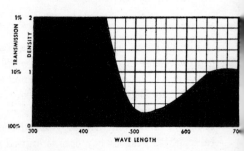

Fig. 18.16a.—Absorption Curves of Wratten Correction Filters in common use.

450

Tricolour Filters (Standard)

For making colour-separation negatives from original subject.

Filter factors	A	B	C
Panchromatic film			
Daylight	7	6	5
Tungsten	4	6	10
Panchromatic plates			
Daylight	6	9	7
Tungsten	3	10	15
Panchromatic half-tone plates			
Tungsten	7	12	12

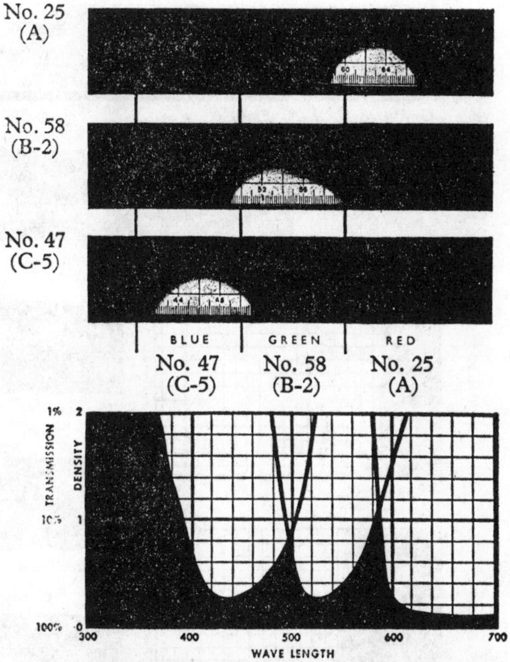
No. 25
(A)
No. 58
(B-2)
No. 47
(C-5)
BLUE
GREEN
RED
No. 47
(C-5)
No. 58
(B-2)
No. 25
(A)
1%
10%
100%
2
1
0
TRANSMISSION
DENSITY
300
400
500
600
700
WAVE LENGTH

Tricolour Filters (Narrow Cut)

For making colour-separation negatives from colour transparencies in tungsten light only.

Filter factors	F	N	C
Panchromatic film	8	7	24
Panchromatic plates	5	12	25
Panchromatic half-tone plates	20	14	35

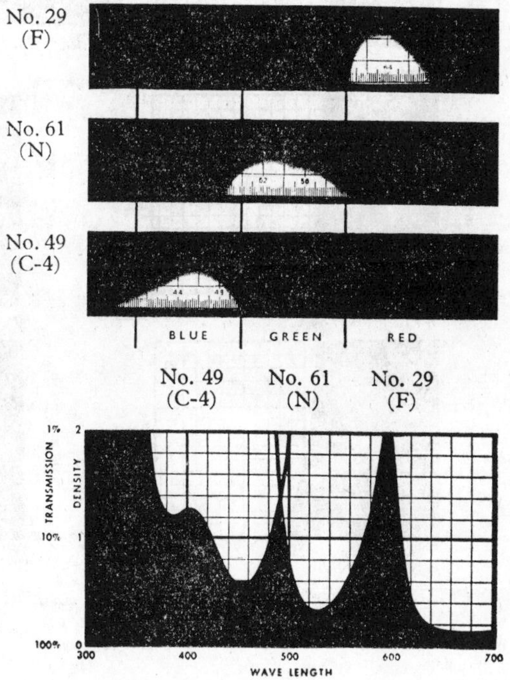
No. 29
(F)
No. 61
(N)
No. 49
(C-4)
BLUE
GREEN
RED
No. 49
(C-4)
No. 61
(N)
No. 29
(F)
1%
10%
100%
2
1
0
TRANSMISSION
DENSITY
300
400
500
600
700
WAVE LENGTH

FIG. 18.16b.—Absorption Curves of Wratten Tricolour Filters.

Unfiltered I.R.E.R. Plate

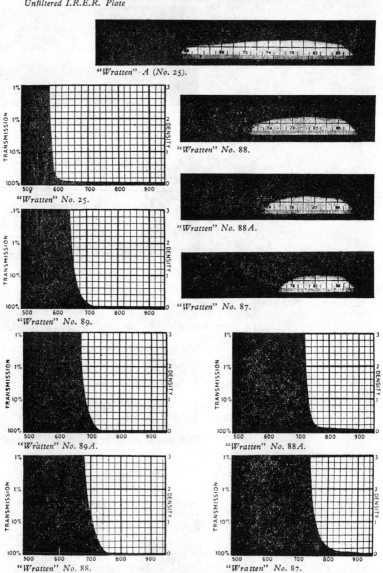

"Wratten" A (No. 25).

"Wratten" No. 25.

"Wratten" No. 88.

"Wratten" No. 89.

"Wratten" No. 88A.

"Wratten" No. 89A.

"Wratten" No. 87.

"Wratten" No. 88.

"Wratten" No. 88A.

"Wratten" No. 87.

Fig. 18.16c.—Wedge spectrograms and transmission curves of infra-red filters.

TABLE 18.5

Liquid Filters for the Isolation of Certain Lines of Mercury Discharge Lamps

STOCK SOLUTIONS

NOTE.—Nickel, cobalt and copper solutions must be free from traces of iron salts. Salts of " Analar " standard have been found suitable (B.D.H. and Hopkin & Williams Ltd.).

A   Copper chloride, $CuCl_2.2H_2O$, 1,000 gm. in 1 litre water.

B   Calcium chloride 3 molar, i.e., 333 gm. anhydrous salt made up to 1 litre solution with water.

C   Potassium dichromate, 15 gm. in 200 c.c. water.

D   Didymium (or neodymium) nitrate, 30 gm. made up to 100 c.c. solution with water.

E   Copper sulphate, $CuSO_4.5H_2O$, 25 gm., 300 c.c. ammonium hydroxide ($d = 0.88$) made up to 1 litre with water.

G   Copper sulphate, $CuSO_4.5H_2O$, 125 gm. made up to 1 litre with water.

H   Copper nitrate, $Cu(NO_3)_2.6H_2O$, 200 gm. in 100 c.c. water.

J   Iodine, 0.75 gm. in 100 c.c. carbon tetrachloride.

K   Sodium nitrite, $NaNO_2$, 75 gm. in 100 c.c. water.

L   Nickel sulphate, $NiSO_4.6-7H_2O$, 145 gm., cobalt sulphate, $CoSO_4.7H_2O$, 41.5 gm., made up to 1 litre with water.

M   Potassium hydrogen phthalate, 5 gm. in 1 litre water.

N   Copper sulphate, $CuSO_4.5H_2O$, 15 gm. in 1 litre water.

P   Potassium iodide, KI, 1.7 gm. in 1 litre water.

R   Potassium iodide 0.14 gm. iodine, 0.1 gm. in 1 litre water.

S   Cobalt chloride, $CoCl_2.6H_2O$, 30 gm. in 100 c.c. of 3M calcium chloride solution.

T   Nickel sulphate, $NiSO_4.7H_2O$, 82 gm. in 100 c.c. of 0.25 M copper sulphate solution.

U   220 gm. $NiSO_4.7H_2O$ + 200 gm. $CoSO_4.7H_2O$ in 1,000 gm. solution.

V   120 gm. $NiSO_4.7H_2O$ + 23.5 gm. $(NH_4)_2SO_4$ + 82.8 gm. aq. NH_3 ($d = 0.925$) in 1,000 gm. solution.

W   Gaseous chlorine at 1 atmosphere in a fused silica cell 3 cm. deep.

Solutions E, M, P and R should be frequently renewed.

TABLE 18.6—*Filter Combinations*

Mercury Line, A	Filter Combinations
5,790, 5,777	10 c.c. *A* with 90 c.c. *B*, 1 cm. combined with either *C*, 2 cm. or Corning glass 344, 3·4 mm.
5,461	20 c.c. *A* with 80 c.c. *B*, 1 cm. combined with either *D*, 1 cm. or Corning glass 512, 5 mm.
4,358	*E*, 2 cm., combined with *K*, 1 cm. or *H*, 2 cm. combined with *K*, 1 cm. (transmits a little 5,461 *A*)
4,047	*H*, 2 cm. combined with *J*, 1 cm.
3,650, 3,663	*G*, 1 cm. combined with Chance's black u.v. glass, 2–3 mm.
3,132	*L*, 10 cm., combined with *M*, 1 cm. or *U*, 2·5 cm., combined with *V*, 2 cm. and *M*, 1 cm.
3,340–3,000	*S*, 1 cm., combined with *T*, 1 cm.
3,340–2,895	*L*, 10 cm., combined with *N*, 1 cm. or *U*, 2·5 cm., combined with *V*, 2 cm., and *N*, 1 cm.
2,650	*L*, 10 cm., combined with *P*, 1 cm. and with *W*, 3 cm., or *U*, 2·5 cm., combined with *V*, 2 cm., and with *P*, 1 cm., and *W*, 3 cm.
2,650–2,537	*L*, 10 cm., combined with *W*, 3 cm., or *U*, 2·5 cm., combined with *V*, 2 cm., and *W*, 3 cm.
2,537	*L*, 10 cm., combined with *R*, 1 cm., and with *W*, 3 cm., or *U*, 2·5 cm., combined with *V*, 2 cm., and with *R*, 1 cm., and *W*, 3 cm.

NOTE.—Glass cells may be used for the visible region down to the 3660*A* line; silica must be used for the ultra-violet region.

A convenient means of obtaining a concentrated beam of light with those filters which include a 10 cm. path in solution *L* is to place this solution in a round flask of 10 cm. diameter (and 500 c.c. capacity) very near to the lamp, followed by the other filters. The reaction cell should be placed behind a diaphragm about 24 cm. from the lamp.

Tables 18.5 and 18.6 are reproduced from *Chemical Aspects of Light* by E. J. Bowen (Clarendon Press) by permission of the author and publishers.

of a number of blades which overlap when the shutter is closed and are made to rotate as in a venetian blind to make the exposure. Louvre shutters are placed usually just behind the lens but they may, in large lenses, be situated between the elements. Finally, in some scientific applications there is the electronic Kerr cell shutter, which, however, is more of a light valve for varying the intensity of the transmitted light than a shutter in the true sense of the word.

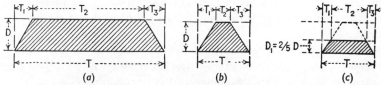

(a)   (b)   (c)

Fig. 18.17.—(a) Efficiency diagram of inter-lens shutter. The total time of operation of the shutter is T; the time during which the leaves are fully open is T_2. During the interval T_1 the shutter is opening whereas during T_3 it is closing. D represents the diameter of the aperture. The efficiency is the ratio of the shaded area to the area of the entire rectangle, and may be expressed as:

$$\eta = \frac{D(T_2 + \frac{1}{2}T_1 + \frac{1}{2}T_3)}{DT}$$

In this case the efficiency is 86·5 per cent.

(b) The efficiency here is much less than in (a); it is 61·1 per cent.

(c) Shows how the efficiency is increased by decreasing the diameter D of the aperture. The efficiency here has been increased to 84·5 per cent.

Since every type of shutter must necessarily take some time to reach its fully open condition and also to close again from its fully open position, it is not possible to have a completely efficient shutter. Fig. 18.17 shows in diagrammatic form the normal efficiency of a shutter. The total time during which the shutter allows light to pass is the exposure time and the ratio of the shaded area to that of the rectangle is the efficiency of the shutter. The time and efficiency of interlens and louvre type shutters can be easily measured by a number of methods and the efficiency of a focal plane shutter can be calculated from the construction when the speed with which the slit traverses the focal plane is known.

One method of testing a shutter consists in taking a series of photographs of the actual shape of the shutter opening at intervals of 1/1000 sec. and from such a test strip the efficiency can be calculated. For an accurate determination of the efficiency the rate of increase of the area and of its decrease must be accurately measured and one way of obtaining such data is to cut out very accurately the shapes in paper and to weigh the pieces. This type of shutter test is carried out by photographing, on a moving film, the shutter blades which are illuminated by an intermittent flashing light. Modern electronic stroboscopic light sources can be used for this purpose but an easier method is to obtain the flashes by means of a rotating mirror device. The mirror block may consist of any convenient number of mirror facets on the periphery of a drum. An extended light source is imaged on the shutter and an auxiliary lens is used to form an image of the shutter on the film which is fixed to the periphery of a rotating film drum.

For the simple determination of exposure time in any camera several methods can be mentioned and the reader can probably devise many more. One very simple method is to photograph an ordinary neon sign tube or mercury arc tube in the ordinary way but to swing the camera during the exposure. A succession of images of the tube will be obtained and their number will depend on the shutter speed and the mains frequency. In a similar manner any laboratory stroboscopic lamp may be photographed. Where such lamps are not available a circular disc can be set up having a white mark from centre to edge on an otherwise black surface and the disc rotated at a known speed while photographs are taken. The resulting photograph will show the white line extended into a sector, the angle of which is a measure of the time.

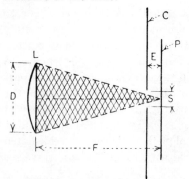

The time of exposure of a focal plane shutter can be measured by the neon sign method or in the laboratory by focusing a point image on the plane of the shutter and making a photographic record on a drum camera. The efficiency of a focal plane shutter can be calculated very simply from the dimensions as shown in Fig. 18.18.

FIG. 18.18.—Efficiency of focal plane shutters.
D is the lens diameter, C is the shutter blind and P is the plate or film. S is the slit width, E the distance from shutter to focal plane and F the focal distance. The efficiency is given by

$$\eta = \frac{1}{1 + \frac{ED}{SF}} = \frac{SF}{SF + ED}$$

The focal plane shutter because of the relatively long time taken by the slit to traverse the focal plane introduces distortion where the object is moving relative to the camera during exposure.

One form of shutter used in ultra high speed cine cameras should be mentioned and consists of a block of glass mounted in an open-sided cylindrical frame as shown in Fig. 18.19. The glass block is rotated

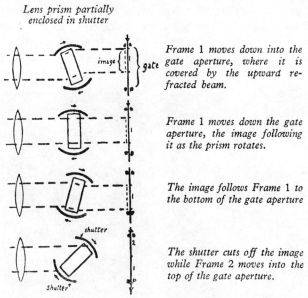

Lens prism partially enclosed in shutter

Frame 1 moves down into the gate aperture, where it is covered by the upward re-fracted beam.

Frame 1 moves down the gate aperture, the image following it as the prism rotates.

The image follows Frame 1 to the bottom of the gate aperture

The shutter cuts off the image while Frame 2 moves into the top of the gate aperture.

FIG. 18.19.—Rotating plane prism in the " Kodak " high speed camera. Note how the image moves as the block rotates.

and thus causes the image to travel along the focal plane. The film is continuously moving at such a speed that the image is effectively stationary and the light is cut off when the cylindrical metal portions mask the opening. Fig. 18.20 shows the interior of the camera, which is very simple.

The testing of shutters has received much attention and several electronic methods are available. In one method the light passing through the shutter during exposure falls on a photo-electric cell which allows a condenser to become charged at a fixed rate. By measuring the resulting potential of the condenser for any pre-determined time rate of charge the exposure time can be found. The voltmeter can in fact be calibrated in time. In another form the actual efficiency curve can be obtained on a cathode ray oscillograph fitted with an afterglow screen by using the Y-plates to measure potential proportional to the light passing through the shutter and any convenient time base. With the addition of a standard known time trace an exceedingly accurate determination can be made. It is, however, not really necessary to strive for extreme accuracy in determining exposure time and efficiency of shutters for the very simple reason that the enormous accelerations, the unknown frictions, variations in springs and inevitable lost motion in linkages all tend to cause large variations in repeated readings, and even if a statistical analysis is made the actual error in any one exposure cannot be predicted.

Fig. 18.20.—Interior of Kodak high speed camera capable of photography on 16 mm. film up to 3,000 frames per second.

Lenses

Details of the types of camera lenses will be found in Chapter 15, but here the relation of the lens to the camera will be discussed.

For normal photography the focal length of a camera lens is usually equal to or very slightly greater than the diagonal of the picture space. A lens is known as " wide angle " if its focal length is much less than the diagonal and as " long focus " if it is much greater than the diagonal. There is often much confusion over the term " telephoto " as applied to a lens. The name telephoto refers to the construction of the lens and means simply that a long focus lens of telephoto construction is placed nearer to the focal plane than an ordinary long focus lens of the same focal length. If the distance from the back of the lens to the focal plane is called the working distance it can be said that normal lenses have a working distance which does not differ much from the focal length. Telephoto lenses have a working distance much less than the focal length and " reversed " telephoto lenses have a working distance much greater than the focal length. Telephoto lenses are used where compactness is essential or for fitting to cameras incapable of long extension and reversed telephoto lenses are used, particularly in some cine cameras, where a very short focal length is required and mechanical obstructions, such as the shutter, make it impossible to fit a normal lens.

Generally speaking a lens should always be used to cover the whole field of view for which it is designed. The balance of the aberrations in lenses is such that the average definition over the field for which the lens is intended is made as good as possible, often at the expense of the best possible definition at the centre. Hence, in particular, if a lens is intended to cover a picture size of, say, 6 in. diagonal it would not necessarily give good definition when used in a cine camera with a frame of 1 in. diagonal or in a miniature camera with a 2-in. diagonal. It is also inadvisable to use a camera lens as a projector lens or in an enlarger and vice versa. Camera lenses are designed for very distant objects and when used at short distances the field curvature becomes excessive and bad definition results. The copying lenses used by process workers are specially designed for their working distance. Lens manufacturers show in their catalogues series of lenses for projection and for enlargers. Projection lenses are supplied normally in plain cylindrical mounts and have no diaphragms. Enlarger lenses frequently have a clicking device in the iris ring to facilitate setting the diaphragm in the dark.

When purchasing a lens in the ordinary way it is not always possible to obtain one whose chromatic correction has been specially adjusted. Normal photographic lenses manufactured before about 1936 are designed so that yellow light corresponding to the D line (5896 A) is focused at the same distance from the lens as the blue violet light corresponding to G' (4340 A). This form of chromatic correction ensures that when a lens is used without a filter in ordinary daylight the visual focus which corresponds roughly with yellow light will coincide with the photographic or actinic focus where the emulsion is most sensitive to light, i.e., in the blue violet region. When using panchromatic films with a yellow or orange filter the D

to G' correction has no value or meaning since the yellow filter is specifically used to prevent blue light from reaching the film. The older type photographic lenses are therefore, relatively speaking, not wholly efficient when used with panchromatic emulsion and a yellow filter, and a lens for such use, provided it is never used without a filter, should be corrected in the yellow and red region. The difficulty becomes enhanced when a red filter is used and even more so when infra-red emulsions with infra-red filters are used. Fig. 18.21 shows

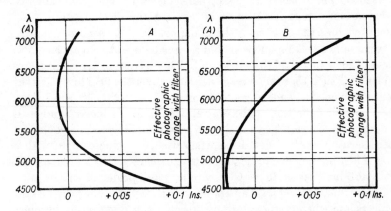

FIG. 18.21.—Typical chromatic aberration curves of a normal camera lens (B) and of a lens corrected for use with a yellow filter (A). The dotted lines show the approximate effective photographic range using a yellow filter. When filters are used the camera should be focused with the filter in position, preferably by repeated trial.

a normal chromatic aberration curve of a lens and the effect with various filters. The result of this chromatic aberration is that the best photographic focus does not coincide with the visual focus and if the optimum results are required a lens in its camera should be focused by making trial exposures until the best definition is obtained and the difference between this focus position and the best visual focus measured and recorded for future use. Those remarks apply particularly to the use of red filters and infra-red filters and emulsions. Modern lenses of the more expensive types are now normally corrected for use with panchromatic materials and for colour photography.

In many lenses the effect of spherical aberration is such that when a lens is stopped down from its full open aperture the position of the best focus shifts, and once again where maximum resolution is required it becomes necessary to measure the difference in the position of best focus for each aperture. Fortunately, this can be done visually by finding the best focus at each aperture, using a fairly powerful microscope to see the image on a ground glass. Fig. 18.22 shows the amount of movement to be expected in a typical wide aperture lens.

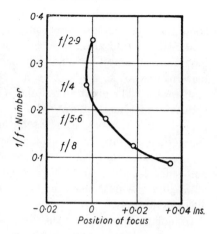

FIG. 18.22.—Effect of stopping down a lens on the position of best focus, caused by spherical aberration. For the best results cameras should be focused with the aperture at which they are to be used.

The reflection of light from the air-glass surfaces of lenses has been mentioned in Chapter 12 and here it is sufficient to say that lenses should always be used with an efficient lens hood to ensure, as far as possible, that only light from the object being photographed falls on the lens. The increase in contrast when a lens hood is used is very marked and is almost equal to the increase in contrast obtained in lenses with " bloomed " surfaces. This does not mean that the blooming of lens surfaces can be dispensed with if a lens hood is used, for even a bloomed lens will give better contrast if a hood is used, and the hood cannot prevent internal reflections but merely minimises their bad effects. Needless to say any dust on a lens surface will cause scattering of light and decrease the contrast and hence lenses should be kept capped when not in use and carefully cleaned with a soft camel-hair brush before use.

Cameras

To attempt to cover all the cameras in use and their properties for research purposes would be impossible and in this book only a few specialised scientific cameras will be very briefly described.

For the straightforward recording by still photography of experimental records, dials of meters, cathode ray tubes and the innumerable other requirements in research almost any commercial camera, properly modified and mounted, can be used, but there are on the market several special cameras of all sizes, having extra long film capacity or specially shaped plate or film holders, and inquiries should always be made before photographic apparatus is purchased.

Mention should also be made here of pin-hole cameras which can have numerous applications. The use of a pin hole with modern fast materials is not so prohibitive, as regards exposure time, as may at first appear. The great advantage of pin-hole work is the undisputed orthoscopy or lack of distortion. An adaptation of the pin-hole camera with a block of glass by introducing necessary distortion enables photographs to be taken with fields of view over a hemisphere. The application to meteorological sky photography is obvious and since lenses with hemispherical fields of view are not readily obtainable the glass block pin hole is a ready to hand substitute of no mean performance.

In moving film cameras the film is driven continuously over a large range of varying speeds and such cameras are useful for the continuous recording of cathode ray traces or when fitted with cylindrical lenses for vibration analysis. Drum cameras are used when the phenomenon to be recorded is of extreme speed and very short duration and in such cases a short length of film wound round the periphery of a drum which is rapidly rotated is most economical. Multichannel recording cameras are available, consisting of a collection of a large number of cameras each recording the trace of an individual cathode ray tube, all the traces appearing side by side on a single moving film.

For normal cinematographic or intermittent recording there are again a multiplicity of useful models for 16 mm. and for 35 mm. film, but care should be taken when choosing a camera that the loading methods are convenient. For 16 mm. film the magazine types of cameras are very convenient, but it frequently happens that the processing must be done by the manufacturer and the cost is certainly somewhat high. An electrically driven 16 mm. magazine camera used in large numbers in the armed forces is now available on the disposals market and can also be obtained from the makers. In 35 mm. cameras very few magazine types are available but there are conveniently arranged daylight loading cameras, both spring and electrically driven. A very useful cine camera which can be used with either 16 or 35 mm. film magazines is the " Cameflex," manufactured in France by the Eclair Company. It is a very versatile camera, with many accessories, having a turret mounting for three lenses, reflex viewing through the taking lens, quickly interchangeable magazines, and is electrically driven from eight to forty pictures per second with 6, 12 or 24 volt motors.

For high speed cinematograph work there are several 16 mm. and 35 mm. cameras giving speeds up to 3,000 frames per second. The Eastman Kodak 16 mm. High Speed camera employs the rotating glass block shutter described above (see Fig. 18.20). Another camera on the same principle is the *Fastax*. For 35 mm. film there are the Debrie, a robust French camera, and the Vinten HS 300, both capable of speeds up to 300 frames per second and using normal intermittent mechanisms. For very high speeds there is the Williamson camera utilising a number of rotating lenses and a Vinten model capable of 3,000 frames per second. Several drum type cameras have been built for even higher speeds but these usually adopt some electronic flash device for obtaining the separate exposures. Some ultra high speed cameras giving repetition rates from 50,000 to 500,000 pictures per second have been made. These cameras normally use some form of rotating mirror or prism device on which a first image of the object is formed. The rotation of the mirror or prism sweeps the light past a number of secondary lenses set round a drum so as to form second images on a stationary length of film on a second drum. The second images are stationary, i.e., they do not move across the film during the exposure provided the first image is formed in the plane of the rotating reflecting surface. One such camera, manufactured by Barr & Stroud of Glasgow (Scotland), taking 100 pictures at a rate of 50,000 per second, is commercially available; most of the others have been made by members of research establishments for their own use.

Extremely high repetition rates have been attained by one form or other of picture dissection. In one form a glass plate having a very large number of narrow clear strips separated by comparatively wide opaque strips is moved rapidly over the very short distance between two adjacent clear strips. This plate is mounted close to the photographic plate. The resulting original negative is quite meaningless but, after processing, it can be again placed against the grating, which can now be moved slowly, and a series of prints can be made by projection showing the instantaneous appearance of the object.

Another form of camera makes use of an image convertor tube in which light from the object falling on the photo-cathode of the tube causes a stream of electrons to be emitted. These electron streams are focused electrically on to a phosphor where they produce a visible

TABLE 18.7

| Manufacturer | Name of Emulsion and Sizes Available | Extent of Spectral Sensitivity and Maximum Sensitivity | | Approximate Emulsion Speed: A.S.A. | | | | Recommended Filters and Beginning of Transmission | Recommended Safelight | Recommended Development to γ 1·8 (with continuous agitation) |
| | | | | Daylight | | Tungsten | | | | |
		Up to—	Maximum	Agfa 82 12	Agfa 83 6	Agfa 82 25	Agfa 83 10			
V.E.B. Filmfabrik Agfa, Wolfen, Kreiss Bitterfeld, Eastern Germany	Infrarapid Film 750 35 mm. film in 36 exposure cassettes, 5 metre rolls; 120 metre or 300 metre rolls for cinematography	8500 A	7600 A					Agfa 82 at 6300 A Agfa 83 at 7100 A	Agfa 108	Agfa 1. 5 min. 65° F.
	Plates in sizes: 6·5 × 9 cm., 9 × 12 cm., 13 × 18 cm., 18 × 24 cm.									
	Agfa-Infrarot Platte 700 Rapid	7500 A	7200 A	5	—	10	—	Both filters apply	,,	Agfa 1. 5 min. 65° F.
	Agfa-Infrarot Platte 700 Hart	7500 A	7200 A	3·2	—	10	—	,, ,,	,,	Agfa 15. 10 min. 65° F.
	Agfa-Infrarot Platte 750 Rapid	8300 A	7700 A	5	2·6	5	3·2	,, ,,	,,	Agfa 1. 5 min. 65° F.
	Agfa-Infrarot Platte 750 Hart	7900 A	7550 A	3·2	2	5	5	,, ,,	,,	Agfa 15. 10 min. 65° F.
	Agfa-Infrarot Platte 800 Rapid	8550 A	8200 A	2·6	2·6	5	3·2	,, ,,	,,	Agfa 1. 5 min. 65° F.
	Agfa-Infrarot Platte 800 Hart	8600 A	8300 A	2	1	5	5	,, ,,	,,	Agfa 15. 10 min. 65° F.
	Agfa-Infrarot Platte 850 Rapid	8900 A	8500 A	1	2	2	2	,, ,,	,,	Agfa 1. 5 min. 65° F.
	Agfa-Infrarot Platte 850 Hart	9000 A	8600 A	1	1	2	2·6	,, ,,	,,	Agfa 15. 10 min. 65° F.
Eastman Kodak Co., Rochester 4, N.Y., U.S.A.	High Speed Infra-red Film No. 546: 16-mm. 100-ft. spool HIR 402: 35 mm. 100-ft. roll, wooden core HIR 40S: 35 mm. 100-ft. roll, modified. No. 10 spool	9700 A	8000 A	*Wratten 87* 25		*Wratten 87* 80		Wratten 87 at 7400 A	None	D 19 7 min. 68° F.
	Infra-red Sheet Film All regularly listed sheet film sizes	8700 A	8000– 8400 A	6		10		Wratten 87 at 7400 A	Wratten Series 7	D 19 7 min. 68° F.

Manufacturer	Film/Plate			6	10			
Ferrania Corso Matteotti, 12 Milan, Italy	Infra-red Film IR 135 35 mm. film, 20 exposure cassettes	8700 A	8000–8400 A			Wratten 87 at 7400 A	Wratten Series 7	D 76 15 min. 68° F. (γ 1·4 only)
	I. 7200 Infra-red Films 35 mm. film, 36 exposure cassettes, 36 exposure refills, 5 metres; 35 mm. cine film in packs suitable for Eyemo, Arriflex, Debrie-Mitchell cameras	7700 A	7200 A	*R. 102* 2·5	*R. 102* 10	R 102 at 5000 A	Ferrania 20	R 6 10 min. 64° F.
	I. 7200 7200 Infra-red Plates, all standard sizes	7700 A	7200 A	*R. 102* 2·5	*R. 102* 10	R 102 at 5900 A	Ferrania 20	R 10 16 min. 64° F.
	I. 8300 8300 Infra-red Plates, all standard sizes	8500 A	8300 A	*R. 103* 1·6	*R. 103* 10	R 103 at 6100 A	Ferrania 20	R 10 15 min. 64° F.
Gevaert Photo-Producten N.V., Mortsel, Antwerp, Belgium	Scientia 52 A 86 Film: 35 mm. film, 36 exposure cassettes, and 20 roll-film. Plates: all standard sizes	8980 A	7800–8000 A	*R. 719* 80	*R. 719* 100	R 719 at 7190 A	Gevinal x535	G 201 3 min. 68° F. (maximum γ 2·7 is reached in 10 min.)
R. Guilleminot, Boespflug & Cie, 22 Rue de Chateaudin, Paris 9e, France	Infra-Guil Plates: 6·5 × 9 cm., 9 × 12 cm., 13 × 18 cm., 18 × 24 cm.	8650 A	8000 A	*Wood* 88 8	*Wood* 88 16	Wood 88 at 7400 A	None	GB 24 4 min. 65° F.
Kodak Ltd., Wealdstone, Harrow, Middlesex, Great Britain	IRER (Kodak Infra-Red Extra-Rapid) Plates: 2¼ × 3¼ in., 3¼ × 4¼ in., 4 × 5 in., 4 × 10 in., 4¾ × 6½ in., 6·5 × 9 cm., 9 × 12 cm. Other sizes up to and including 10 × 12 in. to be ordered under Kodak Scientific Plate II-N	8800 A	8000 A	*Wratten* 87 6	*Wratten* 87 10	Wratten 87 at 7400 A	Wratten Series 9	D 19 b diluted 1 + 2 5½ min. 68° F.
Kodak-Pathé, 37–39, Avenue Montaigne Paris 8e, France	Infra Rouge 5512 35 mm. film, 20 exposure cassettes	8800 A	8200 A	*Wratten* 87 6	*Wratten* 87 10	Wratten 87 at 7400 A	Wratten Series 7	D 19 b diluted 1 + 1 6 min. 68° F. (γ 0·9 only)
Konishiroku Photo Industry Co., No. 1, 3-Chome, Muromachi, Nihonbashi, Chuo-Ku, Tokyo, Japan	Sakura Infra-red Film 750 35 mm. film 20 exposure, dark room loading, 120 roll-film, 8 exposures	8200 A	7500 A	Any filter cutting at 5600 A 6	Any filter cutting at 5600 A 10	Any filter cutting at 5600 A	None	D 76 9 min. 68° F.

image. Electrostatic or electromagnetic means can be used to deflect the beams of electrons rapidly to different parts of the screen and if a camera is arranged to photograph the screen it will record the successive images as they occur. It is possible to obtain about nine separate pictures in this way at phenomenal repetition rates, depending only on the rapidity with which the electric or magnetic fields can be changed.

The problems in ultra high speed cinematography are the disposal of exposed film and the enormous length of film used to record a phenomenon which usually occurs so rapidly as only to appear on a few frames. The time spent in analysing such records should always be considered before embarking on a programme involving ultra high speed cinematography.

Infra-Red and Ultra-Violet Photography

It is well known that photographic emulsions are all sensitive to ultra-violet light, but photographic lenses are almost opaque to this light and it is not possible to photograph objects with a *normal* camera, using ultra-violet illumination. There does not appear to be any short-wave limit to the sensitivity of the emulsion; gamma-rays, X-rays and ultra-violet light are all strongly actinic and will record provided the radiation can reach the sensitive grains of the emulsion; gelatine absorbs light of wave-length less than 2200 A. Air is almost opaque to ultra-violet light of shorter wave-length than about 2000 A and if records are required for such short wave radiation the work must be done in a vacuum. The glasses used in normal photographic lenses include, almost invariably, flint glasses or medium or dense barium crowns and, as shown on page 221, these glasses are almost opaque at wave-lengths shorter than 3800 A. Lenses for UV transmission, as used in photo-micrography, must be made in a transparent substance such as quartz or fluorite or, of course, mirror objectives can be used.

Subjects irradiated with ultra-violet light often fluoresce, or images can be formed on fluorescent screens with ultra-violet light and the visible image can then be photographed in the normal way.

Infra-red radiation on the other hand easily penetrates air and glass is reasonably transparent up to 2·8μ, but normal photographic emulsions are not sensitive to infra-red light. Special infra-red emulsions are available, however, as shown in Table 18.7 and useful photography is possible to about 1·0μ. There are numerous applications of infra-red photography. The haze penetrating properties are made use of in long range landscapes and in air photography, but it must be emphasised that infra-red light will *not* penetrate cloud or fog. Other applications include the detection of camouflage and, in particular, spurious and false work in paintings, including detail hidden under a layer of paint. In medicine and surgery, the added penetration can be made to show under skin infections. A particular advantage of infra-red photography is that no *visible* light need be used. Photoflash tubes are very rich in infra-red radiation and if the flash bulb is entirely covered by an infra-red filter, such as a Wratten 87 or 88A, the flash will be entirely invisible and photography is possible in complete darkness, or without interference to the subject. In surgical operations, for example, infra-red photographs can be taken without in any way inconveniencing the surgeon at work; at boxing matches the contestants are quite unaware of the photograph. In addition to the Wratten or similar filters, cellophane bags are available which can easily and quickly be attached over a flash bulb.

Applications

As a final appendix to this chapter we list below a few subjects in which photographic methods have been used. This list cannot pretend to be exhaustive but may guide the reader in his choice of attack on some problem. References are given where possible to enable the reader to follow up any problem.

(*i*) Astronomical Photography—a very wide field including star maps, stellar spectroscopy. Henney & Dudley, *Handbook of Photography*, Ch. XXV.

(*ii*) Air Photography and Surveying—*Surveying from Air Photographs*, Hotine (Constable).
Special Cameras for Air Photography—Williamson Manfg. Co., Willesden, London. Fairchild Corporation Inc. (U.S.A.).

(*iii*) Infra Red photography in Medicine, etc.—*Photography by Infra Red*, Clark (Chapman & Hall).

(*iv*) Photo Elastic stress analysis—*Photoelasticity*, Coker & Filon (Cambridge).

(*v*) Wave Photography—Admiralty.

(*vi*) Photo Micrography in Black and White, in colour, and in U.V. light, *Practical Photomicrography*, Barnard & Welch (Arnold).
Also Macro structure of Metals, *Practical Microscopic Metallography*, Greeves & Wrighton (Chapman & Hall). *Metallography*, Desch (Longmans).

(*vii*) Radiography of Welds & Castings, Kodak Ltd., Harrow.

(*viii*) Motion Study, Kodak Ltd., Data Book D.11.

(*ix*) Document & Book recording, Kodak Ltd., Recordak Division.

(*x*) Reflex Copying, Kodak Ltd.

(*xi*) Spectrography, Brode, *Chemical Spectroscopy* (Wiley), Hilger & Watts Ltd.

(*xii*) X-Ray diffraction, Bragg, Sir W. H. & W. L. *X-Rays and Crystal Structure* (Bell).

(*xiii*) Gamma Radiography, Crowther, J. A. (editor) *Handbook of Industrial Radiography* (Arnold).

(*xiv*) Ballistics, Bullets, Shells, Bombs, N.P.L., Admiralty, R.A.E., etc.
(*xv*) Cathode ray oscillograph recording, C.R.O. Manufacturers.
(*xvi*) Heat gradients in furnaces, Kodak Ltd.
(*xvii*) Atomic Physics, Wilson Cloud Chamber, etc., Atomic Research Laboratories. Harwell.
(*xviii*) Sound Waves by Schlieren methods, R. W. Wood, *Physical Optics.*
(*xix*) Air Flow in Wind & Supersonic Tunnels, Schlieren & Polarisation Methods, N.P.L., R.A.E.
(*xx*) Sound recording and analysis, E.M.I. Ltd., Hayes.
(*xxi*) Under Water Photography, Admiralty, Siebe Gorman Ltd., London.

Books on Photography

HENNEY & DUDLEY, *Handbook of Photography* (McGraw Hill).
LE CLERC, *Photography, Theory & Practice* (Pitman).
MEES, *The Theory of the Photographic Process* (Macmillan).
NEBLETTE, *Photography* (Van Nostrand).
BOURNE, *Discharge Lamps in Photography and Projection* (Chapman & Hall).
BALY, *Spectroscopy* (Longmans).
BRODE, *Chemical Spectroscopy* (Wiley).
HOTINE, *Surveying from Air Photographs* (Constable).
CLARK, *Photography by Infra Red* (Chapman & Hall).
COKER & FILON, *Photoelasticity* (Cambridge).
JESSOP & HARRIS, *Photoelasticity* (Cleaver Hume).
BARNARD & WELCH, *Practical Photomicrography* (Arnold).
DESCH, *Metallography* (Longmans).
GREAVES & WRIGHTON, *Practical Microscopical Metallography* (Chapman & Hall).
Kodak Ltd., *Kodak Data Book.*
Ilford Ltd., *Ilford Photographic Manual.*
STRONG, *Modern Physical Laboratory Practice* (Blackie).
CHESTERMAN, W. D., *The Photographic Study of Rapid Events* (Oxford).

The above are the more important books on photography in general and a number of applications and there is a very large number of books, many quite good, on practically every possible branch and application of photography.

REFERENCES

BURKIN, A. R., " Ultra Rapid Processing of Photographic Materials," *Phot. Jour.,* **87 B** (Sept. 1947), 108.
TEARLE, J. L., " Accuracy of the Image," *Photo. Jour.,* **87 B** (Nov. 1947), 132.
DUNN, J. F., and PLANT, G. S., " A New Photometric Exposure Meter for Cameras and Enlargers," *Phot. Jour.,* **85 B** (Nov. 1945), 114.
BOURNE, E. K., " Photographic Light Sources," *Phot. Jour.,* **85 B** (Nov. 1945), 129.
SENIOR, D. A., " High Speed Photography of Under-Water Explosions," *Phot. Jour.,* **86 B** (Jan. 1946), 25.
SYMPOSIUM, " Photographic Recording of C.R.T. Screen Traces," *Phot. Jour.* **86 B** (Nov. 1946), 138.
DIGHTON, D. R., & Ross, H. M., " Instrument for Investigating the Operation of Camera Shutters," *Phot. Jour.,* **86 B** (Sept. 1946), 110.
SELWYN, E. W. S., " Photographic and Visual Resolving Power of Lenses," *Phot. Jour.,* **88 B** (Jan., May 1948), 6, 46.
KASHA, M., " Transmission Filters for the Ultra-Violet," *J.O.S.A.,* **38** (1948), 929.
HUSE, " Photographic Resolving Power," *J.O.S.A.,* **1** (1917), 119.
SELWYN, E. W. H., & TEARLE, J. L., " The Performance of Aircraft Camera Lenses," *Proc. Phys. Soc.,* **58** (1946), 493.
GARDNER, I. C., " A Test of Lens Resolution for the Photographer," Nat. Bur. Standards, Washington, Circular C.428 (1941).
COOK, G. H., "Photographic Resolving Power", *Phot. Jour.,* **95 A** (Aug. 1955), 161.

CHAPTER 19

CORROSION IN INSTRUMENTS AND ITS PREVENTION

The general problem

SCIENTIFIC instruments are expected to work satisfactorily in widely varying conditions, and as their fields of application broaden, these conditions tend to become more severe. The problems are probably greatest in the military field, where a number of circumstances combine to make the satisfactory maintenance of instruments difficult. Since we are here concerned with laboratory instruments, we shall only refer incidentally to experience in military applications, though we shall use information which has been obtained for such purposes. Laboratory instruments are used in large numbers in industry and elsewhere where exposure to corrosive agents may occur, and in this chapter we shall consider what may be done to lessen or prevent corrosion in such circumstances.

The most widespread source of corrosion is atmospheric moisture, whose effect is greatly increased by the presence of acid sulphurous vapour from industrial and domestic smoke (see Fig. 19.1). Rapid changes of temperature may give rise to condensation of moisture on surfaces, greatly enhancing the effect, and when large changes of barometric pressure occur (as may happen, for instance, in aircraft) such condensation may form inside the cases of imperfectly sealed instruments. Corrosive fumes are often present in the atmosphere of a chemical laboratory, and although they may and should be confined to fume cupboards, the range of work now undertaken in the presence of such vapours demands instruments which may be used under these conditions. Near the coast, droplets of salt water are encountered in the air, and all these facts make it necessary to give some thought to the possible corrosion which may result from day to day use. In addition, splashing by corrosive liquids must be considered, and such liquids may have to be introduced into an instrument for measurement. We see, then, that problems of corrosion in laboratory instruments may vary greatly ; in many laboratories no special problem exists, whereas in others the prevention of corrosion may be difficult or even, in the sense of a complete solution, impossible. Reduction or elimination of corrosion may conveniently be considered under three headings.

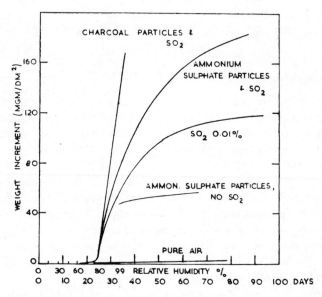

FIG. 19.1.—Corrosion of iron (measured by increase in weight per unit area) exposed to various agencies. The relative humidity was increased up to 100 per cent during the course of the test (Vernon [1]).

Reduction by improving local conditions

In cases where atmospheric moisture is the main source of trouble, it is important to note that the *relative humidity* is one of the most important factors. Local reduction of this factor may easily reduce corrosion (e.g. of iron and steel) to negligible amounts. This reduction can evidently be brought about by the use of drying agents such as silica gel or activated alumina, but this is only practicable if the instrument can be enclosed in some kind of case so that the amount of air to be dried is not too large. Such cases may conveniently be made of transparent plastic materials, and for some purposes a bag or envelope of polyethylene may be used. If protection is to be given in this way for a long time, it becomes necessary to arrange for periodic inspection and renewal of the desiccant, and this is not always convenient, and may also be overlooked. The desiccation of some instru-

470

ments, especially optical instruments, is carried out by passing a stream of dry air through the instrument, either continuously or intermittently according to circumstances. The air stream may be dried by passing it over silica gel or activated alumina, or may be obtained from an arrangement which depends on the expansion of air under high pressure to dry it (Barr & Stroud, Ltd.).

The relative humidity may be lowered, however, without the use of drying agents, simply by raising the temperature of the instrument and its surrounding atmosphere. There is no reason why the instrument should be in an air-tight enclosure, but much less power will be required to maintain the ambient air at the required temperature if this air is enclosed to some extent—otherwise a whole room may have to be heated in order to keep a small piece of apparatus warm. How effective the reduction of relative humidity is in the case of mild steel may be seen from Fig. 19.1. In the experiment ([1]) whose results are shown in this figure, the relative humidity was gradually increased from 0 to 99 per cent in a time of about thirty-six days, after which it was kept constant at this value. The effect of a small amount of sulphur dioxide (normally present in urban atmospheres) is striking. The fact that the presence of inert particles of charcoal (in presence of sulphur dioxide) has much more influence on rusting than is produced by particles of ammonium sulphate is at first sight surprising ; it is connected with the absorbing power of charcoal. Separate experiments at constant relative humidity show that prolonged exposure at 60 per cent relative humidity or less causes no rusting in the presence of 0·01 per cent sulphur dioxide.

Below the critical humidity only an invisible oxide film is formed, which protects the metal from further attack. At higher humidities, however, this film is alternately formed and broken down, and the metal rusts. Since relative humidity varies rapidly with temperature (for a given water content of the air) only a moderate temperature excess is needed to give good protection to iron and steel. For instance, a temperature excess of 10° C. will reduce the relative humidity of air, saturated at 20° C., to only 55 per cent, and this is below the critical humidity which is in the region 60–70 per cent. Such a temperature excess is easily provided by electrical heating, in many cases a low-power lamp being sufficient. It is of course necessary to ensure that the local heating does not cause distillation of moisture from damp, absorbing materials in the enclosure, for this would increase the rate of corrosion. Also, it cannot be assumed that protection will be obtained if the iron or steel surfaces are contaminated with corrosive substances, and handling of bright surfaces with moist, perspiration-covered hands may be expected to result in rusting. From the point of view of corrosion reduction, it is desirable to install a constant source of heat, not to keep the temperature constant by means of a thermostat, since what is needed is a constant *excess* of temperature.

Where a more chemically corrosive atmosphere is present, even the simple precaution of providing a housing will in many cases reduce corrosion considerably, since it reduces the rate of replacement of the corrosive vapour in contact with the vulnerable parts. The protection can obviously be further increased by including an absorbent material within the housing to remove the corrosive vapour.

Use of inhibitors in aqueous solution

It has been found that a variety of chemical compounds, when present in solution in water in which iron or steel is immersed, have the property of retarding or sometimes completely inhibiting the formation of rust on the metal. Such inhibitors find many applications, for instance in preventing the internal rusting of boilers and of the parts of internal combustion engines which are in contact with cooling water. Some such inhibitors must be used with care, because if they are not present in sufficient concentration, the corrosion is localized even though the total amount is reduced, and such a concentration of corrosion in a small region may lead to pitting, perhaps with serious weakening of the metal. Other inhibitors, on the other hand, do not have this property and are classed as " safe."

Sodium benzoate is an example of a safe inhibitor, and at a concentration of 1 per cent or more will protect steel (but not cast iron) immersed in the aqueous solution. If chlorides are present in the water (as for instance in sea water) the concentration of sodium benzoate must be increased to give adequate protection. Sodium nitrite added to water gives protection both to cast iron and steel, but attacks soldered joints. However, a mixture of sodium nitrite and benzoate may be used to protect both cast iron and steel, and suitable mixtures do not attack soldered joints. Such inhibitors can obviously be used with advantage in water baths, thermostats, etc., wherever iron or steel parts are immersed in water. Some of these applications are covered by patents. Further information is contained in refs. 2 and 13.

Vapour-phase inhibitors

It has been found that the vapour of some compounds, if at suitable concentration, will protect bright iron and steel surfaces in a moist, contaminated atmosphere and will even give protection if, subsequently, water is condensed on the surface. These vapour-phase inhibitors find great application in giving temporary protection to machinery, etc., during transport, a great advantage being that greasing and subsequent removal of grease on arrival are rendered unnecessary. The permanence of the protection depends on the amount of inhibitor included in the packing, on the saturated vapour pressure of the inhibitor, and on the efficiency of the means used to prevent escape of the vapour. Of the many substances which have been found to give protection, the nitrite salts of amines, and the amine carbonates appear to be outstanding. Refs. 3–8 deal chiefly with the former ; the use of amine carbonates and other substances is described in ref. 9. Two compounds in particular have been examined in some detail, namely di*cyclo*hexylamine nitrate and *cyclo*hexylamine carbonate; the former is known under the trade name "Shell V.P.I. 260."

These materials are soluble in water, methanol and ethanol, and are used for impregnating paper and board for packaging. The inhibitors may also be applied by spraying, or dusting, or porous bags containing them may be enclosed along with the articles to be protected. The quantities required are small, and in the case of **V.P.I. 260** 1 gram per c. ft. of enclosed space is stated to be ample. Protection is afforded as long as the inhibitor is present.

*Cyclo*hexylamine carbonate gives protection to steel and to cast iron, as well as to aluminium, zinc, chromium plate on steel, tinplate, solder and soldered joints. The corrosion of copper, copper-rich alloys and magnesium is, however, substantially increased.[9] Di*cyclo*hexylamine nitrite protects steel, but does not adequately protect cast iron. The degree of protection given to cast iron is greater if the surface is highly polished than in the rough, cast state. With non-ferrous metals, the results are not alway predictable. It appears desirable to avoid contact between the nitrite and non-ferrous metals, particularly copper, brass and soft solder. Provided that this is observed, deleterious effects (except perhaps in the case of soft solder) appear to be limited to dulling or surface tarnish. Aluminium is given some protection whether in contact with the solid or vapour only.[8]

Many measuring instruments have accurately made sliding surfaces of iron or steel, and such surfaces cannot be protected from rust by painting. Vapour-phase inhibitors may have some application to the protection of such parts, either in use or in store. None of the inhibitors hitherto described in the literature can be considered as the best under all circumstances ; apart from their different behaviour towards various metals, the vapour pressures of the inhibitors in common use differ considerably (Table 19.1). This may influence the choice of inhibitor, for evidently a material with a high vapour pressure will be more quickly dispersed than one with a lower vapour pressure.

Until more is known of the action of vapour-phase inhibitors on non-ferrous metals, care should be taken and preferably a trial should be made in doubtful cases.

TABLE 19.1[7]—*Saturation Vapour Pressures (in mm. Hg.)*

Inhibitor	Temperature		
	25° C.	45° C.	60° C.
*cyclo*hexylamine carbonate	0·4	3·3	13
*dicyclo*hexylamine nitrite	0·002	0·0014	0·007
*diiso*propylamine nitrite	0·005	—	—

As in the case of other corrosion inhibitors, some applications are patented.

Use of suitable materials

Evidently the simple answer to problems of corrosion is to employ materials which are proof against the agencies of corrosion. Generally speaking, organic plastic materials (see Chapter 3) are resistant to an atmosphere contaminated by inorganic vapours, and when they have suitable mechanical and other properties they may be used to replace metal. This is frequently possible, for example, in instrument cases, panels and housings, where the use of wood may also be considered.

Metals differ greatly in their resistance to corrosion, and the behaviour of a given metal varies considerably with circumstances. For instance, since stainless steels owe their inertness to an oxide layer formed on the surface, destruction of the surface when not in contact with oxygen leaves the metal unprotected. A more common cause of corrosion, however, is the proximity of other metals and the electrolytic action which follows when the surfaces are moist. Because of these effects, some attempts to reduce corrosion (for instance, by replacing mild steel screws in light alloy structures by brass or by stainless steel screws) may do more harm than good. The subject of bimetallic corrosion is complicated, and because the behaviour of a given pair of metals varies considerably with their surface condition, many pitfalls exist.[10]

Bimetallic Corrosion

The available information on the behaviour of pairs of metals in contact in moist conditions has recently been collected by the Corrosion and Electrodeposition Committee of the Inter-Services Metallurgical Research Council, and is reproduced in Table 19.2. The original report[11] contains, in addition to this table and a useful introduction, an appendix giving the group numbers to be used in Table 19.2 for a large number of alloys for which standard specifications exist. These include British Standards, Ministry of Supply Aircraft Material Specifications (D.T.D. Series) and S.T.A.7 Schedules. Reference to Table 19.2 will enable the designer to choose suitable combinations of metals, when this is possible, and will indicate whether additional precautions must be taken if, for other reasons, a particular combination must be used. Such precautions are considered below.

It should be noted that the symbols in the table refer only to the *acceleration* of corrosion caused by the proximity of two metals. The basic corrosion resistance of metals is quite distinct and the table gives no information on this aspect. Among other matters dealt with in the Notes (ref. 11) are the effects of complex ions in water in which the metals are immersed. If a reagent is present in this water which forms complex ions with one of the metals, that metal will be rendered less noble and the predictions of Table 19.2 will not be reliable. The effect of relative areas of the metals in contact is important also, for the danger of corrosion is increased if the area of the more noble metal is large compared with that of the other component of the pair. This may be important when bolts, rivets etc. are made of the less noble metal. In a water circulating system, it is possible for small quantities of noble metals such as copper to be dissolved from one part of the

TABLE 19.2—Degree of Corrosion at Bimetallic Contacts

(Reproduced from ref. 11 by permission of the Controller of H.M. Stationery Office.)

[Based on data provided by members of the I.S.M.R.C. Corrosion and Electrodeposition Committee and others, and arranged by Mrs. V. E. Rance.]

A = The corrosion of the "metal considered" is not increased by the "contact metal."
B = The corrosion of the "metal considered" may be slightly increased by the "contact metal."
C = The corrosion of the "metal considered" may be markedly increased by the "contact metal."

(Acceleration is likely to occur only when the metal becomes wet by moisture containing an electrolyte, e.g. salt, acid, combustion products. In ships, acceleration may be expected to occur under in-board conditions, since salinity and condensation are frequently present. Under less severe conditions the acceleration may be slight or negligible.)

D = When moisture is present, this combination is inadvisable, even in mild conditions, without adequate protective measures.

CONTACT METAL (columns →):

1. Gold, platinum, rhodium, silver
2. Monel, Inconel, nickel / molybdenum alloys
3. Cupronickels, silver solder, aluminium-bronzes, tin-bronzes, gunmetals
4. Copper, brasses, "nickel silvers"
5. Nickel
6. Lead, tin and soft solders
7. Steel and cast iron
8. Cadmium
9. Zinc
10. Magnesium and magnesium alloys (chromated)

Stainless Steels —
11. Austenitic 18/8 Cr/Ni
12. 18/2 Cr/Ni
13. 13% Cr

14. Chromium
15. Titanium
16. Aluminium and aluminium alloys

METAL CONSIDERED ↓	1	2	3	4	5	6	7	8	9	10	11	12	13	14	15	16
1. Gold, platinum, rhodium, silver	—	A	A	A	A	A	A	A	A	A	A	A	A	A	A	A
2. Monel, Inconel, nickel / molybdenum alloys	B	—	A	A	A	A	A	A	A	A	A	A	A	B	B	A
3. Cupronickels, silver solder, aluminium-bronzes, tin-bronzes, gunmetals	C(k)	B	—	A	A	A	A	A	A	A	B or C	B	A	B or C	C	A(e)
4. Copper, brasses, "nickel silvers"	C(k)	B or C	B or C(g)	—	B or C	B or C(p)	A	A	A	A	B or C	B or C	A	B or C	C	A(e)
5. Nickel	C	B	A	A	—	A	A	A	A	A	B or C	B or C	A	B or C	C	A
6. Lead, tin and soft solders	C	B or C(t)	B or C(q)	B or C(q)	B	—	A or C(r)	A	A or C(r)	A	B or C	B or C	B or C	C(k)	C	B(m)
7. Steel and cast iron (a)(f)	C	C	C	C	C(k)	C(k)	—	A	A or C(r)	A	C	C	C	C	C	B
8. Cadmium	C	C	C	C	C	B	B	—	A(m)	A	C	C	C	C	C	B
9. Zinc	C	C	C	C	C	B	B	B	—	A	C	C	C	C	C	C(j)
10. Magnesium and magnesium alloys (chromated) (b)(a)	D	D	D	C	D	C	C	B or C	B or C	—	C	C	C	C	C	B or C(e)
11. Stainless steel — Austenitic 18/8	A	A	A	A	A	A	A	A	A	A	—	A	A	A	A	A
12. Stainless steel — 18/2 Cr/Ni	C	A or C(s)	A or C(s)	A or C(s)	A	A	A	A	A	A	A	—	A	A	(o)	A
13. Stainless steel — 13% Cr.	C	C	C	C	B or C	A	A	A	A	A	C	—	—	C	C	A
14. Chromium	A	A	A	A	A	A	A	A	A	A	A	A	A	—	—	A
15. Titanium	A	A	A	A	A	A	A	A	A	A	A	—	A	A	—	A
16. Aluminium and aluminium alloys (n)(a)	D	C	D(e)	D(e)	C(k)	B or C	B or C	A	A	A(c)(h)	B or C	B or C	B or C	B or C(d)	C	—

TABLE 19.2 Notes

(a) The exposure of iron, steel, magnesium alloys and unclad aluminium-copper alloys in an unprotected condition in corrosive environments should be avoided wherever possible even in the absence of bimetallic contact.

(b) Except when used for affording cathodic protection, magnesium and magnesium alloys should not normally be used in an unchromated condition unless otherwise protected. When a volume of water (as opposed to a film of atmospheric moisture) can collect at a bimetallic junction, they should, even when chromated, be insulated from more noble metals. Steel, brass and copper parts such as nuts, bolts, washers, screws and studs, should be galvanised, cadmium plated or otherwise protected. If, however, jointing compound (D.T.D. 369A) is employed, insulation may sometimes be unnecessary but advice should be sought from a Service corrosion specialist.

(c) Where contact between magnesium and aluminium alloys is necessary, the use of aluminium alloys with low or negligible copper content is preferred.

(d) If in contact with thin (decorative) chromium plate, the symbol is C, but with thick plating (as used for wear resistance) the symbol is B.

(e) When contacts between copper or copper-rich materials and aluminium alloys cannot be avoided, a much higher degree of protection against corrosion is obtained by first plating the copper-rich material with tin or nickel and then, with cadmium, than by applying a coating of cadmium of similar thickness. The aluminium in contact with the copper-rich material should be anodised when practicable.

(f) The corrosion of mild steel may sometimes be increased by coupling with cast iron, especially when the exposed area of the mild steel is small compared with the cast iron.

(g) Instances may arise in which corrosion of copper or brasses may be accelerated by contact with bronzes or gunmetals, e.g. the corrosion of copper, seawater-carrying pipe-lines may be accelerated by contact with gunmetal valves, etc.

(h) When magnesium corrodes in sea-water or certain other electrolytes, alkali formed at the aluminium cathode may attack the aluminium.

(i) When it is not practicable to use other more suitable methods of protection, e.g. spraying with aluminium, zinc may be useful for the protection of steel in contact with aluminium, despite the accelerated attack upon the coating.

(k) This statement should not necessarily discourage the use of the "contact metal" as a coating for the "metal considered", provided that continuity is good; under abrasive conditions, however, even a good coating may become discontinuous.

(l) In most supply waters at temperatures above about 60°C., zinc may accelerate the corrosion of steel.

(m) In these cases the "contact metal" may provide an excellent protective coating for the "metal considered", the latter usually being electrochemically protected at gaps in the coating.

(n) When aluminium is alloyed with appreciable amounts of copper it becomes more noble and when alloyed with appreciable amounts of zinc it becomes less noble. These remarks apply to bimetallic contacts and not to the inherent corrosion resistance of the individual aluminium alloy. Such effects are mainly of interest when the aluminium alloys are connected with each other.

(o) No data available.

(p) In some immersed conditions, the corrosion of copper or brass may be seriously accelerated at pores or defects in tin coatings.

(q) In some immersed conditions there may be serious acceleration of the corrosion of soldered seams in copper or copper alloys.

(r) When exposed to the atmosphere in contact with steel or galvanised steel, lead can be rapidly corroded with formation of PbO at narrow crevices where the access of air is restricted.

(s) Serious acceleration of corrosion of 18/2 stainless steel in contact with copper or nickel alloys may occur at crevices where the oxygen supply is low.

Normally the corrosion of lead/tin soldered seams is not significantly increased by their contact with the nickel-base alloys but under a few immersed conditions the seams may suffer enhanced corrosion.

system and deposited on less noble metals elsewhere, giving rise to local corrosion. Severe pitting may arise in this way. These and other complications which may arise from contact effects are considered in greater detail in ref. 11. The information given in Table 19.2 should not be regarded as infallible, though it does represent the best available at present.

Corrosive chemicals

When instruments are to be used in contact with corrosive liquids, it is imperative that suitable materials should be used. Among metals, stainless steels are generally the most useful. They vary considerably in resistance, and may require to have been suitably heat-treated. Information on stainless steels is given in Chapter 3. For containers, pipes etc. to be used with strong acids and alkalies, much use is now made of polyethylene and of polytetrafluorethylene. These materials are sufficiently pliable to allow flexible tubing, bellows etc. to be fabricated and they are very resistant to a wide range of chemicals. The properties of these and other plastic materials are given in Chapter 3. In considering the use of plastics, it must be realised that some plastic materials can be a source of corrosive vapour. For instance, rubber containing free sulphur may give off sulphurous vapour which, in a confined space, will attack copper and some of its alloys. This can be serious in the case of fine copper wire used in electrical measuring instruments, and rubber gaskets used for sealing such instruments should be sulphur-free. Polyvinylchloride, at elevated temperatures, may give off hydrochloric acid, and phenolic resins are said to be unsuitable in closed containers where cadmium-plated parts are present.[12]

Protection by means of paints, lacquers and enamels

Until comparatively recently, the protection of metals (mostly iron and steel) from corrosion has been achieved by the use of paints based on " drying oils," or by vitreous enamels. Drying oils are oils such as linseed oil which oxidise on exposure to the air, changing from liquids to resinous materials in which the constituent long-chain molecules are linked crosswise to form a three-dimensional felt. This "drying " is irreversible, and the dried film cannot be redissolved, though it can be attacked and destroyed by strong chemicals such as acids and alkalies. Paints based on drying oils require a considerable time (several days) before the film acquires its final hardness, although the use of accelerating agents may reduce this time considerably. For this reason, they are not well suited to the finishing of articles produced in large numbers. The film may be given greater hardness and gloss by cooking the oil with a natural resin or gum, to produce what is usually referred to as a varnish, but the objection of slow drying remains.

Cellulose finishes have been much used on metals because of the much shorter time required for drying. These materials are usually based on cellulose nitrate or acetate which is dissolved in a ketone solvent to which is added a variety of other organic liquids, to control the rate of drying, the viscous properties and the cost. In addition, plasticisers are added to impart flexibility to the dried film. These are substances like tricresyl phosphate and dibutyl pthallate which are liquids with very low vapour pressures. Cellulose lacquers dry by simple evaporation and no further polymerisation or cross-linking then takes place. They will in consequence soften or dissolve when further coats are applied, and for this reason spraying rather than brushing is the preferred method of application. It is clear that they are not suitable for use on instruments which are liable to be splashed by a variety of organic solvents.

A number of different classes of synthetic resins are now available for preparing lacquers. Such lacquers include those which dry by solvent evaporation, those which are stoved to induce further polymerisation or cross-linking, and also air-drying lacquers (which do not require stoving) in which cross-linking is brought about by adding another component shortly before using the lacquer. For a general account, the reader may consult ref. 14. Although other classes of resins have good properties, only two, of recent introduction, will be referred to here as being of particular interest for the protection of instruments. These are the epoxide and the silicone resins. The following brief account of these materials will show the scope of their application ; a useful purpose will also have been served if the complexity of the subject is revealed, for it is certain that expert advice should be sought if the best choice is to be made. Information concerning epoxide resins for varnishes may be obtained in the United Kingdom from the Shell Chemical Company Ltd., London and Aero Research Ltd., Cambridge, and in the United States from the Shell Chemical Corporation, New York. Information on silicones may be had from Midland Silicones Ltd., London, and from the Dow-Corning Chemical Corporation, Corning.

Epoxide resins for finishes

Epoxide resins (" Araldite " and " Epikote " resins) are resins of high chemical stability and great versatility. They are large, linear polymeric molecules with the general formula

$$\underset{CH_2-CH-CH_2-}{\overset{O}{\diagup\diagdown}}\left[-O-\bigcirc-\underset{CH_3}{\overset{CH_3}{\underset{|}{\overset{|}{C}}}}-\bigcirc-O-CH_2-\underset{OH}{\overset{OH}{\underset{|}{CH}}}-CH_2\right]_n-$$

$$-O-\bigcirc-\underset{CH_3}{\overset{CH_3}{\underset{|}{\overset{|}{C}}}}-\bigcirc-O-CH_2-\overset{O}{\overset{\diagup\diagdown}{CH}}-CH_2$$

in which n is the degree of polymerisation. Molecular weights of epoxide resins for coating are in the range 1,000–3,800. These resins owe their useful properties to the presence of reactive groups (OH side groups and $\overset{O}{\overset{\diagup\diagdown}{CH_2-CH}}$ (epoxy) end groups). These reactive groups enable the molecular chains to be cross-linked by various means to give a three-dimensional network of great stability, having good resistance to chemical attack. General accounts of the chemistry and uses of epoxide resins may be found in refs. 15–17. There are at present three main ways of using epoxide resins for varnishes.

(1) *Epoxide Ester Resins*

These are made by esterifying the side hydroxyl groups and the epoxy end groups by heating with a monocarboxylic acid. If the fatty acids of drying oils are used, the epoxide ester may be used to make an air-drying varnish, with a suitable drier such as cobalt naphthenate. Such varnishes dry rapidly (hard dry in 3–5 hours, with further hardening up to about a week) to give a very hard finish. They show considerable resistance to mineral acids and alkalies, though with acetic acid (10 per cent) breakdown occurs in about one day (details in refs. 16 and 17). Adhesion to metals is excellent, and their abrasion resistance makes them suitable for the painting of objects subject to hard wear. They have, for instance, been used for floor varnishes.

(2) *Epoxide Resins Cross-Linked with Phenolic or Amino Resins*

A mixture of an epoxide resin with a phenolic or an amino resin, in a suitable solvent system, may be used as a stoving finish. Under the influence of heat, the system becomes cross-linked and a very hard but flexible film of very high chemical resistance is produced. The combination with a phenolic resin is more chemically resistant than that with an amino resin, but rather less flexible, and of somewhat darker colour. The phenolic combination is resistant to all concentrations of caustic soda (three months immersion test, ref. 16). Resistance to mineral acids is also very good ; as with epoxide ether resins, acetic acid appears to be resisted only in dilute form. Epoxide resins linked with amino resins are very suitable where flexibility and good adhesion are required (insulated wire, collapsible tubes etc.)

(3) *Epoxide Resins Cross-Linked with Amines*

The reactive groups of an epoxide resin can be cross-linked by an amine such as ethylene diamine or diethylene triamine. This reaction takes place at room temperature, hence the amine must be stored separately and added to the resin solution shortly before use (such mixed solutions keep for up to a few days, depending on the conditions. It is advantageous to keep the mixture some 16–20 hours before application, to prevent the development of " bloom " if dried in humid conditions). The air-dried film of an amine-linked epoxide resin is hard, flexible and has a chemical resistance which approaches that of a stoved phenolic-linked epoxide resin. This method of using epoxide resins has obvious applications to objects which cannot be stoved, and is much used for the protection of chemical plant and structural work. Alternatively, if stoving can be employed, the drying time is very short. An important advantage of amine linking is that, since no volatile products are produced by the reaction, quite thick films can be applied. Amines, in general, are toxic and care should be observed in using them ; paint manufacturers will be able to say what precautions should be taken when using their products.

Amides are also used for cross-linking epoxy resins and have some advantages over amines. Some curing agents are sensitive to moisture and should therefore be stored in dry conditions.

It will be seen from the above brief account that epoxide resins are very suitable for the protection of laboratory instruments and installations, particularly where exposure to chemically laden atmospheres and splashing with chemicals is to be encountered. They are not, however, completely proof against long immersion to all strong reagents. Since their behaviour in this respect is decidedly specific, enquiries as to suitability for a particular purpose should be made to the manufacturers. The literature gives little specific information as to maximum temperatures to which the epoxide varnishes may be safely subjected : stoving times of about 3 hours at 200° C. produce a golden yellow film with one of the " Araldite " coating resins, whereas 20 minutes at this temperature produces a colourless film, hence there is appreciable, though slow change at 200° C. Stoving temperatures up to 400° C. (in the case of wire enamel with a curing time of 20–50 seconds) are in use.

Any of the epoxy resins may be applied to all metals by dipping, brushing or spraying and all have good adhesive properties. Taken all-round, they give the best protection at present available which can be obtained by the use of lacquers, though as shown in the next section there are certain cases where a silicone lacquer is preferable. The type of epoxy resin chosen for a particular job is to some extent governed by the conditions of application (e.g. whether stoving is admissible or not), though as explained above they do vary somewhat in their properties. Unlike the cellulose lacquers, once they have dried they cannot be removed by solvent action, but require the application of destructive agents.

Silicone finishes

Among the many products based on the silicon-oxygen chain

$$-\overset{|}{O}-\overset{|}{Si}-\overset{|}{O}-\overset{|}{Si}-$$ and its variants are a number of resins, soluble in

liquids like xylene and toluene, which are suitable for the preparation of stoving varnishes. Generally speaking, those resins which give the hardest films are also the least flexible, but suitable blending of the different silicone resins enables control over hardness and flexibility to be obtained. The outstanding characteristic of silicone paints is their heat resistance. The pure resins tend to soften at high temperatures, but this is reduced by the addition of pigments and metallic driers containing cobalt, iron or zinc. White silicone-based gloss paints containing titanium dioxide may be kept at 200° C. indefinitely without yellowing or chalking. Aluminium paint based on silicone resin has a truly remarkable heat resistance. With suitable choice of the silicone resin, aluminium paints are found to give films which remain intact after prolonged exposure at 550° C.

The flow characteristics of silicone varnishes are not good, their adhesion to metals is not outstanding and they require stoving to produce the hardest films. It has been found, however, that some (not all) silicone resins can be blended with other resins to give varnishes and paints which have the good properties of both components. Silicone paints are water-repellent and have very good moisture resistance. Aluminium paints based on silicone resins have been successfully used for protecting steelwork exposed to the weather. Their resistance to moist gases containing oxides of sulphur is not, however, good, nor are they resistant to aromatic hydrocarbon solvents. They are unattacked at room temperatures by many acid, alkali and salt solutions.

Care should be taken in the preparation of metal surfaces which are to be silicone-painted. Adhesion to aluminium surfaces is satisfactory, but may be greatly improved by etching the metal in dilute alkali, or by dipping in a solution containing alcohol, phosphoric acid and zinc chromate. Steel surfaces may be cleaned chemically, or by sand-blasting or scratch-brushing, or by phosphating. This is particularly necessary if resistance to high temperatures is required, the presence of scale being fatal to adhesion at high temperatures. Further information is contained in ref. 18.

Silicone based paints are made by many paint manufacturing firms. Information on the basic materials may be obtained from Midland Silicones Ltd. in Great Britain and from the Dow-Corning Corporation in the United States.

Anti-corrosive finishes for metals (other than paints)

The use of paints, lacquers or varnishes on metallic surfaces is not always admissible or effective, and an alternative is to coat the metal with a more resistant metal, or in some cases to form an oxide or other layer on the surface which requires protection. Metallic coatings are usually made by electrodeposition. Though simple in principle, such processes call for great attention to detail to be satisfactory, and no attempt is made to describe them here. The chief properties of such coatings do, however, require to be known by the instrument designer and user and a description of them finds a place in this chapter. Beside these specialised techniques, there are a few relatively simple processes which can be carried out without difficulty, and a few of those which appear useful have been described. There are, in addition, various proprietary and other methods which may be found in ref. 19, where information on testing for corrosion-resistance may also be found.

Metallic Coatings

The metals most commonly used for plating are zinc, cadmium, nickel and chromium and they are widely used for the protection of iron and steel, and of brass. The following notes are based on information from ref. 19.

Zinc

Zinc coatings 0·0003–0·0005 in. thick (deposited electrolytically) may be used in industrial and urban conditions where the humidity is not very high. The films are adherent and uniform, somewhat harder than cadmium, and may be finished either matt or bright. Zinc is anodic to iron at ordinary temperatures, though cathodic in hot water. At room temperatures, therefore, breaks in the coating do not lead to enhanced rusting of the iron surface, and some protection is afforded by the zinc in the neighbourhood of a break. Zinc is attacked by hot steam, by most acids and alkalies, and also by materials containing sulphur, such as some vulcanised rubbers.

Zinc coatings are also applied by hot dipping, which is the process known as " galvanising, " used for protecting household articles of iron and steel, corrugated iron for roofs, wire netting etc. This gives very good protection to iron, but since the variation in thickness is considerable the method is not used when ·close tolerances are required. Another method of applying zinc is the sheradising process, which consists in heating the articles to be coated in zinc dust at temperatures between 350 and 375° C. in a closed rotating system.

Cadmium

Cadmium coatings 0·0003 in. thick are suitable for protecting iron in marine atmospheres and in conditions of high humidity. Cadmium is not so suitable as zinc in industrial atmospheres. It forms adherent though soft coatings, which may be either matt or bright. The polarity of cadmium to iron is variable, but it is not generally strongly cathodic ; hence no intensification of attack need be feared, as with copper. It is attacked by most acids, and by sulphur-containing compounds, but has good resistance to alkalies. It may be plated on to brass, and is so used to prevent bimetallic corrosion between brass which would otherwise be in contact with light alloys. In such application, much better protection is afforded by first plating the copper-rich material with tin or nickel, followed by cadmium.[11]

Nickel

Nickel films are used to protect steel in marine and urban applications (minimum 0·002 in.). Unlike zinc and cadmium, nickel is cathodic to iron (also to zinc and aluminium). Porosity and breaks in the coating will therefore lead to increased corrosion of the underlying steel. Nickel coatings are porous and uneven unless suitable plating techniques are employed ; avoidance of sharp edges will assist in obtaining an intact coating. Nickel is hard and abrasion-resistant ; in industrial atmospheres nickel coatings do not have a long life, however. The metal is not very resistant to acids, but resistance to strong alkalies and to steam is good. At ordinary temperatures sulphur-containing materials do not affect nickel. Black nickel deposits can be obtained ; they are said to be harder than white nickel, but are no better in respect of corrosion resistance.

Nickel may be deposited chemically without applied E.M.F. by the Kanigen process on aluminium, brass, cobalt, copper, iron (cast or wrought), nickel and steel (including stainless), but not on antimony, bismuth, cadmium, lead or tin ; soldered or brazed parts cannot usually be coated in this way. The process was developed by the General American Transportation Corporation of the United States, and is operated in the United Kingdom by Albright and Wilson.

Kanigen nickel plate consists of an amorphous nickel-phosphorus alloy (about 8·5 per cent phosphorus) which is uniform to ± 10 per cent over the most intricate shape, very adherent and more corrosion-resistant than electrolytically deposited nickel. In a thickness of 0·0002 in. it appears to be non-porous. In addition to its use for protection against corrosion, Kanigen plate is used to provide a wear-resistant coating, and also for building up worn parts which have become undersize.

Chromium

Chromium-plating finds a wide variety of applications for the protection of iron in industrial and marine atmospheres in conditions of high humidity. It is commonly applied to nickel or nickel-copper undercoats. The total thickness of these coats should not be less than 0·002 in., to which the chromium should contribute not less than 0·0001 in. Chromium is cathodic to iron, and tends to be porous unless the plating technique is carefully attended to. On porous coatings, rust spots rapidly develop, and chromium coatings vary greatly in the degree of protection which they afford. Where a good polish is important, the use of soft undercoatings like copper and nickel (which can easily be polished) is advantageous, for a chromium deposit on a polished surface requires less working to produce a good surface than one which is on a rougher substrate. Chromium is very hard and resistant to abrasion. It is resistant to many acids (not, however, to hydrochloric acid), to alkalies and to sulphur compounds. Resistance is very good at high temperatures.

Various processes for protecting iron and steel

Many processes have been devised for coating the surface of iron or steel with black iron oxide. Such coatings are often in some degree porous, and it is usual to seal them in some way, often with oil. An alternative is to use paint, varnish or enamel for sealing, and such a combination affords good protection. Oxide coatings sealed with oil are not suitable in severe conditions, but find considerable use for steel objects which are subject to handling in reasonably dry situations, especially if the coating is occasionally oiled and wiped to renew the sealing. It is important that such coatings should be sealed before handling, which might allow acid perspiration to contaminate the coating. Many proprietary processes exist[19] and have their advantages. For occasional use, however, oxidation in an alkaline bath of sodium or potassium nitrate gives very satisfactory results. The properties of the metal are not affected, and the dimensional changes are very small. Cast iron and some special steels require a preliminary treatment in 5–10 per cent hydrofluoric acid, but mild and carbon steels only require a moderate degree of cleaning. Alternative baths are

$$\left. \begin{array}{lll} \text{NaOH} & 1200\text{--}1500 & \text{g./l.} \\ \text{NaNO}_3 & 300 & \text{g./l.} \end{array} \right\} \text{ in water}$$

Treat for 5–30 minutes at 138–150° C.

and

$$\left. \begin{array}{lll} \text{NaOH} & 500 & \text{g./l.} \\ \text{KNO}_3 & 310 & \text{g./l.} \end{array} \right\} \text{ in water}$$

Treat for 10 minutes at 140° C.

The solution for either bath should be just on the boil, and is best used in a cast or welded iron or steel container. Care should be used, as the solution may sputter. Thorough washing is needed to get rid of alkali, and the objects may be sealed without drying by immersion in " soluble oil." If dried and oiled subsequently, precautions against contamination must be taken. We have found this process very useful for coating small hand tools, measuring instruments etc.

An alternative process (Browning process [20]) is to coat the steel with a thin film of tallow or of linseed oil and stove for 30 minutes at a temperature between 200° and 400° C. Several treatments may be applied. The film is subsequently impregnated with oil, and if the oil is renewed from time to time good protection is said to be given under corrosive atmospheric conditions.

Chemical polishing of steel

A method of polishing steel by chemical attack has recently been described [21] ; this has several applications and might have been considered in other chapters, but since it is of interest in connection with anti-corrosion treatments an account of this and other uses is given here. Iron or steel which has been abraded on a series of emery papers, ending with 0, may be considerably smoothed and to some extent polished by immersion for a period of 30–60 minutes (at room temperatures) in the following solution.

Oxalic acid (crystals)	25 g.
Hydrogen peroxide	13 g.
Sulphuric acid	0·1 g.
Water	1 litre

The steel is degreased, for example by immersion in a hot alkaline metal cleaner, given a short dip in dilute sulphuric acid, rinsed and suspended in the polishing fluid. A considerable degree of smoothing takes place with the periodic and copious evolution of gas, and a noticeable degree of polishing is obtained, which diminishes after the attainment of the maximum effect owing to grain etching which takes place in the later stages. The process may be used, in place of polishing by abrasives, simply to improve the appearance of the metal, but has additional advantages. The polished surface has an increased degree of resistance to mild corrosive conditions, ascribed to the formation of a smooth, dense oxide film about 60 A thick. This film forms a very suitable base on which to deposit nickel electrolytically, for the adhesion of the nickel is very good. In a test, nickel was deposited on pieces of steel treated as above and kept wet in air for times up to 8 minutes before commencing the nickel plating. In each case the adhesion value was of the order of 50 tons/sq. in., the nickel layer shearing at this value. The significance of the time delay of 8 minutes lies in the fact that with the usual etching treatments given to steel, deposition of nickel should follow within 30 seconds if good adhesion is to be obtained.

The removal of metal by the oxalic acid bath is remarkably uniform. A test piece remained flat within the original limits of 1×10^{-5} in. after treatment up to within a few thousandths of an inch from edges and corners. For mild steel, the rate of removal is about 0.4×10^{-3} in./h. Removal of metal is therefore well under control, and could be used in some cases in place of more conventional finishing. Obviously it is particularly useful when the size, but not the shape, is to be altered. It has been successfully used for the recovery of gear wheels which have grown oversize during heat treatments. The smooth surface obtained results in lower friction in the resulting train. Another interesting application is the reduction of thin steel foil, and strong, non-porous foil down to 0.3×10^{-3} in. has been made in this way.

Oxide coatings on aluminium and its alloys

The customary method of protecting aluminium and its alloys is by anodic oxidation, obtained by making the metal the anode in an electrolyte of chromic, sulphuric or oxalic acid. With suitable current densities, very adherent, hard films are produced. Initially such films are porous in the outer parts with a barrier coat next the metal, and will readily absorb oil (and perspiration) as well as many dyes. Boiling in water removes this porosity, apparently because the amorphous Al_2O_3 film is thereby converted into a compact, crystalline form. Details of the process are given in ref. 19. Chromic acid treatments produce soft films of good corrosion resistance, and very hard, wear-resistant golden-yellow films result when oxalic acid is used. With sulphuric acid, the properties depend considerably on the concentration and current density employed. Anodising produces a very good foundation for the application of paints, varnishes etc.

Oxide films may also be produced on aluminium by a simple immersion process, without electrolysis. One such, the M.B.V. process [19,22] gives very adherent films, which are, however, not so resistant to abrasion as anodised films. The process is suitable for pure aluminium and to most of its alloys except those containing considerable amounts of copper. The metal is immersed for 4–5 minutes in an aqueous solution containing 5 per cent crystalline sodium carbonate and $1\frac{1}{2}$ per cent sodium or potassium chromate. The solution, for which pure chemicals must be used, is employed at a temperature of 90–100° C. The treatment is followed by rinsing in water and drying. Greater hardness and corrosion resistance is obtained by a further treatment for 15 minutes in 3–5 per cent aqueous sodium silicate solution at 90° C., after which the objects are rinsed and dried. The silicate finish may be sealed by heating in a flame.

Magnesium and its alloys

Anodic oxidation, to a suitable schedule, gives protection but it is desirable to apply in addition a coating of paint. Phenolic resin primers containing zinc chromate are recommended, followed by finishing coats of phenolic resin varnishes pigmented with aluminium. Epoxy resin varnishes would doubtless also be suitable.

Many immersion processes have been described, some of which are unsuitable for machined surfaces because of the amount of metal removed during the application. The following process (Dow No. 8) is free from this objection.

1. Immerse for 5 minutes in an aqueous solution containing 15–20 per cent (by weight) hydrofluoric acid at room temperature and wash in water.

2. Boil for 45 minutes in a bath containing 3 per cent ammonium sulphate, 3 per cent sodium dichromate and 0·25 per cent ammonium hydroxide in water. Wash in water.

3. Boil for 5 minutes in a solution containing 1 per cent arsenious oxide. Wash in cold and in hot water and dry.

Other immersion processes are described in ref. 19.

The use of hydrofluoric acid is avoided in the chrome-sulphate (Dow No. 11) process, which produces a golden-brown film on magnesium alloys without serious attack of the metal. The treatment consists in immersing the alloy for 15 minutes in an aqueous solution containing 5 per cent magnesium sulphate and 3·7 per cent sodium dichromate (by weight), at 70° C.

Polyethylene protective coatings on metals

The use of polyethylene powder for producing a tough protective coating on metals has been developed by the Telegraph Construction and Maintenance Company Ltd., the name Telcothene being given to the powder. The chief advantage of the process is the complete protection which can be obtained against many corrosive chemicals, such as acids and alkalies. The material is used, for example, for coating vats and tanks. It is available in colours and in the normal colourless, translucent form.

Application may be made by dipping the object (heated to 140–

260° C.) in the powder, shaking off the excess and stoving at 160° C., which will give a smooth, even coat of polymer. Instead of dipping, the heated metal may be sprayed with unheated powder, and this is followed by stoving. A third method is to spray the powder through a flame on to the heated metal, which gives a continuous film without subsequent heating. The first method has the advantage that nothing is required except a supply of powder and an oven.

The adhesion of polyethylene is poor in the case of brass, copper and lead, and it is recommended that with these metals the whole object should be coated, so that the shrinkage which occurs on cooling will cause the film to grip tightly. When coating iron, shot- or sandblasting will improve the adhesion ; phosphate coating of the metal is also useful. Aluminium, when clean (but covered with the oxide film which forms on the metal in air) adheres well to polyethylene.

Although polyethylene is not dissolved by any chemicals at room temperature, it is swollen by hydrocarbons and some other liquids, and is not a suitable coating when used in contact with such liquids. It is not suitable for use in concentrated sulphuric and nitric acids, though proof against concentrated hydrofluoric acid and strong alkalies. More detailed information may be obtained from the manufacturers.

REFERENCES

[1] VERNON, W. H. J., *Trans. Faraday Soc.*, **31** (1935), 1668.
[2] VERNON, W. H. J., *Research*, **5** (1952), 54.
[3] WACHTER, A., and STILLMAN, N., U.S.P. 2,419,327; 2,432,839–40 (1947).
[4] WACHTER, A., and STILLMAN, N., B.P. 600,328 (1948).
[5] WACHTER, A., *Mod. Packaging*, **22** (1948), 147.
[6] WACHTER, A., SKEI, T., and STILLMAN, N., *Corrosion*, **7** (1951), 284.
[7] BENNISTER, H. L., *Research*, **5** (1952), 424.
[8] Shell V.P.I. (Shell Chemicals Ltd., London, 1952).
[9] STROUD, E. G., and VERNON, W. H. J., *J. Appl. Chem.*, **2** (1952), 178.
[10] EVANS, U. R., *Metallic Corrosion, Passivity and Protection* (Arnold, London, 1946); EVANS, U. R., *Research*, **5** (1952), 220.
[11] "Corrosion and its Prevention at Bimetallic Contacts" (H.M. Stationery Office, London, 1956).
[12] WALFORD, J. G., *Trans. Soc. Inst. Technology*, **7** (1955), 124.
[13] THORNHILL, R. S., *Research*, **5** (1952), 324.
[14] HOLLIS, H., *Trans. Inst. Metal Finishing*, **30** (1954), 31.
[15] MARMION, W. J., *Research*, **7** (1954), 351.
[16] WHEELER, R. N., *J. Oil and Colour Chem. Assoc.*, **36** (1953), 305.
[17] BATES, G. C., *Metal Finishing J.*, (March 1955).
[18] Silicone resins for protective coatings. Midland Silicones Technical Data Sheet L1–5 (September 1955).
[19] GAILER, J. W., and VAUGHAN, E. J., *Protective Coatings for Metals* (Charles Griffin & Co. Ltd., London, 1950).
[20] SILMAN, H., *Met. Ind.*, **66** (1945), 21, 330.
[21] MARSHALL, W. A., *Research*, **7** (1954), 89. U.K. Pat. App. 16578/51.
[22] " Aluminium Finishing Processes " (British Aluminium Co., Ltd.).

APPENDIX I

COMPUTATION OF A CORRECTOR PLATE FOR A SCHMIDT CAMERA

FIG. A.1 shows an approximate method of obtaining the profile of a Schmidt corrector plate in terms of depth of glass to be removed from a flat disc. The method is sufficiently accurate for practical purposes, since the final figuring must of necessity be done in conjunction with an optical test.

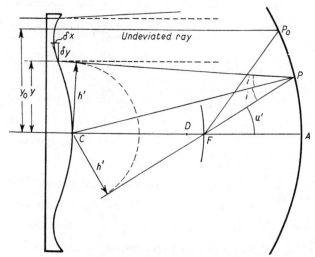

FIG. A.1.—Schmidt camera.

Referring to Figure A.1, the height y_o of the undeviated ray is first found. It has been found empirically that if $y_o = 0\cdot866$ ($\frac{1}{2}\sqrt{3}$) of the radius of the corrector plate the chromatic aberration is a minimum. Then if R is the radius of curvature of the mirror, $y_o/R = \sin i_o$ and $CF = FP_o = y_o \operatorname{cosec} 2i_o$.

For any ray at height y, $\sin u' = y/CF$ since $y = h'$, and $\sin i = h'/R = y/R$. The correction $h' = y \cos\delta$ can be applied in a second computation but is hardly necessary. The deviation $\delta = 2i - u'$ and since the plate can be considered as a prism of small angle, the prism angle will be given by $\delta/(n - 1) = \delta x/\delta y$.

491

By taking small but finite steps for δy it is possible to calculate δx and thus find the co-ordinates (x, y) of the plate surface. In the table on p. 494 a profile has been computed for a radius of curvature of 50 and a plate diameter of 25 arbitrary units.

REFERENCES

Bibliography on Reflecting Optics

ALDIS, H. L., " Fourplate Theorems," *Phot. J.*, **24** (1900), 291.

BAKER, J. G., " The Solid Schmidt Camera,"*Proc. Amer. Phil. Soc.*, **82** (1940), 323.

BAKER, J. G., " A Family of Flat Field Cameras Equivalent in Performance to the Schmidt Camera," *ibid.* 339.

BALLARD, STANLEY S., " Bibliography on Reflecting Optics 1925–50," University of Michigan, 1950.

BOUWERS, A., " Achievements in Optics," (Elsevier), 2nd Edition, 1950.

BOUWERS, A., " Reflecting Microscopes," *Proc. Opt. Conv.*, (Chapman & Hall). London. 1950.

BURCH, C. R., " On the Optical See-Saw Diagram," *M.N.R.A.S.*, **102** (1942), 159.

BURCH, C. R., " On Aspheric Anastigmatic Systems," *Proc. Phys. Soc.*, **55** (1943), 433.

BURCH, C. R., " Reflecting Microscopes," *Nature*, **152** (1943), 748.

BURCH, C. R., " Flatfielded Singlet Aplanats," *Proc. Phys. Soc.*, **57** (1945), 567.

BURCH, C. R., " On Reflecting Microscopes," *ibid.* **59** (1947), 41.

BURCH, C. R., " Semi Aplanat Reflecting Microscopes," *ibid.* **59** (1947), 47.

COLACEVICH, A., " Theory of Two New Astronomical Telescopes of the Schmidt Type," *Atti. Fond. Giorgio Ronchi*, **1** (1946), 139.

COX, H. W., " Construction of a Schmidt Camera," *J. Brit. Astr. Assn.*, **48** (1938), 308, *ibid.* **50** (1939), 61, *ibid.* **51** (1941), 174.

DE GROOT, W., " Optical Aberrations in Lens and Mirror Systems," *Philips Tech. Rev.*, **9** (1947), 301.

FREUNDLICH, E. F., " The Development of the Astronomical Telescope," *J. Sci. Inst.*, **27** (1950), 233.

FREUNDLICH, E. F., " Schmidt-Cassegrain Telescope at Dundee," *Nature*, **165** (1950), 703.

FRIEDMAN, H. S., " Method of Computing Corrector Plates for Schmidt Systems for Rear Projection," *J.O.S.A.*, **37** (1947), 488.

GABOR, D., " Improvements in Photographic Objectives," Brit. Pat., **544** (1941), 694.

GREY, D. S., " A Family of Catadioptric Microscope Objectives," *Proc. Opt. Conv.* (Chapman & Hall), London, 1950.

LINFOOT, E. H., " Applications of the Schmidt Principle to Microscopy," *J. Sci. Inst.*, **15** (1945), 405.

LINFOOT, E. H., " On Some Optical Systems Employing Aspherical Surfaces," *M.N.R.A.S.*, **103** (1943), 210.

LINFOOT, E. H., " Schmidt-Cassegrain Systems and Their Application to Astronomical Photography," *ibid.* **104** (1944), 48.

LINFOOT, E. H., and HAWKINS, D. G., " An Improved Type of Schmidt Camera," *ibid.* **105** (1945), 334.

LINFOOT, E. H., " Achromatized Plate-Mirror Systems," *Proc. Phys. Soc.*, **57** (1945), 199.

LINFOOT, E. H., " Recent Advances in Astronomical Camera Design," *Phot. J.*, **88 B** (1948), 58.

LINFOOT, E. H., and WOLF, E., " On the Corrector Plates of Schmidt Cameras," *J.O.S.A.*, **39** (1949), 752.

LINFOOT, E. H., " On the Optics of the Schmidt Camera," *M.N.R.A.S.*, **109** (1949), 279.

LINFOOT, E. H., and WAYMAN, P. A., " On the Aberrations of the Field Flattened Schmidt Camera," *ibid.* **109** (1949), 535.

LINFOOT, E. H., " The Modern Reflecting Telescope," *Proc. Opt. Conv.* (Chapman & Hall), London, 1950.

LUCY, F. A., " Exact and Approximate Computation of Schmidt Cameras," *J.O.S.A.*, **30** (1940), 251. **31** (1941), 358.

MAKSUTOV, D. D., " New Catadioptric Meniscus Systems," *J.O.S.A.*, **34** (1944), 270.

MARTIN, L. C., " Wide Aperture Aplanatic Single Lenses," *Proc. Phys. Soc.*, **56** (1944), 104.

SCHMIDT, BERNARD, " Ein Lichtstarkes Komafreies Spiegelsystem," *Zentralzeitung,* **52** (1931), 25.

SCHWARTZSCHILD, K., " Theorie der Spiegeltelescope," *Gottingen Abhandlungen,* **2** (1905).

SMILEY, C. H., " A Note on the Schmidt Camera," *J. Brit. Astr. Assn.*, **49** (1938), 34.

SYNGE, J. L., " Theory of the Schmidt Telescope," *J.O.S.A.*, **33** (1943), 129.

WASSERMAN, G. D., and WOLF, E., " On the Theory of Aplanatic Aspherical Surfaces," *Proc. Phys. Soc.*, **62 B** (1949), 2.

WAYMAN, P. A., " The Monocentric Schmidt-Cassegrain Camera," *ibid.* **63 B** (1950), 553.

WOLF, E., " On the Designing of Aspherical Surfaces,". *ibid.* **61** (1948), 494.

WORMSER, E. M., " On the Design of Wide-Angle Schmidt Optical Systems," *J.O.S.A.*, **40** (1950), 412.

WYNNE, C. G., " New Wide-Angle Catadioptric Systems," *M.N.R.A.S.*, **107** (1947), 356.

WYNNE, C. G., " Field Correctors for Parabolic Mirrors," *Proc. Phys. Soc.*, **62 B** (1949), 772.

WYNNE, C. G., " Chromatic Correction of Wide Aperture Catadioptric Systems," *Nature,* **160** (1947), 91.

Discussion, " The Designing of Non-Spherical Systems," *Proc. Phys. Soc.*, **55** (1943), 481.

Some further references, particularly to articles on reflecting microscopes, will be found on page 345.

TABLE A.1—*Calculation of Schmidt Corrector Plate*

$$\sin u' = \frac{y}{CF}$$

$$\sin i = \frac{y}{R}$$

$$\delta = 2i - u'$$

$$\frac{\delta x}{\delta y} = \frac{\delta}{n-1}$$

$$\delta x = \delta y \tan\frac{\delta}{n-1}$$

Radius of Corrector = 25

y_o = height of undeviated ray = $\dfrac{\sqrt{3}}{2} \times 25 = 21\cdot65$

Radius of curvature of mirror = $R = 50$

$\sin i_o = \dfrac{y_o}{R} = \dfrac{21\cdot65}{50} = 0\cdot4330$

$\qquad\qquad = \sin 25°\ 39'$

$2i_o = 51°\ 18'$

$CF = y_o \operatorname{cosec} 2i_o = 21\cdot65 \times 1\cdot2813$

$\qquad\quad = 27\cdot74$

$\log 27\cdot74 = 1\cdot4431$

y	$\log y$	$\log \sin u'$	u'	$\sin i$	i	$2i$	δ	$\dfrac{\delta x}{\delta y}$	δx	δt
25	1·3979	$\bar{1}$·9548	65° 18′	0·5000	30° 00′	60° 00′	− 5° 18′	−10° 36′	0·1871	0·3221
24	1·3802	$\bar{1}$·9371	59 54	0·4800	28 41	57 22	− 2 32	− 5 04	0·0886	0·1350
23	1·3617	$\bar{1}$·9186	56 00	0·4600	27 23	54 46	− 1 14	− 2 28	0·0431	0·0464
22	1·3424	$\bar{1}$·8993	52 28	0·4400	26 06	52 12	− 0 16	− 0 32	0·0033	0·0033
21·65	1·3355	$\bar{1}$·8924	51 18	0·4330	25 39	51 18	0	0	0	0
21	1·3222	$\bar{1}$·8791	49 12	0·4200	24 50	49 40	+ 0 28	+ 0 56	0·0163	0·0163
20	1·3010	$\bar{1}$·8579	46 08	0·4000	23 35	47 10	1 02	2 04	0·0361	0·0524
19	1·2788	$\bar{1}$·8357	43 14	0·3800	22 20	44 40	1 26	2 52	0·0501	0·1025
18	1·2553	$\bar{1}$·8122	40 28	0·3600	21 06	42 12	1 44	3 28	0·0606	0·1631
17	1·2304	$\bar{1}$·7873	37 48	0·3400	19 52	39 44	1 56	3 52	0·0676	0·2307
16	1·2041	$\bar{1}$·7610	35 13	0·3200	18 40	37 20	2 07	4 14	0·0740	0·3047
15	1·1761	$\bar{1}$·7330	32 44	0·3000	17 28	34 56	2 12	4 24	0·0769	0·3816
14	1·1461	$\bar{1}$·7030	30 18	0·2800	16 16	32 32	2 14	4 21	0·0781	0·4597
13	1·1139	$\bar{1}$·6708	27 57	0·2600	15 04	30 08	2 11	4 22	0·0763	0·5350
12	1·0792	$\bar{1}$·6361	25 38	0·2400	13 53	27 46	2 08	4 16	0·0746	0·6096
11	1·0414	$\bar{1}$·5983	23 22	0·2200	12 43	25 26	2 04	4 08	0·0723	0·6819
10	1·000	$\bar{1}$·5569	21 08	0·2000	11 32	23 04	1 56	3 52	0·0676	0·7495
9	0·9542	$\bar{1}$·5111	18 56	0·1800	10 22	20 44	1 48	3 36	0·0629	0·8124
8	0·9031	$\bar{1}$·4600	16 46	0·1600	9 12	18 24	1 38	3 16	0·0571	0·8695
7	0·8451	$\bar{1}$·4020	14 37	0·1400	8 03	16 06	1 29	2 58	0·0519	0·9214
6	0·7782	$\bar{1}$·3351	12 30	0·1200	6 54	13 48	1 18	2 36	0·0454	0·9668
5	0·6990	$\bar{1}$·2559	10 23	0·1000	5 45	11 30	1 07	2 14	0·0396	1·0064
4	0·6021	$\bar{1}$·1590	8 18	0·0800	4 36	9 12	0 54	1 48	0·0314	1·0378
3	0·4771	$\bar{1}$·0340	6 12	0·0600	3 27	6 54	0 42	1 24	0·0244	1·0622
2	0·3010	$\bar{2}$·8579	4 09	0·0400	2 18	4 36	0 27	0 54	0·0157	1·0779
1	0	$\bar{2}$·5569	2 03	0·0200	1 09	2 18	0 15	0 30	0·0087	1·0866

APPENDIX II

NOTES ON RAY-TRACING

1. *Tables.*—The books listed below give full details of ray-tracing and recommend suitable tables. Five-figure tables of logarithms of numbers and of the circular functions are sufficiently accurate but require considerable interpolation which is tiresome and takes time. For those who only occasionally make computations it is quicker to use seven-figure tables as recommended below. For professional use calculating machines are almost essential and are used with tables of natural sines, etc.

2. *Data.*—The data should be carefully tabulated and the logs and co-logs written down. The co-log can be found by inspection by making up each figure to 9, except the last which is made up to 10. Thus the co-log of $\bar{1}\cdot12345$ (9·12345) is 0·87655.

3. *Formulae.*—The standard formulae are as follows :—

Incident ray at height Y parallel to axis ; $\sin I = Y/r$

Incident ray making an angle U with the axis and cutting the axis at a distance L from the vertex ;

$$\frac{L - r}{\sin I} = \frac{r}{\sin U} ; \quad \sin I = \frac{(L - r)\sin U}{r}$$

At refraction ; $n \sin I = n' \sin I'$

After refraction ; $U + I = U' + I' ; \quad U_2 = U'_1$, etc.

For the refracted ray ;

$$\frac{L' - r}{\sin I'} = \frac{r}{\sin U'} ; \quad L' = \frac{r \sin I'}{\sin U'} + r$$

For the next surface ; $L_2 = L'_1 - t$, etc.

For long radii and as a check formula throughout ;

$$\frac{L \sin U}{\cos \frac{1}{2}(I - U)} = \frac{L' \sin U'}{\cos \frac{1}{2}(I' - U')}$$

Another check formula ; $n(L - r)\sin U = n'(L' - r)\sin U'$

4. *Paraxial rays.*—Use the same incident height.

$I = Y/r ; \quad (L - r)/I = r/U ;$

$nI = n'I' ; \quad U + I = U' + I' ;$

$(L' - r)/I' = r/U' ; \quad L_2 = L'_1 - t.$

For long radii, $LU = L'U'$ and as a check, $n(L - r)U = n'(L' - r)U'$

5. *Calculating Machine.*—The same formulae may be used tabulated as in the following table which is the paraxial ray-trace for the same data as in Table A.2

Radii	9·116	− 8·554	− 86·207
n	1·0	1·5097	1·62258
$\overline{n'}$	1·5097	1·62258	1·0
U	0	037036	0264220
$I = U(L - r)/r$	109697	152555	0378447
$I' = In/n'$	072661	141941	0614060
U'	037036	0264220	0499833
$L' = rI'/U' + r$	27·0007	37·3987	19·70091
t	0·32	0·13	
New L	26·6807	37·2687	

$$E.F.L. = Y/U' = 20·00668$$

6. *Oblique rays.*—The computation of oblique rays is made with the same formulae and their intersections with a line perpendicular to the optical axis, drawn through the paraxial focus, is found. For the interpretation of the results the reader should consult a text book on Applied Optics.

BOOKS ON APPLIED OPTICS AND RAY-TRACING

Applied Optics and Optical Design, by A. E. Conrady (Oxford).
  A comprehensive treatise intended for the specialist.
A System of Applied Optics, by H. Dennis Taylor (Macmillan). (Out of print.)
Optical Design and Lens Computation, by B. K. Johnson (Hatton Press).
  Numerical examples based on Conrady.
Technical Optics, Vols. I and II, by L. C. Martin (Pitman).
  A good general text book on Applied Optics.

TABLES

Chambers' Seven-figure Mathematical Tables.
  Contains logs of numbers to seven figures and the natural and logarithmic circular functions to 1 minute.
Shortrede's Seven-figure Tables of the Logarithms of Circular functions for every second.
Bremiker's Five-figure Tables of Logarithms of numbers and of circular functions to 0·01 degree. (H.M.S.O.)

Table A.2—*Ray-tracing*

Ray Trace Through a Cemented Doublet

DATA	Radii (inches)	Thickness (inches)	Refractive index (n_d)	Logarithms	
r_1 + 9·116				log r_1 0·95980	log $1/r_1$ $\bar{1}$·04020
	0·32	1·50970		log n_1 0·17889	log $1/n_1$ $\bar{1}$·82111
r_2− 8·554				log r_2 0·93217(−)	log $1/r_2$ $\bar{1}$·06783(−)
	0·13	1·62258		log n_2 0·21021	log $1/n_2$ $\bar{1}$·78979
r_3 − 86·207				log r_3 1·93554(−)	log $1/r_3$ $\bar{2}$·06446(−)

Diameter 2·0 in.

Schedule		Marginal ray		Paraxial ray	
	Y_1		1·0		
log Y_1	I_1	0·00000	+ 6° 17′ 53″		+ 0·109698
log $1/r_1$	I'_1	$\bar{1}$·04020 +	+ 4° 10′ 01″		+ 0·072662
log sin I_1	$I_1 - I'_1$	$\bar{1}$·04020 +	+ 2° 07′ 52″		+ 0·037036
log $1/n_1$		$\bar{1}$·82111 +			
log sin I'_1	log sin U'_1	$\bar{2}$·86131 +	$\bar{2}$·57038 +	$\bar{2}$·86131 +	$\bar{2}$·56862 +
log $1/\sin U'_1$	$L'_1 - r_1$	1·42962 +	+ 17·813	1·43138 +	+ 17·8850
log r_1	$r_1 - r_2 - t_1$	0·95980 +	+ 17·350	0·95980 +	+ 17·350
log $(L'_1 - r_1)$	$L_2 - r_2$	1·25073 +	+ 35·163	1·25249 +	+ 35·2350
log $(L_2 - r_2)$	I_2	1·54609 +	− 8° 47′ 34″	1·54697 +	− 0·152552
log $1/r_2$	I'_2	$\bar{1}$·06783 −	− 8° 10′ 36″	$\bar{1}$·06783 −	− 0·141938
log sin U_2	$I_2 - I'_2$	$\bar{2}$·57038 +	− 36′ 58″	$\bar{2}$·56862 +	− 0·010614
log sin I_2	U_2	$\bar{1}$·18430 −	+ 2° 07′ 52″	$\bar{1}$·18342 −	+ 0·037036
log n_1/n_2	U'_2	$\bar{1}$·96868 +	+ 1° 30′ 54″	1·96868 +	+ 0·026422
log sin I'_2	log sin U'_2	$\bar{1}$·15298 −	$\bar{2}$·42224 +	$\bar{1}$·15210 −	$\bar{2}$·42197 +
log $1/\sin U'_2$	$L_2' - r_2$	1·57776 +	+ 46·016	1·57803 +	+ 45·9515
log r_2	$r_2 - r_3 - t_2$	0·93217 −	+ 77·523	0·93217 −	+ 77·523
log $(L_2' - r_2)$	$L_3 - r_3$	1·66291 +	+ 123·539	1·66230 +	+ 123·4745
log L_3	L_3	1·57208 +	+ 37·332		(+37·2673)

Schedule		Marginal ray		Paraxial ray	
$\log (L_3 - r_3)$	I_3	$2\cdot09180\ +$	$-\ 2°\ 10'\ 17''$	$2\cdot09158\ +$	$-\ 0\cdot037845$
$\log 1/r_3$	I'_3	$\bar{2}\cdot06446\ -$	$-\ 3°\ 31'\ 29''$	$\bar{2}\cdot06446\ -$	$-\ 0\cdot061407$
$\log \sin U_3$	$I_3 - I'_3$	$\bar{2}\cdot42224\ +$	$+\ 1°\ 21'\ 12''$	$\bar{2}\cdot42197\ +$	$+\ 0\cdot023562$
$\log \sin I_3$	U_3	$\bar{2}\cdot57850\ -$	$+\ 1°\ 30'\ 54''$	$\bar{2}\cdot57801\ -$	$+\ 0\cdot026422$
$\log n_2$	U_3'	$0\cdot21021\ +$	$+\ 2°\ 52'\ 06''$	$0\cdot21021\ +$	$+\ 0\cdot049984$
$\log \sin I_3'$	$\log \sin U_3'$	$\bar{2}\cdot78871\ -$	$2\cdot69933\ +$	$\bar{2}\cdot78822\ -$	$\bar{2}\cdot69883\ +$
$\log 1/\sin U'_3$	$L'_3 - r_3$	$1\cdot30067\ +$	$+\ 105\cdot9059$	$1\cdot30117\ +$	$+\ 105\cdot9083$
$\log r_3$	r_3	$1\cdot93554\ -$	$-\ 86\cdot207$	$1\cdot93554\ -$	$-\ 86\cdot207$
$\log (L'_3 - r_3)$	L'_3	$2\cdot02492\ +$	$+\ 19\cdot6989$	$2\cdot02493\ +$	$+\ 19\cdot7013$
$\log Y_1$		$0\cdot00000$		$0\cdot00000$	
$\log 1/\sin U'_3$		$1\cdot30067\ +$		$1\cdot30117\ +$	
$\log Y_1/\sin U'_3$	$Y_1/\sin U'_3$	$1\cdot30067\ +$	$+\ 19\cdot9835$	$1\cdot30117\ +$	$+\ 20\cdot0067$
$\log L_3$	$\tfrac{1}{2}I_3$	$1\cdot57208\ +$	$-\ 1°\ 05'\ 09''$		
$\log \sin U_3$	$\tfrac{1}{2}U_3$	$\bar{2}\cdot42224\ +$	$+\ \ \ 45'\ 27''$		
$\log 1/\cos \tfrac{1}{2}(I_3-U_3)$	$\tfrac{1}{2}(I_3-U_3)$	$0\cdot00022\ +$	$-\ 1°\ 50'\ 36''$	Check for long	
			$-\ 1°\ 45'\ 45''$	radius and accept	
$\log 1/\sin U'_3$	$\tfrac{1}{2}I'_3$ $\tfrac{1}{2}U'_3$	$1\cdot30067\ +$	$+\ 1°\ 26'\ 03''$	value of L'_3	
$\log \cos \tfrac{1}{2}(I'_3-U'_3)$	$\tfrac{1}{2}(I'_3-U'_3)$	$\bar{1}\cdot99932\ +$	$-\ 3°\ 11'\ 48''$		

$$\underline{\underline{\log L'_3}} \qquad \underline{\underline{L'_3}} \qquad 1\cdot29453\ + \qquad +\ 19\cdot7029$$

Spherical aberration (para–marg) $= 19\cdot7013 - 19\cdot7029 = -\ 0\cdot0016$

(OSC) = Offence against the sine condition = Coma

$$= 1 - U'_3 L'_3 \text{ (parax.)} / \sin U'_3 L'_3 \text{ (marg.)}$$

$$= 1 - \frac{20\cdot0067 \times 19\cdot7013}{19\cdot9835 \times 19\cdot7029} \qquad\qquad = +\ 0\cdot0013$$

APPENDIX III

ANGULAR MEASUREMENT

Many methods have been devised for the measurement of angles and Table A.3 shows how the various units of angular measure are related.

The commonest division of the circle is in degrees (360), minutes (60) and seconds (60), but this division has obvious disadvantages when calculating machines are used and most computers are now using degrees and decimals of a degree. The grade (400) and its centigrade minutes and seconds has many advantages but has not been adopted to any extent except in Germany. The radian is the most useful theoretical measure and its extension into milliemes (mils) is of great practical value. The radian is the angle subtended at the centre of a circle by an arc equal in length to the radius and the measure of an angle in radians is given by the simple relation :—

Angle in radians = arc/radius.

For practical purposes an angle of 1/1000 radian is called a millieme, or mil, and is the angle subtended by (say) 1 yd. at a distance of 1,000 yd. Since it is not possible to divide a circular scale in radian measure, because of its incommensurability, the practical mil of 1/6400 circle has been adopted.

	Degrees	Minutes	Seconds	Grades	Centigrade Minutes	Centigrade Seconds	Radians	Milliemes (Mils)			
								Theoretical	Practical	"Rimaillo"	Russian
	1	2	3	4	5	6	7	8	9	10	11
Circle (2πR) contains	360	21,600	1,296,000	400	40,000	4,000,000	6·28318	6283·1853	6,400	6,000	5,760
1. Degree contains	1	60	3,600	1·1	111·1	11111·1	0·01745	17·4532	17·7	16·6	16
2. Minute contains	0·016	1	60	0·0185	1·85185	185·185	0·00029	0·29091	0·296	0·27	0·26
3. Second contains	0·00027	0·016	1	0·00031	0·03086	3·08640	0·0000048	0·00485	0·00494	0·00463	0·004
4. Grade contains	0·9	54	3,240	1	100	10,000	0·01571	15·70796	16	15	14·4
5. Centigrade Minute contains	0·009	0·54	32·4	0·01	1	100	0·00016	0·15708	0·16	0·15	0·144
6. Centigrade Second contains	0·00009	0·0054	0·324	0·0001	0·01	1	0·0000016	0·00157	0·0016	0·0015	0·00144
7. Radian contains	57·295	3437·75	206,264	63·66	6366·19	636619·77	1	1,000	1018·591	954·929	916·73
8. Theoretical Millieme contains	0·05729	3·43775	206·264	0·06366	6·36619	636·61977	0·001	1	1·01859	0·95493	0·91673
9. Practical Millieme contains	0·05625	3·375	202·5	0·0625	6·25	625	0·00098	0·98175	1	0·9375	0·9
10. "Rimaillo" Millieme contains	0·06	3·6	216	0·06	6·6	666·6	0·00105	1·04719	1·06 …	1	0·96
11. Russian Millieme contains	0·0625	3·75	225	0·0694	6·94	694·4	0·00109	1·09083	1·1 …	1·0416…	1

APPENDIX IV

NUCLEAR RADIATION, PROTECTION AND STABILIZED GLASS

A problem of some importance in nuclear research, in industry and in hospitals is protection against X-rays, gamma rays and harmful radiations whilst ensuring good visibility. Plate glass and most optical glasses, particularly the glasses containing lead, afford good protection if sufficiently thick or dense, but they become discoloured under intense radiation. Special stabilized glasses have, however, been evolved which remain more transparent even after considerable doses of radiation. These special glasses need only be used on the "hot" side, while retaining ordinary plate glass for the safe "cold" side of windows.

Table A.4.1 gives the properties of some of the stabilized glasses available from Chance-Pilkington and Table A.4.2 shows how these glasses compare for transmission, throughout the spectrum, with similar unstabilized glasses after being subjected to radiation dosages of up to 6×10^6 Roentgens.

The stabilized glasses may be used in the construction of optical instruments subjected to radiation, but it is probably better to protect the instruments from the harmful effects by means of optically worked windows of the special glasses. Large viewing windows may be made up of a multiplicity of glass sheets mounted in a tank containing liquid of similar refractive index to that of the glass. Only the first few plates on the "hot" side need be stabilized, the remainder being ordinary white plate.

TABLE A.4.1—*Stabilized Optical Glass (Chance-Pilkington)*

Type	Cat. No.	n_d	V	C–F	Specific Gravity	Lead Equivalent
HC	519604-N	1·52119	60·0	0·00869	2·53	0·22
LBC	541595-N	1·54107	58·9	0·00918	2·87	0·25
MBC	572577-N	1·57203	57·9	0·00988	3·14	0·28
DF	620362-N	1·62285	36·3	0·01717	3·63	0·32
OW7 EDF	700303-N	1·70035	30·3	0·02313	4·3	0·38
OW8 DEDF	927210-N	1·92707	21·0	0·04412	6·1	0·54

Table A.4.2—*Effect of Gamma Radiation on Stabilized and Unstabilized Glass*

Thickness 1 inch

Percentage spectral Transmission after Dosage at Rate of 6,400 Roentgens/min.

(N-type glasses are stabilized)

Glass Type	Dose Roentgens	Percentage Transmissions at Wave-lengths (A)									
		3500	4000	4500	5000	5500	6000	6500	7000	7500	8000
HC	0	84	88·5	89	89	89	90	90·4	90·5	90·5	91
	1×10^6				1·7	4·5	7·6	11·5	23·5	44·5	63·5
	6×10^6						1·4	3·3	10·5	29·5	53
HC-N	0		84·5	87	88	88·5	89	89·5	89·5	90	90
	1×10^6		60	78	84	86·5	89	89·5	89·5	90	90
	6×10^6		46	71	80	84	87	87·5	88	88·5	89
DF	0	74	87·5	88·5	88	88·5	89	89	89	89	89
	1×10^6					2·5	10	18	21	24	30
	6×10^6					2	8·2	15·5	18	21·5	28
DF-N	0		44·5	84	86·5	87	88·5	88·5	89	89	89
	1×10^6		28	77·5	84	86·5	88·5	88·5	88·5	89	89
	6×10^6		22	75	84	86	87·5	88	88·5	88·5	89
MBC	0	75	87·5	88·5	89	89	89·5	89·5	89·5	89·5	89·5
	1×10^6				4·1	11·5	21·5	31·5	43·5	55	65
	6×10^6				2·7	8·5	17	27·5	40	53	63·5
MBC-N	0		73·5	86	87·5	88	89	89·5	89·5	89·5	89·5
	1×10^6		34·5	68·5	79	84	87	87·5	88	88	89
	6×10^6		21	60	75·5	82	86	87	88	88·5	89
LBC	0	87	89	89·5	89·5	89·5	90	90	90	90·5	90·5
	1×10^6				1·3	3·5	5·2	8	15	35	57·5
	6×10^6					0·9	1·4	3	8·5	25	48·5
LBC-N	0		81	88·5	89	89	89·6	90·4	90·2	90·5	90·8
	1×10^6		69	83·5	86·5	88	89·5	90	90	90·5	90·5
	6×10^6		55	77·5	83	86·5	88·5	89	90	90	90

Chance-Pilkington: Leaflet O.S. 41.A.

In general it is desirable for the window not to be thicker than the wall structure in which it is set. If the wall is concrete, of average density, 2·5 grms/cc., normal lime-soda plate glass, also of density 2·5 may be used. If the wall is of Barytes concrete of density about 3·3 grms./cc. or the concrete is loaded with iron to an average density of about 5·6 grms./cc., the glass may be extra-dense-flint of density 4·3 or 6·1 in which both stabilized and unstabilized types are available.

The protective efficiency of windows can be expressed in terms of their *"lead equivalent"*, i.e. the thickness of metallic lead which gives the same absorption of radiation from a cobalt 60 source as unit thickness of glass. The lead equivalent of many heavy lead glasses of refractive index form 1·7 to 1·93 can be calculated from the empiric formula:—

Lead equivalent $= 0.088 \times$ density (grm./cc.)

In Table A.4.1 the lead equivalent calculated by this formula is tabulated.

Mention may be made here of the zinc bromide window where normal concrete, with a density of 2·5 is used for the cell construction. Zinc bromide solution is contained in a steel tank with a stabilized glass window for the inner wall and normal glass for the outer wall. Another application of glass in nuclear research is the measurement of visible " Cerenkov " light produced by the passage of high energy electrons in a cylindrical block of glass of the extra dense flint type having good transmission in the ultra violet. The light is collected by means of a photo multiplier and the method has been used for high energy gamma ray spectroscopy.

REFERENCES

KANTZ & HOFSTADTER, *Nucleonics*, **12**, No. 3, 36 (1954).
CASSELS, J. M., Nuclear Physics Laboratory, University of Liverpool—Private Communications.
CHANCE-PILKINGTON, St. Asaph, Flintshire—Private Communications.

APPENDIX V

TABLE FOR USE WITH SAYCE RESOLUTION CHART

(See Fig. 18.8 (c) p. 436)

Resolving power in lines /mm. $= \dfrac{R \text{ (Corresponding to finest line resolved. } N)}{L \text{ (Length in mm. of chart image)}}$

N	R	N	R	N	R	N	R
1	23·6	26	81·0	51	138·4	76	195·9
2	25·9	27	83·3	52	140·7	77	198·2
3	28·1	28	85·6	53	143·0	78	200·5
4	30·4	29	87·9	54	145·3	79	202·8
5	32·7	30	90·2	55	147·6	80	205·1
6	35·0	31	92·5	56	149·9	81	207·3
7	37·3	32	94·8	57	152·2	82	209·6
8	39·6	33	97·1	58	154·5	83	211·9
9	41·9	34	99·4	59	156·8	84	214·2
10	44·2	35	101·7	60	159·1	85	216·5
11	46·5	36	104·0	61	161·4	86	218·8
12	48·8	37	106·3	62	163·7	87	221·1
13	51·1	38	108·6	63	166·0	88	223·4
14	53·4	39	110·9	64	168·3	89	225·7
15	55·7	40	113·2	65	170·6	90	228·0
16	58·0	41	115·4	66	172·9		
17	60·3	42	117·7	67	175·2		
18	62·6	43	120·0	68	177·5		
19	64·9	44	122·3	69	179·8		
20	67·2	45	124·6	70	182·1		
21	69·5	46	126·9	71	184·4		
22	71·8	47	129·2	72	186·7		
23	74·1	48	131·5	73	189·0		
24	76·4	49	133·8	74	191·3		
25	78·7	50	136·1	75	193·6		

NOTES

1. Read on chart finest line resolved (N). Note peaks of chart are at 10, 20, 30, etc., and depressions at 5, 15, 25, etc.
2. Measure length of chart image in mm. (L)
3. From Table find R corresponding to N
4. Resolving power in lines/mm. $P = R/L$
5. Angular resolution in radians $= 1/P \times F$
   ($F =$ focal length of lens in mm.).
6. Angular resolution in seconds $= 206265/P \times F$

INDEX